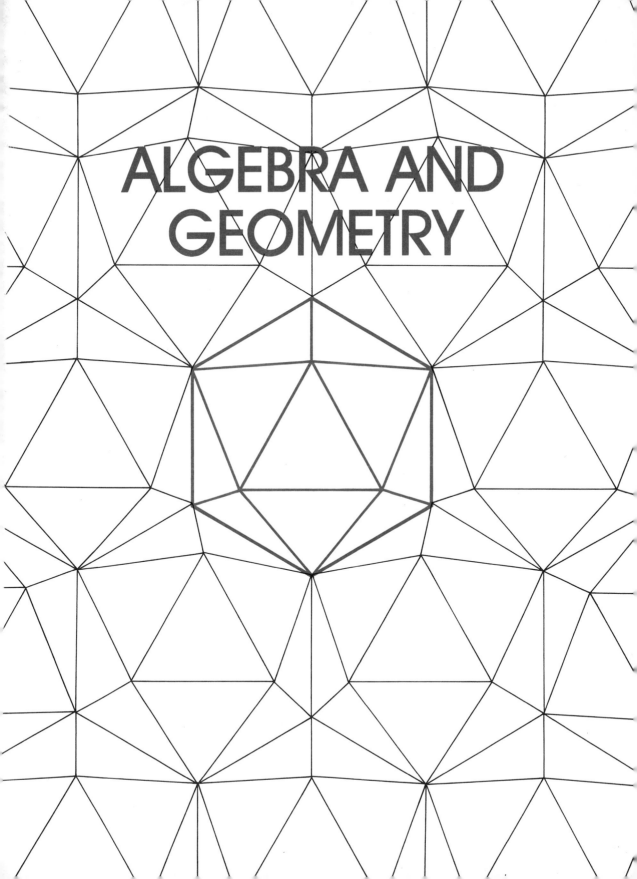

ALGEBRA AND GEOMETRY

THE McGRAW-HILL RYERSON
MATHEMATICS PROGRAM

LIFE MATH 1
LIFE MATH 2
LIFE MATH 3

INTERMEDIATE MATHEMATICS 1
INTERMEDIATE MATHEMATICS 2
INTERMEDIATE MATHEMATICS 3

TEACHER'S EDITION FOR:
INTERMEDIATE MATHEMATICS 1
INTERMEDIATE MATHEMATICS 2
INTERMEDIATE MATHEMATICS 3

BLACKLINE MASTERS FOR:
INTERMEDIATE MATHEMATICS 1
INTERMEDIATE MATHEMATICS 2

APPLIED MATHEMATICS 9
APPLIED MATHEMATICS 10
APPLIED MATHEMATICS 11
APPLIED MATHEMATICS 12

TEACHER'S GUIDE FOR:
AM9
AM10
AM11
AM12

FOUNDATIONS OF MATHEMATICS 9
FOUNDATIONS OF MATHEMATICS 10
FOUNDATIONS OF MATHEMATICS 11
FOUNDATIONS OF MATHEMATICS 12

TEACHER'S GUIDE FOR:
FM9
FM10
FM11
FM12

FINITE MATHEMATICS
ALGEBRA AND GEOMETRY
CALCULUS: A FIRST COURSE

ALGEBRA AND GEOMETRY

James Stewart, Ph.D.
Professor of Mathematics, McMaster University

Thomas M.K. Davison, Ph.D.
Professor of Mathematics, McMaster University

O. Michael G. Hamilton, M.Sc.
Department Head, Ridley College, St. Catharines

James Laxton, M.Sc.
Delta Secondary School, Hamilton

M. Patricia Lenz, M.Sc.
Department Head, St. John's College, Brantford

Consultant
John Carter, M.Sc.
Department Head, North Toronto Collegiate Institute, Toronto

McGraw-Hill Ryerson Limited

Toronto   Montreal   New York   Auckland   Bogotá   Cairo   Caracas   Hamburg   Lisbon
London   Madrid   Mexico   Milan   New Delhi   Panama   Paris   San Juan
São Paulo   Sydney   Tokyo

ALGEBRA AND GEOMETRY

ISBN 0-07-549602-X

13 14 BP 02 01

Printed and bound in Canada

Cover and Text Design by Daniel Kewley

Technical Illustrations by Sam Graphics Inc. and Warren Macdonald

Canadian Cataloguing in Publication Data

Main entry under title:

Algebra and geometry

(The McGraw-Hill Ryerson mathematics program)
Includes index.
ISBN 0-07-594602-X

1. Algebra. 2. Geometry. I. Stewart, James.

QA152.2.A584 1989   512'.12   C88-094620-2

TABLE
OF
CONTENTS

REVIEWERS

Ivy Brown
North Park CVI
Brantford, Ontario

Ken McDonald
Bluevale CI
Waterloo, Ontario

Hugh Welbourn
Applewood Heights Secondary School
Mississauga, Ontario

CREDITS

pp. 75, 248, 320; *Mathematical People: Profiles and Interviews*, Donald J. Albers and G.L. Alexanderson. Published by Birkhäuser Boston © 1985.
pp. 158, 408; *International Mathematical Congresses: An Illustrated History 1893–1986*, Donald J. Albers, G.L. Alexanderson, and Constance Reid. Published by Springer-Verlag © 1987.
pp. 189, 293; photos: courtesy of Don Ford.

PREFACE

This textbook on Algebra and Geometry is part of a three-volume series, also including books on Calculus and Finite Mathematics, for courses that represent the culmination of a high school mathematics program.

GEOMETRIC APPROACH

In Algebra and Geometry, geometric vectors are emphasized as the more general approach and Cartesian vectors are introduced through a consideration of the restrictions placed on the more general approach. Vectors are used again in the study of conic sections with transformations and matrices. The geometric approach also deepens the understanding of complex number arithmetic.

APPLICATIONS/MOTIVATION

Among the diverse applications of this theory that we include are the following:
- Forces in a traction apparatus are used to motivate the study of operations on geometric vectors.
- Vector subtraction is used to determine the velocity of one moving body relative to another.
- The work done in performing a task leads to the definition of the dot product of two vectors.
- The cross product of two vectors is used to find the position of a bicycle pedal at which the turning force is maximized.
- Complex numbers are used to express the admittance in an electric network.

PROBLEM SOLVING EMPHASIS

Our educational philosophy has been strongly influenced by the books of George Polya and the lectures of both Polya and Gabor Szego at Stanford University. They consistently introduced a topic by relating it to something concrete or familiar. In this spirit, we have tried to motivate new topics by relating mathematical concepts to the students' experience.

The influence of Polya's work on problem solving can be seen throughout the book. In the pages following this preface we give an introduction to some of the problem-solving strategies that he has explained at greater length in his books *How to Solve It*, *Mathematical Discovery*, and *Mathematics and Plausible Reasoning*. When these strategies occur in examples, we highlight their use with margin captions.

In addition to the graded exercise sets, we have included special problems, called PROBLEMS PLUS, that require a higher level of problem-solving skill.

OPTIONAL SECTIONS

Sections that are labelled optional in the curriculum for the Ontario Academic Course in Algebra and Geometry have been indicated by an asterisk. Enrichment topics that go beyond this curriculum are indicated by double asterisks.

TWENTIETH CENTURY MATHEMATICIANS

Many people have the mistaken impression that all of mathematics was done centuries ago. To show that mathematics is still very much alive and is still being created, we have included biographies of five contemporary mathematicians: H.S.M. Coxeter, Henri Poincaré, Garret Birkhoff, Olga Taussky-Todd, and David Hilbert.

ACKNOWLEDGMENTS

In addition to the reviewers listed earlier and our consultant John Carter, who attended all our authors' meetings, we wish to thank our teaching colleagues for their valuable advice, the editorial and production staff at McGraw-Hill Ryerson for a superb job, and those close to us who understandingly put up with the long hours that we devoted to this project.

James Stewart
Thomas M.K. Davison
O. Michael G. Hamilton
James Laxton
M. Patricia Lenz

There are no hard and fast rules that will ensure success in solving problems. However, it is possible to outline some general steps in the problem-solving process and to give some principles that may be useful in the solution of certain problems. These steps and principles are just common sense made explicit. They have been adapted from George Polya's book *How to Solve It*.

1. Understand the Problem

The first step is to read the problem and make sure that you understand it clearly. Ask yourself the following questions:

> *What is the unknown?*
> *What are the given quantities?*
> *What are the given conditions?*

For many problems it is useful to

> *draw a diagram*

and identify the given and required quantities on the diagram.

Usually it is necessary to

> *introduce suitable notation.*

In choosing symbols for the unknown quantities we often use letters such as a, b, c, ..., m, n, ..., x, y, ... , but in some cases it helps to use initials as suggestive symbols, for instance, V for volume, t for time.

2. Think of a Plan

Find a connection between the given information and the unknown that will enable you to calculate the unknown. If you do not see the connection immediately, the following ideas may be helpful in devising a plan.

(a) *Try to recognize something familiar.* Relate the given situation to previous knowledge. Look at the unknown and try to recall a more familiar problem having a similar unknown.

(b) *Try to recognize patterns.* Some problems are solved by recognizing that some kind of pattern is occurring. The pattern could be geometric, or numerical, or algebraic. If you can see regularity or repetition in a problem, then you might be able to guess what the continuing pattern is, and then prove it.

(c) *Use analogy.* Try to think of an analogous problem, that is, a similar and related problem, but one that is easier than the original problem. If you can solve the similar, simpler problem, then it might give you the clues you need to solve the original, more difficult one. For instance, if a problem involves very large numbers, you could first try a similar problem with smaller numbers. Or if the problem is in three-dimensional geometry, you could look for a similar problem in two-dimensional geometry. Or if the problem you start with is a general one, you could first try a special case.

(d) *Introduce something extra.* It may sometimes be necessary to introduce something new, an auxiliary aid, to help make the connection between the given and the unknown. For instance, in geometry the auxiliary aid could be a new line drawn in a diagram. In algebra it could be a new unknown that is related to the original unknown.

(e) *Take cases.* You may sometimes have to split a problem into several cases and give a different argument for each of the cases.

(f) *Work backwards.* Sometimes it is useful to imagine that your problem is solved and work backwards, step by step, till you arrive at the given data. Then you may be able to reverse your steps and thereby construct a solution to the original problem.

(g) *Use indirect reasoning.* Sometimes it is appropriate to attack a problem indirectly. For instance, in a counting argument it might be best to count the total number of objects and subtract the number of objects that do *not* have the required property. Another example of indirect reasoning is *proof by contradiction* in which we assume that the desired conclusion is false and eventually arrive at a contradiction.

(h) *Use mathematical induction.* In proving statements that involve a positive integer n, it is frequently helpful to use the Principle of Mathematical Induction, which is discussed in Chapter 11.

3. Carry Out the Plan

In Step 2 a plan was devised. In carrying out that plan you have to check each stage of the plan and write the details that prove that each stage is correct.

4. Look Back

Having completed your solution, it is wise to look back over it, partly to see if there are errors in the solution, and partly to see if there is an easier way to solve the problem. Another reason for looking back is that it will familiarize you with the method of solution and this may be useful for solving a future problem. Descartes said, "Every problem that I solved became a rule which I then used in solving other problems."

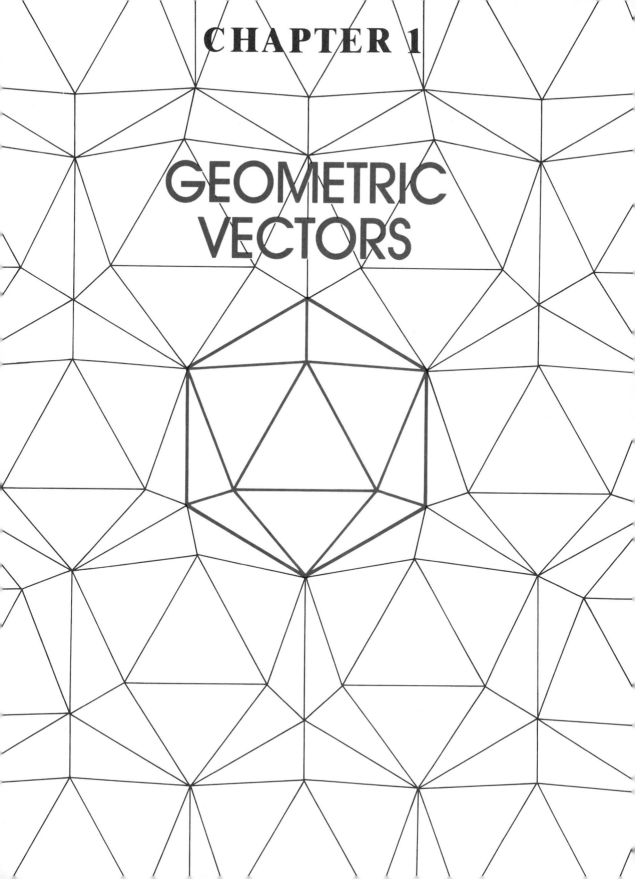

CHAPTER 1

GEOMETRIC VECTORS

REVIEW AND PREVIEW TO
CHAPTER 1

EXERCISE 1   **Solution of Triangles**

$a^2 = b^2 + c^2$

$\sin \theta = \dfrac{\text{opp}}{\text{hyp}}$

$\cos \theta = \dfrac{\text{adj}}{\text{hyp}}$

$\tan \theta = \dfrac{\text{opp}}{\text{adj}}$

1. Solve the following triangles. Find the angles to the nearest degree and the lengths to one decimal place.

   (a)
   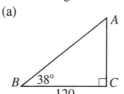

   (b)
   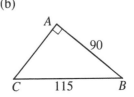

   (c)

   (d)
   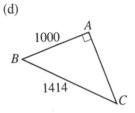

   (e)

   (f)
   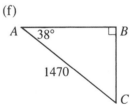

2. Solve each triangle. Find the angles to the nearest degree and the lengths to one decimal place.

Law of Sines

$\dfrac{\sin A}{a} = \dfrac{\sin B}{b} = \dfrac{\sin C}{c}$

Law of Cosines

$a^2 = b^2 + c^2 - 2bc \cos A$

   (a)
   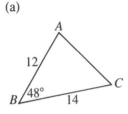

   (b)
   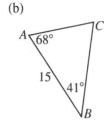

   (c)
   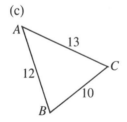

   (d)
   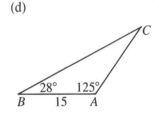

(e)

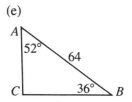

(f)

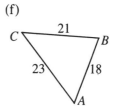

INTRODUCTION

The patient in the picture is experiencing the effects of *force*. The traction apparatus designed by an orthopedic surgeon combines masses, rods, and wires to produce a force acting against the mass of the patient's body. In this way a broken bone is pulled back into position so that it may heal properly.

Geometric vectors provide a mathematical model for physical phenomena such as force and *velocity*. In this chapter we develop the mathematical theory of geometric vectors necessary to investigate such physical situations.

1.1 DIRECTED LINE SEGMENTS

A **vector** is a mathematical object with both magnitude (length) and direction.

A vector can be represented geometrically by a directed line segment, that is, a line segment with an arrow on one end to indicate the intended direction. The end of the line segment with no arrow is called the **tail** or **initial point** of the vector. The end with the arrow is its **tip** or **terminal point**.

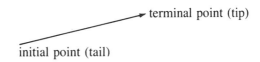

In drawing vector diagrams, the length and direction of the line segments should reflect the length and direction of the vectors represented in the diagram. For example, if a vector is drawn as follows:

(a)   a vector twice as long as this vector could be drawn as follows:

(b)   a vector at right angles to the original vector could be drawn as:

(c)   and a vector 1.7 times as long at an angle of 38° to the original vector could be drawn as:

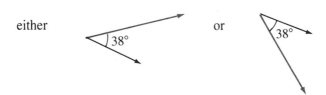

We will use the arrow notation.

Various symbols are used to denote vectors. One practice is to use lower-case letters marked in a special way, for example:

topped with an arrow $\vec{u}, \vec{x}$

bold-face **u**, **x**

topped with a bar $\bar{u}, \bar{x}$

or underlined $\underline{u}, \underline{x}$

When the initial and terminal points of a directed line segment that gives one representation of the vector are known, it can be represented using them. For example, we write $\overrightarrow{PQ}$ to represent a vector from point P to point Q.

Note, however, that this line segment PQ is only one copy of the vector $\overrightarrow{PQ}$, for a vector is determined completely by its magnitude and direction; its position in space is not fixed. Such vectors are referred to as **free vectors**.

In learning about vectors it is often useful to recall what we know about positive and negative numbers (that is, numbers with a direction indicated by the sign). For a number, to specify only its size while disregarding its sign, we use the absolute value function. For example, $|-7|$ is 7, that is, the absolute value of -7 is 7, meaning the distance from 0 to -7 is 7 units.

Similarly, for vector $\vec{u}$, $|\vec{u}|$ is used to symbolize the **magnitude of the vector $\vec{u}$**.

When mathematicians begin to deal with a new class of mathematical objects, they consider several basic issues. One of these issues is the notion of equality, that is, "For these objects, under what conditions will we consider two of them to be identical or equal?" Because the only important features of a geometric vector are its length and direction, we define vector equality as follows:

Vector Equality

Two vectors are equal vectors if, and only if, they have the same magnitude and the same direction. Notation: If vectors $\vec{u}$ and $\vec{v}$ are equal then we write $\vec{u} = \vec{v}$.

Example 1 Figure $ABCD$ in the diagram is a parallelogram. F is the point of intersection of its diagonals. By recalling relevant properties of a parallelogram, name all equal vectors in the diagram.

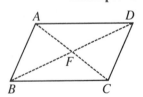

Solution   Because opposite sides of a parallelogram are equal and parallel,
$$\overrightarrow{AB} = \overrightarrow{DC} \quad \text{and} \quad \overrightarrow{AD} = \overrightarrow{BC}.$$
(This could also be stated as
$$\overrightarrow{BA} = \overrightarrow{CD} \quad \text{and} \quad \overrightarrow{DA} = \overrightarrow{CB}.)$$
Because diagonals of a parallelogram bisect each other,
$$\overrightarrow{AF} = \overrightarrow{FC} \quad \text{and} \quad \overrightarrow{BF} = \overrightarrow{FD}.$$

EXERCISE 1.1

1. For which of the following situations would vectors be a suitable mathematical model?
(a) the cost of a dance ticket
(b) the path from your desk to the classroom door
(c) the air speed of a jet as it heads due north
(d) the current in a river
(e) the number of players in the annual dramatic production

2. (a) Name the initial point of each vector drawn below.
(i)

(ii)

(b) Name the terminal point of each vector in (a).

3. Name all equal vectors in each diagram. (Use the geometric properties of each figure shown.)
(a)

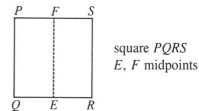

square $PQRS$
E, F midpoints

(b)

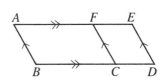

(c)

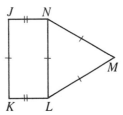

B **4.** Redraw the vector shown below in your notebook, then draw the indicated related vectors:

(a) a vector half as long in the same direction
(b) a vector at 180° to the original, three times as long
(c) two different vectors perpendicular to the original, with the same magnitude.

5. Name all equal vectors in the diagrams below.

(a)
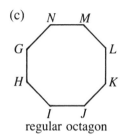

(b)

(c)
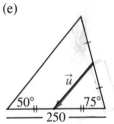

regular octagon

(d)
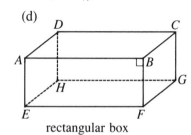

rectangular box

6. Find the magnitude of $\vec{u}$.

(a)
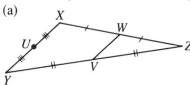

(b)
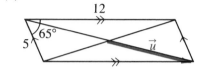

(c)
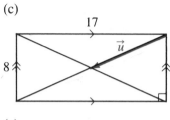

(d)
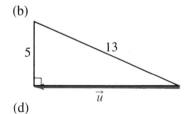

(e)
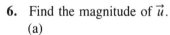
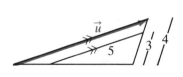

7. Consider the statement: $|\vec{u}| = |\vec{v}|$.

    (a) What information does this convey about $\vec{u}$ and $\vec{v}$?

    (b) What other significant information about $\vec{u}$ and $\vec{v}$ is not conveyed by this statement?

✓1.2 ADDING AND SUBTRACTING VECTORS

At several points in a traction apparatus, forces are combined to produce the required effect, a pull on the broken bone or suspension of the limb above the hospital bed. In mathematical terms, the force vectors are added.

In considering the notion of adding vectors, we seek a technique that looks like adding as we are used to it in other mathematical settings. Usually adding two mathematical objects produces a third of the same type of object.

Keeping this in mind, we define vector addition as follows:

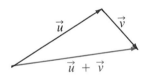

The Triangle Law of Vector Addition

For vectors $\vec{u}$ and $\vec{v}$, the **sum** (or **resultant**) **of** $\vec{u}$ **and** $\vec{v}$ is a vector from the tail of $\vec{u}$ to the tip of $\vec{v}$, when the tail of $\vec{v}$ is placed at the tip of $\vec{u}$. Notation: The sum of $\vec{u}$ and $\vec{v}$ is denoted by $\vec{u} + \vec{v}$.

Example 1   Draw a diagram of $\overrightarrow{PQ} + \overrightarrow{XY}$ for vectors $\overrightarrow{PQ}$ and $\overrightarrow{XY}$ as shown.

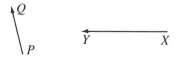

Solution   It is first necessary that we place the tail of $\overrightarrow{XY}$ at the tip of $\overrightarrow{PQ}$ by drawing a copy of $\overrightarrow{XY}$. This is allowed because the position of a vector in space is not fixed.

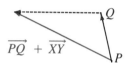

The resultant $\overrightarrow{PQ} + \overrightarrow{XY}$ is the vector from the tail of $\overrightarrow{PQ}$ to the tip of the copy of $\overrightarrow{XY}$. ⬡

Vector addition is useful in modelling trips as in the following example.

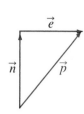

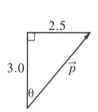

Example 2   When they set out on their canoe trip, Jamie and Kaari travelled 3.0 km north, then turned to travel 2.5 km due east along the bank of the river to a point where they put the canoes in the water. Lorne set out later, wanting to take the most direct route to meet his friends.

(a) Draw a diagram of this situation.

(b) Describe Lorne's path (its length and direction).

Solution   (a)

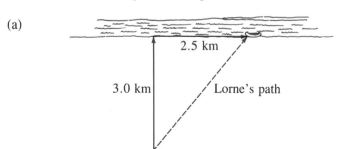

2.5 km

3.0 km   Lorne's path

(b) Let $\vec{p}$ represent Lorne's path, while $\vec{n}$ and $\vec{e}$ represent the two legs of the trip taken by the others.

To find the magnitude of $\vec{p}$, take advantage of the right angle at the river to apply the Pythagorean Theorem:

$$|\vec{p}|^2 = |\vec{n}|^2 + |\vec{e}|^2$$

so, $|\vec{p}| \doteq 3.9$

To find the direction of $\vec{p}$:

let θ represent the acute angle at the beginning of both trips.

$$\tan \theta = \frac{2.5}{3}$$

so, $\theta \doteq 40°$

Thus, Lorne's most direct route would be at an angle 40° east of north. He would travel 3.9 km in that direction to meet his friends.

In considering vector subtraction, it is again useful to recall what we do with numbers. To subtract two numbers we add the opposite (of the second number). We start with the following definition:

For a vector, $\vec{u}$, the **opposite of $\vec{u}$** is a vector with the same magnitude as $\vec{u}$ but exactly opposite direction.

Notation: The opposite of $\vec{u}$ is denoted by $-\vec{u}$.

Note that the sum of a vector and its opposite is a vector with zero magnitude. This vector is called the **zero vector** and is denoted by $\vec{0}$. For any vector $\vec{u}$, $\vec{u} + (-\vec{u}) = \vec{0}$.

Now we are ready to define vector subtraction as "adding the opposite."

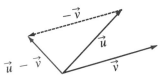

For vectors $\vec{u}$ and $\vec{v}$, the **difference**, $\vec{u} - \vec{v}$, is $\vec{u} + (-\vec{v})$.

Note that $\vec{u} - \vec{v}$ can also be illustrated as in the following diagram.

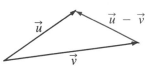

Example 3   (a) Show that $\overrightarrow{PQ} - \overrightarrow{RQ} = \overrightarrow{PR}$.

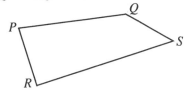

(b) Write $\overrightarrow{PR}$ in terms of $\overrightarrow{PQ}$, $\overrightarrow{QS}$, and $\overrightarrow{RS}$.

Solution   (a)

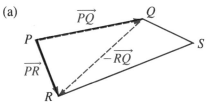

$$\overrightarrow{PQ} - \overrightarrow{RQ} = \overrightarrow{PQ} + (-\overrightarrow{RQ})$$
$$= \overrightarrow{PQ} + \overrightarrow{QR}$$
$$= \overrightarrow{PR}$$

(b)

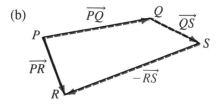

$$\overrightarrow{PR} = \overrightarrow{PQ} + \overrightarrow{QS} + \overrightarrow{SR}$$
$$= \overrightarrow{PQ} + \overrightarrow{QS} + (-\overrightarrow{RS})$$
$$= \overrightarrow{PQ} + \overrightarrow{QS} - \overrightarrow{RS}$$

EXERCISE 1.2

A 1. Express each vector as the sum or difference of two other vectors.
(a)

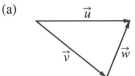

(b)

(c)

(d)

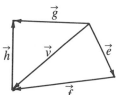

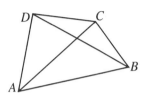

2. Name a single vector equal to each combination of vectors.
   (a) $\overrightarrow{AB} + \overrightarrow{BC}$ (b) $\overrightarrow{AB} + \overrightarrow{BD}$
   (c) $\overrightarrow{CD} + \overrightarrow{DA}$ (d) $\overrightarrow{BC} - \overrightarrow{DC}$
   (e) $\overrightarrow{AB} + \overrightarrow{BC} + \overrightarrow{CD}$

3. Express $\vec{v}$ as the sum of other vectors.
   (a)

   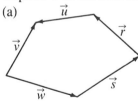

   (b)

   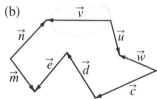

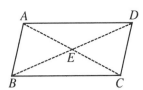

4. Given that $ABCD$ is a parallelogram, name a single vector equal to
   (a) $\overrightarrow{AD}$ (b) $\overrightarrow{ED}$
   (c) $\overrightarrow{AE}$ (d) $\overrightarrow{CD}$
   (e) $\overrightarrow{AE} + \overrightarrow{EB}$ (f) $\overrightarrow{BC} + \overrightarrow{BA}$
   (g) $\overrightarrow{AE} + \overrightarrow{AE}$ (h) $\overrightarrow{AD} - \overrightarrow{AB}$
   (i) $\overrightarrow{BA} + \overrightarrow{AE} + \overrightarrow{ED} + \overrightarrow{DC}$

B 5. Using a suitable scale, draw a diagram to represent each of the following vector sums:
   (a) 7 km south followed by 10 km west
   (b) 12 km east followed by 8 km north
   (c) 6 km south followed by 8 km southeast
   (d) 14 km north, 20 km west, 8 km southwest.

6. Consider parallelogram $QRST$ with $\overrightarrow{QR} = \vec{u}$ and $\overrightarrow{QT} = \vec{v}$. Explain why $\vec{u} + \vec{v} = \overrightarrow{QS}$.

   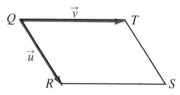

   Note: This method of adding vectors is known as the *Parallelogram Law of Vector Addition*.

7. Redraw the following pairs of vectors and find their sum using:
   (i) the Triangle Law,
   (ii) the Parallelogram Law.
   For example, for

   and

   (i) by the Triangle Law   (ii) by the Parallelogram Law

(a)   (b)   (c)

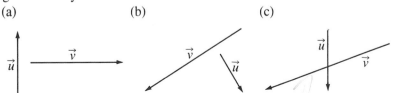

8. Redraw the following vectors and find the difference $\vec{u} - \vec{v}$ geometrically.

(a)   (b)   (c)

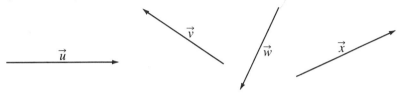

9. Redraw the following vectors and find $\vec{u} + \vec{v} - \vec{w} + \vec{x}$ geometrically.

10. (a) Give a geometric argument to show that $|\vec{u} + \vec{v}| \leq |\vec{u}| + |\vec{v}|$ for any vectors $\vec{u}$ and $\vec{v}$.

(b) When does the equal sign hold?

11. A rectangular box has parallel faces *ABCD* and *EFGH*. Find a single vector equal to each of the following.

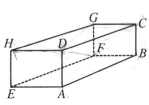

(a) $\overrightarrow{AB} + \overrightarrow{BC}$ (b) $\overrightarrow{GF} + \overrightarrow{FB}$ (c) $\overrightarrow{AD} + \overrightarrow{AB}$

(d) $\overrightarrow{HD} - \overrightarrow{BA}$ (e) $\overrightarrow{EC} - \overrightarrow{BC}$ (f) $\overrightarrow{AB} + \overrightarrow{AD} + \overrightarrow{AE}$

(g) $\overrightarrow{HE} + \overrightarrow{AF}$ (h) $\overrightarrow{FD} + \overrightarrow{AE}$ (i) $\overrightarrow{HE} - \overrightarrow{GA} + \overrightarrow{FC}$

12. On the soccer field, the goalie Gina stands in the middle of the goal crease on the goal line. She kicks the ball 25 m on an angle of 35° to the goal line. Her teammate Louisa takes this pass and kicks it 40 m further, parallel to the sideline.

(a) What is the resultant displacement of the ball?

(b) If the field is 110 m long, how far must the next striker kick the ball to take a good shot at the centre of the goal, and in approximately what direction?

C **13.** If vectors $\vec{u}$ and $\vec{v}$ are at right angles to each other, derive formulas for the magnitudes of each of the following in terms of $|\vec{u}|$ and $|\vec{v}|$.

(a) $\vec{u} + \vec{v}$ (b) $\vec{u} - \vec{v}$

14. Using the results of Question 13, verify that, for mutually perpendicular vectors,

$$|\vec{u} + \vec{v}|^2 + |\vec{u} - \vec{v}|^2 = 2(|\vec{u}|^2 + |\vec{v}|^2)$$

1.3 FORCES AND VELOCITIES

As was mentioned at the beginning of this chapter, both force and velocity are examples of vectors. Thus, the techniques we have developed in Sections 1.1 and 1.2 can be used in analysing both forces and velocities.

Force

Intuitively, we can think of a force as describing a push or a pull on an object. For example, a horizontal push of a book across a table or the downward pull of the earth's gravity on a ball are forces. To describe a force it is necessary to state

  (i) its direction,

 (ii) the point at which it is applied, and

(iii) its magnitude.

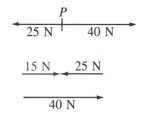

For example, the diagram shows forces of 40 N and 25 N acting, in opposite directions, at point P. The combined effect of these two forces is a 15 N force acting to the right. This single force that has the same effect as the other two forces combined is called the resultant. The **resultant** is the sum of the vectors representing the two forces. The **equilibrant** is the opposite force, that is, the force that would exactly counterbalance the resultant force.

The force exerted by gravity on two golf balls is about one newton (1 N).

Example 1 Two draft horses pull a load. The chains between the horses and the load are at an angle of 60° to each other. One horse pulls with a force of 230 N, the other with a force of 340 N.

(a) What is the resultant force on the load? In what direction is this force?

(b) What is the equilibrant force on the load? In what direction is this force?

Solution Let $\vec{f}$ and $\vec{e}$ represent the 230 and 340 N forces respectively. Let $\vec{r}$ represent the resultant force.

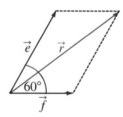

(a) We wish to find the magnitude of $\vec{r}$. We first note that the angle opposite $\vec{r}$ is 120°.

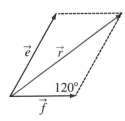 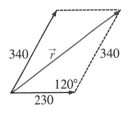

According to the Law of Cosines,

$$|\vec{r}|^2 = |\vec{f}|^2 + |\vec{e}|^2 - 2|\vec{f}||\vec{e}|\cos 120°$$
$$= 230^2 + 340^2 - 2(230)(340)\cos 120°$$

thus, $|\vec{r}| \doteq 497$ N

We wish to find the angle at which $\vec{r}$ acts. Let θ represent the angle between $\vec{r}$ and the 230 N force.

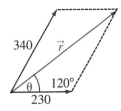

According to the Law of Sines,

$$\frac{\sin \theta}{340} = \frac{\sin 120°}{497}$$

so, $\theta \doteq 36°$

Accurate to two significant digits

The resultant force has a magnitude of 500 N and acts at an angle of 36° to the 230 N force.

(b) The equilibrant force (that is, the force that would counteract this force) is a force of 500 N acting at an angle of 144° to the 230 N force.

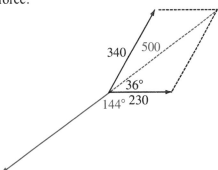

Example 2 A traffic sign with a mass of 5 kg is suspended above the street as shown. Find the tensions (forces) in the wires.

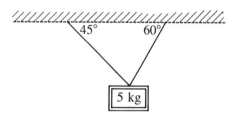

Solution The force acting on the sign is due to gravity. Thus, we have a force of

force = mass
× acceleration

$$5 \times 9.8 = 49 \text{ N down}$$

This force is balanced by the forces (*tensions*) in the two wires. Let $\vec{t}_1$ represent the tension in one wire and $\vec{t}_2$ represent the tension in the other. We represent these balanced forces in a diagram.

acceleration due to
gravity $\doteq 9.8 \text{ m/s}^2$

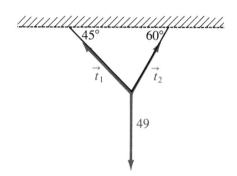

Note that, because the force $\vec{t}_1$ makes an angle of 45° with the horizontal and the force $\vec{t}_2$ makes an angle of 60° with the horizontal, the angle between $\vec{t}_1$ and $\vec{t}_2$ is 105°.

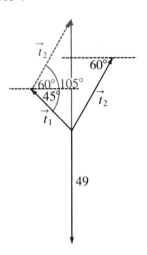

To find the magnitude of $\vec{t}_1$:

Note that the angle between $\vec{t}_1$ and the 49 N equilibrant force is 45°. This is because it is in the triangle formed by the $\vec{t}_1$ force, the horizontal, and a portion of the 49 N force. Similarly, the angle between $\vec{t}_2$ and the 49 N equilibrant force is 30° because it is in the triangle formed by a portion of the 49 N force, the horizontal, and $\vec{t}_2$.

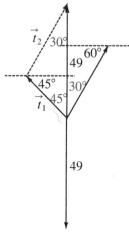

So, by the Law of Sines,

$$\frac{|\vec{t}_1|}{\sin 30°} = \frac{49}{\sin 105°}$$

Thus, $|\vec{t}_1| = \dfrac{49 \sin 30°}{\sin 105°}$

$$\doteq 25$$

Similarly, to find the magnitude of $\vec{t}_2$:

$$\frac{|\vec{t}_2|}{\sin 45°} = \frac{49}{\sin 105°}$$

Thus, $|\vec{t}_2| = \dfrac{49 \sin 45°}{\sin 105°}$

$$\doteq 35$$

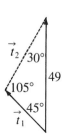

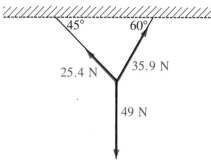

The tensions are 25 N and 36 N in the directions of the wires.

Velocity

Since velocity is speed in a direction, it can be represented as a vector. When a plane flies, its velocity relative to the earth is the resultant of:
(i) the plane's velocity through still air
(ii) the velocity of the wind.

Example 3 A plane is steering at N45°E at an air speed (speed in still air) of 525 km/h. The wind is from N60°W at 98 km/h. (The direction *from* which the wind comes is usually specified.) Find the groundspeed and track (or course) of the plane.

Solution

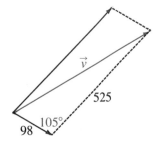

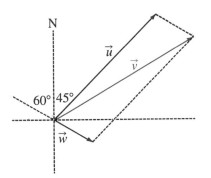

This diagram illustrates an alternate technique for adding vectors, the Parallelogram Law.

Let $\vec{u}$ represent the vector of the plane's velocity in still air and $\vec{w}$ the wind's velocity. Let $\vec{v}$ represent the plane's actual velocity.

We wish to calculate the plane's groundspeed, that is, the magnitude of the velocity along the ground:

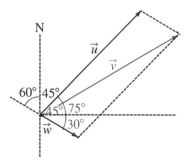

Because the angle between the two vectors is 75°, the angle opposite the vector $\vec{v}$ is 105°.

By the Law of Cosines,

$$|\vec{v}|^2 = |\vec{u}|^2 + |\vec{w}|^2 - 2|\vec{u}||\vec{w}|\cos 105°$$
$$= 525^2 + 98^2 - 2(525)(98)\cos 105°$$
$$\doteq 311\ 861$$

So, $|\vec{v}| \doteq 558$

Now we determine the plane's course.
Let θ represent the angle between $\vec{v}$ and $\vec{u}$.
By the Law of Sines,

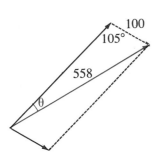

$$\frac{\sin \theta}{|\vec{w}|} = \frac{\sin 105°}{|\vec{v}|}$$

$$\frac{\sin \theta}{100} = \frac{\sin 105°}{558}$$

$$\sin \theta = \frac{100 \sin 105°}{558}$$

So, $\theta \doteq 10°$

The plane is actually travelling $(45 + 10)$ degrees east of north.

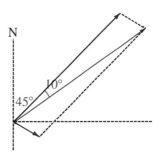

Thus, the plane's ground velocity is 560 km/h at N55°E.

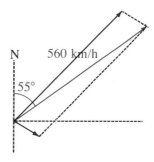

Relative Velocity

Consider the highway situation indicated in the diagram involving a car (C) travelling at 100 km/h, a bus (B) travelling at 80 km/h, and a truck (T) travelling at 90 km/h in the indicated directions.

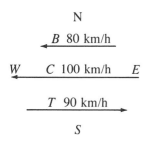

To an observer in a helicopter hovering over the vehicles, their actual velocities are 100 km/h west, 80 km/h west, and 90 km/h east. To someone sitting in the bus the car is passing at 20 km/h. We say that the velocity of the car relative to the bus is 20 km/h west. The velocity of the truck relative to the car is 190 km/h east.

Einstein's Theory of Relativity is based on the principle that all velocities are relative.

This phenomenon occurs because all velocities are relative to something else. In the strictest sense the velocity of the car is 100 km/h relative to the earth. The earth itself is flying through space at approximately 100 000 km/h and spinning as it goes, yet we do not notice this motion. In other words, when we look at a moving object, even though we are moving ourselves, we see the object as though we were stationary. The **velocity of an object** is its velocity relative to the frame of reference of some observer in a given situation. The following, then, is the important principle for relative velocity problems.

> The **velocity of an object A relative to an object B** is $\vec{v}_A - \vec{v}_B$ where $\vec{v}_A$ is the velocity of A and $\vec{v}_B$ is the velocity of B.

Example 4 A ship is steering east at 15 kn. A tug 2 M to the south is steering N45°E at 20 kn.
(a) Find the velocity of the ship relative to the tug.
(b) Will the ship pass in front of or behind the tug?

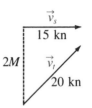

Solution To an observer above the two vessels the vectors would appear as in the diagram.

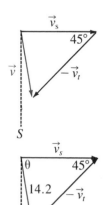

(a) To an observer on the tug the velocity $\vec{v}$ of the ship is $\vec{v}_s - \vec{v}_t$ or $\vec{v}_s + (-\vec{v}_t)$.

By the Law of Cosines,

$$|\vec{v}|^2 = 15^2 + 20^2 - 2(15)(20)\cos 45°$$

so, $\qquad |\vec{v}| \doteq 14.2$

By the Law of Sines,

$$\frac{\sin \theta}{20} = \frac{\sin 45°}{14.2}$$

$$\sin \theta = \frac{20 \sin 45°}{14.2}$$

so, $\qquad \theta \doteq 85°$

Thus, to an observer on the tug the ship is steering S5°E at 14 kn.

(b) A diagram illustrates the path of the ship relative to the tug. It shows that the ship passes in front of the tug.

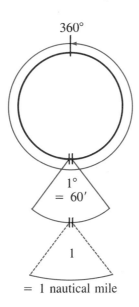

360°

1°
= 60'

1

= 1 nautical mile

1 M = 1 nautical mile
   = 1.852 km
1 kn = 1 M/h
Note: The nautical mile and the
nautical mile per hour, or knot, are
not SI units. And M and kn are not SI
symbols (though M, k, and n are SI
prefixes, meaning 10^6, 10^3, and 10^{-9}
respectively). The nautical mile and
knot are permitted for use in SI for
the time being because of their wide
use in navigation. The nautical mile is
based on the geometry of the earth. It
is the mean length of an arc of 1′
along a great circle route of the earth.

EXERCISE 1.3

A 1. State the resultant of each of the following systems of forces acting
at a point P.

(a)

11 N P 15 N

(b)
8 N P 7 N

10 N

(c)

8 N P 12 N

10 N

(d)

18 N P 22 N

20 N   16 N

2. State the equilibrant of each of the following systems of forces
acting at a point P.

(a)
7 N P 13 N

9 N

(b)
28 N P 35 N

37 N   29 N

3. The diagram shows a highway situation involving a bus (B), car (C),
truck (T), and van (V). Determine:
(a) the velocity of the car relative to the truck
(b) the velocity of the bus relative to the car
(c) the velocity of the bus relative to the van
(d) the velocity of the van relative to the bus
(e) the velocity of the truck relative to the van
(f) the velocity of the car relative to the van
(g) the velocity of the truck relative to the car.

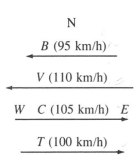

N

B (95 km/h)

V (110 km/h)

W C (105 km/h) E

T (100 km/h)

S

B **4.** Determine the magnitude and direction (to the nearest degree, relative to the first force) of the *resultant* of each of the following systems of forces:
   (a) forces of 7 N and 8 N acting at an angle of 90° to each other
   (b) forces of 62 N and 48 N acting at an angle of 60° to each other
   (c) forces of 12 N and 31 N acting at an angle of 153° to each other.

5. Determine the magnitude and direction (to the nearest degree) of the *equilibrant* of each of the following systems of forces:
   (a) forces of 55 N and 37 N acting at an angle of 30° to each other
   (b) forces of 12 N and 9 N acting at an angle of 120° to each other
   (c) forces of 11 N and 15 N acting at an angle of 34° to each other.

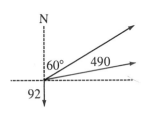

6. A plane is steering N60°E at an air speed of 490 km/h. The wind is from the north at 92 km/h. Find the groundspeed and track of the plane.

7. If the wind is from the east at 91 km/h and a plane is steering southwest at an airspeed of 340 km/h, find the velocity of the plane.

8. A pilot wants his plane to track N60°W with a groundspeed of 380 km/h. If the wind is from S80°E at 85 km/h, what heading should the pilot steer and at what airspeed should he fly?

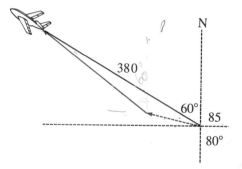

9. A ship is steering west at 12 kn. A submarine 3 M to the north is steering southwest at 16 kn.
   (a) Find the velocity of the submarine relative to the ship.
   (b) Will the submarine pass in front of or behind the ship?

10. A 3 kg metal bar is suspended from the middle of a 2 m chain whose ends are attached to a support beam 1.5 m apart. Find the tensions in each part of the chain.

11. Two tug boats pull a barge directly against the current of the river. The tow ropes from the tugs are at an angle of 37° to each other; the forces exerted by the tugs along the ropes are both 4200 N. If the current produces a force of 45 N, what is the force with which the barge is pulled forward?

12. A ship is steering north at 16 kn. Radar detects a submarine 2 M to the east with a relative velocity of 13 kn at S75°E. What is the actual velocity of the submarine?

13. A pilot maps out her flight plan and determines that to reach her destination on time her plane must travel S10°E at 510 km/h. If the wind is from S40°W at 55 km/h, what heading should the pilot steer and at what airspeed should she fly the plane?

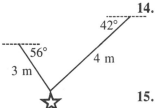

14. Ropes of 3 m and 4 m in length are fastened to a holiday decoration to be suspended over the town square. The decoration has a mass of 5 kg. The ropes, fastened at different heights, make angles of 56° and 42° respectively with the horizontal. Calculate the tension in each rope.

15. A plane is heading S70°W with a groundspeed of 625 km/h. If the pilot is steering west at an airspeed of 665 km/h, what must be the windspeed and wind direction?

C 16. A submarine detects a ship 5 M to the north. The ship is steering east at 20 kn. The submarine's attack speed is 30 kn. What course should the submarine steer to intercept the ship?

17. Three forces act on an object. Two of the forces (one 25 N, the other 12 N) are at an angle of 100° to each other. The third is perpendicular to the plane of these two forces and has a magnitude of 45 N. Calculate the magnitude of the equilibrant in this situation.

18. A boater wishes to cross a canal which is 3.0 km wide. He wishes to land at a point 2.0 km upstream from his starting point. If the current in the canal flows at 3.5 km/h and the speed of his boat is 13 km/h,
   (a) what course should he steer?
   (b) how long will the trip take?

1.4 MULTIPLYING VECTORS BY SCALARS

When the orthopedic surgeon checks on the progress of her patient, she may add more mass to the situation to increase the pull on the broken bone or remove some mass to decrease the force. Such actions are modelled by the operation of scalar multiplication of vectors.

In light of what we know so far about geometric vectors, what would make sense as a meaning for the expression $3\vec{u}$? Consider the following diagram.

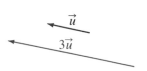

What would make sense as a meaning for $-4.3\vec{v}$?
Again, consider the following diagram.

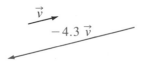

In each case the new object created is a vector. Its magnitude has been adjusted by a factor corresponding to the size of the multiplier. Its direction has remained the same when the multiplier is positive and become opposite when the multiplier is negative.

In this fashion, we define multiplication of a vector by a scalar (that is, a real number):

If $c = 0$, $c\vec{u} = \vec{0}$.

> For vector $\vec{u}$ and real number c, the **scalar multiple of $\vec{u}$ by c** is a vector with the following characteristics
> magnitude: $|c||\vec{u}|$
> direction: if $c > 0$, same as that of $\vec{u}$,
>   if $c < 0$, opposite to that of $\vec{u}$.
> Notation: $c\vec{u}$.

In words, the magnitude of $c\vec{u}$ is the absolute value of c multiplied by the magnitude of $\vec{u}$; vectors $\vec{u}$ and $c\vec{u}$ are parallel.

Example 1   For vectors $\vec{u}$ and $\vec{v}$ shown below, draw a diagram of $2\vec{u} + 3\vec{v}$.

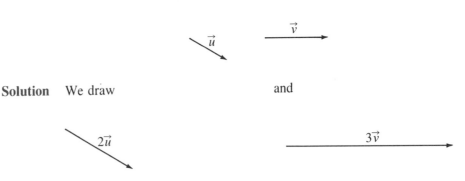

Solution   We draw   and

Then we place them with the tip of $2\vec{u}$ at the tail of $3\vec{v}$ and draw the resultant.

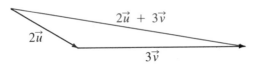

EXERCISE 1.4

A **1.** Express $\vec{u}$ as a scalar multiple of $\vec{v}$, where possible.

(a)

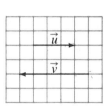

(b)

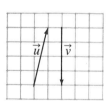

(c)

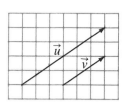

(d)

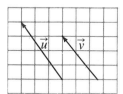

B **2.** For vectors $\vec{u}$ and $\vec{v}$ as shown, draw:

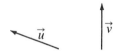

(a) $\frac{1}{2}\vec{u}$ (b) $-3\vec{v}$

(c) $5.2\vec{u}$ (d) $2\vec{u} + \vec{v}$

(e) $3.5\vec{u} - 4\vec{v}$ (f) $-0.4\vec{u} - 3\vec{v}$

3. In the school track and field meet, three competitors participated in the senior division discus event. The second competitor threw the discus about one and a half times as far as the first, however the third competitor threw it only about four-fifths as far. Draw a vector diagram representing the displacements of the discus for the three competitors, assuming that all throws were in roughly the same direction.

4. Draw two non-parallel vectors $\vec{u}$ and $\vec{v}$. For these vectors, draw:

(a) $4\vec{u}$ (b) $-3.5\vec{v}$

(c) $\vec{u} + \frac{1}{3}\vec{v}$ (d) $2\vec{v} - 5\vec{u}$

(e) $-4\vec{u} - \frac{3}{2}\vec{v}$

5. $ABCD$ is a parallelogram with P and Q the midpoints of AB and DA respectively. If $\vec{u} = \overrightarrow{BP}$ and $\vec{v} = \overrightarrow{AQ}$, express the following vectors in terms of $\vec{u}$ and $\vec{v}$.

(a) $\overrightarrow{AD}$ (b) $\overrightarrow{PA}$ (c) $\overrightarrow{CD}$ (d) $\overrightarrow{PQ}$

(e) $\overrightarrow{BD}$ (f) $\overrightarrow{PD}$ (g) $\overrightarrow{AC}$

6. For vector $\vec{u}$, calculate the magnitude of $\frac{1}{|\vec{u}|}\vec{u}$.

7. Illustrate that $\vec{u} + \vec{u} + \vec{u} = 3\vec{u}$; that is, that our definitions of vector addition and scalar multiplication of a vector are consistent.

C 8. Assuming that $\vec{u}$ and $\vec{v}$ are mutually perpendicular, derive a formula for the magnitude of each vector in terms of $|\vec{u}|$ and $|\vec{v}|$.
   - (a) $\vec{u} + 3\vec{v}$
   - (b) $4\vec{u} - 2\vec{v}$
   - (c) $\frac{1}{2}\vec{v} - 5\vec{u}$
   - (d) $|\vec{u}|\vec{v} + |\vec{v}|\vec{u}$

9. Prove that, for non-zero vectors $\vec{u}$ and $\vec{v}$, $\vec{u}$ and $\vec{v}$ are parallel if and only if $\vec{u} = c\vec{v}$ for some scalar c.

PROBLEMS PLUS

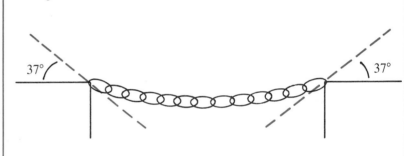

The tension T at each end of the chain is 25 N. What is the weight of the chain?

1.5 PROPERTIES OF VECTOR OPERATIONS

The operations on vectors that we have introduced have many similarities to addition, subtraction, and multiplication of numbers. Let us explore the extent of these similarities by examining the properties (rules) which hold for these operations.

At this stage, we are content to use illustrations of several of the properties to persuade ourselves that they hold. Proofs of these rules are left until we look at these objects from an algebraic point of view in Chapter 4 (because the algebraic forms of the proofs are more straightforward).

Example 1 Illustrate geometrically the *associative property of vector addition*, that is,
for vectors $\vec{u}$, $\vec{v}$, and $\vec{w}$, $(\vec{u} + \vec{v}) + \vec{w} = \vec{u} + (\vec{v} + \vec{w})$

Illustration   Consider vectors $\vec{u}$, $\vec{v}$ and $\vec{w}$ in space as shown.

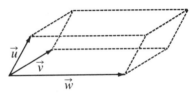

First, we draw $(\vec{u} + \vec{v}) + \vec{w}$.

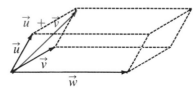   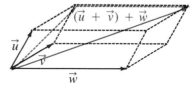

Then, we draw $\vec{u} + (\vec{v} + \vec{w})$.

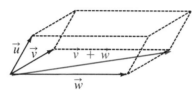   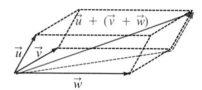

The resultant vectors in the two cases are apparently equal.

We summarize some other familiar properties. For illustrations of these statements, see Questions 3, 4, and 5 in Exercise 1.5.

For vectors $\vec{u}$ and $\vec{v}$, scalars a and b,
$$\vec{u} + \vec{v} = \vec{v} + \vec{u}$$
$$(a + b)\vec{u} = a\vec{u} + b\vec{u}$$
$$a(\vec{u} + \vec{v}) = a\vec{u} + a\vec{v}$$

Such properties are useful in dealing with expressions involving vectors and vector operations.

Example 2   Use the distributive and commutative properties stated above and the associative property of vector addition to simplify each of the following:
(a) $3\vec{u} + 2\vec{u} - 5\vec{u}$
(b) $4\vec{u} - 3\vec{v} + 7\vec{u} + 2\vec{v}$

Solution   (a) $3\vec{u} + 2\vec{u} - 5\vec{u} = (3\vec{u} + 2\vec{u}) - 5\vec{u}$
$$= ((3 + 2)\vec{u}) - 5\vec{u}$$
$$= 5\vec{u} - 5\vec{u}$$
$$= (5 - 5)\vec{u}$$
$$= 0\vec{u}$$
$$= \vec{0}$$

(b) $4\vec{u} - 3\vec{v} + 7\vec{u} + 2\vec{v} = 4\vec{u} + (-3\vec{v} + (7\vec{u} + 2\vec{v}))$
$$= 4\vec{u} + (-3\vec{v} + (2\vec{v} + 7\vec{u}))$$
$$= 4\vec{u} + ((-3\vec{v} + 2\vec{v}) + 7\vec{u})$$
$$= 4\vec{u} + ((-3 + 2)\vec{v} + 7\vec{u})$$
$$= 4\vec{u} + (-1\vec{v} + 7\vec{u})$$
$$= 4\vec{u} + (7\vec{u} + (-1\vec{v}))$$
$$= (4\vec{u} + 7\vec{u}) - \vec{v}$$
$$= (4 + 7)\vec{u} - \vec{v}$$
$$= 11\vec{u} - \vec{v}$$

Note that, although these are exactly what we would have hoped for as results considering our previous encounters with adding, subtracting, and multiplying numbers, it is necessary to go through such exercises a few times in this new mathematical setting before being assured that the same behaviour holds.

EXERCISE 1.5

A **1.** (a) Is the sum of two vectors always a vector? Explain why or why not.
    (b) Is the difference between two vectors always a vector? Explain.
    (c) Is the scalar multiple of any vector still a vector? Explain.

B **2.** (a) Draw a vector diagram to illustrate the effect of adding the zero vector to any vector.
    (b) Illustrate a similar property for scalar multiplication of vectors. What scalar must you use?

3. Using the given vectors, demonstrate the commutative property of vector addition.

4. (a) Draw two parallel vectors. Use these to illustrate the commutative property of vector addition.
    (b) Repeat (a) using two non-parallel vectors.

5. (a) Using vector $\vec{v}$ as shown and scalars, $a = 2$ and $b = 5$, illustrate the following distributive property:
$$(a + b)\vec{v} = a\vec{v} + b\vec{v}$$

  (b) Draw two vectors $\vec{u}$ and $\vec{v}$ and choose a positive scalar c. Use these to illustrate this other distributive property of vectors
$$c(\vec{u} + \vec{v}) = c\vec{u} + c\vec{v}$$

  (c) Repeat (b) using a negative scalar.

6. Illustrate the following property of vector operations. For vector $\vec{u}$ and scalars a and b,
$$(ab)\vec{u} = a(b\vec{u})$$

7. Simplify the following expressions using the properties of vector operations:

  (a) $2\vec{u} + 3\vec{v} - 9\vec{u} + \vec{v}$

  (b) $4(\vec{u} - \vec{v}) + 3\vec{u} - \vec{v}$

  (c) $4(2\vec{v}) + (\vec{w} - \vec{v})$

  (d) $6(3\vec{v} - 2\vec{u}) + 4\vec{u} - (\vec{v} - \vec{w})$

  (e) $5(\vec{u} - 3\vec{v}) + \vec{u} + 15\vec{v}$

8. Given that $\vec{u} = 2\vec{x} - \vec{y}, \vec{v} = 3\vec{y} - 5\vec{x}, \vec{x} = \vec{i} + \vec{j}, \vec{y} = 4\vec{i} + 2\vec{j}$; write $\vec{u}, \vec{v}, \vec{u} + \vec{v}, \vec{u} - \vec{v}$ in terms of $\vec{i}$ and $\vec{j}$.

9. Prepare a summary listing of all the properties of vector operations dealt with in this section. State all properties in general form with a suitable name: for example,

  commutative property of vector addition:
  For vectors $\vec{u}$ and $\vec{v}, \vec{u} + \vec{v} = \vec{v} + \vec{u}$

10. Using properties of vector operations, prove that for any two vectors $\vec{u}$ and $\vec{v}$, there is a third vector $\vec{w}$ for which
$$\vec{u} + \vec{v} + \vec{w} = \vec{0}.$$

PROBLEMS PLUS

A plane is capable of flying 180 km/h in still air. The pilot, Captain Carl, takes off from an airfield and heads due north according to the plane's compass. After 30 minutes of flight time, Captain Carl notices that, due to the wind, the plane has actually travelled 80 km at an angle 5° east of north.

  (a) What is the wind velocity?

  (b) In what direction should the pilot have headed to reach the intended destination?

1.6 REVIEW EXERCISE

1. Which of the following are true statements?
   (a) If $|\overrightarrow{AB}| = |\overrightarrow{AC}|$ then $\overrightarrow{AB} = \overrightarrow{AC}$
   (b) If $\overrightarrow{AB} = -\overrightarrow{AC}$ then $|\overrightarrow{AB}| = |\overrightarrow{AC}|$
   (c) $3\overrightarrow{BB} = -2\overrightarrow{BB}$
   (d) $-5\overrightarrow{AB} = 5(-\overrightarrow{AB})$
   (e) $2\overrightarrow{AB}$ and $-4\overrightarrow{BA}$ have the same direction.

2. For the vectors shown on the diagram, write $\vec{u}$ in terms of
   (a) $\vec{v}, \vec{w}, \vec{q}$, and $\vec{r}$
   (b) $\vec{v}, \vec{w}$, and $\vec{z}$
   (c) $\vec{v}, \vec{x}, \vec{y}, \vec{p}$, and $\vec{q}$

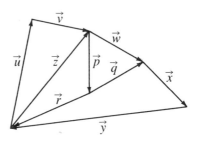

3. Name all equal vectors on the diagram.

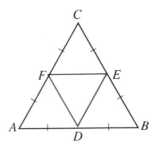

4. Draw two vectors at an angle of 45° to each other, one twice as long as the other.
   (a) Using the Parallelogram Law, draw the sum of these vectors.
   (b) Using the Triangle Law, draw the resultant of these vectors.

5. For vectors $\vec{u}$ and $\vec{v}$ as shown, draw each of the following:

   (a) $\vec{u} + 2\vec{v}$ (b) $3\vec{v} - 2\vec{u}$

6. What is the magnitude of $\frac{1}{|\vec{v}|}\vec{v}$?

7. Find the magnitude of the resultant force in each case.
    (a) Forces of 33 N and 47 N acting at a point at an angle of 40° to
         each other.
    (b) Forces of 9 N and 12 N acting at a point at an angle of 100°·to
         each other.

8. Find the equilibrant for each set of forces.
    (a)

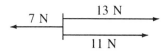

    (b)

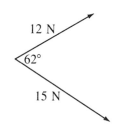

9. Find the resultant velocity in each case.
    (a) 26 m/s at N70°E, 5 m/s at S60°E
    (b) 3 km/h north, 4 km/h east, 6 km/h northeast

10. Simplify each expression using the properties of vector operations.
    (a) $-4(3\vec{u}) + \vec{u}$
    (b) $3\vec{v} + 5\vec{u} - 7\vec{v} + \vec{u}$
    (c) $2\vec{u} + 3(\vec{v} + \vec{u}) + 5\vec{v}$
    (d) $-2(6\vec{u}) - 3(\vec{u} - \vec{v})$
    (e) $10\vec{u} + 2(\vec{v} - 5\vec{u})$

11. A force of magnitude 12 N is the resultant of two forces, one of
    which has a magnitude of 7 N and acts at 30° to the resultant. Find
    the magnitude and direction of the other force.

12. A sheet with a mass of 2 kg is hung by a corner from the centre of a
    line 20 m long whose ends are fastened to poles 18 m apart. What is
    the tension in each portion of the line?

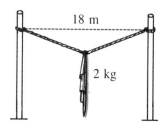

13. A plane is steering N50°E with an airspeed of 310 km/h; the wind is from the north at 54 km/h. Find the ground velocity of the plane.

14. A ship is steering east at 15 kn. A submarine 5 M to the north is steering S60°E at 20 kn.
    (a) Find the velocity of the submarine relative to the ship.
    (b) Will the submarine pass in front of or behind the ship?

15. For vectors $\vec{x}$ and $\vec{y}$ at right angles to each other, find expressions in terms of $|\vec{x}|$ and $|\vec{y}|$ for
    (a) $|\vec{x} + \vec{y}|$ \qquad (b) $|\vec{x} - \vec{y}|$
    (c) $|2\vec{x} + 5\vec{y}|$ \qquad (d) $|3\vec{y} - \vec{x}|$

16. With vectors $\vec{u}$, $\vec{v}$, and $\vec{w}$ as shown, illustrate geometrically

    (a) the associative property of vector addition
    (b) $(a + b)\vec{u} = a\vec{u} + b\vec{u}$ for scalars $a = 1$ and $b = 3$
    (c) $k(\vec{v} + \vec{w}) = k\vec{v} + k\vec{w}$ for scalar $k = -3$.

PROBLEMS PLUS

A car is stuck on the side of the road and the driver has only a long piece of nonstretchable rope. Seeing a tree 20 m away from the car he ties the rope to the tree and then to the car such that it is quite tight and any sag is negligible. The driver then pushes the rope at the midpoint of the rope with a push perpendicular yet horizontal to the line made by the rope. What force does the rope exert on the car if the driver can push the rope to a distance of 2 m with a force of 600 N?

PROBLEMS PLUS

A clothesline is tied between two poles, 8 m apart. The line is quite taut and has negligible sag. When a wet shirt with a mass of 0.8 kg is hung at the middle of the line, the midpoint is pulled down 8 cm. What is the tension in the clothesline at this time?

1.7 CHAPTER 1 TEST

1. When is $|\vec{u} + \vec{v}| = |\vec{u}| + |\vec{v}|$?

2. Given the information on the diagram, write
    (a) $\overrightarrow{AF}$ in terms of $\overrightarrow{AC}$
    (b) $\overrightarrow{AE}$ in terms of $\overrightarrow{AB}$ and $\overrightarrow{BC}$
    (c) $\overrightarrow{AB}$ in terms of $\overrightarrow{AF}$ and $\overrightarrow{EC}$.

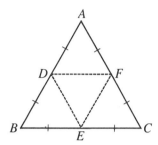

3. For *PQRS*, a quadrilateral with $\overrightarrow{PQ} = 2\vec{u}$, $\overrightarrow{QR} = 3\vec{v}$, and $\overrightarrow{QS} = 3(\vec{v} - \vec{u})$, express $\overrightarrow{PS}$ in terms of $\vec{u}$ and $\vec{v}$.

4. Illustrate geometrically the following property of vector operations: For vectors $\vec{u}$ and $\vec{v}$ and scalar a, $a(\vec{u} + \vec{v}) = a\vec{u} + a\vec{v}$

5. Find the magnitude of the resultant of two forces of 15 N and 11 N acting at a point at 55° to each other.

6. An aircraft pilot wishes to fly from an airfield to a point lying S20°E from the airfield. If there is a wind of 45 km/h blowing from N80°E and the cruising speed of her aircraft is 550 km/h,
    (a) what direction should the pilot take?
    (b) what will be her actual ground speed?

7. Simplify using the properties of vector operations.
    $$3(4\vec{u} + \vec{v}) - 2\vec{u} + 3(\vec{u} - \vec{v})$$

8. A 14 m steel cable is suspended between two fixed points that are 10 m apart. A force of 12 N pulls the cable down at a point 6 m from the end of the cable. Determine the tension in each section of the cable.

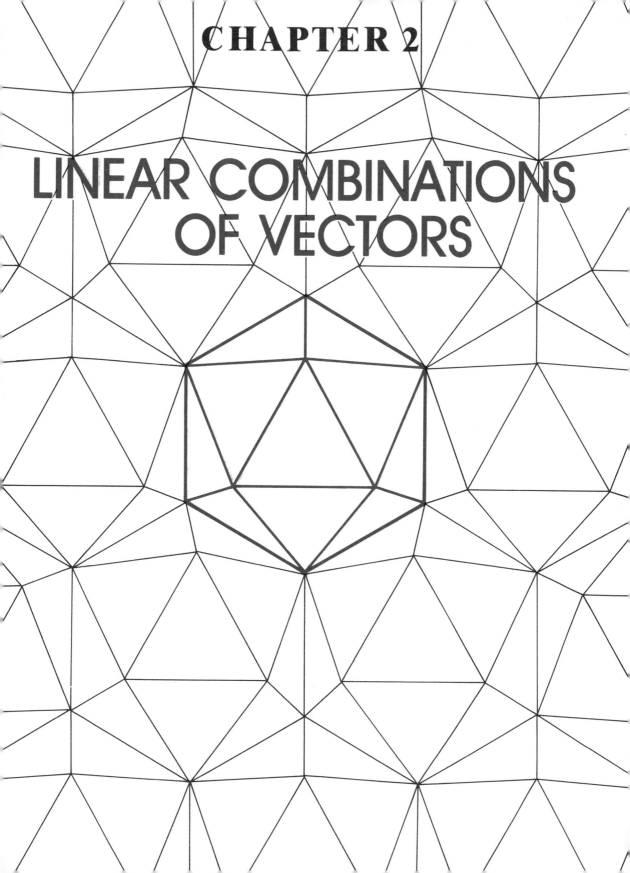

CHAPTER 2

LINEAR COMBINATIONS OF VECTORS

REVIEW AND PREVIEW TO
CHAPTER 2

Division of a Line Segment

Suppose that X lies on PQ where $PX = 3$ cm and $XQ = 6$ cm.

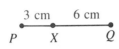

Then $\dfrac{PX}{XQ} = \dfrac{3}{6} = \dfrac{1}{2}$

We say X **divides the segment PQ internally** in the ratio $1:2$.
Suppose that X lies on PQ produced where $PX = 20$ cm,
$XQ = 15$ cm.

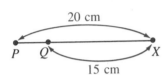

Then $\dfrac{PX}{XQ} = \dfrac{20}{15} = \dfrac{4}{3}$

We say X **divides the segment PQ externally** in the ratio $4:3$.
In general, for points P, Q, and X,

X **divides PQ in the ratio $a:b$** means that

$$\frac{PX}{XQ} = \frac{a}{b}$$

If X lies on PQ, the division is **internal**.
If X lies on PQ or QP produced, the division is **external**.

EXERCISE 1

1. State the ratio in which X divides the line segment. State whether
    the division is internal or external.

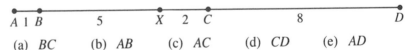

    (a) BC (b) AB (c) AC (d) CD (e) AD

2. In what ratio does P divide XY in each case?
    (a) $XY = 12$ cm, $PY = 18$ cm
    (b) $XP = 4$ cm, $PY = 18$ cm
    (c) $XY = 10$ cm, $XP = 17$ cm

3. If Q divides the line segment CD internally in the ratio $3:5$ and
    $CD = 18$ cm, find the lengths of CQ and QD.

4. If P divides AB externally in the ratio $7:4$ and $AB = 10$ cm, find
    the lengths of AP and PB.

EXERCISE 2   Solving Systems of Linear Equations

Solve each system.

1. $a + b = 5$
   $a - c = 8$
   $a + b + c = -1$

2. $a + b = 1$
   $2b = c$
   $2a + b = 1$

3. $a + b = 4$
   $2a + c = 0$
   $b + c = 1$

4. $a + 4b = 2$
   $2a + c = 0$
   $8b - 3c = 0$

5. $a = b$
   $2b = d$
   $2a + 3c = -1$
   $4a - d = 2$

6. $a + b = 1$
   $c - d = 1$
   $a + c = 4$
   $b + d = 2$

INTRODUCTION

Depending on the relationship between the vectors used, we can produce a linear combination of vectors that is either trivial or extremely powerful. We examine these two situations; linearly dependent vectors and linearly independent vectors. Using an extension of the notion of division of a line segment we look at linear combinations of fixed vectors in order to characterize points that are collinear or coplanar. Finally we apply both the results about fixed vectors and the theory of linear independence of vectors to prove statements of Euclidean geometry.

2.1 LINEAR COMBINATIONS OF VECTORS

In Chapter 1 we produced both resultants and scalar multiples of vectors. Now we use both of these operations together. A **linear combination of vectors** $\vec{u}$ and $\vec{v}$ is a vector $\vec{w}$ of the form $\vec{w} = c\vec{u} + d\vec{v}$ for scalars c and d. Indeed this concept of linear combination can be applied to any number of vectors. In a linear combination the vector operations dealt with in the preceding chapter are used to produce "new vectors from old."

Example 1   For the vectors shown in the diagram, write
(a) $\vec{v}$ as a linear combination of $\vec{u}$ and $\vec{x}$;
(b) $\vec{v}$ as a linear combination of $\vec{u}$, $\vec{w}$, and $\vec{y}$;
(c) $\vec{u}$ as a linear combination of $\vec{v}$, $\vec{w}$, and $\vec{y}$.

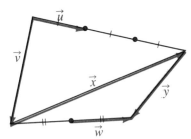

Solution   (a) $\vec{v} = 3\vec{u} + (-\vec{x}) = 3\vec{u} - \vec{x}$
(b) $\vec{v} = 3\vec{u} + \vec{y} + (-2)\vec{w} = 3\vec{u} + \vec{y} - 2\vec{w}$
(c) Using the linear combination from part (b), we find that

$$3\vec{u} = \vec{v} - \vec{y} + 2\vec{w}$$

So, $\vec{u} = \frac{1}{3}\vec{v} - \frac{1}{3}\vec{y} + \frac{2}{3}\vec{w}$

Example 2   Three coplanar vectors $\vec{u}$, $\vec{v}$, and $\vec{w}$ are shown in the diagram. If their magnitudes are 4, 6, and 10 respectively, write $\vec{u}$ as a linear combination of $\vec{v}$ and $\vec{w}$.

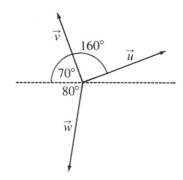

Solution   Let $\vec{u} = k\vec{v} + l\vec{w}$. Then $\cos 60° = \dfrac{|\vec{u}|}{|l\vec{w}|} = \dfrac{|\vec{u}|}{|l||\vec{w}|} = \dfrac{4}{10|l|}$.

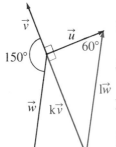

But $\cos 60° = \frac{1}{2}$, so $\frac{1}{2} = \dfrac{4}{10|l|}$. Thus $10|l| = 8$ and $|l| = \frac{4}{5}$.

Similarly, $\tan 60° = \dfrac{|k\vec{v}|}{|\vec{u}|} = \dfrac{|k||\vec{v}|}{|\vec{u}|} = \dfrac{6|k|}{4}$.

But $\tan 60° = \sqrt{3}$ so $\sqrt{3} = \dfrac{6|k|}{4}$. Thus $4\sqrt{3} = 6|k|$ and

$$|k| = \dfrac{2\sqrt{3}}{3}.$$

From the diagram we see that both k and l must be negative so

$$\vec{u} = -\dfrac{2\sqrt{3}}{3}\vec{v} - \tfrac{4}{5}\vec{w}$$

The relationships between the vectors used in a linear combination are of interest.

Vectors $\vec{u}_1, \vec{u}_2, \vec{u}_3, \ldots, \vec{u}_n$ are **linearly dependent**, if there exist scalars $a_1, a_2, a_3, \ldots, a_n$, not all zero, such that $a_1\vec{u}_1 + a_2\vec{u}_2 + a_3\vec{u}_3 + \ldots + a_n\vec{u}_n = \vec{0}$.

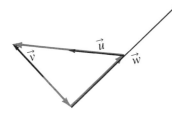

Intuitively, the directions of linearly dependent vectors bear some relationship to one another. This relationship is such that, if you travel for some distance in the direction of one vector (or its opposite) and then for some distance in the direction of the next vector (or its opposite) and so on, it is possible to arrive back at your starting point; that is, you have gone nowhere.

Example 3   (a)   Prove that vectors $\vec{u}$ and $\vec{v}$ are linearly dependent.

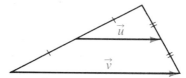

(b) Prove that vectors $\vec{x}$, $\vec{y}$, $\vec{z}$, and $\vec{w}$ are linearly dependent.

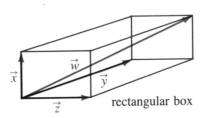

rectangular box

Proof (a) Because the vectors are directed line segments joining the mid-points of sides of the triangle, we know that $2\vec{u} = \vec{v}$.

Thus, $2\vec{u} - \vec{v} = \vec{0}$

We have found two scalars, 2 and -1, not both zero, that produce the zero vector as a linear combination of $\vec{u}$ and $\vec{v}$, so

$\vec{u}$ and $\vec{v}$ are linearly dependent.

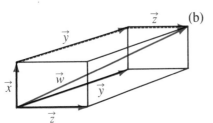

(b) Because opposite sides of each face of the box are equal and parallel, we can draw copies of $\vec{y}$ and $\vec{z}$ as shown. Thus we see that

$$\vec{x} + \vec{y} + \vec{z} - \vec{w} = \vec{0}$$

We have scalars, 1, 1, 1, -1, not all zero which produce $\vec{0}$ as a linear combination of $\vec{x}$, $\vec{y}$, $\vec{z}$, and $\vec{w}$,

so, $\vec{x}$, $\vec{y}$, $\vec{z}$, and $\vec{w}$ are linearly dependent.   ⬡

Linear dependence of two vectors

In Example 3(a) we see that $2\vec{u} - \vec{v} = \vec{0}$ or, equivalently, that $2\vec{u} = \vec{v}$.

When we consider only two vectors $\vec{u}$ and $\vec{v}$, the notion of linear dependence is equivalent to the condition that one vector is a scalar multiple of the other according to the following reasoning.

If $\vec{u} = c\vec{v}$, then $1\vec{u} - c\vec{v} = \vec{0}$, that is, the zero vector can be written as a linear combination of $\vec{u}$ and $\vec{v}$ where at least one scalar, 1, is not zero.

On the other hand, if we start with such a linear combination, that is, $a\vec{u} + b\vec{v} = \vec{0}$, where not both a and b are zero, we can do the following.

By assuming that b is a non-zero scalar, we can write $\vec{v} = -\frac{a}{b}\vec{u}$; however, if $b = 0$ then $a \neq 0$; so we could write $\vec{u} = -\frac{b}{a}\vec{v}$.

In Example 3(a), we see that $\vec{u}$ and $\vec{v}$ are parallel.

Using the characterization of dependent vectors as vectors for which one is a scalar multiple of the other we can show also that two linearly dependent vectors are two parallel vectors.

If two vectors $\vec{u}$ and $\vec{v}$ are parallel, then their directions are either the same or exactly opposite. If the directions are the same, we can write $\vec{u} = \frac{|\vec{u}|}{|\vec{v}|} \vec{v}$; that is, we multiply $\vec{v}$ by a factor that adjusts its magnitude to that of $\vec{u}$ (multiplying $\vec{v}$ by $\frac{1}{|\vec{v}|}$ to adjust the magnitude to 1, then by $|\vec{u}|$). Otherwise, we write $\vec{u} = -\frac{|\vec{u}|}{|\vec{v}|} \vec{v}$. So, if two vectors are parallel, one is a scalar multiple of the other.

Conversely, if one vector is a scalar multiple of another, $\vec{u} = c\vec{v}$, then, according to the definition of scalar multiplication, the direction of $\vec{u}$ is either the same as that of $\vec{v}$ (if $c > 0$) or opposite to that of $\vec{v}$ (if $c < 0$). So, the vectors are parallel.
Note: This proof was requested in Question 9 of Exercise 1.4.

In discussing relationships between points, the term *collinear* is used to indicate that the points all lie on the same line. Because the position of a free vector in space is not fixed, the definition of collinearity for vectors is adapted as follows.

> Vectors are **collinear vectors** if they lie on a straight line *when they are arranged tail-to-tail*.

Note that, according to this definition, any vector is collinear with the zero vector, $\vec{0}$. This concept of collinear vectors is obviously equivalent to the condition that the vectors are parallel. We now summarize the results of the preceding discussions.

> The following conditions are equivalent for vectors $\vec{u}$ and $\vec{v}$:
> - vectors $\vec{u}$ and $\vec{v}$ are linearly dependent
> - at least one vector is a scalar multiple of the other
> - vectors $\vec{u}$ and $\vec{v}$ are parallel
> - vectors $\vec{u}$ and $\vec{v}$ are collinear

Linear Dependence of Three Vectors

> **Theorem:** Three vectors are linearly dependent if and only if at least one of the vectors can be written as a linear combination of the other two vectors.

Proof   Consider three dependent vectors $\vec{u}$, $\vec{v}$, and $\vec{w}$. Because these are dependent we can find scalars a, b, and c, not all zero, such that $a\vec{u} + b\vec{v} + c\vec{w} = \vec{0}$.

Assume that $a \neq 0$; then we can write $\vec{u} = -\frac{b}{a}\vec{v} - \frac{c}{a}\vec{w}$, that is, $\vec{u}$ is a linear combination of $\vec{v}$ and $\vec{w}$. (If $a = 0$, we could use either b or c in the same manner.)

Thus, at least one of the vectors can be written as a linear combination of the other two.

Now, we consider three vectors $\vec{x}$, $\vec{y}$, and $\vec{z}$ for which $\vec{x}$ is a linear combination of $\vec{y}$ and $\vec{z}$; that is, there are scalars k and l such that $\vec{x} = k\vec{y} + l\vec{z}$. Then we can write $-1\vec{x} + k\vec{y} + l\vec{z} = \vec{0}$; that is, we can write $\vec{0}$ as a linear combination of $\vec{x}$, $\vec{y}$, and $\vec{z}$ with not all scalars zero.

Thus, $\vec{x}$, $\vec{y}$, and $\vec{z}$ are dependent vectors.

Vectors are **coplanar vectors**, if they lie on a plane *when they are arranged tail-to-tail.*

Example 4   (a)   For vectors $\vec{u}$ and $\vec{v}$ as shown here, draw the linear combination $3\vec{u} - 5\vec{v}$ using the Parallelogram Law for vector addition (see Questions 6 and 7 in Exercise 1.2).

$\xleftarrow{\quad \vec{u} \quad}$ $\diagup \vec{v}$

(b)   Explain why vectors $\vec{u}$, $\vec{v}$, and $3\vec{u} - 5\vec{v}$ are coplanar vectors.

Solution   (a)

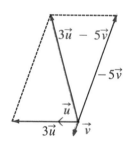

(b)   The vectors $\vec{u}$, $\vec{v}$ and $3\vec{u} - 5\vec{v}$ are tail to tail. Since $3\vec{u}$ and $\vec{u}$ are collinear, as are $-5\vec{v}$ and $\vec{v}$, the plane on which $\vec{u}$, $\vec{v}$ lie is the plane on which $3\vec{u}$ and $-5\vec{v}$ lie. From (a) we see that $3\vec{u} - 5\vec{v}$ is constructed using the parallelogram law (see diagram) in the plane of $3\vec{u}$ and $-5\vec{v}$. So, $3\vec{u} - 5\vec{v}$ lies in the same plane as $\vec{u}$ and $\vec{v}$. Hence $\vec{u}$, $\vec{v}$, and $3\vec{u} - 5\vec{v}$ are coplanar.

In general, for vectors $\vec{u}$, $\vec{v}$, and scalars a, b, the three vectors $\vec{u}$, $\vec{v}$, and $a\vec{u} + b\vec{v}$ are coplanar vectors. The proof is left for the reader as Question 13(b) in Exercise 2.1. The proof of the following statement is also left as an exercise as Question 14.

> If three vectors are linearly dependent, then they are coplanar.

We have now laid the foundation for a characterization of three linearly dependent vectors similar to that for two dependent vectors developed in this section. We will complete this characterization in the next section of this chapter.

EXERCISE 2.1

A 1. Given $5\vec{u} + \vec{v} - 7\vec{w} + 3.5\vec{z} = \vec{0}$, express each vector as a linear combination of the other three.

2. For the vectors shown in the parallelogram, give

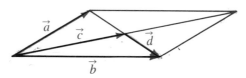

(a) $\vec{a}$ as a linear combination of $\vec{b}$ and $\vec{c}$;
(b) $\vec{a}$ as a linear combination of $\vec{c}$ and $\vec{d}$;
(c) $\vec{b}$ as a linear combination of $\vec{a}$, $\vec{c}$, and $\vec{d}$.

B 3. Draw vectors $\vec{u}$ and $\vec{v}$ at right angles to each other with $|\vec{u}| = 3$ and $|\vec{v}| = 4.5$. Then draw the following linear combinations of $\vec{u}$ and $\vec{v}$.
(a) $\vec{u} + \vec{v}$ (b) $2\vec{u} - \vec{v}$
(c) $2.5\vec{u} + 2\vec{v}$ (d) $3\vec{v} - 5\vec{u}$

4. For the given vectors $\vec{u}$, $\vec{v}$, and $\vec{w}$, draw each of the following linear combinations.

(a) $\vec{u} + \vec{v} + \vec{w}$ (b) $\vec{u} - 3\vec{v} + \vec{w}$
(c) $2\vec{u} + 2\vec{v} + 2\vec{w}$ (d) $1.5\vec{v} + \vec{w} - 3\vec{u}$

5. Consider vectors $\vec{u}$, $\vec{v}$, and $\vec{w}$ as shown in the diagram. If $|\vec{u}| = 6$, $|\vec{v}| = 9$, and $|\vec{w}| = 12$,
(a) write $\vec{w}$ as a linear combination of $\vec{u}$ and $\vec{v}$,
(b) write $\vec{u}$ as a linear combination of $\vec{v}$ and $\vec{w}$.

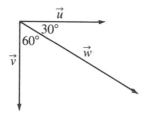

6. For vectors $a\vec{u}$, $b\vec{v}$, and $\vec{w}$ as shown where a and b are positive scalars, $|\vec{u}| = 1$, $|\vec{v}| = 5$, and $|\vec{w}| = 8$, write $\vec{w}$ as a linear combination of $\vec{u}$ and $\vec{v}$.

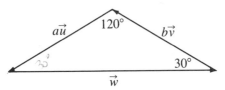

7. Consider vectors $\vec{x}$, $\vec{y}$, and $\vec{z}$ as shown in the diagram. If $|\vec{x}| = 10$, $|\vec{y}| = 4$, and $|\vec{z}| = 3$,
   (a) write $\vec{z}$ as a linear combination of $\vec{x}$ and $\vec{y}$,
   (b) write $\vec{x}$ as a linear combination of $\vec{y}$ and $\vec{z}$.

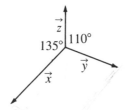

8. (a) For vectors $\vec{u}$ and $\vec{v}$, write $3\vec{u} - 4\vec{v}$ as a linear combination of $\vec{u} + \vec{v}$ and $\vec{u} - \vec{v}$.
   (b) What geometric conclusion can then be reached about $\vec{u} + \vec{v}$, $\vec{u} - \vec{v}$, and $3\vec{u} - 4\vec{v}$?

9. (a) Draw a diagram to illustrate four linearly dependent vectors in the plane.
   (b) Draw a diagram to illustrate four linearly dependent vectors in space.
   (c) Form a conclusion about vectors $\vec{u}$, $\vec{v}$, $\vec{w}$, and $\vec{z}$ in Question 1 of this exercise.

10. (a) Prove, using the definition of linearly dependent vectors, that for any vector $\vec{u}$, the two vectors $\vec{0}$ and $\vec{u}$ are dependent.
    (b) Prove, for any vectors $\vec{u}$ and $\vec{v}$, that $\vec{0}$, $\vec{u}$, and $\vec{v}$ are dependent vectors.

11. Prove that vectors $\vec{u}$, $\vec{v}$, and $\vec{w}$ are dependent if any two of them are dependent.

12. (a) Write a definition of **one dependent vector.**
    (b) What is the only *single dependent vector*?

13. (a) Prove (from first principles): For vectors $\vec{u}$ and $\vec{v}$, $\vec{u}$, $\vec{v}$, and $4\vec{u} + 7\vec{v}$ are coplanar.
    (b) Prove: For vectors $\vec{u}$ and $\vec{v}$ and scalars a and b, $\vec{u}$, $\vec{v}$, and $a\vec{u} + b\vec{v}$ are coplanar. [Hint: See Example 4.]

14. Prove: If three vectors are linearly dependent, then they are coplanar. [Hint: Use the result of Question 13.]

2.2   LINEAR INDEPENDENCE OF VECTORS

Linearly dependent vectors are related to each other in such a way that it is impossible to travel very far using just linear combinations of such vectors. Vectors not related in this way can take us a long way.

> Vectors $\vec{u}_1$, $\vec{u}_2$, $\vec{u}_3$, ... , $\vec{u}_n$ are **linearly independent if** the *only* linear combination of $\vec{u}_1$, $\vec{u}_2$, $\vec{u}_3$, ... , $\vec{u}_n$ that produces the zero vector is $0\vec{u}_1 + 0\vec{u}_2 + 0\vec{u}_3 + ... + 0\vec{u}_n$.

Intuitively, this means that travelling a certain distance in the direction of $\vec{u}_1$ (or its opposite) and then for a certain distance in the direction of $\vec{u}_2$ (or its opposite) and so on *cannot* bring us back to the starting point.

Note that this is equivalent to the statement that vectors are linearly independent if and only if they are not linearly dependent.

Example 1   In each diagram, name two dependent vectors and two independent vectors:

(a)

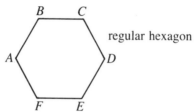

regular hexagon

(b)

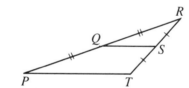

Solution   (a)   Two dependent vectors must be parallel, so any pair of parallel vectors may be used. We locate parallel vectors using the properties of regular polygons. So, $\overrightarrow{AB}$ and $\overrightarrow{DE}$ (or $\overrightarrow{AF}$ and $\overrightarrow{CD}$ or ...) are two dependent vectors.

Two independent vectors are not dependent, in other words, they must not be parallel; so we may name any pair of non-parallel vectors. Thus, $\overrightarrow{AB}$ and $\overrightarrow{BC}$ (or $\overrightarrow{AF}$ and $\overrightarrow{ED}$ or ...) are two independent vectors.

(b)   By recognizing that the line joining the midpoints of two sides of a triangle is parallel to the third side, we locate parallel vectors. So, $\overrightarrow{QS}$ and $\overrightarrow{PT}$ are two dependent vectors.

Because $\overrightarrow{PR}$ and $\overrightarrow{RT}$ are vectors along sides of a triangle we know they are not parallel; so $\overrightarrow{PR}$ and $\overrightarrow{RT}$ are two independent vectors.

Example 2   Assuming that the vectors in a given expression are (linearly) independent, solve for the unknown scalars, where possible.

(a) $(2a + 4)\vec{u} + (3b - 1)\vec{v} = \vec{0}$

(b) $(3a - 6)\vec{u} = (2a - 5)\vec{v}$

(c) $(b - a)\vec{u} + (3 - c)\vec{v} + (a + b)\vec{w} = \vec{0}$

Solution   (a)   Because $\vec{u}$ and $\vec{v}$ are independent, the only possible values for $2a + 4$ and $3b - 1$ are 0.

So, $\begin{aligned}2a + 4 &= 0 \\ 2a &= -4 \\ a &= -2\end{aligned}$ and $\begin{aligned}3b - 1 &= 0 \\ 3b &= 1 \\ b &= \tfrac{1}{3}\end{aligned}$

(b)   The given expression is equivalent to
$$(3a - 6)\vec{u} + (5 - 2a)\vec{v} = \vec{0}.$$
Because $\vec{u}$ and $\vec{v}$ are independent,

$\begin{aligned}3a - 6 &= 0 \\ 3a &= 6 \\ a &= 2\end{aligned}$ and $\begin{aligned}5 - 2a &= 0 \\ 5 &= 2a \\ a &= \tfrac{5}{2}\end{aligned}$

Because a cannot take on both of these values, there is no value for a that satisfies this equation.

(c)   Because $\vec{u}, \vec{v},$ and $\vec{w}$ are independent vectors,
$$b - a = 0 \quad \text{and} \quad 3 - c = 0 \quad \text{and} \quad a + b = 0$$
So, $c = 3$ and we solve the system $a + b = 0, a - b = 0$, to find values for a, b.

Adding the two equations, we obtain $2b = 0$, so $b = 0$. Subtracting the two equations, we obtain $2a = 0$, so $a = 0$.

Thus, $a = b = 0, c = 3$

We continue with a consideration of vectors that lie in the same plane, that is, **planar vectors**.

Two planar vectors form a **basis for a plane** if every vector in that plane can be written as a linear combination of the two vectors.

The importance of linearly independent planar vectors lies in the following theorem.

Basis Theorem for the Plane

Any two independent planar vectors form a basis for the plane in which they are located.

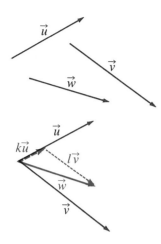

Proof

Consider the independent vectors $\vec{u}$ and $\vec{v}$ and a third vector $\vec{w}$ lying in the same plane as $\vec{u}$ and $\vec{v}$. Arrange these vectors tail-to-tail.

Draw a vector parallel to $\vec{v}$ from $\vec{u}$ to the tip of $\vec{w}$. (This can always be done because $\vec{u}$ and $\vec{v}$ are not parallel. See Example 3.) Because the vector is parallel to $\vec{v}$ we can name it $l\vec{v}$ for some scalar l. Because the vector from the tail of $\vec{u}$ to the tail of $l\vec{v}$ is parallel to $\vec{u}$, we can name it $k\vec{u}$.

Then, $\vec{w} = k\vec{u} + l\vec{v}$

that is, $\vec{w}$ can be written as a linear combination of $\vec{u}$ and $\vec{v}$.

So, the two independent vectors form a basis for the plane in which they lie.

Note: Any two vectors that form a basis for the plane are linearly independent. The proof of this statement is requested in Exercise 2.2.

Example 3

The vectors $\vec{u}$ and $\vec{v}$ are linearly independent.

Draw each vector as a linear combination of these two vectors following the technique used in the proof of the Basis Theorem for the Plane.

(a)   (b)

(c)   (d)

Solution   (a)   (b)

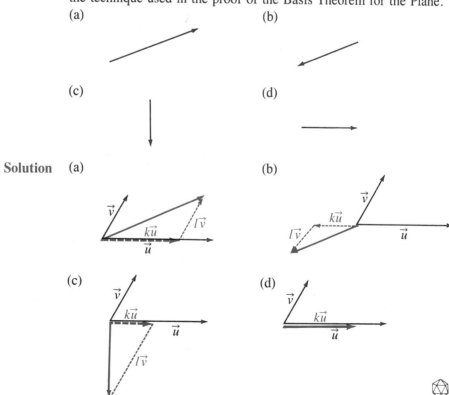

(c)   (d)

For basis vectors $\vec{u}$ and $\vec{v}$ and vector $\vec{w}$ in the plane of $\vec{u}$ and $\vec{v}$ such that $\vec{w} = a\vec{u} + b\vec{v}$, the scalars a and b are called the **co-ordinates of $\vec{w}$ with respect to the basis $\vec{u}$ and $\vec{v}$.**

> **Theorem:** The co-ordinates of a planar vector with respect to a given basis are unique.

Note: The technique used to prove this statement, known as *proof by contradiction*, is a valuable mathematical tool. In applying this technique we assume that the given conditions are true but that the statement which is to be proved is false. From these combined assumptions we are lead logically to some contradictory statement. At this point we conclude that the statement to be proved must therefore be true.

Proof   Choose basis vectors $\vec{u}$ and $\vec{v}$ and a third vector $\vec{w}$ in the plane of $\vec{u}$ and $\vec{v}$. We assume that there are two *different* pairs of scalars a_1, b_1 and a_2, b_2 such that

INDIRECT REASONING

$$a_1\vec{u} + b_1\vec{v} = \vec{w}$$
and $$a_2\vec{u} + b_2\vec{v} = \vec{w}$$

By subtracting these two equations we obtain

$$(a_1\vec{u} + b_1\vec{v}) - (a_2\vec{u} + b_2\vec{v}) = \vec{w} - \vec{w}$$
$$(a_1 - a_2)\vec{u} + (b_1 - b_2)\vec{v} = \vec{0}$$

Because $\vec{u}$ and $\vec{v}$ are linearly independent, we conclude that

$$a_1 - a_2 = 0 \quad \text{and} \quad b_1 - b_2 = 0$$
So, $$a_1 = a_2 \quad \text{and} \quad b_1 = b_2$$

However, this contradicts our choice of a_1, b_1 and a_2, b_2 as *different* pairs of scalars. Thus, there cannot be different pairs of scalars producing $\vec{w}$ as a linear combination of $\vec{u}$ and $\vec{v}$; in other words, the co-ordinates of $\vec{w}$ with respect to $\vec{u}$ and $\vec{v}$ are unique.

Using the notion of linear independence of vectors we return to the task of developing a characterization of three linearly dependent vectors begun in the preceding section.

Example 4   Prove that, if three vectors are coplanar, then they are linearly dependent.

Proof   We choose three coplanar vectors $\vec{u}$, $\vec{v}$, and $\vec{w}$.
There are two possible cases to consider. *Either* (i) no pair of the vectors is collinear (dependent) *or* (ii) at least one pair of the vectors is collinear (dependent).

TAKE CASES

(i) In the first case, we choose one of the pairs of linearly independent vectors, say $\vec{u}$ and $\vec{v}$, as a basis for the plane. Then $\vec{w} = a\vec{u} + b\vec{v}$ for some scalars a and b.

So, $a\vec{u} + b\vec{v} + (-1)\vec{w} = \vec{0}$

We have scalars, a, b, -1, not all of which are zero, for which $\vec{0}$ is a linear combination of $\vec{u}$, $\vec{v}$, and $\vec{w}$. So, we conclude that $\vec{u}$, $\vec{v}$, and $\vec{w}$ are linearly dependent vectors.

(ii) In the other case, we choose a pair of linearly dependent vectors, say $\vec{u}$ and $\vec{v}$. There are scalars c and d, not both zero, for which $c\vec{u} + d\vec{v} = \vec{0}$.

Thus, $c\vec{u} + d\vec{v} + 0\vec{w} = \vec{0}$,

that is, we can find scalars, c, d, 0, not all zero, producing $\vec{0}$ as a linear combination of $\vec{u}$, $\vec{v}$, and $\vec{w}$. We conclude that $\vec{u}$, $\vec{v}$, and $\vec{w}$ are linearly dependent vectors. ⬡

This statement combines with statements proved in Section 2.1 to give the following set of equivalent statements about three linearly dependent vectors.

The following statements about vectors $\vec{u}$, $\vec{v}$, and $\vec{w}$ are equivalent:
- $\vec{u}$, $\vec{v}$, and $\vec{w}$ are linearly dependent
- at least one of the vectors can be written as a linear combination of the other two
- $\vec{u}$, $\vec{v}$, and $\vec{w}$ are coplanar

In the following example we prove a statement about linear dependence and independence of vectors using once again the technique of proof by contradiction.

Example 5 For three linearly independent vectors $\vec{u}$, $\vec{v}$, and $\vec{w}$, prove that $\vec{w}$ and any non-zero linear combination of $\vec{u}$ and $\vec{v}$ are two linearly independent vectors.

Proof Given that $\vec{u}$, $\vec{v}$, and $\vec{w}$ are linearly independent, we assume that there exist scalars a and b, not both zero, such that $a\vec{u} + b\vec{v}$ and $\vec{w}$ are *not*

INDIRECT REASONING

linearly independent; that is, $a\vec{u} + b\vec{v}$ and $\vec{w}$ are dependent vectors. So, we can find scalars k and l, not both zero, such that

$$k(a\vec{u} + b\vec{v}) + l\vec{w} = \vec{0}$$
Thus, $ka\vec{u} + kb\vec{v} + l\vec{w} = \vec{0}$
Because $\vec{u}$, $\vec{v}$, and $\vec{w}$ are linearly independent,

$$ka = 0 \quad \text{and} \quad kb = 0 \quad \text{and} \quad l = 0$$
Because $l = 0$ and k and l are not both zero, $k \neq 0$. So $a = b = 0$. But this contradicts our assumption that a and b are not both zero. So $a\vec{u} + b\vec{v}$ and $\vec{w}$ must be linearly independent vectors. ⬡

The basis theorem holds also for three linearly independent vectors.

Basis Theorem for Space

Any three linearly independent vectors form a basis for space; that is, any vector in space can be written as a linear combination of the three vectors.

Note: The proof of this statement relies on two other results:
1.   The Basis Theorem for the Plane, and
2.   The result that, if any three vectors are linearly independent then any two of the vectors are also linearly independent (to be proved as Question 9 in Exercise 2.2).

Proof   Consider three linearly independent vectors, $\vec{u}$, $\vec{v}$, and $\vec{w}$ and a fourth vector $\vec{z}$.

There are two cases to consider.

TAKE CASES

Case 1: $\vec{z}$ is coplanar with one pair of the vectors, say $\vec{u}$ and $\vec{v}$.

Because $\vec{u}$, $\vec{v}$, and $\vec{w}$ are linearly independent, $\vec{u}$ and $\vec{v}$ are also independent. Because $\vec{z}$ is in the same plane as these independent vectors, it can be written as a linear combination of them; that is, $\vec{z} = a\vec{u} + b\vec{v}$ for some scalars a and b.

So, $\vec{z} = a\vec{u} + b\vec{v} + 0\vec{w}$; that is, $\vec{z}$ can be written as a linear combination of $\vec{u}$, $\vec{v}$, and $\vec{w}$.

Case 2: $\vec{z}$ is not coplanar with any pair of the vectors.

In particular, $\vec{z}$, $\vec{u}$, and $\vec{v}$ are not coplanar. This means that $\vec{z}$, $\vec{u}$, and $\vec{v}$ are linearly independent and, thus, $\vec{u}$ and $\vec{z}$ are independent. The independent vectors $\vec{u}$ and $\vec{z}$ form a basis for the plane in which they lie, as do the independent vectors $\vec{v}$ and $\vec{w}$. Along the line of intersection of these planes, we choose a non-zero vector $\vec{x}$.

Then, $\vec{x} = k\vec{v} + l\vec{w}$ (Basis Theorem for the Plane)
so, $\vec{x}$ and $\vec{u}$ are independent   (Example 5)

Because $\vec{z}$ is coplanar with the independent vectors $\vec{x}$ and $\vec{u}$,

$$\vec{z} = m\vec{x} + n\vec{u}$$
$$= m(k\vec{v} + l\vec{w}) + n\vec{u}$$
$$= n\vec{u} + mk\vec{v} + ml\vec{w}$$

that is, $\vec{z}$ can be written as a linear combination of $\vec{u}$, $\vec{v}$, and $\vec{w}$. Thus, three linearly independent vectors form a basis for space. ⬡

We note that, as in the plane, the coordinates of a vector in space with respect to a given basis are unique.

Several of the results from this section will be of more practical use when we consider vectors from a different point of view in Chapter 4 of this text.

EXERCISE 2.2

A **1.** Give a geometric interpretation of each of the following concepts:
   (a) two linearly dependent vectors
   (b) three linearly independent vectors.

2. Assume that the vectors in each situation are linearly independent. Wherever possible, give values for the variables.
   (a) $(2a + 4)\vec{u} + (b - 3)\vec{v} = \vec{0}$
   (b) $(a - 7)\vec{u} + (2a - 3)\vec{v} + 5\vec{w} = \vec{0}$
   (c) $(a^2 - 1)\vec{u} + (a + 1)\vec{v} = \vec{0}$

3. From each diagram, name two dependent and two independent vectors.

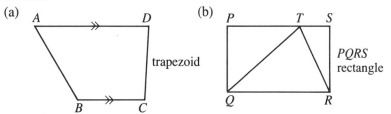

(a) A ———»— D   trapezoid

(b) P   T S   PQRS rectangle

B **4.** Wherever possible, draw the vector $\vec{w}$ as a linear combination of the given vectors $\vec{u}$ and $\vec{v}$. Where it is not possible, explain why not.

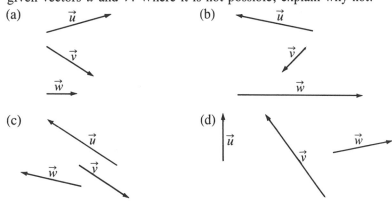

(a) $\vec{u}$
(b) $\vec{u}$
(c)
(d)

5. From the given information, what geometric conclusions can you draw about relationships between the given vectors?
   (a) $\vec{u} = -5\vec{v}$
   (b) $\vec{u} = 3\vec{v} + 7\vec{w}$
   (c) $\vec{0} = 2\vec{u} - 5\vec{v} + 0\vec{w}$
   (d) $\vec{u} + \vec{v} + \vec{w} = \vec{0}$

6. Assuming that all of the vectors involved are linearly independent, find values for the scalar variables wherever possible.
   (a) $(3a - 2)\vec{u} + (4b + 3)\vec{v} = \vec{0}$
   (b) $c\vec{w} = \dfrac{(2a + 1)}{3}\vec{u} + (12b - 5)\vec{v}$
   (c) $\overrightarrow{DC} + (-m)\overrightarrow{DC} + \overrightarrow{CB} + (-k)\overrightarrow{CB} = \vec{0}$
   (d) $a(\vec{u} + \vec{v}) - m(\vec{v} - \vec{u}) = \vec{u}$

7. The vectors $\vec{u}$, $\vec{v}$, and $\vec{w}$ are linearly independent. Prove that $\vec{u}$, $\vec{v}$, $\vec{w}$, and $\vec{z}$ are linearly dependent for any other vector $\vec{z}$ in the space of $\vec{u}$, $\vec{v}$, and $\vec{w}$.

8. Given: $\vec{u}$ and $\vec{v}$ are linearly independent vectors, a and b non-zero scalars
    Prove: $a\vec{u}$ and $b\vec{v}$ are linearly independent vectors.

9. Prove that, if three vectors are linearly independent, then any two of the vectors are also linearly independent. [Hint: Try the technique of *proof by contradiction*.]

10. Prove that any two vectors that form a basis for the plane in which they lie must be linearly independent.

C 11. Consider n independent vectors $\vec{u_1}$, $\vec{u_2}$, $\vec{u_3}$, ... , $\vec{u_n}$. Prove that none of these is $\vec{0}$. [Hint: Try *proof by contradiction*.]

12. Using the notions equivalent to linear dependence and independence of two and three vectors, many of the results from the last two sections can be reworded. For example, the statement ''If three vectors are linearly independent, then any two of the vectors are linearly independent'' (Question 9 of this exercise) could be stated as:

    If three vectors are not coplanar, then no two of the vectors are collinear.

    Write each of the indicated statements in a different form using these equivalent concepts.
    (a) Question 10(a) in Exercise 2.1
    (b) Question 10(b) in Exercise 2.1
    (c) Question 11 in Exercise 2.1
    (d) The Basis Theorem for the Plane
    (e) The Basis Theorem for Space
    (f) Example 5 in Section 2.2
    (g) Question 7 of this exercise
    (h) Question 8 of this exercise

2.3 DIVISION OF A LINE SEGMENT

The concept of *division of a line segment* is a way of describing the relative locations of several collinear points. We use this concept in the context of vectors to express both relative distances and placement of points.

The situation shown in the diagram below can be described in many different ways using the idea of division of a line segment.

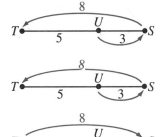

For example,
U divides $\overrightarrow{TS}$ *internally* in the ratio $5:3$

because $\left|\frac{\overrightarrow{TU}}{\overrightarrow{US}}\right| = \frac{5}{3}$ and $\overrightarrow{TU}$ and $\overrightarrow{US}$ have the same direction.

OR

U divides $\overrightarrow{ST}$ internally in the ratio $3:5$

because $\left|\frac{\overrightarrow{SU}}{\overrightarrow{UT}}\right| = \frac{3}{5}$ and $\overrightarrow{SU}$ and $\overrightarrow{UT}$ have the same direction.

OR

S divides $\overrightarrow{UT}$ *externally* in the ratio $3: -8$

because $\left|\frac{\overrightarrow{US}}{\overrightarrow{ST}}\right| = \frac{3}{8}$ and $\overrightarrow{US}$ and $\overrightarrow{ST}$ have opposite directions.

OR

S divides $\overrightarrow{UT}$ externally in the ratio $-3:8$
for the same reasons as in the previous example.

OR

T divides $\overrightarrow{US}$ externally in the ratio $5: -8$. Why?

OR

T divides $\overrightarrow{US}$ externally in the ratio $-5:8$. Why?

Notice that the use of the terms *internal* and *external* are somewhat redundant because the relative direction of the line segments is conveyed by the signs of the numbers in the ratio. That is, if the numbers have the same signs, the division is internal; if they have opposite signs, the division is external.

Example 1   For points A, B, and C as shown in the diagram:
(a) Write a statement about the division of $\overrightarrow{AC}$ by B.
(b) Write a statement about the division of $\overrightarrow{AB}$ by C.
(c) In what ratio does B divide $\overrightarrow{CA}$?
(d) In what ratio does A divide $\overrightarrow{BC}$?

Solution

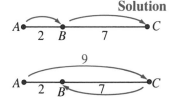

(a) Because $\left|\frac{\overrightarrow{AB}}{\overrightarrow{BC}}\right| = \frac{2}{7}$ and $\overrightarrow{AB}$ and $\overrightarrow{BC}$ have the same direction, B divides $\overrightarrow{AC}$ (internally) in the ratio $2:7$.

(b) Because $\left|\frac{\overrightarrow{AC}}{\overrightarrow{CB}}\right| = \frac{9}{7}$ and $\overrightarrow{AC}$ and $\overrightarrow{CB}$ have opposite directions, C divides $\overrightarrow{AB}$ (externally) in the ratio $9: -7$.

(c) Because $\left|\frac{\overrightarrow{CB}}{\overrightarrow{BA}}\right| = \frac{7}{2}$ and $\overrightarrow{CB}$ and $\overrightarrow{BA}$ have the same direction, B divides $\overrightarrow{CA}$ in the ratio $7:2$.

(d) Because $\left|\frac{\overrightarrow{BA}}{\overrightarrow{AC}}\right| = \frac{2}{9}$ and $\overrightarrow{BA}$ and $\overrightarrow{AC}$ have opposite directions, A divides $\overrightarrow{BC}$ in the ratio $2: -9$ or $-2:9$.

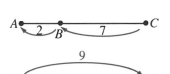

Example 2   If P divides $\overrightarrow{QR}$ in the ratio $4: -5$,

(a)   draw a diagram showing the relative positions of points P, Q, and R,

(b)   write a statement about the division of $\overrightarrow{RP}$ by the point Q.

Solution   (a)   From the statement we learn that $\frac{\left|\overrightarrow{QP}\right|}{\left|\overrightarrow{PR}\right|} = \frac{4}{5}$ and $\overrightarrow{QP}$ and $\overrightarrow{PR}$ are in opposite directions. We draw a line segment 4 units long from point Q to point P. Then we change direction and move 5 units from point P to point R.

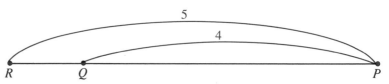

Note that this information also gives rise to a diagram that is a mirror image of this. However, both diagrams are acceptable because they both illustrate the *relative* positions of the points P, Q, and R.

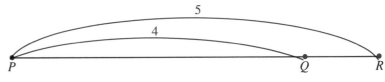

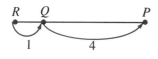

(b)   Using the diagram constructed in part (a), we reason that $\frac{\left|\overrightarrow{RQ}\right|}{\left|\overrightarrow{QP}\right|} = \frac{1}{4}$ and $\overrightarrow{RQ}$ and $\overrightarrow{QP}$ have the same direction. Thus, Q divides $\overrightarrow{RP}$ (internally) in the ratio $1:4$.

In dealing with more than three points, it is important to remember that the numbers in the ratio are relative, that is, that they are not given in standard units.

Example 3   Given that point X divides $\overrightarrow{YZ}$ (externally) in the ratio $5: -7$ and T divides $\overrightarrow{XY}$ in the ratio $1:3$,

(a)   draw a diagram showing the relative positions of the points T, X, Y, and Z,

(b)   state the ratio in which T divides $\overrightarrow{XZ}$,

(c)   state the ratio in which T divides $\overrightarrow{YZ}$.

Solution   (a)   In order to distinguish between the units in the two statements we consider that X divides $\overrightarrow{YZ}$ in the ratio $5a: -7a$ and T divides $\overrightarrow{XY}$ in the ratio $1b:3b$.

From the first statement, we learn that $\left|\overrightarrow{YX}\right| = 5a$ and $\left|\overrightarrow{XZ}\right| = 7a$ and that $\overrightarrow{YX}$ and $\overrightarrow{XZ}$ have opposite directions. So, beginning at point Y we draw a line segment $5a$ units long to point X, then reverse direction and move $7a$ units to point Z.

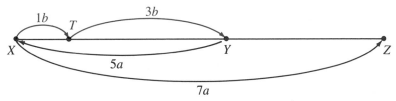

From the second statement, we learn that $\left| \overrightarrow{XT} \right| = 1b$ and $\left| \overrightarrow{TZ} \right| = 3b$ and that $\overrightarrow{XT}$ and $\overrightarrow{TY}$ have the same directions. So, beginning at point X we draw a line segment $1b$ units long to point T, then move on $3b$ more units to point Y.

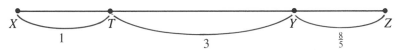

(b) In order to write a statement about T dividing $\overrightarrow{XZ}$, we must translate the lengths on the diagram to common units.
Considering the magnitude of $\overrightarrow{XY}$, we obtain

$$5a = 1b + 3b = 4b$$

So, $a = \frac{4}{5}b$

Thus, $2a = \frac{8}{5}b$

and the lengths on our diagram can be adjusted as follows:

or

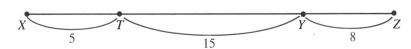

Now, we can see that $\dfrac{\left| \overrightarrow{XT} \right|}{\left| \overrightarrow{TZ} \right|} = \frac{5}{23}$ and $\overrightarrow{XT}$ and $\overrightarrow{TZ}$ are in the same direction. So, T divides $\overrightarrow{XZ}$ in the ratio $5 : 23$.

(c) Using the lengths as calculated for part (b), we see that $\dfrac{\left| \overrightarrow{YT} \right|}{\left| \overrightarrow{TZ} \right|} = \frac{15}{23}$ and $\overrightarrow{YT}$ and $\overrightarrow{TZ}$ are in opposite directions. So, T divides $\overrightarrow{YZ}$ in the ratio $15 : -23$.

EXERCISE 2.3

A **1.** For the points X, Y, and Z as shown in each diagram, give the ratio in which X divides $\overrightarrow{YZ}$.

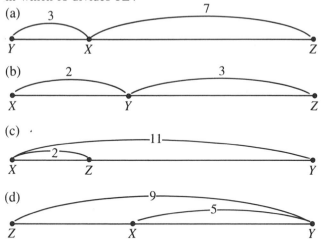

(a)

3   7

Y X Z

(b)

2   3

X Y Z

(c)

—11—

—2→

X Z Y

(d)

—9—

—5—

Z X Y

2. For each diagram in Question 1 give a statement involving
(i) internal division of a line segment,
(ii) external division of a line segment.

B **3.** From the given information, draw a diagram for each situation.
(a) A divides $\overrightarrow{BC}$ internally in the ratio $1:6$
(b) P divides $\overrightarrow{QR}$ externally in the ratio $3:-2$
(c) X divides $\overrightarrow{YZ}$ externally in the ratio $-7:8$
(d) D divides $\overrightarrow{EF}$ in the ratio $3:10$
(e) S divides $\overrightarrow{TU}$ in the ratio $5:-12$

4. Assume that A divides $\overrightarrow{XY}$ (internally) in the ratio $3:11$.
(a) What fraction of $\overrightarrow{XY}$ is $\overrightarrow{AX}$?
(b) Express $\overrightarrow{AY}$ as a fraction of $\overrightarrow{XY}$.
(c) What fraction of $\overrightarrow{XA}$ is $\overrightarrow{AY}$?

5. For each diagram in Question 1, express the rightmost line segment as a fraction of the entire line segment.

6. For each situation in Question 1, what fraction is the rightmost line segment of the leftmost segment?

7. Given that point P divides $\overrightarrow{QR}$ in the ratio $5:-3$, explain why $\overrightarrow{PQ}$ and $\overrightarrow{QR}$ are linearly dependent vectors.

8. Assume that A divides $\overrightarrow{BC}$ in the ratio $5:1$ and D divides $\overrightarrow{AC}$ in the ratio $3:4$.
(a) Draw a diagram showing the relative positions of the points A, B, C, and D.
(b) In what ratio does D divide $\overrightarrow{AB}$?
(c) Express $\overrightarrow{CD}$ as a fraction of $\overrightarrow{BD}$.

9. If X divides $\overrightarrow{YZ}$ in the ratio $4:1$, in what ratio does Y divide $\overrightarrow{XZ}$?

10. Consider collinear vectors $\overrightarrow{AB}$ and $\overrightarrow{AC}$ such that $\overrightarrow{AB} = 5\overrightarrow{AC}$. In what ratio does B divide $\overrightarrow{AC}$?

11. If M divides $\overrightarrow{KL}$ in the ratio $3:-2$ and N divides $\overrightarrow{MK}$ in the ratio $5:4$, in what ratio does K divide $\overrightarrow{LN}$?

C 12. Given the following information, draw a diagram representing the relative locations, including distances, of the six points:

    D divides $\overrightarrow{AE}$ in the ratio $2:1$

    A divides $\overrightarrow{BD}$ in the ratio $3:-5$

    E divides $\overrightarrow{CD}$ in the ratio $7:-2$

    $\overrightarrow{DF} = \frac{8}{5}\overrightarrow{DE}$

13. Assume that vectors $\overrightarrow{XY}$ and $\overrightarrow{YZ}$ are linearly dependent so that $\overrightarrow{XY} = c\overrightarrow{YZ}$ for some scalar c. Write a statement about division of the line segment $\overrightarrow{XY}$ by the point Z.

2.4 POSITION VECTORS

The geometric vectors that we have dealt with up to now are referred to as **free vectors** because the position of such a vector in space is not considered. At this stage we begin to consider vectors that start at a specific point in space and, thus, are referred to as **fixed vectors**. These vectors include the force vectors dealt with in Chapter 1 because any force vector starts at the point at which the force is applied.

In order to develop representations of lines and planes as linear combinations of vectors we introduce the idea of a vector associated with a point. First, we choose a point of reference. This point, usually denoted by O, is the **origin** for our fixed vectors. Then we associate with each point a fixed vector in the following manner:

> A **position vector for a point** X (with respect to origin O) is the fixed vector $\overrightarrow{OX}$.

Example 1   For each of the given points, draw its position vector with respect to the given point O.

(a)

(b)

B

A

• O

C

D

Solution (a)

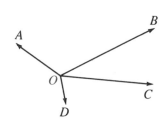

(b)

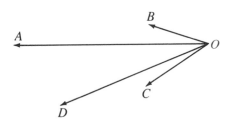

Example 2 Consider collinear points P, Q, and R. Consider also a reference point O. Write $\overrightarrow{OQ}$ as a linear combination of $\overrightarrow{OP}$ and $\overrightarrow{OR}$ if:
(a) Q divides $\overrightarrow{PR}$ (internally) in the ratio $3:5$
(b) Q divides $\overrightarrow{PR}$ (externally) in the ratio $-2:7$

Solution (a) From the given information, we draw a diagram.

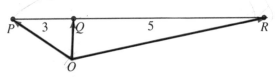

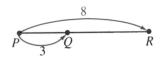

Then $\overrightarrow{PQ} = \tfrac{3}{8}\overrightarrow{PR}$

So, $\overrightarrow{OQ} = \overrightarrow{OP} + \overrightarrow{PQ}$

$= \overrightarrow{OP} + \tfrac{3}{8}\overrightarrow{PR}$

$= \overrightarrow{OP} + \tfrac{3}{8}(\overrightarrow{PO} + \overrightarrow{OR})$

$= \overrightarrow{OP} + \tfrac{3}{8}(-\overrightarrow{OP} + \overrightarrow{OR})$

$= \overrightarrow{OP} - \tfrac{3}{8}\overrightarrow{OP} + \tfrac{3}{8}\overrightarrow{OR}$

$= \tfrac{5}{8}\overrightarrow{OP} + \tfrac{3}{8}\overrightarrow{OR}$

So, we can write $\overrightarrow{OQ}$ as a linear combination of $\overrightarrow{OP}$ and $\overrightarrow{OR}$ as follows:

$$\overrightarrow{OQ} = \tfrac{5}{8}\overrightarrow{OP} + \tfrac{3}{8}\overrightarrow{OR}$$

(b) From the given information, we draw a diagram.

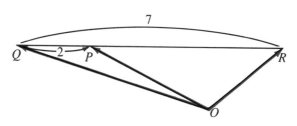

Then $\overrightarrow{PQ} = -\tfrac{2}{5}\overrightarrow{PR}$

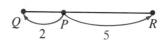

Thus, $\overrightarrow{OQ} = \overrightarrow{OP} + \overrightarrow{PQ}$

$$= \overrightarrow{OP} + (-\tfrac{2}{5}\overrightarrow{PR})$$

$$= \overrightarrow{OP} - \tfrac{2}{5}\overrightarrow{PR}$$

$$= \overrightarrow{OP} - \tfrac{2}{5}(\overrightarrow{PO} + \overrightarrow{OR})$$

$$= \overrightarrow{OP} - \tfrac{2}{5}(-\overrightarrow{OP} + \overrightarrow{OR})$$

$$= \overrightarrow{OP} + \tfrac{2}{5}\overrightarrow{OP} - \tfrac{2}{5}\overrightarrow{OR}$$

$$= \tfrac{7}{5}\overrightarrow{OP} - \tfrac{2}{5}\overrightarrow{OR}$$

So, we can write $\overrightarrow{OQ}$ as a linear combination of $\overrightarrow{OP}$ and $\overrightarrow{OR}$ as follows:

$$\overrightarrow{OQ} = \tfrac{7}{5}\overrightarrow{OP} - \tfrac{2}{5}\overrightarrow{OR}$$

Note that, in both parts of Example 2, the scalars in the linear combination add to 1. This is not a coincidence but a general result.

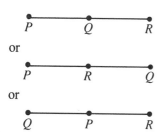

> **Theorem 1:** Three points P, Q, and R are collinear if and only if, for any point O, $\overrightarrow{OQ}$ can be written as a linear combination of $\overrightarrow{OP}$ and $\overrightarrow{OR}$,
>
> $$\overrightarrow{OQ} = a\overrightarrow{OP} + b\overrightarrow{OR}, \text{ such that } a + b = 1.$$

Proof Consider three collinear points P, Q, and R. From these we produce two collinear vectors $\overrightarrow{PQ}$ and $\overrightarrow{PR}$. So, for some scalar c,

$$\overrightarrow{PQ} = c\overrightarrow{PR}$$

Thus,
$$\begin{aligned}
\overrightarrow{OQ} &= \overrightarrow{OP} + \overrightarrow{PQ} \\
&= \overrightarrow{OP} + c\overrightarrow{PR} \\
&= \overrightarrow{OP} + c(\overrightarrow{PO} + \overrightarrow{OR}) \\
&= \overrightarrow{OP} + c(-\overrightarrow{OP} + \overrightarrow{OR}) \\
&= \overrightarrow{OP} - c\overrightarrow{OP} + c\overrightarrow{OR} \\
&= (1 - c)\overrightarrow{OP} + c\overrightarrow{OR}
\end{aligned}$$

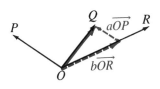

So, we can write $\overrightarrow{OQ}$ as a linear combination of $\overrightarrow{OP}$ and $\overrightarrow{OR}$ as follows:

$$\overrightarrow{OQ} = a\overrightarrow{OP} + b\overrightarrow{OR} \text{ where } a + b = (1 - c) + c = 1$$

Conversely, consider points P, Q, and R for which

$$\overrightarrow{OQ} = a\overrightarrow{OP} + b\overrightarrow{OR} \text{ where } a + b = 1$$

Then,
$$\begin{aligned}
\overrightarrow{PQ} &= \overrightarrow{PO} + \overrightarrow{OQ} \\
&= \overrightarrow{PO} + a\overrightarrow{OP} + b\overrightarrow{OR} \\
&= \overrightarrow{PO} - a\overrightarrow{PO} + b\overrightarrow{OR} \\
&= (1 - a)\overrightarrow{PO} + b\overrightarrow{OR} \\
&= b\overrightarrow{PO} + b\overrightarrow{OR} \\
&= b(\overrightarrow{PO} + \overrightarrow{OR}) \\
&= b\overrightarrow{PR}
\end{aligned}$$

Therefore $\overrightarrow{PQ}$ and $\overrightarrow{PR}$ are collinear vectors with a common point (P); so the points P, Q, and R are collinear. ⬡

In fact, a linear combination as in Theorem 1 includes enough information to describe the relative locations of the three points on the line and, conversely, given information about the relative locations of three collinear points, it is possible to produce such a linear combination.

Q divides $\overrightarrow{PR}$ in the ratio $b:a$ where $a + b = 1$ because:

$$\begin{aligned}
\overrightarrow{PQ} &= b\overrightarrow{PR} \\
&= b(\overrightarrow{PQ} + \overrightarrow{QR}) \\
&= b\overrightarrow{PQ} + b\overrightarrow{QR}
\end{aligned}$$

So,
$$\begin{aligned}
(1 - b)\overrightarrow{PQ} &= b\overrightarrow{QR} \\
a\overrightarrow{PQ} &= b\overrightarrow{QR} \\
\overrightarrow{PQ} &= \tfrac{b}{a}\overrightarrow{QR}
\end{aligned}$$

We use this fact to produce linear combinations as in Example 2, or, conversely, to describe the relative locations of collinear points. Note the reversal of the scalars between the ratio and the linear combination.

For collinear points P, Q, and R,
$\overrightarrow{OQ} = a\overrightarrow{OP} + b\overrightarrow{OR}$ with $a + b = 1$ and Q divides $\overrightarrow{PR}$ in the ratio $b:a$

Example 3   (a)   For points X, Y, and Z, and origin O, $\overrightarrow{OX} = \frac{3}{7}\overrightarrow{OY} + \frac{4}{7}\overrightarrow{OZ}$.
What can be said about the points X, Y, and Z?

(b)   Three collinear points A, B, and C are located so that B divides $\overrightarrow{AC}$ in the ratio $5:-2$. For another point O, write $\overrightarrow{OB}$ as a linear combination of $\overrightarrow{OA}$ and $\overrightarrow{OC}$.

Solution   (a)   Because the scalars in the linear combination, $\frac{3}{7}$ and $\frac{4}{7}$, add to 1, we conclude that the points X, Y, and Z are collinear. Using the ratio of the scalars, $\frac{4}{7}:\frac{3}{7}$ or $4:3$, we conclude that X divides $\overrightarrow{YZ}$ in the ratio $4:3$. We show this in a diagram:

(b)   We use the ratio $5:-2$ to find the scalars for the linear combination. We need an equivalent ratio whose parts add to 1, that is, $\frac{5}{3}:-\frac{2}{3}$. Thus, according to our theory,

$$\overrightarrow{OB} = -\frac{2}{3}\overrightarrow{OA} + \frac{5}{3}\overrightarrow{OC}$$

We can extend these ideas to deal with four points.

Theorem 2: Four points P, Q, R, and S are coplanar if and only if, for any point O, $\overrightarrow{OQ} = a\overrightarrow{OP} + b\overrightarrow{OR} + c\overrightarrow{OS}$ where $a + b + c = 1$.

Proof

TAKE CASES

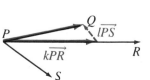

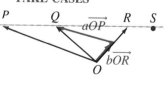

Consider four coplanar points P, Q, R, and S.
Case 1:   four collinear points
If all four of the points are collinear, we use Theorem 1 with one of the scalars equal to zero to obtain the result.
For example, $\overrightarrow{OQ} = a\overrightarrow{OP} + b\overrightarrow{OR} + 0\overrightarrow{OS}$
Case 2:   at least one point not collinear with the others
If at least one of the points, say S, is not on the line with the other points, we can produce a pair of linearly independent vectors $\overrightarrow{PR}$ and $\overrightarrow{PS}$. They form a basis for the plane determined by the points P, R, and S.

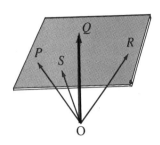

Because vector $\overrightarrow{PQ}$ is in this plane, there exist scalars k and l such that

$$\overrightarrow{PQ} = k\overrightarrow{PR} + l\overrightarrow{PS}$$

Then, $\overrightarrow{OQ} = \overrightarrow{OP} + \overrightarrow{PQ}$

$$= \overrightarrow{OP} + k\overrightarrow{PR} + l\overrightarrow{PS}$$
$$= \overrightarrow{OP} + k(\overrightarrow{PO} + \overrightarrow{OR}) + l(\overrightarrow{PO} + \overrightarrow{OS})$$
$$= \overrightarrow{OP} + k(-\overrightarrow{OP} + \overrightarrow{OR}) + l(-\overrightarrow{OP} + \overrightarrow{OS})$$
$$= (1 - k - l)\overrightarrow{OP} + k\overrightarrow{OR} + l\overrightarrow{OS}$$

So, $\overrightarrow{OQ} = a\overrightarrow{OP} + b\overrightarrow{OR} + c\overrightarrow{OS}$

where $a + b + c = (1 - k - l) + k + l = 1$

Conversely, if four points P, Q, R, and S are such that

$$\overrightarrow{OQ} = a\overrightarrow{OP} + b\overrightarrow{OR} + c\overrightarrow{OS} \text{ where } a + b + c = 1$$

then, $\overrightarrow{PQ} = \overrightarrow{PO} + a\overrightarrow{OP} + b\overrightarrow{OR} + c\overrightarrow{OS}$

$$= (1 - a)\overrightarrow{PO} + b\overrightarrow{OR} + c\overrightarrow{OS}$$
$$= (b + c)\overrightarrow{PO} + b\overrightarrow{OR} + c\overrightarrow{OS}$$
$$= b\overrightarrow{PO} + b\overrightarrow{OR} + c\overrightarrow{PO} + c\overrightarrow{OS}$$
$$= b(\overrightarrow{PO} + \overrightarrow{OR}) + c(\overrightarrow{PO} + \overrightarrow{OS})$$
$$= b\overrightarrow{PR} + c\overrightarrow{PS}$$

Because $\overrightarrow{PQ}$ can be written as a linear combination of $\overrightarrow{PR}$ and $\overrightarrow{PS}$, the vectors $\overrightarrow{PQ}$, $\overrightarrow{PR}$, and $\overrightarrow{PS}$ are coplanar. Because these coplanar vectors have a point (P) in common, the points P, Q, R, and S are coplanar. ⬡

Example 4   From the given information, draw a conclusion, where possible, about the relationship between the specified points. If it is not possible to make any conclusion, explain why not. (O is the origin.)

(a) $\overrightarrow{OX} = \frac{1}{2}\overrightarrow{OP} + \frac{1}{2}\overrightarrow{OQ}$ (b) $\overrightarrow{OA} = \frac{2}{5}\overrightarrow{OB} + \frac{1}{5}\overrightarrow{OC} + \frac{2}{5}\overrightarrow{OD}$

(c) $4\overrightarrow{OR} - 7\overrightarrow{OS} + 3\overrightarrow{OT} = \vec{0}$ (d) $\overrightarrow{OY} = \frac{3}{5}\overrightarrow{OX} - \frac{2}{5}\overrightarrow{OZ}$

Solution   (a) Because the scalars $\frac{1}{2}$ and $\frac{1}{2}$ add to 1, we conclude that the points P, Q, and X are collinear. Further, we conclude that X divides $\overrightarrow{QP}$ in the ratio $\frac{1}{2} : \frac{1}{2}$; in other words, X is the midpoint of the line segment PQ.

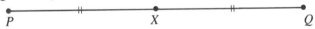

(b) Because the scalars $\frac{2}{5}$, $\frac{1}{5}$, and $\frac{2}{5}$ add to 1, we conclude that the points A, B, C, and D are coplanar.

(c) From the given information we look for a representation of one position vector in terms of the other two, for example, $\overrightarrow{OR}$ in terms of $\overrightarrow{OS}$ and $\overrightarrow{OT}$.

$$4\overrightarrow{OR} = 7\overrightarrow{OS} - 3\overrightarrow{OT}$$
$$\overrightarrow{OR} = \frac{7}{4}\overrightarrow{OS} - \frac{3}{4}\overrightarrow{OT}$$

Because the scalars $\frac{7}{4}$ and $-\frac{3}{4}$ add to 1, we conclude that the points R, S, and T are collinear. Further we reason that R divides $\overrightarrow{ST}$ in the ratio $-\frac{3}{4} : \frac{7}{4}$ or $-3 : 7$ so that the points are located as in the diagram.

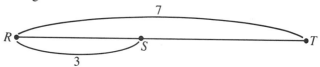

(d) Because the scalars $\frac{3}{5}$ and $-\frac{2}{5}$ do not add to 1 we can form no conclusion about the points X, Y, and Z. ⬡

EXERCISE 2.4

A **1.** In each case, from the given information, decide whether the point A divides the line segment BC internally or externally.

(a) $\overrightarrow{OA} = \frac{5}{6}\overrightarrow{OB} + \frac{1}{6}\overrightarrow{OC}$ (b) $9\overrightarrow{OA} = -2\overrightarrow{OB} + 11\overrightarrow{OC}$

(c) $\overrightarrow{OA} = \frac{11}{6}\overrightarrow{OB} - \frac{5}{6}\overrightarrow{OC}$ (d) $\overrightarrow{OB} = 2\overrightarrow{OA} - \overrightarrow{OC}$

2. For each situation in Question 1, state the ratio in which A divides $\overrightarrow{BC}$.

3. In each case, give an expression for $\overrightarrow{OX}$ such that X divides $\overrightarrow{YZ}$ in the ratio given.

(a) X divides $\overrightarrow{YZ}$ in the ratio $5:2$

(b) X divides $\overrightarrow{YZ}$ in the ratio $1:-5$

(c) X divides $\overrightarrow{YZ}$ in the ratio $9:4$

(d) X divides $\overrightarrow{YZ}$ in the ratio $-7:2$

B **4.** Draw the position vectors with respect to origin O of each of the points.

5. Determine whether the specified points are collinear, coplanar, or neither. Give reasons for your answer. (O is the origin.)

(a) $\overrightarrow{OA} = 2\overrightarrow{OB} + 3\overrightarrow{OC} - 4\overrightarrow{OD}$

(b) $3\overrightarrow{OX} = 2\overrightarrow{OY} + \overrightarrow{OZ}$

(c) $8\overrightarrow{OP} - 7\overrightarrow{OQ} - \overrightarrow{OR} = \vec{0}$

(d) $4\overrightarrow{OA} - 3\overrightarrow{OB} = \frac{1}{2}\overrightarrow{OC} + \frac{1}{2}\overrightarrow{OD}$

6. From the given information, draw a diagram for each situation showing the relative positions of the points.

   (a) $\overrightarrow{OA} = \frac{1}{4}\overrightarrow{OB} + \frac{3}{4}\overrightarrow{OC}$ (b) $\overrightarrow{OX} = \frac{5}{2}\overrightarrow{OY} - \frac{3}{2}\overrightarrow{OZ}$

   (c) $7\overrightarrow{OP} = 3\overrightarrow{OQ} + 4\overrightarrow{OR}$ (d) $-4\overrightarrow{OS} - 7\overrightarrow{OT} + 11\overrightarrow{OU} = \vec{0}$

7. Using the technique of Example 2 and Theorem 1, that is, *from first principles*, write $\overrightarrow{OX}$ as a linear combination of $\overrightarrow{OY}$ and $\overrightarrow{OZ}$ from the given information.

   (a) X divides $\overrightarrow{YZ}$ in the ratio $3:7$

   (b)

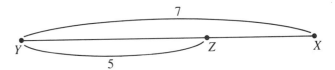

8. Using Theorem 1, express $\overrightarrow{OA}$ as a linear combination of $\overrightarrow{OB}$ and $\overrightarrow{OC}$ from the given information.

   (a) A divides $\overrightarrow{BC}$ in the ratio $3:-2$

   (b) $\overrightarrow{AB} = -\frac{1}{3}\overrightarrow{BC}$

   (c)

   (d) C divides $\overrightarrow{AB}$ in the ratio $2:9$

9. Three points P, Q, and R are located so that $\overrightarrow{OP} = 5\overrightarrow{OQ} - 4\overrightarrow{OR}$ for a point O. Prove, from first principles, that the points are collinear.

10. Two distinct points are sufficient to completely determine a line. Using Theorem 1 of this section show that a (vector) equation of the line through distinct points A and B is given by
$$\overrightarrow{OX} = a\overrightarrow{OA} + b\overrightarrow{OB}$$ where X is any point on the line, O is the origin and $a + b = 1$.

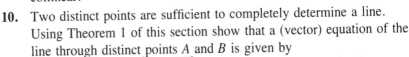

11. Four points X, Y, Z, and W are located so that
$$\overrightarrow{OX} = 7\overrightarrow{OY} + 5\overrightarrow{OZ} - 11\overrightarrow{OW}$$ for a point O.
Prove, from first principles, that the points are coplanar.

12. Three non-collinear points completely determine a plane. Using Theorem 2 of this section show that a (vector) equation of the plane through non-collinear points A, B, and C is given by
$$\overrightarrow{OX} = a\overrightarrow{OA} + b\overrightarrow{OB} + c\overrightarrow{OC}$$ where X is any point on the plane, O is the origin and $a + b + c = 1$.

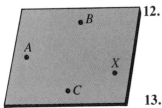

13. B divides $\overrightarrow{AD}$ in the ratio $2:9$. C divides $\overrightarrow{AB}$ in the ratio $3:-2$.

   (a) Express $\overrightarrow{OA}$ as a linear combination of $\overrightarrow{OC}$ and $\overrightarrow{OD}$.

   (b) Express $\overrightarrow{OC}$ in terms of $\overrightarrow{OB}$ and $\overrightarrow{OD}$.

C 14. Given: points P, Q, and R such that P divides $\overrightarrow{QR}$ in the ratio $m:n$ where $m + n \neq 0$.

Prove, from first principles, that

$$\overrightarrow{OP} = \frac{n}{m + n}\overrightarrow{OQ} + \frac{m}{m + n}\overrightarrow{OR}$$

*2.5 VECTOR PROOFS IN GEOMETRY

The geometric vector concepts from this chapter can be applied to prove many theorems of geometry. In the proofs of this section we will be careful not to use results from the study of Euclidean geometry but to rely only on definitions and the results proved here using vector methods.

Example 1 A quadrilateral has one pair of opposite sides equal and parallel. Prove that the other pair of opposite sides is equal and parallel.

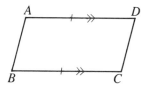

Proof Consider quadrilateral $ABCD$ with sides AB and CD parallel and of equal length; that is, in vector terms, $\overrightarrow{AB} = \overrightarrow{DC}$.

We are to prove that $\overrightarrow{AD} = \overrightarrow{BC}$.

From this point we can proceed in different ways, for example:

Proof (a):

$$\begin{aligned}
\overrightarrow{AD} &= \overrightarrow{AB} + \overrightarrow{BD} &&\text{(vector addition)} \\
&= \overrightarrow{DC} + \overrightarrow{BD} &&(\overrightarrow{AB} = \overrightarrow{DC}) \\
&= \overrightarrow{BD} + \overrightarrow{DC} &&\text{(commutativity)} \\
&= \overrightarrow{BC} &&\text{(vector addition)}
\end{aligned}$$

or *Proof (b):*

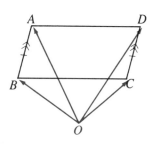

For origin O,

$$\overrightarrow{AO} + \overrightarrow{OB} = \overrightarrow{DO} + \overrightarrow{OC}$$

So,

$$-\overrightarrow{OA} + \overrightarrow{OB} = -\overrightarrow{OD} + \overrightarrow{OC}$$

and,

$$\overrightarrow{OD} = \overrightarrow{OA} - \overrightarrow{OB} + \overrightarrow{OC}$$

But,

$$\overrightarrow{AD} = \overrightarrow{AO} + \overrightarrow{OD}$$

So

$$\begin{aligned}
\overrightarrow{AD} &= \overrightarrow{AO} + (\overrightarrow{OA} - \overrightarrow{OB} + \overrightarrow{OC}) \\
&= \overrightarrow{AO} + \overrightarrow{OA} + \overrightarrow{BO} + \overrightarrow{OC} \\
&= \overrightarrow{BO} + \overrightarrow{OC} \\
&= \overrightarrow{BC}
\end{aligned}$$

In both cases we have shown that the other sides are equal and parallel.

In most situations many different approaches are possible to complete the required proof. We choose an approach as in Proof (b) of Example 1, which has the advantage of being adaptable to proofs in a wide variety of cases even though it may sometimes produce a longer proof than an alternate method. In order to practise this technique we do the following example.

Example 2   Given $\triangle XYZ$ with points A and B as shown

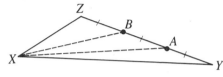

Prove: $\overrightarrow{XA} + \overrightarrow{XB} = \overrightarrow{XY} + \overrightarrow{XZ}$

Proof   From the given information about the location of points A and B, we write

$$\overrightarrow{OA} = \tfrac{2}{3}\overrightarrow{OY} + \tfrac{1}{3}\overrightarrow{OZ}$$

and $\overrightarrow{OB} = \tfrac{1}{3}\overrightarrow{OY} + \tfrac{2}{3}\overrightarrow{OZ}$ for any point O

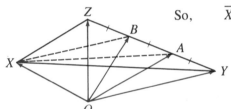

So, $\overrightarrow{XA} + \overrightarrow{XB} = \overrightarrow{XO} + \overrightarrow{OA} + \overrightarrow{XO} + \overrightarrow{OB}$

$= \overrightarrow{XO} + (\tfrac{2}{3}\overrightarrow{OY} + \tfrac{1}{3}\overrightarrow{OZ}) + \overrightarrow{XO} + (\tfrac{1}{3}\overrightarrow{OY} + \tfrac{2}{3}\overrightarrow{OZ})$

$= \overrightarrow{XO} + \tfrac{2}{3}\overrightarrow{OY} + \tfrac{1}{3}\overrightarrow{OY} + \overrightarrow{XO} + \tfrac{1}{3}\overrightarrow{OZ} + \tfrac{2}{3}\overrightarrow{OZ}$

$= (\overrightarrow{XO} + \overrightarrow{OY}) + (\overrightarrow{XO} + \overrightarrow{OZ})$

$= \overrightarrow{XY} + \overrightarrow{XZ}$

In summary, the approach we use to apply vector methods to proving geometric results always depends on formulating the given information and desired result in vector terms, then expressing the relevant vectors in terms of position vectors. In some situations, the concept of linear independence is also useful.

Example 3   Prove that the diagonals of a parallelogram bisect each other.

Proof   Consider parallelogram $ABCD$ with X the point of intersection of the diagonals AC and BD. In vector terms we are to prove that X divides both $\overrightarrow{AC}$ and $\overrightarrow{BD}$ in the ratio $1:1$, that is, for any point O,

$$\overrightarrow{OX} = \tfrac{1}{2}\overrightarrow{OA} + \tfrac{1}{2}\overrightarrow{OC} = \tfrac{1}{2}\overrightarrow{OB} + \tfrac{1}{2}\overrightarrow{OD}$$

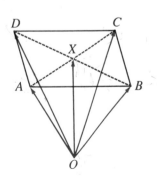

Because A, X, and C are collinear, according to Theorem 1 of Section 2.4 we can write

$$\overrightarrow{OX} = k\overrightarrow{OA} + l\overrightarrow{OC} \text{ for scalars } k \text{ and } l \text{ where } k + l = 1$$

Similarly, we can write

$$\overrightarrow{OX} = m\overrightarrow{OB} + n\overrightarrow{OD} \text{ for scalars } m \text{ and } n \text{ where } m + n = 1$$

If we choose the origin O so that it is not on the plane then the position vectors of any three of the vertices of the parallelogram are linearly independent vectors. In order to solve for the variables k, l, m, and n, we write $\overrightarrow{OX}$ in terms of these independent vectors, then use the fact that co-ordinates with respect to a given basis are unique (Section 2.2).

We use the result that $\overrightarrow{AB} = \overrightarrow{DC}$ which follows from the statement that opposite sides of a parallelogram are equal. (This statement is to be proved as Question 5 in Exercise 2.5.)

Thus, $\overrightarrow{AO} + \overrightarrow{OB} = \overrightarrow{DO} + \overrightarrow{OC}$.

So, $-\overrightarrow{OA} + \overrightarrow{OB} = -\overrightarrow{OD} + \overrightarrow{OC}$

and $\overrightarrow{OD} = \overrightarrow{OA} - \overrightarrow{OB} + \overrightarrow{OC}$

So, $\overrightarrow{OX} = m\overrightarrow{OB} + n(\overrightarrow{OA} - \overrightarrow{OB} + \overrightarrow{OC})$
$= m\overrightarrow{OB} + n\overrightarrow{OA} - n\overrightarrow{OB} + n\overrightarrow{OC}$
$= n\overrightarrow{OA} + (m - n)\overrightarrow{OB} + n\overrightarrow{OC}$.

Since $\overrightarrow{OX} = k\overrightarrow{OA} + l\overrightarrow{OC}$, using the Theorem of Section 2.2 and Theorem 1 of Section 2.4, we have the following system of equations to solve for k, l, m, and n.

$k = n$ and $0 = m - n$ and $l = n$
(so $m = n$)
and $k + l = 1$ and $m + n = 1$

So, $2n = 1$; therefore $n = \frac{1}{2}$

Thus, $k = l = m = n = \frac{1}{2}$

that is, X is the midpoint of both diagonals; in other words, the diagonals of a parallelogram bisect each other.

An alternate proof of the statement from Example 3 is requested as Question 4 in Exercise 2.5.

Example 4   For $\triangle XYZ$, point P divides $\overrightarrow{XZ}$ in the ratio 3:1 and Q is the midpoint of XY. If R is the point of intersection of PY and QZ, find PR:RY.

Solution   We draw a diagram using the given information.

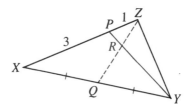

We wish to find scalars a and b such that, for origin O not on the plane,

$$\overrightarrow{OR} = a\overrightarrow{OP} + b\overrightarrow{OY} \text{ where } a + b = 1$$
(so that R divides $\overrightarrow{PY}$ in the ratio $b:a$)

In so doing we also work with scalars c and d such that

$$\overrightarrow{OR} = c\overrightarrow{OQ} + d\overrightarrow{OZ} \text{ where } c + d = 1$$

From the given information about the locations of P and Q,

we can write $\quad \overrightarrow{OP} = \frac{1}{4}\overrightarrow{OX} + \frac{3}{4}\overrightarrow{OZ}$

and $\quad\qquad \overrightarrow{OQ} = \frac{1}{2}\overrightarrow{OX} + \frac{1}{2}\overrightarrow{OY}$

We now write $\overrightarrow{OR}$ in two ways as a linear combination of the independent vectors $\overrightarrow{OX}$, $\overrightarrow{OY}$, and $\overrightarrow{OZ}$.

$$\overrightarrow{OR} = a(\tfrac{1}{4}\overrightarrow{OX} + \tfrac{3}{4}\overrightarrow{OZ}) + b\overrightarrow{OY}$$

$$= \tfrac{1}{4}a\overrightarrow{OX} + b\overrightarrow{OY} + \tfrac{3}{4}a\overrightarrow{OZ}$$

and $\quad \overrightarrow{OR} = c(\tfrac{1}{2}\overrightarrow{OX} + \tfrac{1}{2}\overrightarrow{OY}) + d\overrightarrow{OZ}$

$$= \tfrac{1}{2}c\overrightarrow{OX} + \tfrac{1}{2}c\overrightarrow{OY} + d\overrightarrow{OZ}$$

But the co-ordinates of the vector $\overrightarrow{OR}$ with respect to independent vectors $\overrightarrow{OX}$, $\overrightarrow{OY}$, and $\overrightarrow{OZ}$ are unique (Section 2.2),

so $\quad \tfrac{1}{4}a = \tfrac{1}{2}c, \quad b = \tfrac{1}{2}c, \quad \text{and} \quad \tfrac{3}{4}a = d$

thus $\quad\qquad\qquad 2b = c$

We also know that

$$a + b = 1 \quad \text{and} \quad c + d = 1$$

By substituting for c and d in the second equation, we find

$$2b + \tfrac{3}{4}a = 1$$

Next we substitute $1 - a$ for b in this equation

$$2(1 - a) + \tfrac{3}{4}a = 1$$

$$8 - 8a + 3a = 4$$

$$-5a = -4$$

So, $\quad a = \tfrac{4}{5}; \quad \text{hence } b = \tfrac{1}{5}$

Thus, R divides $\overrightarrow{PY}$ in the ratio $\tfrac{1}{5} : \tfrac{4}{5}$ or $1 : 4$.

PROBLEMS PLUS

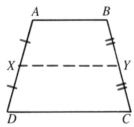

Median of a Trapezoid

Prove that the median of a trapezoid is parallel to the bases and that its length is one-half the sum of the lengths of its bases.

EXERCISE 2.5

A 1. From the given information express the vector $\overrightarrow{OA}$ in terms of the other position vectors for origin O.
   (a) A divides $\overrightarrow{BC}$ in the ratio $4:7$
   (b) A divides $\overrightarrow{XY}$ in the ratio $3:-7$
   (c) P divides $\overrightarrow{AB}$ in the ratio $1:2$
   (d)

   (e) M is the midpoint of $\overrightarrow{AB}$

B 2. Solve for the unknowns.
   (a) $a + b = 1$ $\qquad c + d = 1$
   $\qquad\quad a = \frac{1}{2}d$ $\qquad\quad \frac{1}{2}b = c$ $\qquad\quad b = d$
   (b) $k + l = 1$ $\qquad m + n = 1$
   $\qquad\quad \frac{3}{7}l = m - n$ $\qquad k = n$ $\qquad\quad \frac{4}{7}l = n$

Two different diagrams are possible.

3. Prove that, if the diagonals of a quadrilateral bisect each other, then it is a parallelogram. [Hint: Use the technique of Example 1.]

4. Given: parallelogram $ABCD$
   Prove: The diagonals of a parallelogram bisect each other.
   [Hint: Let X be the midpoint of $\overrightarrow{AC}$. Show that $\overrightarrow{BX} = \overrightarrow{XD}$.]

5. Prove that the opposite sides of a parallelogram are equal.
   (Recall: A parallelogram is a quadrilateral with opposite sides parallel. Hint: Use the technique of Example 3 with $\overrightarrow{XY} = m\overrightarrow{WZ}$ and $\overrightarrow{XW} = n\overrightarrow{YZ}$.

6. Given: P, Q, R, and S any four non-collinear points
   A and B the midpoints of PR and QS respectively
   Prove: $\overrightarrow{PQ} + \overrightarrow{RS} = 2\overrightarrow{AB}$
   [Hint: Use the method of Example 2.]

7. Prove that the line joining the midpoints of two sides of a triangle is parallel to the third side and half its length.

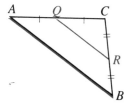

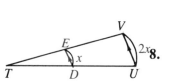

8. Prove that a line parallel to one side of a triangle and half as long as that side intersects the other sides at their respective midpoints.

9. For $\triangle PQR$ with X dividing $\overrightarrow{PR}$ in the ratio $2:3$, Y the midpoint of $\overrightarrow{PQ}$, and Z the point of intersection of QX and RY, prove that Z divides $\overrightarrow{RY}$ in the ratio $3:1$.
[Hint: Use the method of Example 3.]

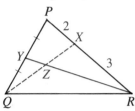

10. Given parallelogram $PQRS$ with A dividing $\overrightarrow{SR}$ in the ratio $3:4$, B and C the points of trisection of $\overrightarrow{QR}$, and T the point of intersection of $\overrightarrow{QA}$ and $\overrightarrow{SB}$, show that $BT:TS = 4:9$.

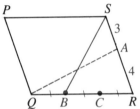

11. For parallelogram $PQRS$, show that $2\overrightarrow{PQ} = \overrightarrow{PR} + \overrightarrow{SQ}$.

12. For $\triangle ABC$ with D dividing $\overrightarrow{AB}$ in the ratio $5:1$, E dividing $\overrightarrow{AC}$ in the ratio $3:2$ and F the point of intersection of BE and CD, find the ratio in which F divides $\overrightarrow{BE}$.

13. Given: parallelogram $ABCD$
E divides $\overrightarrow{AD}$ in the ratio $5:2$
F divides $\overrightarrow{BC}$ in the ratio $1:4$
G is the point of intersection of AF and BE
Find: the ratio in which G divides $\overrightarrow{AF}$
and the ratio in which G divides $\overrightarrow{BE}$

C **14.** For $\triangle KLM$, points D and E divide $\overrightarrow{KL}$ and $\overrightarrow{KM}$ respectively in the ratio $m:n$.
(a) Prove that DE is parallel to LM.
(b) Express the length of DE as a multiple of the length of LM.

15. Figure $PQRS$ is a tetrahedron. A, B, C, X, Y, and Z are the midpoints of its sides.
Prove that AY bisects BX, and, similarly, AY and BX both bisect CZ.

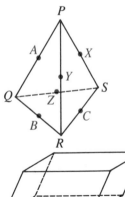

16. In parallelogram $FGHT$, A divides $\overrightarrow{FG}$ in the ratio $1:k$, $k > 0$ and X is the point of intersection of AJ and FH. Prove that X divides $\overrightarrow{FH}$ in the ratio $1:(k + 1)$.

17. Given: A parallelepiped is a figure with six faces for which opposite faces are parallel parallelograms of equal size.
Prove: The internal diagonals of a parallelepiped bisect each other.

2.6 REVIEW EXERCISE

1. Express each vector as a linear combination of the specified vectors using the given information.
   (a) $\vec{v}$ as a combination of $\vec{u}$ and $\vec{w}$ where $2\vec{u} + 3\vec{v} - 5\vec{w} = \vec{0}$
   (b) $\vec{x}$ as a combination of $\vec{y}$ and $\vec{z}$

   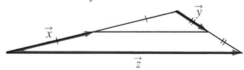

   (c) $\vec{a}$ as a combination of $\vec{b}$ and $\vec{c}$ where $|\vec{a}| = 10$, $|\vec{b}| = 4$, $|\vec{c}| = 3$

   (d) $2\vec{v} - \vec{u}$ as a combination of $\vec{u} + \vec{v}$ and $\vec{u} - \vec{v}$
   (e) $\overrightarrow{OA}$ as a linear combination of $\overrightarrow{OB}$ and $\overrightarrow{OC}$ where A divides $\overrightarrow{BC}$ in the ratio $2:1$
   (f) $\overrightarrow{OX}$ as a combination of $\overrightarrow{OY}$ and $\overrightarrow{OZ}$ where Z divides $\overrightarrow{XY}$ in the ratio $3:-1$
   (g) $\overrightarrow{OQ}$ as a combination of the position vectors of the other two points

2. Prove, from first principles, that $\vec{u}$, $\vec{v}$, and $3\vec{u} - 7\vec{v}$ are coplanar, for any vectors $\vec{u}$ and $\vec{v}$.

3. Give a geometric interpretation of
   (a) 2 linearly independent vectors,
   (b) 3 linearly dependent vectors.

4. Solve for the variables assuming that the vectors are linearly independent.
   (a) $(c - 3)\vec{u} + (5d - 4)\vec{v} = \vec{0}$
   (b) $3\vec{u} + 2\vec{v} = 5a\vec{u} + 3b\vec{v}$

5. Draw vectors based on the given information.
   (a) For $|\vec{x}| = 2$, $|\vec{y}| = 3.5$ with $\vec{x}$ and $\vec{y}$ in opposite directions, draw $\vec{x} - \vec{y}$.
   (b) For $\vec{u}$ and $\vec{v}$ as shown, draw (i) $2\vec{u} + 3\vec{v}$ (ii) $5\vec{v} - \vec{u}$
   (c) Draw $\vec{x}$ as a linear combination of $\vec{y}$ and $\vec{z}$.

   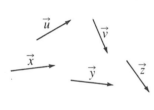

6. From the given information what conclusions can you form about the given vectors?
   (a) $3\vec{u} = 2\vec{v}$ (b) $\vec{x} = \vec{u} - \vec{v}$

7. Prove that, if vectors $2\vec{u} - 3\vec{v}$ and $\vec{w}$ are linearly dependent, then $\vec{u}, \vec{v},$ and $\vec{w}$ are also dependent.

8. (a) Prove, geometrically, that the zero vector is coplanar with any two planar vectors.
   (b) Prove, algebraically, that the zero vector is coplanar with any two planar vectors.

9. Prove that three vectors are coplanar if any two of those vectors are parallel.

10. From the given information, determine the ratio in which X divides $\overrightarrow{YZ}$ in each case. For parts (c) and (d), draw a diagram showing the relative positions of the points.

    (a)

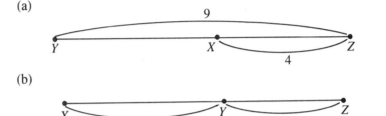

    (b)

    (c) $\overrightarrow{OX} = \frac{3}{5}\overrightarrow{OY} + \frac{2}{5}\overrightarrow{OZ}$ (d) $7\overrightarrow{OX} - 9\overrightarrow{OY} + 2\overrightarrow{OZ} = \vec{0}$

11. Three points A, B, and C are located so that, for any point O, $\overrightarrow{OA} = \frac{5}{4}\overrightarrow{OB} - \frac{1}{4}\overrightarrow{OC}$. Prove, from first principles, that the points are collinear.

12. Y divides $\overrightarrow{XZ}$ in the ratio $2:5$. T divides $\overrightarrow{XY}$ in the ratio $5:-3$.
    (a) Draw a diagram showing the relative positions of the four points.
    (b) Express $\overrightarrow{OT}$ as a linear combination of $\overrightarrow{OX}$ and $\overrightarrow{OZ}$, for any point O.

13. The following are statements about the position vectors of points for the origin O.
    Where it is possible form a conclusion about the relationships between the points. Where it is not possible, explain why not.
    (a) $5\overrightarrow{OA} = 4\overrightarrow{OB} - \overrightarrow{OC}$ (b) $\overrightarrow{OP} = 3\overrightarrow{OQ} - 5\overrightarrow{OR} + 3\overrightarrow{OS}$

14. Prove that the figure formed by joining consecutive midpoints of a quadrilateral is a parallelogram.

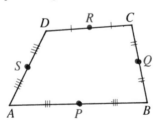

15. For $\triangle ABC$, P divides $\overrightarrow{AB}$ in the ratio $3:1$, Q is the midpoint of $\overrightarrow{BC}$, E is the point of intersection of $\overrightarrow{AQ}$ and $\overrightarrow{PC}$. Find the ratio in which E divides $\overrightarrow{AQ}$.

16. (a) Show that the medians of a triangle intersect in a single point. (This point is called the *centroid of the triangle*.)
(b) Prove that the centroid divides each median internally in the same ratio, specify the ratio.

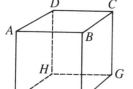

17. The figure shown is a cube.
(a) Show that diagonals AG, BH, CE, and DF intersect in a common point.
(b) Prove that the point of intersection of the diagonals is also the point of intersection of the lines joining the midpoints of opposite sides.

18. A tetrahedron has four triangular faces. The *medians of the tetrahedron* are the line segments joining a vertex to the centroid of its opposite face.
(a) Show that the medians intersect in a single point. (This point is called the *centroid of the tetrahedron*.)
(b) Prove that the centroid divides each median internally in the same ratio; specify the ratio.

PROBLEMS PLUS

Ceva's Theorem

(a) This theorem is credited to seventeenth century Italian mathematician Giovanni Ceva. Prove it using vector methods.

Ceva's Theorem: The three lines drawn from the vertices A, B, and C of $\triangle ABC$, meeting the opposite sides in points D, E, and F respectively, are concurrent if and only if $\dfrac{AF}{FB} \times \dfrac{BD}{DC} \times \dfrac{CE}{EA} = 1$.

(b) The importance of Ceva's Theorem lies in its use to prove many classic results in geometry. Use Ceva's Theorem to prove each of the following results:
   (i) The medians of any triangle are concurrent.
   (ii) The altitudes of any triangle are concurrent.
   (iii) The interior angle bisectors of a triangle are concurrent.

2.7 CHAPTER 2 TEST

1. For vectors $\vec{u}$, $\vec{v}$, and $\vec{w}$ such that $\vec{w} = 5\vec{v} + 2\vec{u}$ where $\vec{u} = 2\vec{x} + \vec{y}$ and $\vec{v} = \vec{x} - \vec{y}$, write $\vec{w}$ as a linear combination of $\vec{x}$ and $\vec{y}$.

2. For vectors $\vec{u}$, $\vec{v}$, and $\vec{w}$, shown, draw a diagram showing $\vec{v}$ as a linear combination of $\vec{u}$ and $\vec{w}$.

3. Assuming that vectors $\vec{x}$, $\vec{y}$, and $\vec{z}$ are linearly independent, solve for the scalar variables (if possible).
$$(c^2 - 4)\vec{x} + d\vec{y} + c\vec{z} = 3\vec{y} + 2\vec{z}$$

4. Given: vectors $\vec{x}$, $\vec{y}$, and $\vec{z}$ which are not coplanar, and nonzero scalars a, b
Prove: $a\vec{x} + b\vec{y}$ and $\vec{z}$ are not parallel.

5. (a) From the given information form a conclusion about vectors $\vec{u}$, $\vec{v}$, and $\vec{w}$ if possible. Give a reason for any conclusion.
$$3\vec{u} + 2\vec{v} - \vec{w} = \vec{0}$$
   (b) From the information given form a conclusion about points A, B, C, and D if possible. Give a reason for any conclusion.
$$\overrightarrow{OA} + \overrightarrow{OB} - 2\overrightarrow{OC} + \overrightarrow{OD} = \vec{0}$$

6. The point A divides $\overrightarrow{BC}$ in the ratio $3 : -2$.
   (a) Draw a diagram showing the relative positions of the points A, B, and C.
   (b) Write $\overrightarrow{OC}$ as a linear combination of $\overrightarrow{OA}$ and $\overrightarrow{OB}$.

7. Prove, from first principles, that points X, Y, and Z are collinear if, for origin O, $\overrightarrow{OX} = k\overrightarrow{OY} + l\overrightarrow{OZ}$ where $k + l = 1$.

8. For $\triangle PQR$, the line joining the midpoints, A and B, of PQ and PR is extended to S so that it is equal in length to QR. Prove using vector methods that figure $AQRS$ is a parallelogram.

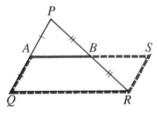

9. For parallelogram $WXYZ$, U divides $\overrightarrow{WZ}$ in the ratio $3 : 2$ and V divides $\overrightarrow{YZ}$ in the ratio $2 : 1$. For T the point of intersection of $\overrightarrow{XU}$ XU and $\overrightarrow{WV}$ WV, show that T is the midpoint of $\overrightarrow{WV}$ WV.

TWENTIETH CENTURY MATHEMATICIANS

D r. H.S.M. Coxeter of the University of Toronto has been credited with the revival of geometry as a university subject in North America. He has written more than ten books on geometry, many of them best-selling university texts and has made prize-winning films.

He was born and educated in England but has been associated with the University of Toronto for more than fifty years. Many people who are currently mathematics teachers at high school or university attended his classes or the classes of his students.

Groups generated by reflections are named Coxeter groups in his honour, and special diagrams used in advanced mathematics and physics are called Coxeter diagrams.

When asked what geometry is, he said: "I suppose it's the study of shapes and patterns." This answer includes the topics of packing and tiling.

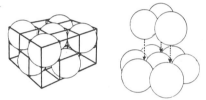

Cubic and hexagonal closepacking.

The sphere packing problem concerns putting together congruent balls in space as economically as possible. He says: "Are the cubic closepacking and the hexagonal closepacking the best, or could you possibly get anything better? That has been solved if you assume that the centres of the spheres are arranged in straight rows in a 'lattice packing.' But if you don't insist on having a lattice, the question is, could you do better than 74% density?"

The packing problem in *n*-dimensional space, which generalizes the above, has important applications in coding theory which is a branch of electrical and communications engineering.

Professor Coxeter says this about tiling: "What are the possible ways in which you can take a convex polygon and repeat it so as to get congruent replicas of it which, when fitted together, fill and cover the plane? Even tiling with pentagons which was supposed to be solved, still isn't. Nobody knows quite what are all the possible shapes of a pentagon that can be repeated by congruent transformation to cover the plane. People seem to keep on thinking of new ones."

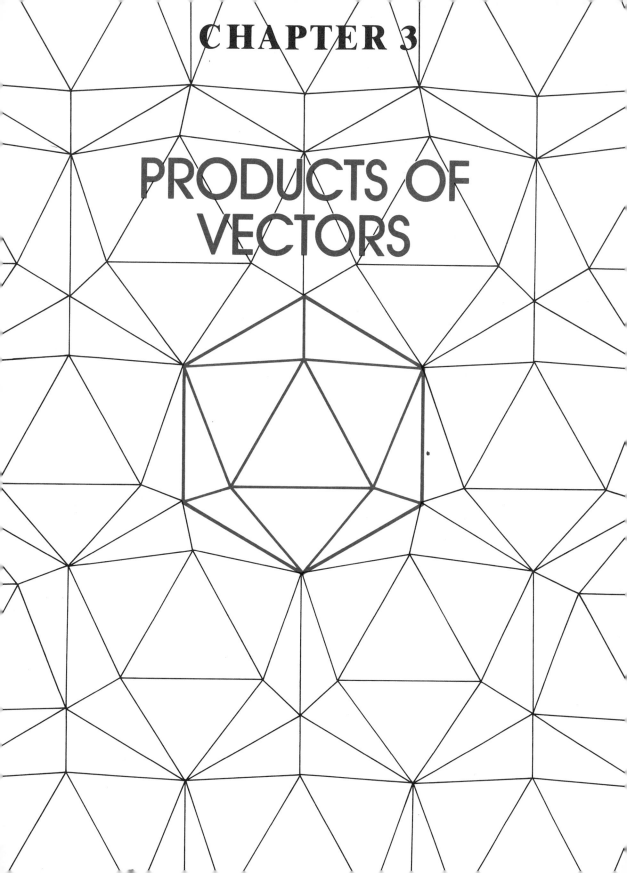

CHAPTER 3

PRODUCTS OF VECTORS

REVIEW AND PREVIEW TO
CHAPTER 3

Trigonometric Ratios of Any Angle

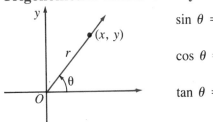

$$\sin \theta = \frac{y}{r} \qquad \csc \theta = \frac{r}{y}$$

$$\cos \theta = \frac{x}{r} \qquad \sec \theta = \frac{r}{x}$$

$$\tan \theta = \frac{y}{x} \qquad \cot \theta = \frac{x}{y}$$

$$r = \sqrt{x^2 + y^2}$$

Example 1   Show that $\sin(180° - \theta) = \sin \theta$.

Solution

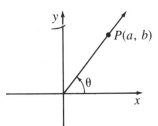 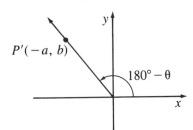

If $P(a, b)$ lies on the terminal arm of θ in standard position, then $P'(-a, b)$ lies on the terminal arm of $(180° - \theta)$ following a reflection in the y-axis. Now

$$\sin \theta = \frac{b}{\sqrt{a^2 + b^2}} \qquad \text{and} \qquad \sin(180° - \theta) = \frac{b}{\sqrt{(-a)^2 + b^2}}$$

$$= \frac{b}{\sqrt{a^2 + b^2}}$$

Therefore $\sin \theta = \sin(180° - \theta)$.

EXERCISE 1

1. Find the six trigonometric ratios of the indicated angle in standard position if the given point lies on the terminal arm.

(a)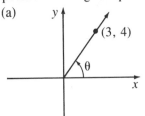

(b)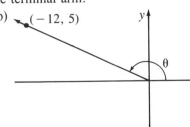

(c)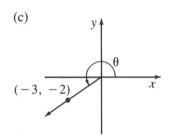

(d)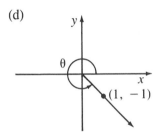

2. Find the six trigonometric ratios of an angle in standard position if the given point is on the terminal arm.

   (a) $(-6, 8)$ (b) $(5, -2)$ (c) $(-2, -5)$ (d) $(0, -3)$

3. Prove each identity.

   (a) $\cos(180° - \theta) = -\cos \theta$ (b) $\tan(180° - \theta) = -\tan \theta$

   (c) $\sin(-\theta) = -\sin \theta$ (d) $\cos(-\theta) = \cos \theta$

   (e) $\tan(-\theta) = -\tan \theta$ (f) $\sin(90° - \theta) = \cos \theta$

   (g) $\cos(90° - \theta) = \sin \theta$

4. Find the six trigonometric ratios of the following angles.

   (a) $0°$ (b) $90°$ (c) $180°$ (d) $270°$

Special Triangles

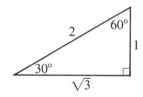

EXERCISE 2

1. Use the given triangles to find the following.

   (a) $\sin 45°$ (b) $\cos 30°$

   (c) $\tan 60°$ (d) $\cos 135°$

   (e) $\tan 225°$ (f) $\sin 330°$

   (g) $\cos 315° + \tan 225°$ (h) $\sin 240° - \cos 240°$

Radian Measure

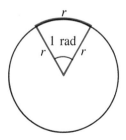

An angle subtended at the centre of a circle by an arc equal in length to the radius has a measure of one radian.

$$\pi \text{ rad} = 180°$$

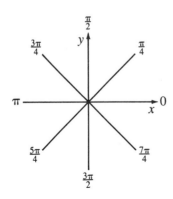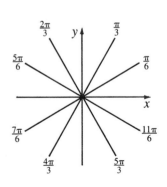

EXERCISE 3

1. Evaluate each of the following.

(a) $\sin \dfrac{\pi}{3}$

(b) $\cos \dfrac{\pi}{4}$

(c) $\tan \dfrac{\pi}{6}$

(d) $\sin \dfrac{7\pi}{6}$

(e) $\cos \dfrac{3\pi}{2}$

(f) $\tan \dfrac{5\pi}{4}$

(g) $\sin\left(-\dfrac{2\pi}{3}\right) + \cos \dfrac{11\pi}{6}$

(h) $\tan(-\pi) - \cos\left(-\dfrac{4\pi}{3}\right)$

INTRODUCTION

In Chapter 1 we saw how vectors could be added and multiplied by a scalar. In this chapter we see how vectors can be combined in other ways. We use the concept of *work* to define the *dot product* and the *moment of a vector* to define the *cross product* of two vectors.

3.1   RESOLUTION OF A VECTOR

In this section we limit our discussion to coplanar vectors.

Suppose $\vec{a}$ and $\vec{b}$ are two non-collinear vectors; then any vector $\vec{u}$, in the plane determined by $\vec{a}$ and $\vec{b}$, can be uniquely written as a linear combination of them.

$$\vec{u} = k\vec{a} + l\vec{b}, \quad k, l \in R$$

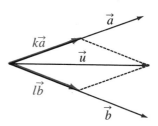

The vectors $k\vec{a}$ and $l\vec{b}$ are called the **vector components** of $\vec{u}$ along $\vec{a}$ and $\vec{b}$. We say $\vec{u}$ has been **resolved** into its vector components in the directions of $\vec{a}$ and $\vec{b}$.

Example 1   A boat is pulled onto shore using two ropes, as shown in the diagram. If a force of 255 N is needed, find the magnitude of the force in each rope.

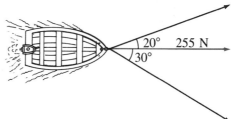

Solution   Let $\vec{f}_1$ and $\vec{f}_2$ represent the vector components of the 255 N force along the ropes.

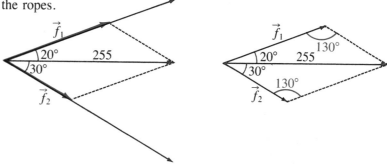

Using the Law of Sines,

$$\frac{|\vec{f_1}|}{\sin 30°} = \frac{255}{\sin 130°} \qquad \text{and} \qquad \frac{|\vec{f_2}|}{\sin 20°} = \frac{255}{\sin 130°}$$

$$|\vec{f_1}| \doteq 166 \qquad\qquad\qquad |\vec{f_2}| \doteq 114$$

Therefore the forces in the ropes have magnitudes of 166 N and 114 N.

Example 2 The wind exerts a force of 175 N perpendicular to the sail of a boat as shown in the diagram. Resolve this force into two vector components, one parallel and one perpendicular to the keel of the boat.

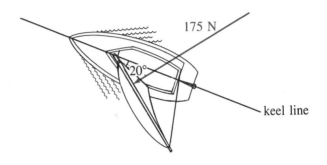

Solution Let $\vec{f_1}$ and $\vec{f_2}$ be the vector components of the 175 N force parallel and perpendicular to the keel of the boat, respectively.

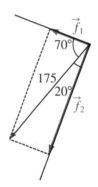

Now

$$\frac{|\vec{f_1}|}{175} = \cos 70° \qquad \text{and} \qquad \frac{|\vec{f_2}|}{175} = \cos 20°$$

$$|\vec{f_1}| \doteq 59.8 \qquad\qquad\qquad |\vec{f_2}| \doteq 164$$

Therefore the force directed parallel to the keel has a magnitude of 59.8 N and the force perpendicular to the keel has a magnitude of 164 N.

Example 3 At a school dance, a reflective ball is suspended from the ceiling by two wires that make angles of 20° and 30° with the ceiling. If the ball exerts a force of 123 N under gravity, find the tensions in the wires.

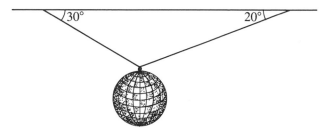

Solution Let $\vec{f}$ represent the 123 N force. Then $-\vec{f}$ represents the equilibrant force.

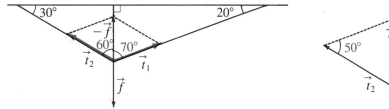

Let the vector components of $-\vec{f}$ along the wires be $\vec{t}_1$ and $\vec{t}_2$, as shown. Using the Law of Sines,

$$\frac{|\vec{t}_1|}{\sin 60°} = \frac{|-\vec{f}|}{\sin 50°} \qquad \text{and} \qquad \frac{|\vec{t}_2|}{\sin 70°} = \frac{|-\vec{f}|}{\sin 50°}$$

$$|\vec{t}_1| = \frac{123(\sin 60°)}{\sin 50°} \qquad\qquad\qquad |\vec{t}_2| = \frac{123(\sin 70°)}{\sin 50°}$$

$$|\vec{t}_1| \doteq 139 \qquad\qquad\qquad\qquad |\vec{t}_2| \doteq 151$$

Therefore the tensions in the wires are 139 N and 151 N.

Example 4 The neon sign for "Mike's Diner" is held out from the side of his building by a horizontal aluminum pole. A wire, fastened to the building at an angle of 55° to the vertical, supports the entire weight of the sign. If the sign has a weight of 630 N under gravity, find the tension in the wire and the *compression* in the aluminum pole.

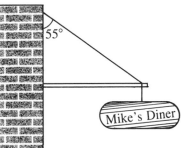

Solution Let $\vec{f}$ represent the 630 N force. Then $-\vec{f}$ represents the equilibrant force.

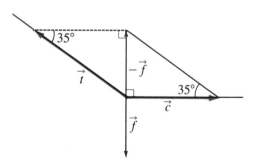

Let the vector components of $-\vec{f}$ along the wire and along the pole be $\vec{t}$ and $\vec{c}$, respectively. Now

$$\frac{|\vec{t}|}{|-\vec{f}|} = \csc 35° \qquad \text{and} \qquad \frac{|\vec{c}|}{|-\vec{f}|} = \cot 35°$$

$$|\vec{t}| = 630(\csc 35°) \qquad\qquad |\vec{c}| = 630(\cot 35°)$$

$$\doteq 1100 \qquad\qquad\qquad\qquad \doteq 900$$

Therefore the tension in the wire is 1100 N and the compression in the pole is 900 N.

EXERCISE 3.1

B **1.** Resolve each of the following into vector components in the given directions.

(a)

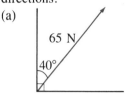

(b)

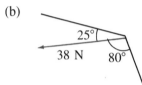

(c)

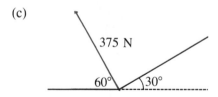

2. A force of 25 N is resolved into two vector components with magnitudes of 12 N and 21 N. Find the angle each vector component makes with the 25 N force.

3. In the diagram shown, $\vec{u}_1$ and $\vec{u}_2$ are **rectangular vector components** of $\vec{u}$; that is, $\vec{u}_1$ and $\vec{u}_2$ are **orthogonal** (or perpendicular). Find $|\vec{u}_1|$ and $|\vec{u}_2|$ for each of the following values for $|\vec{u}|$ and θ.

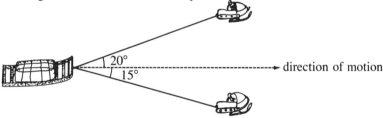

   (a) $|\vec{u}| = 50$, $\theta = \dfrac{\pi}{6}$

   (b) $|\vec{u}| = 250$, $\theta = 40°$

   (c) $|\vec{u}| = 110$, $\theta = \dfrac{\pi}{2}$

4. A 30 N force is resolved into rectangular vector components, $\vec{f}_1$ and $\vec{f}_2$, such that $|\vec{f}_1| = 2|\vec{f}_2|$. Find $|\vec{f}_1|$ and the angle between $\vec{f}_2$ and the 30 N force.

5. A sled is being towed by two snowmobiles. The tow ropes make angles of 20° and 15° with the direction of motion. If the resultant force has a magnitude of 850 N, along the direction of motion, find the magnitude of each vector component.

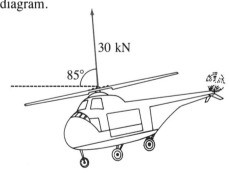

6. A force of 30 kN is developed by the main rotor of a helicopter as shown in the diagram.

   (a) Resolve this force into vector components parallel and perpendicular to the ground.

   (b) Explain what physical effect is caused by each component on the helicopter.

7. A traffic sign hanging over the road is supported by two wires attached to poles on either side of the road. Both wires make angles of 10° with the horizontal. If the sign weighs 468 N, find the tension in each wire.

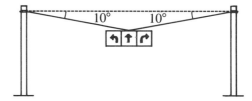

8. A tennis net is supported at each end by a steel post. If the tension in the net cord is 250 N and the angles are as shown in the diagram, find the tension in the guy wire and the compression in the post.

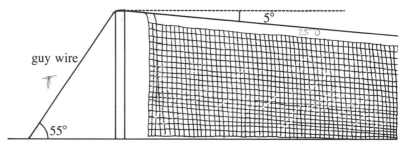

9. An arrow is drawn back against a bowstring with a force of 215 N. If the arrow makes angles of 60° with the string above and below, find the tensions in the strings.

10. A hot air balloon is anchored to the earth by ropes each 50 m long (one on each side in the same plane). The distance between the ropes at ground level is 70 m. If the balloon exerts an upward force of 1200 N, find the tensions in the ropes.

11. A weight of 12 N is suspended by two strings that make angles of 20° and 40° with the vertical. Find the tensions in the strings.

12. A basketball hoop and backboard are held out from a wall by a steel pole. A wire, fastened to the wall at an angle of 60°, supports the entire weight of the structure. If the hoop and backboard have a weight of 1950 N under gravity, find the tension in the wire and the compression in the steel pole.

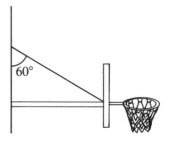

3.2 VECTOR PROJECTIONS

An aircraft's velocity, represented by $\vec{v}$, makes an angle of θ with the vertical. A simple question we might ask is: "How fast is the aircraft climbing?"

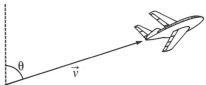

A wagon is pulled along a flat road by a force represented by $\vec{f}$, inclined at an angle of θ to the horizontal. Here we might want to ask: "How much of the force is actually being used to pull the wagon along?"

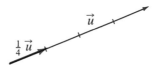

Questions like these have motivated the mathematical definitions in this section.

We begin by making the following definition.

> A **unit vector** is a vector with magnitude 1.

Suppose $\vec{u}$ is a vector with magnitude 4. By the definition of scalar multiplication for vectors, $\frac{1}{4}\vec{u}$ is a vector with the same direction as $\vec{u}$ and a quarter of its magnitude, that is, with magnitude 1.

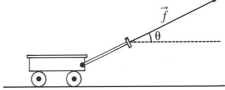

We generalize this idea.

> If $\vec{u}$ is a non-zero vector, $\hat{u} = \dfrac{1}{|\vec{u}|}\vec{u}$ is a unit vector with the same direction as $\vec{u}$.

Proof

First, since $\dfrac{1}{|\vec{u}|} > 0$, $\hat{u} = \dfrac{1}{|\vec{u}|}\vec{u}$ is a positive scalar multiple of $\vec{u}$ and so has the same direction as $\vec{u}$.

Second, $\left| \vec{u} \right| = \left| \dfrac{1}{\left| \vec{u} \right|} \vec{u} \right|$

$$= \left| \dfrac{1}{\left| \vec{u} \right|} \right| \left| \vec{u} \right|$$

$$= \dfrac{1}{\left| \vec{u} \right|} \left| \vec{u} \right|$$

$$= 1$$

Another way of stating the result is to write

$$\vec{u} = \left| \vec{u} \right| \hat{u}$$

Now suppose $\vec{u}$ and $\vec{v}$, $\vec{v} \neq \vec{0}$, are two vectors with a common initial point and with θ the angle between them, $0 \leq \theta \leq \pi$. The vector we obtain by projecting $\vec{u}$ perpendicularly onto the line through $\vec{v}$ is called the **vector projection of $\vec{u}$ on $\vec{v}$** and is denoted by $\mathbf{proj_{\vec{v}}}\, \vec{u}$.

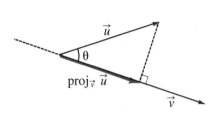 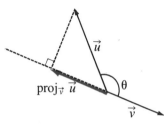

$$0 < \theta < \tfrac{\pi}{2} \qquad\qquad \tfrac{\pi}{2} < \theta < \pi$$

$\mathrm{proj}_{\vec{v}}\vec{u}$ is a vector, so $\left| \mathrm{proj}_{\vec{v}}\vec{u} \right|$ denotes the magnitude of this vector.

> For vectors $\vec{u}$ and $\vec{v}$, $\vec{v} \neq \vec{0}$,
> $$\mathbf{proj_{\vec{v}}}\, \vec{u} = \left| \vec{u} \right| \cos \theta\, \hat{v}$$
> where θ is the angle between $\vec{u}$ and $\vec{v}$, $0 \leq \theta \leq \pi$.

Proof

There are two cases to consider.

Case 1 $\quad 0 \leq \theta \leq \dfrac{\pi}{2}$

From the diagram

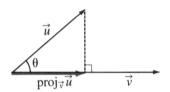

$$\dfrac{\left| \mathrm{proj}_{\vec{v}}\, \vec{u} \right|}{\left| \vec{u} \right|} = \cos \theta$$

so $\qquad \left| \mathrm{proj}_{\vec{v}}\, \vec{u} \right| = \left| \vec{u} \right| \cos \theta$

Since $\mathrm{proj}_{\vec{v}}\, \vec{u}$ and $\vec{v}$ have the same direction,

$$\mathrm{proj}_{\vec{v}}\, \vec{u} = \left| \vec{u} \right| \cos \theta\, \hat{v}$$

Case 2 $\dfrac{\pi}{2} \leqslant \theta \leqslant \pi$

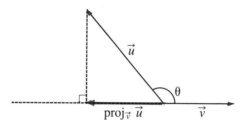

From the diagram

$$\dfrac{\left|\text{proj}_{\vec{v}}\,\vec{u}\right|}{\left|\vec{u}\right|} = \cos(\pi - \theta)$$

so $\left|\text{proj}_{\vec{v}}\,\vec{u}\right| = \left|\vec{u}\right| \cos(\pi - \theta)$

$$= -\left|\vec{u}\right| \cos \theta \qquad [\cos(\pi - \theta) = -\cos \theta]$$

Since $\text{proj}_{\vec{v}}\,\vec{u}$ and $\vec{v}$ have opposite directions,

$$\text{proj}_{\vec{v}}\,\vec{u} = -\left|\vec{u}\right| \cos \theta\,(-\hat{v})$$
$$= \left|\vec{u}\right| \cos \theta\,\hat{v}$$

Therefore, in either case

$$\text{proj}_{\vec{v}}\,\vec{u} = \left|\vec{u}\right| \cos \theta\,\hat{v}$$

The scalar $\left|\vec{u}\right|\;\cos\theta$ is referred to as the **scalar component of $\vec{u}$ on $\vec{v}$** or simply the **component of $\vec{u}$ on $\vec{v}$**.

Example 1   The angle between two vectors $\vec{u}$ and $\vec{v}$ is $\dfrac{\pi}{3}$. If $\left|\vec{u}\right| = 13$, find the projection of $\vec{u}$ on $\vec{v}$.

Solution

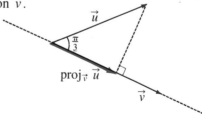

$$\text{proj}_{\vec{v}}\,\vec{u} = \left|\vec{u}\right| \cos \theta\,\hat{v}$$
$$= 13 \cos \dfrac{\pi}{3}\,\hat{v}$$
$$= 6.5\,\hat{v}$$

Note: $\text{proj}_{\vec{v}}\,\vec{u}$ is dependent on the angle between $\vec{u}$ and $\vec{v}$ and on the magnitude of $\vec{u}$, but *not* on the magnitude of $\vec{v}$.

Example 2 $\vec{u}$, $\vec{v}$, and $\vec{w}$ are three coplanar vectors. $\vec{v}$ makes an angle of 38° with $\vec{u}$. $\vec{w}$ makes an angle of 163° with $\vec{u}$ (in the same sense as $\vec{v}$). If $\left|\vec{w}\right| = 8$, find the component of $\vec{w}$ on $\vec{v}$.

Solution

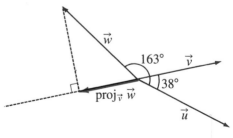

The angle between $\vec{v}$ and $\vec{w}$ is 125°, so

$$\text{component of } \vec{w} \text{ on } \vec{v} = \left|\vec{w}\right| \cos 125°$$
$$= 8 \cos 125°$$
$$\doteq -4.6$$

Example 3   A sled is pulled up a hill by exerting a 150 N force applied at an angle of 30° to the hill. Find the magnitude of the force in the direction of motion.

Solution   Let $\vec{f}$ represent the force at an angle of 30° to the hill.
Let $\vec{u}$ represent a vector directed up the hill.

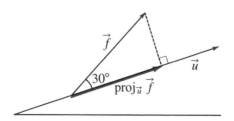

The magnitude of the required force is

$$\left|\text{proj}_{\vec{u}}\, \vec{f}\right| = \left|\left|\vec{f}\right| \cos 30°\right|$$
$$= \left|\vec{f}\right| \cos 30°$$
$$= 150 \cos 30°$$
$$\doteq 130$$

Therefore the force in the direction of motion is 130 N.

Example 4   An aircraft is travelling at 550 km/h at an angle of 25° to the level ground below. Find the horizontal ground speed, in kilometres per hour, and the rate of climb, in metres per minute, of the aircraft.

Solution

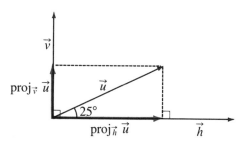

Let $\vec{u}$ represent the velocity of the aircraft.

Let $\vec{h}$ and $\vec{v}$ be vectors in the horizontal and vertical directions, respectively, coplanar with $\vec{u}$.

Now, the horizontal ground speed is

$$\left| \text{proj}_{\vec{h}}\, \vec{u} \right| = \left| \|\vec{u}\| \cos 25^\circ \right|$$
$$= |\vec{u}| \cos 25^\circ$$
$$= 550 \cos 25^\circ$$
$$\doteq 500$$

and the rate of climb is

$$\left| \text{proj}_{\vec{v}}\, \vec{u} \right| = \left| \|\vec{u}\| \cos 65^\circ \right|$$
$$= |\vec{u}| \cos 65^\circ$$
$$= 550 \cos 65^\circ$$
$$\doteq 230$$

Therefore the horizontal ground speed of the aircraft is 500 km/h and the rate of climb is 230 km/h or 3900 m/min. ⬡

Example 5   A box with a mass of 12 N rests on a frictionless ramp inclined at an angle of 25° to the level ground. Find the magnitude of the force, directed up the ramp, that must be applied to keep the box at rest.

Solution   Let $\vec{f}$ represent the 12 N force. Let $\vec{r}$ be a vector directed down the ramp.

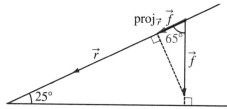

The magnitude of the force directed down the ramp is

$$\left| \text{proj}_{\vec{r}}\, \vec{f} \right| = \left| \|\vec{f}\| \cos 65^\circ \right|$$
$$= |\vec{f}| \cos 65^\circ$$
$$= 12 \cos 65^\circ$$
$$\doteq 5.1$$

Therefore, since the box is to remain at rest, a 5.1 N force must be applied up the ramp. ⬡

EXERCISE 3.2

B **1.** The angle between two vectors $\vec{u}$ and $\vec{v}$ is 20°. If $|\vec{u}| = 15$, find $\text{proj}_{\vec{v}}\, \vec{u}$.

2. The angle between two vectors $\vec{a}$ and $\vec{b}$ is 130°. If $|\vec{a}| = 15$ and $|\vec{b}| = 20$, find:
(a) $\text{proj}_{\vec{b}}\, \vec{a}$,
(b) the component of $\vec{b}$ on $\vec{a}$.

3. The angle between two vectors $\vec{u}$ and $\vec{v}$ is 115°. If $|\vec{u}| = 18$, find $\text{proj}_{-\vec{v}}\, \vec{u}$.

4. The angle between two vectors $\vec{u}$ and $\vec{v}$ is θ. Find $\text{proj}_{\vec{v}}\, \vec{u}$ and the component of $\vec{u}$ on $\vec{v}$ in each of the following situations.
(a) $\theta = 0°$
(b) $\theta = 90°$
(c) $\theta = 180°$

5. For non-zero vectors $\vec{u}$ and $\vec{v}$, under what conditions will
(a) the component of $\vec{u}$ on $\vec{v}$ equal the component of $\vec{v}$ on $\vec{u}$?
(b) $\text{proj}_{\vec{v}}\, \vec{u} = \text{proj}_{\vec{u}}\, \vec{v}$?

6. The vectors $\vec{u}$, $\vec{v}$, and $\vec{w}$ are coplanar and non-zero. The vectors $\vec{u}$ and $\vec{v}$ are perpendicular. If the component of $\vec{w}$ on $\vec{u}$ and the component of $\vec{w}$ on $\vec{v}$ are equal, find the angle between $\vec{u}$ and $\vec{w}$. (There are two possibilities.)

7. An aircraft is travelling with an airspeed of 735 km/h at an angle of 15° to the level ground below. Find the horizontal ground speed, in kilometres per hour, and the rate of climb, in metres per minute, of the aircraft.

8. A log is being pulled along level ground by a 370 N force exerted at an angle of 35° to the ground. Find the magnitude of the force in the direction of motion and of the force tending to lift the log.

9. A crate is being dragged up a ramp by a 125 N force applied at an angle of 40° to the ramp. Find the magnitude of the force in the direction of motion.

10. In Question 9, if the ramp makes an angle of 20° with the level ground, find the magnitude of the force tending to lift the crate vertically.

11. An aircraft headed due east is climbing at an angle of 15° to the level ground below at a speed of 435 km/h. It is affected by a 25 km/h horizontal wind blowing from the north. What is the aircraft's rate of climb, in metres per minute, and its horizontal ground speed, in kilometres per hour?

12. A crate with a weight of 57 N rests on a frictionless ramp inclined at an angle of 30° to the horizontal. What force must be applied at an angle of 20° to the ramp so that the crate remains at rest?

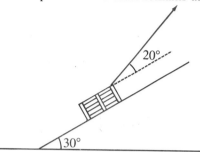

13. A box with a weight of 215 N rests on a ramp. There is a frictional force of 27 N exerted on the box directed up the ramp. If the ramp is inclined at 30°, what force must be applied at an angle of 40° to the ramp to maintain equilibrium?

C 14. A block with a weight of 155 N resting on a ramp is maintained in equilibrium by a 63 N force at an angle of 30° to the ramp. The force, directed up the ramp, due to friction is 22 N. Find the angle of inclination of the ramp.

15. (a) If $\vec{u}$ and $\vec{v}$ are vectors such that $\hat{u} = \hat{v}$, show that $\vec{u} = k\vec{v}$ where $k > 0$.

    (b) If $\hat{u} = -\hat{v}$, show that $\vec{u} = k\vec{v}$ where $k < 0$.

PROBLEMS PLUS

Centre of Mass

If a number of particles of masses m_1, m_2, m_3, ..., m_n have position vectors $\overrightarrow{OP}_1$, $\overrightarrow{OP}_2$, $\overrightarrow{OP}_3$, ..., $\overrightarrow{OP}_n$, respectively, the position vector of their **centre of mass** is defined by

$$\overrightarrow{OP} = \frac{m_1\overrightarrow{OP}_1 + m_2\overrightarrow{OP}_2 + m_3\overrightarrow{OP}_3 + \dots m_n\overrightarrow{OP}_n}{m_1 + m_2 + m_3 + \dots + m_n}$$

(a) Find the position of the centre of mass of three particles having masses $m_1 = 1$, $m_2 = 2$, and $m_3 = 3$ located at the corners of an equilateral triangle.

(b) Find the position of the centre of mass of four particles having masses $m_1 = 1$, $m_2 = 2$, $m_3 = 3$, and $m_4 = 4$ located at the corners of a square.

3.3 THE DOT PRODUCT

There are situations in physics where vectors can be combined in ways other than addition. In this section we will investigate one of these situations.

Example 1 A mass rests on a ramp, inclined at 20° to the level ground, at a point A. A force, $\vec{f}$, is applied to the mass at an angle of θ to the ramp and moves the mass to a point B.

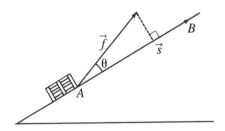

There are two vectors in this example: a force vector, $\vec{f}$, and a displacement vector, $\overrightarrow{AB}$, indicated on the diagram by $\vec{s}$. In physics, the scalar quantity *work* is defined as 'the displacement travelled multiplied by the magnitude of the applied force in the direction of motion.

$$\text{work} = |\vec{s}| \, (|\vec{f}| \cos \theta)$$
$$= |\vec{f}| \, |\vec{s}| \cos \theta$$

Note that work is a scalar quantity. It has no direction. However, its value does depend on the angle between the force and displacement vectors.

We use the preceding example to motivate the following definition.

For non-zero vectors $\vec{u}$ and $\vec{v}$, we define the **dot product** of $\vec{u}$ and $\vec{v}$ as
$$\vec{u} \cdot \vec{v} = |\vec{u}| \, |\vec{v}| \cos \theta$$
where θ is the angle between $\vec{u}$ and $\vec{v}$, $0 \leq \theta \leq \pi$.
If either $\vec{u}$ or $\vec{v}$ is the zero vector, then $\vec{u} \cdot \vec{v} = 0$.

This is called the dot product because of the notation; it is also called the **scalar product** because $\vec{u} \cdot \vec{v}$ is a scalar quantity.

In Example 1 it would make no sense for the angle between $\vec{f}$ and $\vec{s}$ to be 90° or larger, because movement from A to B could not occur. However, we make no such restriction in our definition and allow θ to be any angle from 0° through 180° inclusive.

Example 2 Find the dot product of $\vec{u}$ and $\vec{v}$ in each of the following, where θ is the angle between $\vec{u}$ and $\vec{v}$.

(a) $|\vec{u}| = 16, |\vec{v}| = 12, \theta = \dfrac{\pi}{3}$

(b) $|\vec{u}| = 10, |\vec{v}| = 21, \theta = \dfrac{\pi}{2}$

(c) $|\vec{u}| = 8.1, |\vec{v}| = 4.7, \theta = 126°$

Solution (a) $\vec{u} \cdot \vec{v} = |\vec{u}| |\vec{v}| \cos \dfrac{\pi}{3}$

$\qquad = (16)(12)(0.5)$

$\qquad = 96$

(b) $\vec{u} \cdot \vec{v} = |\vec{u}| |\vec{v}| \cos \dfrac{\pi}{2}$

$\qquad = (10)(21)(0)$

$\qquad = 0$

(c) $\vec{u} \cdot \vec{v} = |\vec{u}| |\vec{v}| \cos 126°$

$\qquad \doteq (8.1)(4.7)(-0.5878)$

$\qquad \doteq -22.4$

We now investigate some of the properties of the dot product.

Property 1

For non-zero vectors $\vec{u}$ and $\vec{v}$,
$\vec{u}$ and $\vec{v}$ are perpendicular if, and only if,
$\vec{u} \cdot \vec{v} = 0$

Proof

First suppose $\vec{u}$ and $\vec{v}$ are perpendicular, then the angle, θ, between $\vec{u}$ and $\vec{v}$ is $\dfrac{\pi}{2}$ and $\cos \theta = 0$. Since $\vec{u} \cdot \vec{v} = |\vec{u}| |\vec{v}| \cos \theta$, $\vec{u} \cdot \vec{v} = 0$.

Conversely suppose $\vec{u} \cdot \vec{v} = 0$, then $|\vec{u}| |\vec{v}| \cos \theta = 0$. Since $\vec{u}$ and $\vec{v}$ are non-zero vectors, $|\vec{u}|$ and $|\vec{v}|$ are not zero. Therefore $\cos \theta = 0$ and hence $\theta = \dfrac{\pi}{2}$.

Property 2

For any vectors $\vec{u}$ and $\vec{v}$,
$$\vec{u} \cdot \vec{v} = \vec{v} \cdot \vec{u}$$
Thus the dot product is commutative.

The proof of this statement is requested in Exercise 3.3.

Property 3

For any vector $\vec{u}$,
$$\vec{u} \cdot \vec{u} = |\vec{u}|^2$$

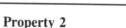

Proof

$$\vec{u} \cdot \vec{u} = |\vec{u}| \, |\vec{u}| \cos 0$$
$$= |\vec{u}|^2 \, (1)$$
$$= |\vec{u}|^2$$

Property 4

For any vectors $\vec{u}$ and $\vec{v}$, with $k \in R$,
$$(k \, \vec{u}) \cdot \vec{v} = k(\vec{u} \cdot \vec{v}) = \vec{u} \cdot (k \, \vec{v})$$

The proof of this statement is requested in Exercise 3.3.

Property 5

For any vectors $\vec{u}$, $\vec{v}$ and $\vec{w}$,
$$\vec{u} \cdot (\vec{v} + \vec{w}) = \vec{u} \cdot \vec{v} + \vec{u} \cdot \vec{w}$$
Thus the dot product is distributive over addition.

If any of the vectors $\vec{u}$, $\vec{v}$, or $\vec{w}$ are the zero vector, then the result is obvious. In the following proof, we assume that none of the vectors are the zero vector.

Proof

Let θ be the angle between $\vec{u}$ and $\vec{v} + \vec{w}$, θ_1 be the angle between $\vec{u}$ and $\vec{v}$, and θ_2 be the angle between $\vec{u}$ and $\vec{w}$.

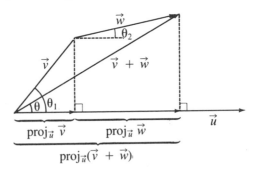

$$\text{proj}_{\vec{u}}(\vec{v} + \vec{w}) = \text{proj}_{\vec{u}} \vec{v} + \text{pro}_{\vec{u}} \vec{w}$$
that is $\quad |\vec{v} + \vec{w}| \cos \theta \, \hat{u} = |\vec{v}| \cos \theta_1 \, \hat{u} + |\vec{w}| \cos \theta_2 \, \hat{u}$

Therefore
$$|\vec{v} + \vec{w}| \cos \theta \, \hat{u} = \left(|\vec{v}| \cos \theta_1 + |\vec{w}| \cos \theta_2\right)\hat{u}$$
or $\quad |\vec{v} + \vec{w}| \cos \theta = |\vec{v}| \cos \theta_1 + |\vec{w}| \cos \theta_2$

Multiplying both sides by $|\vec{u}|$, we obtain
$$|\vec{u}| \, |\vec{v} + \vec{w}| \cos \theta = |\vec{u}| \, |\vec{v}| \cos \theta_1 + |\vec{u}| \, |\vec{w}| \cos \theta_2$$
or $\quad\quad \vec{u} \cdot (\vec{v} + \vec{w}) = \vec{u} \cdot \vec{v} + \vec{u} \cdot \vec{w}$

Since the dot product is commutative, it follows that

$$\boxed{(\vec{u} + \vec{v}) \cdot \vec{w} = \vec{u} \cdot \vec{w} + \vec{v} \cdot \vec{w}}$$

Example 3   Use the properties of dot product to expand and simplify each of the following
(a) $(k\vec{u}) \cdot (\vec{u} + \vec{v})$
(b) $(\vec{u} + \vec{v}) \cdot (\vec{u} + \vec{v})$

Solution   (a) $(k\vec{u}) \cdot (\vec{u} + \vec{v}) = (k\vec{u}) \cdot \vec{u} + (k\vec{u}) \cdot \vec{v}$
$\qquad\qquad\qquad\quad = k(\vec{u} \cdot \vec{u}) + k(\vec{u} \cdot \vec{v})$
$\qquad\qquad\qquad\quad = k|\vec{u}|^2 + k(\vec{u} \cdot \vec{v})$
$\qquad$ (b) $(\vec{u} + \vec{v}) \cdot (\vec{u} + \vec{v}) = (\vec{u} + \vec{v}) \cdot \vec{u} + (\vec{u} + \vec{v}) \cdot \vec{v}$
$\qquad\qquad\qquad\qquad\quad = \vec{u}\cdot\vec{u} + \vec{v}\cdot\vec{u} + \vec{u}\cdot\vec{v} + \vec{v}\cdot\vec{v}$
$\qquad\qquad\qquad\qquad\quad = |\vec{u}|^2 + \vec{u}\cdot\vec{v} + \vec{u}\cdot\vec{v} + |\vec{v}|^2$
$\qquad\qquad\qquad\qquad\quad = |\vec{u}|^2 + 2\vec{u}\cdot\vec{v} + |\vec{v}|^2$

EXERCISE 3.3

A 1.   State whether each of the following is a vector or scalar quantity;
$k, l \in R$.
(a) $k\vec{u}$
(b) $|\vec{v}|$
(c) $\vec{u} \cdot \vec{v}$
(d) $k(\vec{u} + \vec{v})$
(e) $(k + l)\vec{u}$
(f) $k(\vec{u} \cdot \vec{v})$
(g) $\text{proj}_{\vec{v}}\, \vec{u}$
(h) $\vec{u} \cdot (\vec{v} + \vec{w})$
(i) $(\vec{u} \cdot \vec{v})\vec{w}$
(j) the component of $\vec{u}$ on $\vec{v}$
(k) $|\vec{u} + \vec{v}|$
(l) $\vec{u} \cdot \vec{v} + \vec{w} \cdot \vec{x}$

2.   State whether each of the following has meaning. If not, explain why.
(a) $\vec{u} \cdot (\vec{v} \cdot \vec{w})$
(b) $|\vec{u} \cdot \vec{v}|$
(c) $(\vec{u} + \vec{v}) \cdot (\vec{w} + \vec{x})$
(d) $\vec{u}\, \vec{v}$
(e) $\vec{u}(\vec{v} \cdot \vec{w})$
(f) $|\vec{u}|^2$
(g) $\vec{v}^2$
(h) (component of $\vec{u}$ on $\vec{v}$) $\cdot \vec{w}$

B 3.   Find the value of $\vec{u} \cdot \vec{v}$ in each of the following. θ is the angle between $\vec{u}$ and $\vec{v}$.

(a) $|\vec{u}| = 6$, $\qquad\qquad |\vec{v}| = 10$, $\qquad\qquad \theta = \dfrac{\pi}{6}$

(b) $|\vec{u}| = 30$, $\qquad\qquad |\vec{v}| = 15$, $\qquad\qquad \theta = 120°$

(c) $|\vec{u}| = 5.8$, $\qquad\qquad |\vec{v}| = 13.4$, $\qquad\qquad \theta = \pi$

(d) $|\vec{u}| = 4.0$, $\qquad\qquad |\vec{v}| = 6.1$, $\qquad\qquad \theta = \dfrac{\pi}{2}$

(e) $|\vec{u}| = 8550$, $\qquad\qquad |\vec{v}| = 4680$, $\qquad\qquad \theta = 58°$

(f) $|\vec{u}| = 16$, $\qquad\qquad |\vec{v}| = 2|\vec{u}|$, $\qquad\qquad \theta = 153°$
(g) $\vec{u}$ and $\vec{v}$ are unit vectors, $\qquad\qquad\qquad\qquad \theta = 120°$

4. The vector $\vec{u}$ is a unit vector. Find the value of $\vec{u} \cdot \vec{v}$ in each of the following figures.

(a)

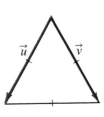

(b)

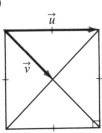

(c)

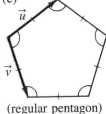

(regular pentagon)

(d)

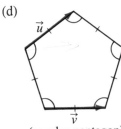

(regular pentagon)

5. Use the properties of dot product to expand and simplify each of the following; $k, l \in R$.
   (a) $\vec{u} \cdot (k\vec{u} + \vec{v})$
   (b) $(k\vec{u} - \vec{v}) \cdot (l\vec{v})$
   (c) $(\vec{u} + \vec{v}) \cdot (\vec{u} - \vec{v})$
   (d) $(\vec{u} + \vec{v}) \cdot (\vec{w} + \vec{x})$

6. (a) If $|\vec{u}| = 4$ and $|\vec{v}| = 2$, what values can $\vec{u} \cdot \vec{v}$ take?
   (b) Prove the Cauchy-Schwarz Inequality; that is
   $$|\vec{u} \cdot \vec{v}| \leq |\vec{u}||\vec{v}|$$

7. If $\vec{u} \cdot \vec{v} = \vec{u} \cdot \vec{w}$, does it follow that $\vec{v} = \vec{w}$? Illustrate your answer with a diagram.

8. Prove that for any vectors $\vec{u}$ and $\vec{v}$, $\vec{u} \cdot \vec{v} = \vec{v} \cdot \vec{u}$.

9. The diagram of a unit cube is given. Find $\vec{u} \cdot \vec{v}$.

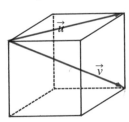

10. Show that $(\vec{b} \cdot \vec{b})\vec{a} - (\vec{a} \cdot \vec{b})\vec{b}$ is perpendicular to $\vec{b}$.

11. If $\vec{a}$ and $\vec{b}$ are parallel, prove
    $$|\vec{a}|^2|\vec{b}|^2 - (\vec{a} \cdot \vec{b})^2 = 0$$

C **12.** Prove that for any vectors $\vec{u}$ and $\vec{v}$, with $k \in R$;
$$(k\vec{u}) \cdot \vec{v} = k(\vec{u} \cdot \vec{v}) = \vec{u} \cdot (k\vec{v})$$
[Hint: Consider three cases; $k = 0$, $k > 0$, and $k < 0$.]

13. If $\vec{a} \cdot \vec{u} = \vec{a} \cdot \vec{v}$ for all vectors $\vec{a}$, prove that $\vec{u} = \vec{v}$.

14. The Parallelogram Law states that
$$|\vec{a} + \vec{b}|^2 + |\vec{a} - \vec{b}|^2 = 2|\vec{a}|^2 + 2|\vec{b}|^2$$

(a) Give a geometric interpretation of the Parallelogram Law.

(b) Prove the Parallelogram Law.
[Hint: Use the fact that $|\vec{a} + \vec{b}|^2 = (\vec{a} + \vec{b}) \cdot (\vec{a} + \vec{b})$ and use Property 5 of the dot product.]

3.4 APPLICATIONS OF THE DOT PRODUCT

I Geometry and Trigonometry

The properties of dot products proved in Section 3.3 will be used extensively in this section. In particular, we use the fact that two non-zero vectors are perpendicular if their dot product is zero.

Example 1   In $\triangle ABC$, $MA = MB = MC$. Use vector methods to prove $\angle BAC = 90°$.

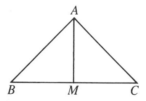

Solution   To prove $\angle BAC = 90°$, it is sufficient to show $\overrightarrow{AB} \cdot \overrightarrow{AC} = 0$.

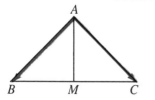

$$\begin{aligned}
\overrightarrow{AB} \cdot \overrightarrow{AC} &= (\overrightarrow{AM} + \overrightarrow{MB}) \cdot (\overrightarrow{AM} + \overrightarrow{MC}) \\
&= (\overrightarrow{AM} + \overrightarrow{MB}) \cdot (\overrightarrow{AM} - \overrightarrow{MB}) \\
&= \overrightarrow{AM} \cdot \overrightarrow{AM} - \overrightarrow{AM} \cdot \overrightarrow{MB} + \overrightarrow{MB} \cdot \overrightarrow{AM} - \overrightarrow{MB} \cdot \overrightarrow{MB} \\
&= |\overrightarrow{AM}|^2 - |\overrightarrow{MB}|^2 \\
&= 0 \quad (\text{since } |\overrightarrow{AM}| = |\overrightarrow{MB}|)
\end{aligned}$$

Since $\overrightarrow{AB} \cdot \overrightarrow{AC} = 0$, the angle between $\overrightarrow{AB}$ and $\overrightarrow{AC}$ is 90°; that is, $\angle BAC = 90°$.

Another useful technique in this sort of proof is to express the length of a line segment in terms of the dot product using $|\vec{u}|^2 = \vec{u} \cdot \vec{u}$ (Property 3).

Example 2 Use the dot product to prove the Law of Cosines.

Solution Let $\vec{a}$, $\vec{b}$, and $\vec{c}$ represent the sides of a triangle with θ the angle between $\vec{a}$ and $\vec{b}$.

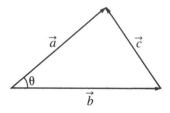

The Law of Cosines states

$$|\vec{c}|^2 = |\vec{a}|^2 + |\vec{b}|^2 - 2|\vec{a}||\vec{b}|\cos\theta$$

To prove this we express $\vec{c}$ in terms of $\vec{a}$ and $\vec{b}$.

$$\vec{c} = -\vec{b} + \vec{a}$$
$$= \vec{a} - \vec{b}$$

Now

$$|\vec{c}|^2 = \vec{c} \cdot \vec{c}$$
$$= (\vec{a} - \vec{b}) \cdot (\vec{a} - \vec{b})$$
$$= \vec{a} \cdot \vec{a} - \vec{a} \cdot \vec{b} - \vec{b} \cdot \vec{a} + \vec{b} \cdot \vec{b}$$
$$= |\vec{a}|^2 + |\vec{b}|^2 - 2\vec{a} \cdot \vec{b}$$

But

$$\vec{a} \cdot \vec{b} = |\vec{a}||\vec{b}|\cos\theta,$$

so

$$|\vec{c}|^2 = |\vec{a}|^2 + |\vec{b}|^2 - 2|\vec{a}||\vec{b}|\cos\theta$$

II Work

As we mentioned in Section 3.3, the work, W, done in moving an object through a displacement, $\vec{s}$, under an applied force, $\vec{f}$, acting at an angle θ to the displacement vector is $W = |\vec{f}||\vec{s}|\cos\theta$. Now we can write this more simply as

$$W = \vec{f} \cdot \vec{s}$$

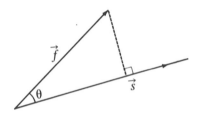

Example 3 A crate on a ramp is hauled 8 m up the ramp under a constant force of 20 N applied at an angle of 30° to the ramp. Find the work done.

Solution Let $\vec{f}$ and $\vec{s}$ represent the force and displacement vectors, respectively.

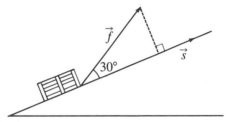

$$W = \vec{f} \cdot \vec{s}$$
$$= |\vec{f}| |\vec{s}| \cos 30°$$
$$= (20)(8) \cos 30°$$
$$\doteq 140$$

Therefore the work done is 140 N·m or 140 J (Joules).

EXERCISE 3.4

Use vector methods in the following questions.

B **1.** In quadrilateral *ABCD*, all sides are equal in length and opposite sides are parallel. Prove that the diagonals are perpendicular.

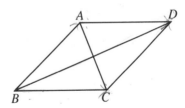

2. Prove that ∠*ADB* inscribed in a semicircle with centre *C* is a right angle.

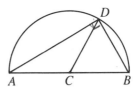

3. *ABC* is an isosceles triangle with base *BC*. Prove that the median from *A* is perpendicular to *BC*.

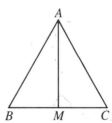

4. Prove that for a parallelogram *ABCD*, the sum of the squares of the lengths of the diagonals equals the sum of the squares of the lengths of the sides. (Assume that the opposite sides of a parallelogram are equal in length.)

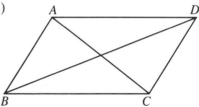

5. *ABC* is an isosceles triangle with base *BC*. Prove that the lengths of the medians, *BM* and *CN*, are equal.

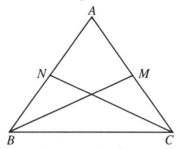

6. A sled is pulled through a distance of 150 m by an 85 N force applied at an angle of 45° to the direction of travel. Find the work done.

7. An orange crate is dragged through 22 m along level ground by a 90 N force applied at an angle of 40° to the ground. It is then dragged up a 6 m ramp onto a truck by the same force. If the ramp is inclined at 25° to the ground, find the total work done.

8. A box is lifted through a distance of 0.5 m and placed on a wagon by exerting a force of 65 N. The wagon is then pulled through a distance of 15 m by a 22 N force applied at an angle of 35° to the ground. Find the total work done.

C 9. Show that for any tetrahedron, the sum of the squares of the lengths of its six edges is equal to four times the sum of the squares of the lengths of the three line segments joining the midpoints of opposite edges

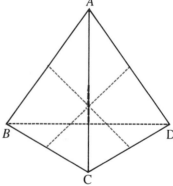

10. X is the midpoint of the line segment AB. For any point O, prove that
$$|\overrightarrow{OA}|^2 + |\overrightarrow{OB}|^2 = |\overrightarrow{XA}|^2 + |\overrightarrow{XB}|^2 + 2|\overrightarrow{XO}|^2$$
Hence $|\overrightarrow{OA}|^2 + |\overrightarrow{OB}|^2 \geq |\overrightarrow{XA}|^2 + |\overrightarrow{XB}|^2$ and the equality holds only if O is the midpoint of AB.

11. X is the centroid of $\triangle ABC$. For any point O, prove that
$$|\overrightarrow{OA}|^2 + |\overrightarrow{OB}|^2 + |\overrightarrow{OC}|^2 = |\overrightarrow{XA}|^2 + |\overrightarrow{XB}|^2 + |\overrightarrow{XC}|^2 + 3|\overrightarrow{XO}|^2$$
Hence $|\overrightarrow{OA}|^2 + |\overrightarrow{OB}|^2 + |\overrightarrow{OC}|^2 \geq |\overrightarrow{XA}|^2 + |\overrightarrow{XB}|^2 + |\overrightarrow{XC}|^2$ and the equality holds only if O is the centroid of $\triangle ABC$.
[The centroid of a triangle is the point where the medians intersect.]

3.5   THE CROSS PRODUCT

In Section 3.3 we showed how two vectors could be combined to form a new scalar quantity, the dot product. In this section we define another product for vectors, the *cross product*. Unlike the dot product, the cross product is a vector quantity. We introduce this product with the following situation from physics.

When a threaded bolt is tightened by a force applied to a wrench, a measure of the *'turning effect'* of the force on the bolt is called the **moment** of the force about the centre of the bolt. It is denoted by $\overrightarrow{M}$.

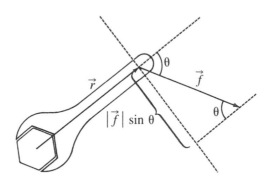

The magnitude of this turning effect will depend on two things:
(1)   the distance between the bolt and the point where the force is applied, and
(2)   the magnitude of the force directed perpendicular to the wrench.
We define
$$|\overrightarrow{M}| = |\overrightarrow{r}|(|\overrightarrow{f}| \sin \theta)$$

where θ is the angle between $\overrightarrow{r}$ and $\overrightarrow{f}$. The direction of the turning effect is perpendicular to the plane containing $\overrightarrow{r}$ and $\overrightarrow{f}$. If the bolt is right-threaded the direction of the moment will be into the page.

We use the preceding example to motivate the following mathematical definition.

For vectors $\vec{u}$ and $\vec{v}$, we define the **cross product** of $\vec{u}$ and $\vec{v}$ as

$$\vec{u} \times \vec{v} = (|\vec{u}||\vec{v}| \sin \theta)\, \hat{n}$$

where θ is the angle between $\vec{u}$ and $\vec{v}$, and $\hat{n}$ is a unit vector perpendicular to both $\vec{u}$ and $\vec{v}$ such that $\vec{u}$, $\vec{v}$, and $\hat{n}$ form a right-handed system, as indicated in the diagram.

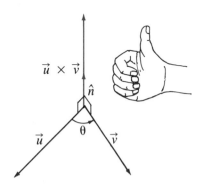

The name, right-handed system, comes from the fact that we could use our right hand to indicate the directions of the three vectors. If the fingers of your right hand curl in the direction of a rotation (through an angle less than 180°) from $\vec{u}$ to $\vec{v}$, then your thumb points in the direction of $\vec{u} \times \vec{v}$.

If $\vec{u}$ and $\vec{v}$ are not collinear, then $\vec{u} \times \vec{v}$ is perpendicular to the plane determined by $\vec{u}$ and $\vec{v}$. Thus $\vec{u}$, $\vec{v}$, and $\vec{u} \times \vec{v}$ are not coplanar.

This is called the cross product, because the symbol used is a cross. It is also called the **vector product** because the result is a vector quantity.

Example 1 If $|\vec{u}| = 8$, $|\vec{v}| = 5$, and the angle between $\vec{u}$ and $\vec{v}$ is 30° (as indicated in the diagram,) find

(a) $\vec{u} \times \vec{v}$

(b) $\vec{v} \times \vec{u}$

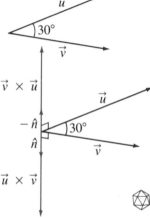

Solution (a) $\vec{u} \times \vec{v} = (|\vec{u}||\vec{v}| \sin 30°)\hat{n}$

$\qquad\qquad = (8)(5)(0.5)\, \hat{n}$

$\qquad\qquad = 20\, \hat{n}$

(b) $\vec{v} \times \vec{u} = (|\vec{v}||\vec{u}| \sin 30°)(-\hat{n})$

$\qquad\qquad = (5)(8)(0.5)(-\hat{n})$

$\qquad\qquad = 20(-\hat{n})$

From the preceding example it is clear that $\vec{u} \times \vec{v}$ and $\vec{v} \times \vec{u}$ are not equal vectors. That is, the cross product is **not commutative**. In fact

$$\vec{u} \times \vec{v} = -(\vec{v} \times \vec{u})$$

Example 2   A right-threaded bolt is tightened by applying a 50 N force to a 0.2 m wrench as shown in the diagram. Find the moment of the force about the centre of the bolt.

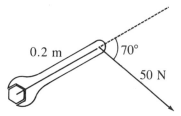

0.2 m   70°

50 N

Solution   Let $\vec{f}$ be the 50 N force. Let $\vec{r}$ be the displacement vector directed from the centre of the bolt to the point where the force is applied.

$$\vec{M} = \vec{r} \times \vec{f}$$
$$= |\vec{r}||\vec{f}| \sin 70° \, \hat{n}$$
$$= (50)(0.2) \sin 70° \, \hat{n}$$
$$\doteq 9.4 \, \hat{n}$$

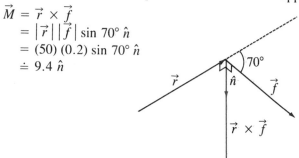

$\vec{r}$ $\hat{n}$ 70° $\vec{f}$

$\vec{r} \times \vec{f}$

Therefore the moment of $\vec{f}$ about the centre of the bolt has a magnitude of 9.4 N·m and is directed down (as shown in the diagram).

One of the important properties of the dot product is that two non-zero vectors are perpendicular if and only if their dot product is zero. There is a similar property for the cross product.

For non-zero vectors $\vec{u}$ and $\vec{v}$,
$\vec{u}$ and $\vec{v}$ are collinear if, and only if, $\vec{u} \times \vec{v} = \vec{0}$

Proof

First suppose $\vec{u}$ and $\vec{v}$ are collinear, then the angle, θ, between $\vec{u}$ and $\vec{v}$ is 0 or π and $\sin \theta = 0$. Since $\vec{u} \times \vec{v} = |\vec{u}| \, |\vec{v}| \sin \theta \, \hat{n}$, $\vec{u} \times \vec{v} = \vec{0}$.

Conversely suppose $\vec{u} \times \vec{v} = \vec{0}$; then $|\vec{u}| \, |\vec{v}| \sin \theta \, \hat{n} = \vec{0}$. Since $\vec{u}$ and $\vec{v}$ are non-zero vectors, $|\vec{u}|$ and $|\vec{v}|$ are not zero. Therefore $\sin \theta = 0$ and hence $\theta = 0$ or π. This shows $\vec{u}$ and $\vec{v}$ are collinear.

An immediate consequence of this fact is

> $\vec{u}$ and $\vec{v}$ are not collinear if, and only if, $\vec{u} \times \vec{v} \neq \vec{0}$

There are other properties of the cross product that we state here for comparison with the corresponding results for the dot product.

> **Properties**
>
> For any vectors $\vec{u}$, $\vec{v}$, and $\vec{w}$, and $k, l \in R$.
> 1. $\vec{u} \times (\vec{v} + \vec{w}) = \vec{u} \times \vec{v} + \vec{u} \times \vec{w}$
> 2. $(\vec{u} + \vec{v}) \times \vec{w} = \vec{u} \times \vec{w} + \vec{v} \times \vec{w}$
> 3. $(k\vec{u}) \times \vec{v} = k(\vec{u} \times \vec{v}) = \vec{u} \times (k\vec{v})$

The proof of Property 3 is requested in Exercise 3.5. The proofs of Properties 1 and 2 are more difficult and the student is asked to accept the results without proof.

Example 3 Use the cross product to prove the Law of Sines.

Solution Let $\vec{a}$, $\vec{b}$, and $\vec{c}$ represent the sides of $\triangle ABC$ as shown in the diagram.

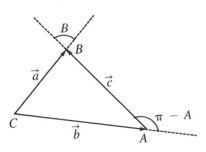

The Law of Sines states that

$$\frac{\sin A}{|\vec{a}|} = \frac{\sin B}{|\vec{b}|} = \frac{\sin C}{|\vec{c}|}$$

To prove this we express $\vec{c}$ in terms of $\vec{a}$ and $\vec{b}$.

$$\vec{c} = -\vec{b} + \vec{a}$$
$$= \vec{a} - \vec{b}$$

Now
$$\vec{c} \times \vec{c} = \vec{0}$$
$$\vec{c} \times (\vec{a} - \vec{b}) = \vec{0}$$
$$\vec{c} \times \vec{a} - \vec{c} \times \vec{b} = \vec{0}$$
$$\vec{c} \times \vec{a} = \vec{c} \times \vec{b}$$
$$|\vec{c} \times \vec{a}| = |\vec{c} \times \vec{b}|$$
$$|\vec{c}||\vec{a}| \sin B = |\vec{c}||\vec{b}| \sin(\pi - A)$$
$$|\vec{c}||\vec{a}| \sin B = |\vec{c}||\vec{b}| \sin A \quad [\sin(\pi - A) = \sin A]$$

Dividing through by $\left|\vec{a}\right|\left|\vec{b}\right|\left|\vec{c}\right|$, we obtain

$$\frac{\sin B}{\left|\vec{b}\right|} = \frac{\sin A}{\left|\vec{a}\right|}$$

Similarly we can show that $\dfrac{\sin C}{\left|\vec{c}\right|} = \dfrac{\sin B}{\left|\vec{b}\right|}$.

Therefore $\dfrac{\sin A}{\left|\vec{a}\right|} = \dfrac{\sin B}{\left|\vec{b}\right|} = \dfrac{\sin C}{\left|\vec{c}\right|}$

An interpretation of $\left|\vec{u}\times\vec{v}\right|$ is the area of the parallelogram with adjacent sides $\vec{u}$ and $\vec{v}$.

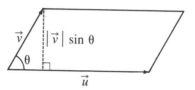

Proof:

$$\begin{aligned}
\text{area} &= (\text{base}) \times (\text{height}) \\
&= \left|\vec{u}\right| (\left|\vec{v}\right| \sin \theta) \\
&= \left|\vec{u}\times\vec{v}\right|
\end{aligned}$$

Example 4   Find the area of the parallelogram below.

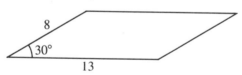

Solution $\begin{aligned}
\text{area} &= \left|\vec{u}\times\vec{v}\right| \\
&= \left|\vec{u}\right|\left|\vec{v}\right|\sin\theta \\
&= (8)(13)\sin 30° \\
&= 52
\end{aligned}$

PROBLEMS PLUS

Three vectors $\vec{u}$, $\vec{v}$, and $\vec{w}$ have a common initial point. Their endpoints form a triangle. Prove that the magnitude of the vector

$$\tfrac{1}{2}(\vec{u}\times\vec{v} + \vec{v}\times\vec{w} + \vec{w}\times\vec{u})$$

is equal to the area of the triangle. Such a vector is called **the vector area** of the triangle.

EXERCISE 3.5

A **1.** State whether each expression has meaning. If not, explain why. If so, state whether it is a vector or scalar quantity.

(a) $\vec{u} \cdot (\vec{v} \times \vec{w})$ (b) $\vec{u} \times (\vec{v} \cdot \vec{w})$

(c) $\vec{u} \times (\vec{v} \times \vec{w})$ (d) $(\vec{u} \cdot \vec{v}) \times \vec{w}$

(e) $(\vec{u} \times \vec{v}) + (\vec{u} \times \vec{w})$ (f) $(\vec{u} \cdot \vec{v}) \times (\vec{u} \cdot \vec{w})$

(g) $(\vec{u} \times \vec{v}) \cdot (\vec{w} \times \vec{x})$

2. For each of the following pairs of vectors, $\vec{u}$ and $\vec{v}$, state whether $\vec{u} \times \vec{v}$ is directed into the page or out of the page.

(a)

(b)

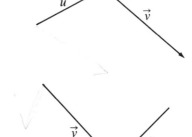

(c)

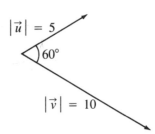

B **3.** For each of the following

(i) determine $|\vec{u} \times \vec{v}|$,

(ii) state whether $\vec{u} \times \vec{v}$ is directed into the page or out of the page.

(a)

$|\vec{u}| = 5$

$60°$

$|\vec{v}| = 10$

(b)

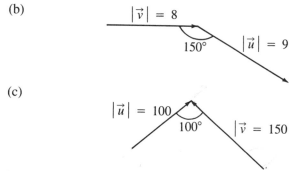

(c)

4. In each of the following diagrams determine the magnitude of the moment of the force about the fixed point A.

(a)

(b)

(c)

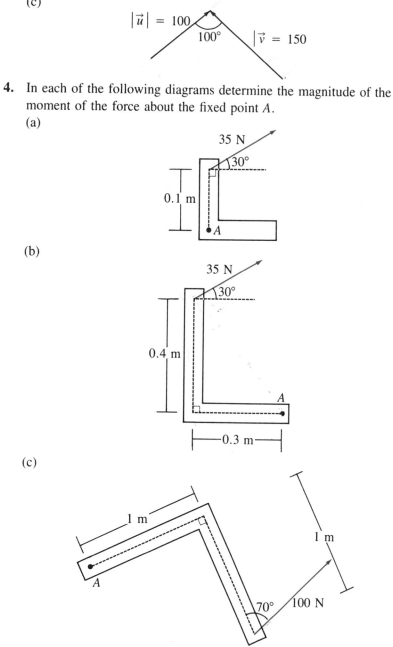

5. A bicycle pedal is pushed by a 75 N force exerted by the foot of its rider, as shown in the diagram. If the shaft of the pedal is 0.15 m long, find the magnitude of the moment of the force about A. [Your answer will be in Newton-metres.]

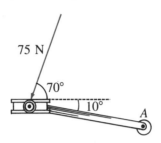

6. Two of the guy wires used to secure an antenna are shown in the diagram. If the tension in wire AB is 550 N and the tension in wire CD is 780 N, find the magnitude of the moment due to each of these tensions about the point P.

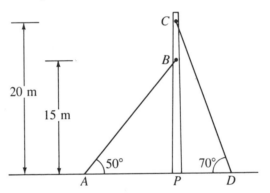

7. Use the cross product to find the area of each of the following parallelograms.
   (a)

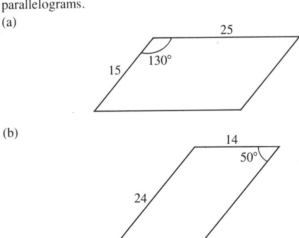

   (b)

8. Show that for any vector $\vec{u}$, $\vec{u} \times \vec{u} = \vec{0}$.

9. If $\vec{u} \cdot \vec{v} = 0$ and $\left| \vec{u} \right| = \left| \vec{v} \right| = 1$, show that $(\vec{u} \times \vec{v}) \times \vec{u} = \vec{v}$.

10. The cross product is **not associative**; that is, in general,
$$\vec{u} \times (\vec{v} \times \vec{w}) \neq (\vec{u} \times \vec{v}) \times \vec{w}$$
By choosing $\vec{u} = \vec{v}$, show that this is so.

11. Given two non-collinear vectors $\vec{u}$ and $\vec{v}$, determine expressions for three mutually perpendicular vectors.

C 12. (a) Show that $\left| \vec{u} \times \vec{v} \right|^2 = \left| \vec{u} \right|^2 \left| \vec{v} \right|^2 - (\vec{u} \cdot \vec{v})^2$.

   (b) Use the result of part (a) to prove $\left| \vec{u} \cdot \vec{v} \right| \leq \left| \vec{u} \right| \left| \vec{v} \right|$.

   (c) Using the result from part (a) show that $\vec{u}$ and $\vec{v}$ are collinear if, and only if, $\left| \vec{u} \cdot \vec{v} \right| = \left| \vec{u} \right| \left| \vec{v} \right|$.

13. Prove that for any vectors $\vec{u}$ and $\vec{v}$ with $k \in R$,
$$(k\,\vec{u}) \times \vec{v} = k(\vec{u} \times \vec{v}) = \vec{u} \times (k\,\vec{v})$$
[Hint: Consider the cases $k = 0$, $k > 0$, and $k < 0$.]

PROBLEMS PLUS

Let ABC be a triangle. Prove that the perpendiculars from A to BC, from B to CA, and from C to AB are concurrent.

PROBLEMS PLUS

Gram-Schmidt Orthogonalization

Let $\vec{u}$, $\vec{v}$, and $\vec{w}$ be three linearly independent vectors. The following procedure, is known as the **Gram-Schmidt** process.

(1) Let $\vec{a} = \dfrac{\vec{u}}{\left| \vec{u} \right|}$.

(2) Find $proj_{\vec{a}}\vec{v}$.

(3) Let $\vec{v}' = \vec{v} - proj_{\vec{a}}\vec{v}$.

(4) Let $\vec{b} = \dfrac{\vec{v}'}{\left| \vec{v}' \right|}$.

(5) Find $proj_{\vec{a}}\vec{w} + proj_{\vec{b}}\vec{w}$.

(6) Let $\vec{w}' = \vec{w} - (proj_{\vec{a}}\vec{w} + proj_{\vec{b}}\vec{w})$.

(7) Let $\vec{c} = \dfrac{\vec{w}'}{\left| \vec{w}' \right|}$.

Explain what the vectors $\vec{a}$, $\vec{b}$, and $\vec{c}$ represent.

3.6 REVIEW EXERCISE

1. Resolve each of the following into vector components along the given directions.

(a)   (b)

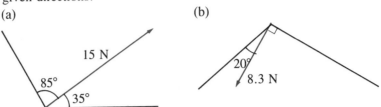

2. An advertising sign for a popular cola manufacturer is held out from the front of a store building by a horizontal steel pole. A wire, fastened to the store at an angle of 35° to the vertical, supports the entire weight of the sign. If the sign has a weight of 934 N under gravity, find the tension in the wire and the compression in the steel pole.

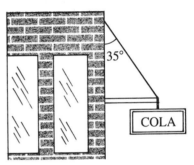

3. While camping in northern regions at night, people often keep food out of the reach of animals by hanging it between two trees. If a food bag weighing 435 N is tied between two trees 6 m apart by two ropes that are 4 m and 5 m long, find the tension in each rope.

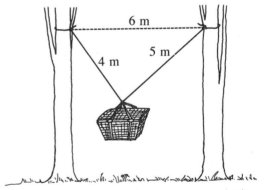

4. The angle between two vectors $\vec{u}$ and $\vec{v}$ is 120°. If $|\vec{u}| = 28$ and $|\vec{v}| = 43$, find
   (a) $\text{proj}_{\vec{v}}\vec{u}$,
   (b) the component of $\vec{v}$ on $\vec{u}$.

5. A box with a mass of 155 N rests on a frictionless ramp inclined at an angle of 25° to the level ground. What force must be applied at an angle of 45° to the ramp so the box remains at rest?

6. An aircraft travelling with an airspeed of 625 km/h is at an angle of 20° to the level ground below. Find the horizontal ground speed, in kilometres per hour, and the rate of climb, in metres per minute, of the aircraft.

7. For each of the following, state whether it is a vector or scalar quantity; $k, l \in R$.
    (a) $\vec{u} \cdot \vec{v}$ (b) $\vec{u} \times \vec{v}$
    (c) $\vec{u} \cdot (\vec{v} \times \vec{w})$ (d) $(\vec{u} \cdot \vec{v})\vec{w}$
    (e) $\vec{u} \times (\vec{v} \times \vec{w})$

8. For each of the following, state whether it has meaning. If not, explain why.
    (a) $(\vec{u} \cdot \vec{v}) \times \vec{w}$ (b) $(\vec{u} \times \vec{v}) \times (\vec{w} \times \vec{x})$
    (c) $\vec{u} \cdot (\vec{v} \cdot \vec{w})$

9. Find the value of $\vec{u} \cdot \vec{v}$ in each of the following. θ is the angle between $\vec{u}$ and $\vec{v}$.

    (a) $|\vec{u}| = 12$ $|\vec{v}| = 23$ $\theta = \dfrac{\pi}{3}$

    (b) $|\vec{u}| = 125$ $|\vec{v}| = 95$ $\theta = 135°$

    (c) $|\vec{u}| = 8.7$ $|\vec{v}| = 5.3$ $\theta = \pi$

10. The diagram of a unit cube is given. Find $\vec{u} \cdot \vec{v}$.

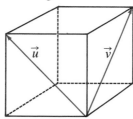

11. Use the properties of dot product to expand and simplify each of the following.
    (a) $(\vec{u} - \vec{v}) \cdot (\vec{w} - \vec{x})$ (b) $(k\vec{u} + \vec{v}) \cdot k\vec{u}$

12. If the diagonals of a parallelogram are perpendicular, use vector methods to prove that it is a rhombus.

13. A refrigerator is fastened to a dolly and is pulled a distance of 13 m by a 185 N force applied at an angle of 15° to the level ground. Find the work done.

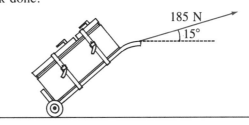

14. A wagon is pulled from a point A to a point B by a child. If the child exerts a constant force of 68 N at an angle of 30° to the level ground, find the total work done.

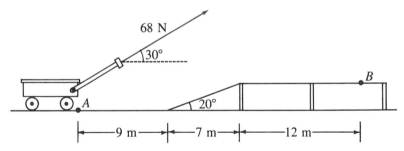

15. For each of the following, determine $\left| \vec{u} \times \vec{v} \right|$ and state whether $\vec{u} \times \vec{v}$ is directed into the page or out of the page.

(a)   (b)

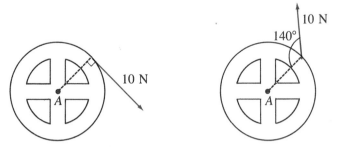

16. For each of the following diagrams, the radius of the wheel is 0.15 m. Determine the magnitude of the moment of the force about the fixed point A.

(a)   (b)

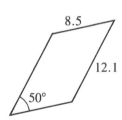

17. Use the cross product to find the area of the following parallelograms.

(a)   (b)

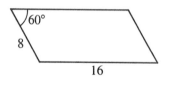

18. A diving board is 5.5 m long. It is fastened to its supporting structure at a point A, 1.0 m from one end. A boy standing at a point 0.1 m from the other end exerts a force of 125 N, under gravity. Find the magnitude of the moment of this force about the point A.

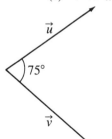

19. For each of the following, state whether the property is true or false for the vectors involved.

(a) $\vec{u} \cdot \vec{v} = \vec{v} \cdot \vec{u}$

(b) $\vec{u} \times \vec{v} = \vec{v} \times \vec{u}$

(c) $|\vec{u} \times \vec{v}| = |\vec{v} \times \vec{u}|$

(d) $\vec{u} \cdot (\vec{v} + \vec{w}) = \vec{u} \cdot \vec{v} + \vec{u} \cdot \vec{w}$

(e) $\vec{u} \times (\vec{v} + \vec{w}) = \vec{u} \times \vec{v} + \vec{u} \times \vec{w}$

(f) $(\vec{u} + \vec{v}) \cdot \vec{w} = \vec{u} \cdot \vec{w} + \vec{v} \cdot \vec{w}$

(g) $(\vec{u} + \vec{v}) \times \vec{w} = \vec{u} \times \vec{w} + \vec{v} \times \vec{w}$

(h) $\vec{u} \times (\vec{v} \times \vec{w}) = \vec{u} \times \vec{v} + \vec{u} \times \vec{w}$

(i) $(k\vec{u}) \cdot \vec{v} = k(\vec{u} \cdot \vec{v})$

(j) $(k\vec{u}) \times \vec{v} = k(\vec{u} \times \vec{v})$

20. The angle between two vectors $\vec{u}$ and $\vec{v}$ is 75° as shown in the diagram. If $|\vec{v}| = 14$ and $|\vec{v}| = 10$, find

(a) $\text{proj}_{\vec{v}}\vec{u}$ (b) component of $\vec{v}$ on $\vec{u}$

(c) $\vec{u} \cdot \vec{v}$ (d) $\vec{v} \cdot \vec{u}$

(e) $\vec{u} \times \vec{v}$ (f) $\vec{v} \times \vec{u}$

$\vec{u}$

75°

$\vec{v}$

PROBLEMS PLUS

Prove that

$$(\vec{u} \times \vec{v}) \cdot ((\vec{v} \times \vec{w}) \times (\vec{w} \times \vec{u})) = (\vec{u} \cdot (\vec{v} \times \vec{w}))^2$$

3.7 CHAPTER 3 TEST

1. If $|\vec{u}| = 4$, $|\vec{v}| = 9$, and the angle, θ, between $\vec{u}$ and $\vec{v}$ is 120°, determine each of the following.
   (a) $\text{proj}_{\vec{v}}\vec{u}$
   (b) component of $\vec{v}$ on $\vec{u}$
   (c) $\vec{u} \cdot \vec{v}$
   (d) $|\vec{u} \times \vec{v}|$

2. The diagram of a unit cube is given.
   Find a simpler expression for each of the following.
   (a) $\vec{u} \times \vec{v}$
   (b) $\vec{v} \times \vec{w}$
   (c) $\vec{u} \times \vec{w}$

3. Referring to the diagram, evaluate
   $(\vec{u} + \vec{v}) \cdot (\vec{v} + \vec{w})$.

4. A tennis net is supported at each end by a steel post. If the tension in the net cord is 325 N and the angles are as shown in the diagram, find the tension in the guy wire and the compression in the post.

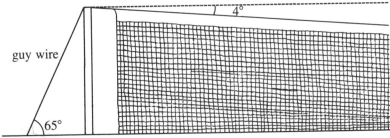

5. A crate with a mass of 195 N is placed on a ramp. There is a frictional force of 25 N exerted on the crate directed up the ramp. If the ramp is inclined at 15° to the horizontal, what force must be applied at an angle of 30° to the ramp to maintain equilibrium?

6. A box is dragged 16 m by a 75 N force applied at an angle of 35° to the level ground. It is then dragged to the top of a 6 m ramp by the same force. If the ramp is inclined at 20° to the ground, find the total work done.

7. *ABC* is an isosceles triangle with base *BC*. Use vector methods to prove that the median from *A* is perpendicular to *BC*.

8. A bicycle pedal is pushed by a force $\vec{f}$ exerted by the foot of its rider, as shown in the diagram. At what position(s) of the pedal will the magnitude of the moment of the force about *A* be a maximum?

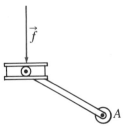

CUMULATIVE REVIEW FOR CHAPTERS 1 TO 3

1. For vectors $\vec{u}$, $\vec{v}$, and $\vec{w}$, draw each of the following:

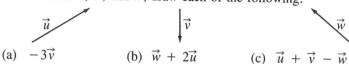

   (a) $-3\vec{v}$ (b) $\vec{w} + 2\vec{u}$ (c) $\vec{u} + \vec{v} - \vec{w}$

2. Find the resultant (magnitude and direction) of each pair of vectors.

   (a)   (b)

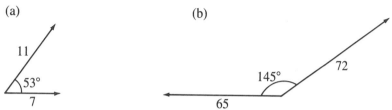

   (c) vector $\vec{u}$ with magnitude 32, direction N20°E
       vector $\vec{v}$ with magnitude 17, direction S15°E

3. If $7|\vec{u}| = 3|\vec{v}|$, under what further condition(s) will $7\vec{u}$ and $3\vec{v}$ be equal vectors?

4. Find the magnitude of the resultant for the forces shown.

   (a)   (b)

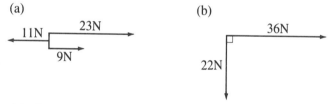

   (c) forces of 215 N and 127 N acting at an angle of 112° to each other

5. Find the equilibrant of each set of forces.

   (a)   (b)

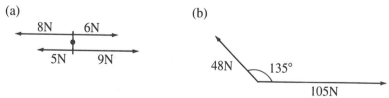

   (c) forces of 56 N and 18 N acting at angle of 65° to each other

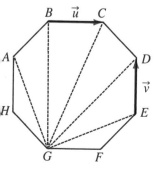

6. Vectors $\vec{u}$ and $\vec{v}$ form two mutually perpendicular sides of the regular octagon shown.

   (a) Express each of the other six sides of the octagon in terms of $\vec{u}$ and $\vec{v}$.

   (b) Express each of the five diagonals indicated in terms of $\vec{u}$ and $\vec{v}$.

7. At the grand opening of the Bartonville Community Centre a banner is strung across the front of the building as shown in the picture. If the mass of the banner is 1.4 kg, what is the tension in each section of the rope?

8. A tall ship is sailing N40°W at a speed of 22 knots. A current of 6 knots is travelling from S50°W. Calculate the actual velocity of the ship.

9. A pilot wishes to fly from his home field to a destination 625 km S20°E. The cruising speed of the aircraft is 535 km/h. If there is a wind of 72 km/h blowing from N80°W, what heading should the pilot take in order to reach his destination and how long will the flight take (to the nearest minute)?

10. A child runs across the aisle of a 747 jumbo jet. If the airliner is flying SW at 695 km/h and the child's ground speed is 694 km/h at S46°W, what was the speed at which the child ran across the plane?

11. The pair of diagrams shown illustrates the property that, for vectors $\vec{u}$ and $\vec{v}$, and scalar k, $k(\vec{u} + \vec{v}) = k\vec{u} + k\vec{v}$.

For each pair of diagrams, write, in general form, the statement of the property that it illustrates.

(a)

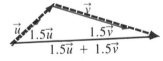

(b)

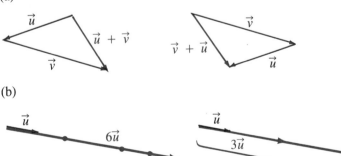

(c)

$5\vec{u} = (2 + 3)\vec{u}$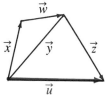

12. Simplify each expression using the properties of vector operations.
    (a) $5(-2\vec{u}) + 3\vec{v} - 2\vec{u}$ (b) $3(\vec{u} + 4\vec{v}) + 2(\vec{w} - \vec{v}) - \vec{u}$

13. Write the indicated vector as a linear combination of the other vectors.
    (a) $\vec{u}$ as a combination of $\vec{x}, \vec{y}, \vec{z}$, and $\vec{w}$,

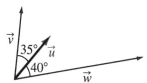

    (b) $\vec{u}$ as a combination of $\vec{v}$ and $\vec{w}$ where $|\vec{u}| = 5, |\vec{v}| = 13,$
        $|\vec{w}| = 22,$

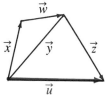

    (c) $\overrightarrow{AX}$ as a linear combination of sides of the parallelogram $ABCD$,

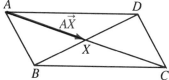

    (d) $\overrightarrow{OA}$ as a linear combination of $\overrightarrow{OB}$ and $\overrightarrow{OC}$ where B divides AC
        externally in the ratio $3:-7$.

14. Give a geometric interpretation of each situation:
    (a) two dependent vectors
    (b) three independent vectors

15. Using the definition of linearly dependent vectors, prove that vectors
    $\vec{u}, \vec{v}$, and $\vec{w}$ are dependent.

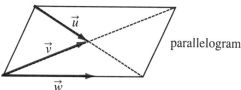

parallelogram

16. Are four vectors in space linearly dependent or independent?

17. Assuming that the vectors in each question are linearly independent,
    solve for the scalars wherever possible.
    (a) $(2a + 1)\vec{u} - \vec{v} = b\vec{v} + (3c - 2)\vec{w}$
    (b) $(3 - m)\vec{u} + (2 - 5m)\vec{v} = \vec{0}$

18. Prove that, if vectors $\vec{u}$, $\vec{v}$, and $\vec{w}$ are not coplanar, then vectors $2\vec{u} - \vec{v}$ and $\vec{w}$ are not collinear.

19. Given: A divides $\overrightarrow{PQ}$ internally in the ratio 7:5
    X divides $\overrightarrow{AP}$ externally in the ratio $4:-1$
    (a) Draw a diagram of this situation.
    (b) In what ratio does A divide $\overrightarrow{XQ}$?

20. If vectors $\overrightarrow{PQ}$ and $\overrightarrow{QR}$ are dependent with $\overrightarrow{PQ} = k\overrightarrow{QR}$, in what ratio does R divide $\overrightarrow{PQ}$?

21. Draw a diagram illustrating each linear combination.
    (a) $\vec{w}$ as a linear combination of $\vec{u}$ and $\vec{v}$

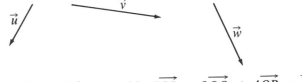

    (b) $\overrightarrow{OX} = \frac{3}{7}\overrightarrow{OY} + \frac{4}{7}\overrightarrow{OZ}$ (c) $5\overrightarrow{OP} - 9\overrightarrow{OQ} + 4\overrightarrow{OR} = \vec{0}$

22. Assuming that points K, L, and M are collinear with M dividing $\overrightarrow{KL}$ in the ratio 7:1, prove, from first principles, that
$$\overrightarrow{OM} = \tfrac{1}{8}\overrightarrow{OK} + \tfrac{7}{8}\overrightarrow{OL}$$

23. For the points shown in the diagram and origin O, express
    (a) $\overrightarrow{OA}$ in terms of $\overrightarrow{OB}$ and $\overrightarrow{OC}$, and
    (b) $\overrightarrow{OC}$ in terms of $\overrightarrow{OA}$ and $\overrightarrow{OD}$.

24. For triangle ABC with X dividing $\overrightarrow{AC}$ in the ratio 3:5, Y the midpoint of $\overrightarrow{AB}$, and Z the point of intersection of $\overrightarrow{BX}$ and $\overrightarrow{CY}$, use vector methods to find the ratio in which Z divides $\overrightarrow{BX}$.

25. In parallelogram $ABCD$, F is the midpoint of $\overrightarrow{AD}$, and E divides $\overrightarrow{BC}$ internally in the ratio 3:2. If P is the point of intersection of $\overrightarrow{AE}$ and $\overrightarrow{BF}$, show that P divides $\overrightarrow{AE}$ in the ratio 5:6.

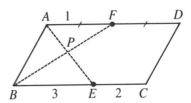

26. G is the centroid of $\triangle ABC$, that is, the point of intersection of its medians.
    (a) Prove that G divides each median in the ratio 2:1.
    (b) Prove that $\overrightarrow{AG} + \overrightarrow{BG} + \overrightarrow{CG} = \vec{0}$.

27. Is it possible that the magnitude of the projection of a vector is greater than the magnitude of the vector? Give a reason for your answer.

28. In each situation the vector $\vec{v}$ is resolved into components. Find the missing information.

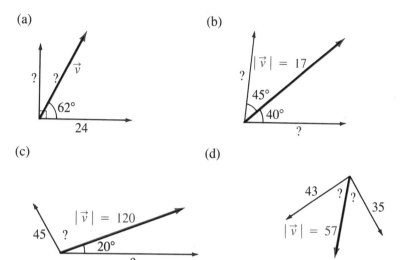

(a)

(b)

(c)

(d)

29. Each of the planters along Main St. is suspended over the street with a hinged rod and a cable as shown. Assuming that the rod is weightless find the tension in the cable and the force exerted by the hinge.

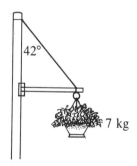

30. A cable car weighing 5025 N stops over the gorge so that the supporting cables make angles of 15° and 12° with the horizontal as shown. At this time what is the tension in each section of the cable?

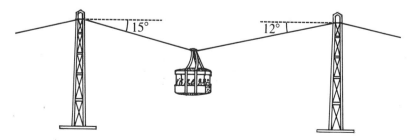

31. For vectors $\vec{u}$ and $\vec{v}$ as described find
    (i) the projection of $\vec{u}$ and $\vec{v}$, and
    (ii) the component of $\vec{v}$ on $\vec{u}$.
    (a) $|\vec{u}| = 12$, $|\vec{v}| = 7$, angle between $\vec{u}$ and $\vec{v}$ is $27°$,
    (b)

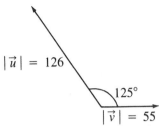

32. An aerobatic plane climbs steeply as it begins its air show display. If its airspeed is 355 km/h and its path makes an angle of $42°$ with the ground, what is its groundspeed, in kilometres per hour, and its rate of climb, in metres per minute?

33. Terri drags a Christmas tree up the ramp into the barn.
    (a) If the force she exerts is 132 N at an angle of $40°$ to the ramp, what is the magnitude of the force in the direction of the motion?
    (b) If the ramp is at an angle of $15°$ to the ground, what is the magnitude of the force tending to lift the tree vertically?

34. Find the dot product of vectors $\vec{u}$ and $\vec{v}$.
    (a) $|\vec{u}| = 312$, $|\vec{v}| = 276$, the angle between $\vec{u}$ and $\vec{v}$ is $29°$
    (b) $|\vec{u}| = 12$, $|\vec{v}| = 38$, the angle between $\vec{u}$ and $\vec{v}$ is $\frac{2\pi}{3}$

(c)   (d)

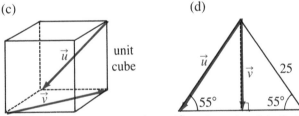

35. For each pair of vectors $\vec{u}$ and $\vec{v}$ in Question 34, find the magnitude of the cross product $\vec{u} \times \vec{v}$.

36. (a) The dot product of two vectors is sometimes called the *scalar product*. Why?
    (b) The cross product of two vectors is sometimes called the *vector product*. Why?

37. How much work is done in each situation?
    (a) Rookaya pushes a box of library books five metres along the floor to the shelving unit against a frictional force of 180 N.
    (b) D'Arcy drags his backpack 25 metres down the hall with a force of 63 N at angle of $32°$ to the floor.

(c) On his summer construction job, Cesar carries a load of building materials up a ramp that is at an angle of 25° to the ground. He carries them under constant force of 175 N to the end of the ramp that rests at a height of five metres against the first floor level of the house under construction.

38. Find the area of each parallelogram using the cross product operation.

(a)

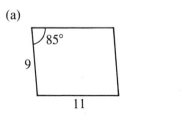

(b)

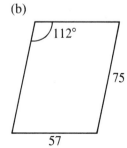

39. A bar 4.0 m long is mounted so that it is inclined at an angle of 30° with the horizontal. An 8.0 kg body is hung 3.0 m from the lower end of the rod. What is the moment of the force
(a) at the point at the lower end of the rod?
(b) at the upper end of the rod?
(c) at the midpoint of the rod?

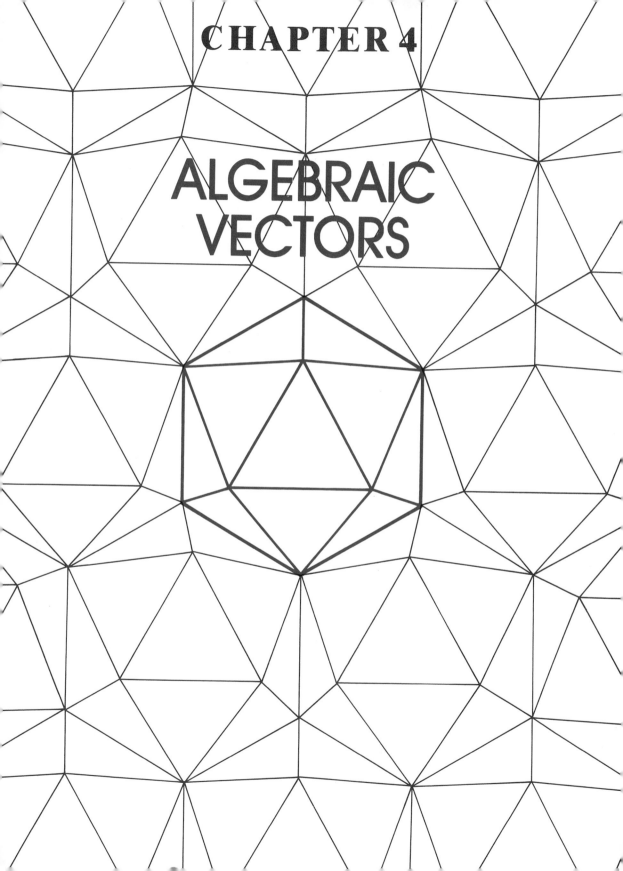

CHAPTER 4

ALGEBRAIC VECTORS

R E V I E W   A N D   P R E V I E W   T O
CHAPTER 4

Solving Systems of Two Equations in Two Unknowns

Example 1   Solve $x - 2y = 5$ ①
$3x + 4y = 10$ ②

Solution   We use the technique usually referred to as *elimination*. One of the equations is used to eliminate a variable from the other equation. In this case we use Equation 1 to eliminate y from Equation 2.
② + 2 × ① gives

$$5x = 20$$
$$x = 4$$

Substituting in Equation 2, we get

$$3(4) + 4y = 10$$
$$4y = -2$$
$$y = -\tfrac{1}{2}$$

Therefore $x = 4$ and $y = -\tfrac{1}{2}$.

EXERCISE 1

Solve each of the following systems of equations.
1. $3x + 2y = -4$
$x - 3y = -5$

2. $2k - l = 3$
$k + l = 6$

3. $2m + 3n = 6$
$3m - 2n = 6$

4. $-k + 2l = 5$
$3k + 4l = 8$

Solving Systems of Three Equations in Two Unknowns

Example 2   Solve $2k + l = 1$ ①
$-k - l = 3$ ②
$k + l = 11$ ③

Solution   We solve Equations 1 and 2, then check our solution in Equation 3.
① + ② gives

$$k = 4$$

Substituting in Equation 1, we get

$$2(4) + l = 1$$
$$l = -7$$

We now check this solution in Equation 3.

$$4 + (-7) = -3 \neq 11$$

Therefore there is no solution to this system of equations.

EXERCISE 2

Solve each of the following systems of equations.

1. $2k + l = 1$
$-k + l = -5$
$-2k + l = -7$

2. $k + 2l = -1$
$-k + l = -1$
$-k + 4l = -1$

3. $x - y = -3$
$x + y = 1$
$2x + 3y = 4$

4. $2r - s = 5$
$r + s = 4$
$-3r + s = 8$

Solving Systems of Three Equations in Three Unknowns

Example 3   Solve $k + l - m = 2$ ①
$k + l + m = 1$ ②
$2k + l + m = 4$ ③

Solution   We use Equation 1 to eliminate m from Equations 2 and 3.
② + ① gives

$$2k + 2l = 3 \quad ④$$

③ + ① gives

$$3k + 2l = 6 \quad ⑤$$

We now solve Equations 4 and 5.
⑤ − ④ gives

$$k = 3$$

Substituting in Equation 4, we get

$$2(3) + 2l = 3$$
$$2l = -3$$
$$l = -\tfrac{3}{2}$$

Substituting these values for k and l in Equation 2, we get

$$3 - \tfrac{3}{2} + m = 1$$
$$m = 1 - 3 + \tfrac{3}{2}$$
$$m = -\tfrac{1}{2}$$

Therefore $k = 3$, $l = -\tfrac{3}{2}$, and $m = -\tfrac{1}{2}$.

EXERCISE 3

Solve each of the following systems of equations.

1. $k + l - m = 1$
  $k + 2l - m = 0$
  $k + 3l + m = -1$

2. $k + l + m = 1$
  $k - l + m = 3$
  $k + l - m = 1$

3. $x + 3y - z = -14$
  $4x - 2y - 5z = 11$
  $7x + 6y + z = 1$

4. $r - 2s + t = 7$
  $2r + s - t = 1$
  $3r + s + 2t = 6$

INTRODUCTION

Descartes and Fermat created the branch of mathematics called **analytic geometry** or **coordinate geometry** by linking algebra and geometry. In this chapter we see how these connections can be applied to geometric vectors and how some operations with vectors can be made easier.

4.1   ALGEBRAIC VECTORS

Vectors in the Plane

We coordinatize the points in the plane in the following way. First we choose two perpendicular lines and refer to them as the **x-axis** and **y-axis**. Their point of intersection, O, is the **origin**. It is conventional to draw the positive portions of the x-axis and the y-axis so that if the positive x-axis were rotated onto the positive y-axis with the origin fixed, the rotation would be counter-clockwise.

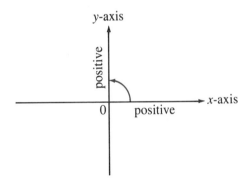

By taking a fixed distance as unit length, the points in the plane then correspond to ordered pairs of real numbers. Each point P in the plane is uniquely determined by a pair of real numbers (a, b) that we call its **coordinates**.

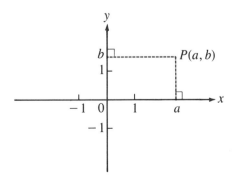

Let $\vec{u}$ be any vector in the plane. If we position $\vec{u}$ so that its tail is at the origin O, then its tip will be at some point $P(a, b)$. In this way $\vec{u}$ can be interpreted as the position vector of P and we write $\vec{u} = \overrightarrow{OP} = (a, b)$. Thus every vector in the plane has a unique algebraic description.

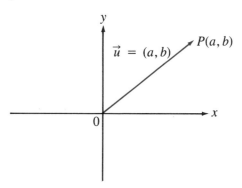

It is important to realize that (a, b) has two meanings: the coordinates of some point P in the plane or the position vector of the point P. It should be clear from the context which is the case.

Let $\vec{i}$ and $\vec{j}$ be unit vectors directed along the positive x-axis and positive y-axis respectively. If $\overrightarrow{OP} = (a, b)$, by resolving $\overrightarrow{OP}$ along $\vec{i}$ and $\vec{j}$ and then by applying the Parallelogram Law for the addition of geometric vectors we obtain

$$\overrightarrow{OP} = a\vec{i} + b\vec{j}$$

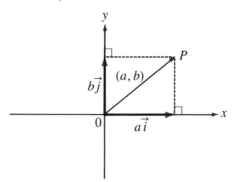

Every vector $\overrightarrow{OP}$ in the plane can be written as

$$\overrightarrow{OP} = (a, b) \quad \text{or} \quad \overrightarrow{OP} = a\vec{i} + b\vec{j}$$

Thus $(a, b) = a\vec{i} + b\vec{j}$

The vectors $a\vec{i}$ and $b\vec{j}$ are the vector components of $\overrightarrow{OP}$ along $\vec{i}$ and $\vec{j}$ respectively. We call a and b the scalar components or simply the **components** of $\overrightarrow{OP}$.

Since $\vec{i} = 1\vec{i} + 0\vec{j}$ and $\vec{j} = 0\vec{i} + 1\vec{j}$, we have

$$\vec{i} = (1, 0) \quad \text{and} \quad \vec{j} = (0, 1)$$

Vectors in Space

Points in space may be coordinatized in a similar fashion. First we choose three mutually perpendicular lines intersecting at a point. We refer to the lines as the x-axis, y-axis, and z-axis. Their point of intersection, O, is the origin. It is conventional to draw the positive portions of the axes so that they form a **right-handed system**. Having chosen a positive x-direction and a positive y-direction, the positive z-direction is obtained by curling the fingers of your right hand in the direction of a rotation (through an angle less than 180°) from the positive x-axis to the positive y-axis. Your thumb then points in the direction of the positive z-axis.

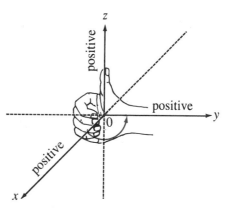

By taking a fixed distance as unit length, the points in space then correspond to ordered triples of real numbers. Each point in space is uniquely determined by a triple of real numbers (a, b, c) we call its **coordinates**.

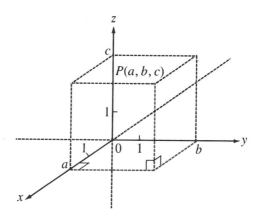

Example 1   Plot the following points.
(a) $(1, 2, 1)$ (b) $(-1, 3, 2)$
(c) $(2, -1, -3)$ (d) $(-1, -1, -1)$

Solution   (a)

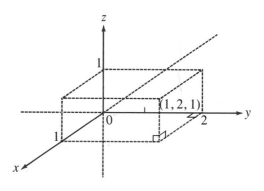

(b)

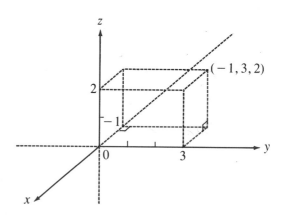

(c)

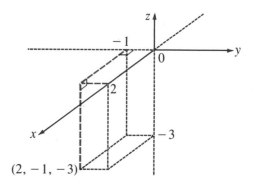

(d)

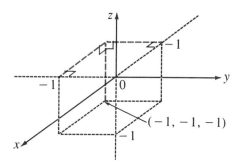

Let $\vec{u}$ be any vector in space. If we position $\vec{u}$ so that its tail is at the origin O, then its tip will be at some point $P(a, b, c)$. In this way $\vec{u}$ can be interpreted as the position vector of P and we write $\vec{u} = \overrightarrow{OP} = (a, b, c)$. Thus every vector in space has a unique algebraic description.

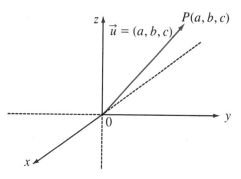

Notice that (a, b, c) has two meanings: again, the coordinates of some point P in space or the position vector of the point P. It should be clear from the context which is the case.

Let $\vec{i}$, $\vec{j}$, and $\vec{k}$ be unit vectors directed along the positive x-axis, y-axis, and z-axis respectively. If $\overrightarrow{OP} = (a, b, c)$ we can extend the method of resolution as follows. Instead of drawing a rectangle we now draw a box as shown.

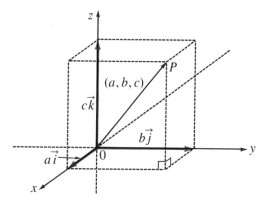

The edges of the box along the axes are the required vector components.

$$\overrightarrow{OP} = a\vec{i} + b\vec{j} + c\vec{k}$$

Every vector $\overrightarrow{OP}$ in space can be written as

$$\overrightarrow{OP} = (a, b, c) \quad \text{or} \quad \overrightarrow{OP} = a\vec{i} + b\vec{j} + c\vec{k}$$

Thus $(a, b, c) = a\vec{i} + b\vec{j} + c\vec{k}$

The vectors $a\vec{i}$, $b\vec{j}$, and $c\vec{k}$ are the vector components of $\overrightarrow{OP}$ along $\vec{i}$, $\vec{j}$, and $\vec{k}$ respectively. We call a, b, c the scalar components or simply the **components** of $\overrightarrow{OP}$.

Since $\vec{i} = 1\vec{i} + 0\vec{j} + 0\vec{k}$, $\vec{j} = 0\vec{i} + 1\vec{j} + 0\vec{k}$, and $\vec{k} = 0\vec{i} + 0\vec{j} + 1\vec{k}$, we have

---

$$\vec{i} = (1, 0, 0) \qquad \vec{j} = (0, 1, 0) \qquad \vec{k} = (0, 0, 1)$$

Vector Equality

Since equal vectors have the same position vectors, their corresponding components are equal. Thus if $\vec{u} = (u_1, u_2, u_3)$ and $\vec{v} = (v_1, v_2, v_3)$,

$$\vec{u} = \vec{v} \quad \text{if, and only if,} \quad u_1 = v_1, \; u_2 = v_2, \; \text{and} \; u_3 = v_3$$

EXERCISE 4.1

A **1.** Express each of the following as a sum of the vectors $\vec{i}$ and $\vec{j}$ or $\vec{i}$, $\vec{j}$, and $\vec{k}$.

   (a) $(3, -5)$ (b) $(-3, -6, 9)$ (c) $(5, 0, -7)$

2. Express each of the following vectors in the form (a, b) or (a, b, c).

   (a) $3\vec{i} + 8\vec{j}$ (b) $-5\vec{i} - 2\vec{k}$ (c) $7\vec{i} - 4\vec{j} + 9\vec{k}$

3. State the vector represented in each of the following diagrams.

   (a)   (b)

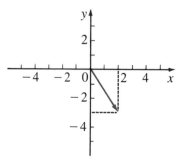
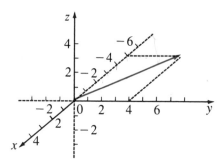

(c)   (d)

4. Taking the left front corner of the floor of your classroom as the origin and taking one metre as unit length, estimate the coordinates of the following rounded to the nearest metre.
(a) the classroom clock
(b) the teacher's head
(c) the base of the school flag pole
(d) the principal's chair
(e) all other corners in the room

B **5.** Plot each of the following points.
(a) $(1, -2, 3)$ (b) $(-3, -1, 0)$ (c) $(2, 3, -3)$

6. Draw each of the following vectors.
(a) $(-1, 2, -3)$ (b) $(2, 2, 2)$ (c) $(0, -3, -1)$

7. Give a geometric interpretation to each of the following sets of vectors.
(a) $(0, 2, 0)$ $(0, 5, 0)$ $(0, -3, 0)$
(b) $(1, -2, 0)$ $(3, 4, 0)$ $(-2, -2, 0)$
(c) $(0, 1, 1)$ $(0, -3, -1)$ $(0, -2, 2)$
(d) $(2, 0, -1)$ $(0, 0, 3)$ $(-1, 0, -3)$

8. For each of the following vectors $\vec{u}$, position it so that its tail is at the origin and find the components of $\vec{u}$.
(a)   (b)

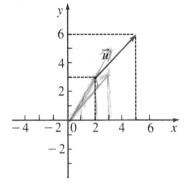

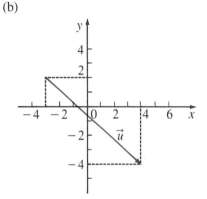

(c)

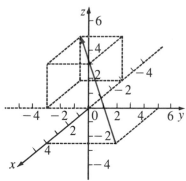

9. In each of the following find a and b such that the vectors $\vec{u}$ and $\vec{v}$ are collinear.

(a) $\vec{u} = (2, a)$ $\vec{v} = (-4, 7)$

(b) $\vec{u} = (a, -3, 6)$ $\vec{v} = (-8, 12, b)$

(c) $\vec{u} = a\vec{i} + 2\vec{j}$ $\vec{v} = -3\vec{i} - 6\vec{j} - b\vec{k}$

10. If $\vec{u} = a\vec{i} + 5\vec{j} - 3\vec{k}$ and $\vec{v} = (b, -15, c)$ are collinear vectors, find c and a relationship between a and b.

4.2 VECTOR OPERATIONS IN COMPONENT FORM

In Chapter 1, addition, subtraction, scalar multiplication, and length of geometric vectors were defined. In this section we determine the rules for performing these operations when the vectors are given in terms of their components.

Vector Addition in Component Form

If $\vec{u} = (u_1, u_2)$ and $\vec{v} = (v_1, v_2)$, then $\vec{u} + \vec{v} = (u_1 + v_1, u_2 + v_2)$.

If $\vec{u} = (u_1, u_2, u_3)$ and $\vec{v} = (v_1, v_2, v_3)$, then $\vec{u} + \vec{v} = (u_1 + v_1, u_2 + v_2, u_3 + v_3)$.

Proof

(We prove only the second result. The proof of the first is similar and is requested in Exercise 4.2.)

$$\begin{aligned}
\vec{u} + \vec{v} &= (u_1, u_2, u_3) + (v_1, v_2, v_3) \\
&= u_1\vec{i} + u_2\vec{j} + u_3\vec{k} + v_1\vec{i} + v_2\vec{j} + v_3\vec{k} \\
&= (u_1 + v_1)\vec{i} + (u_2 + v_2)\vec{j} + (u_3 + v_3)\vec{k} \\
&= (u_1 + v_1, u_2 + v_2, u_3 + v_3)
\end{aligned}$$

Scalar Multiplication in Component Form

If $\vec{u} = (u_1, u_2)$ and $k \in R$, then $k\vec{u} = (ku_1, ku_2)$

If $\vec{u} = (u_1, u_2, u_3)$ and $k \in R$, then $k\vec{u} = (ku_1, ku_2, ku_3)$.

Proof

(Again we prove only the second result.)

$$\begin{aligned}
k\vec{u} &= k(u_1, u_2, u_3) \\
&= k(u_1\vec{i} + u_2\vec{j} + u_3\vec{k}) \\
&= ku_1\vec{i} + ku_2\vec{j} + ku_3\vec{k} \\
&= (ku_1, ku_2, ku_3)
\end{aligned}$$

Vector Subtraction in Component Form

If $\vec{u} = (u_1, u_2)$ and $\vec{v} = (v_1, v_2)$, then $\vec{u} - \vec{v} = (u_1 - v_1, u_2 - v_2)$.

If $\vec{u} = (u_1, u_2, u_3)$ and $\vec{v} = (v_1, v_2, v_3)$ then $\vec{u} - \vec{v} = (u_1 - v_1, u_2 - v_2, u_3 - v_3)$.

Proof

(of the second result)

$$\begin{aligned}
\vec{u} - \vec{v} &= \vec{u} + (-\vec{v}) \\
&= (u_1, u_2, u_3) + (-v_1, -v_2, -v_3) \\
&= (u_1 + (-v_1), u_2 + (-v_2), u_3 + (-v_3)) \\
&= (u_1 - v_1, u_2 - v_2, u_3 - v_3)
\end{aligned}$$

Example 1   If $\vec{u} = (2, -3, 4)$ and $\vec{v} = (5, -3, -4)$ find

(a) $\vec{u} + \vec{v}$ (b) $-3\vec{u}$ (c) $4\vec{u} - \vec{v}$

Solution   (a) $\vec{u} + \vec{v} = (2, -3, 4) + (5, -3, -4) = (2+5, -3-3, 4-4)$
$= (7, -6, 0)$

(b) $-3\vec{u} = -3(2, -3, 4) = (-3(2), -3(-3), -3(4))$
$= (-6, 9, -12)$

(c) $4\vec{u} - \vec{v} = 4(2, -3, 4) - (5, -3, -4)$
$= (8, -12, 16) - (5, -3, -4) = (3, -9, 20)$

Components of a Vector Between Two Points

Given $P_1(x_1, y_1)$ and $P_2(x_2, y_2)$, then $\overrightarrow{P_1P_2} = (x_2 - x_1, y_2 - y_1)$.

Given $P_1(x_1, y_1, z_1)$ and $P_2(x_2, y_2, z_2)$ then $\overrightarrow{P_1P_2} = (x_2 - x_1, y_2 - y_1, z_2 - z_1)$.

Proof

(of the second result)

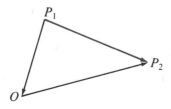

$$\begin{aligned}
\overrightarrow{P_1P_2} &= \overrightarrow{P_1O} + \overrightarrow{OP_2} \\
&= \overrightarrow{OP_2} - \overrightarrow{OP_1} \\
&= (x_2, y_2, z_2) - (x_1, y_1, z_1) \\
&= (x_2 - x_1, y_2 - y_1, z_2 - z_1)
\end{aligned}$$

Example 2 If $P_1(2, -3, 4)$ and $P_2(-5, -2, 6)$ find $\overrightarrow{P_1P_2}$ and $\overrightarrow{P_2P_1}$.

Solution
$$\overrightarrow{P_1P_2} = (-5, -2, 6) - (2, -3, 4) = (-7, 1, 2)$$
$$\overrightarrow{P_2P_1} = (2, -3, 4) - (-5, -2, 6) = (7, -1, -2)$$

Note: $\overrightarrow{P_1P_2} = -\overrightarrow{P_2P_1}$ as expected.

Length of a Vector in Component Form

If $\vec{u} = (u_1, u_2)$, then $|\vec{u}| = \sqrt{u_1^2 + u_2^2}$
If $\vec{u} = (u_1, u_2, u_3)$, then $|\vec{u}| = \sqrt{u_1^2 + u_2^2 + u_3^2}$.

Proof

(of the second result)

Let $\vec{u} = (u_1, u_2, u_3)$ be the position vector of the point P. Construct the perpendicular through P to intersect the xy-plane at Q.

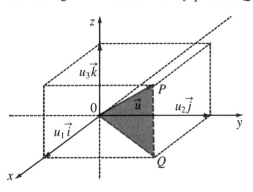

Now, by the Pythagorean Theorem
$$|\vec{u}|^2 = |\overrightarrow{OQ}|^2 + |\overrightarrow{QP}|^2$$
$$= (|u_1\vec{i}|^2 + |u_2\vec{j}|^2) + |u_3\vec{k}|^2$$
$$= u_1^2 + u_2^2 + u_3^2$$
So $\quad |\vec{u}| = \sqrt{u_1^2 + u_2^2 + u_3^2}$

Example 3 If $\vec{u} = (-2, 4, 5)$ and $\vec{v} = (4, -3, 1)$ find
(a) $|\vec{u}|$

(b) $|\vec{u} - \vec{v}|$

Solution
(a) $|\vec{u}| = \sqrt{(-2)^2 + 4^2 + 5^2} = \sqrt{45} = 3\sqrt{5}$
(b) $\vec{u} - \vec{v} = (-2, 4, 5) - (4, -3, 1) = (-6, 7, 4)$
so $|\vec{u} - \vec{v}| = \sqrt{(-6)^2 + 7^2 + 4^2} = \sqrt{101}$

Example 4 Given the points $A(-2, 1)$, $B(3, 4)$, and $C(-1, 6)$, find the perimeter of $\triangle ABC$.

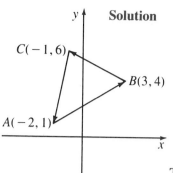

Solution

$$\overrightarrow{AB} = (3,4) - (-2,1) = (5,3)$$
$$\text{so } |\overrightarrow{AB}| = \sqrt{5^2 + 3^2} = \sqrt{34}$$
$$\overrightarrow{BC} = (-1,6) - (3,4) = (-4,2)$$
$$\text{so } |\overrightarrow{BC}| = \sqrt{(-4)^2 + 2^2} = \sqrt{20} = 2\sqrt{5}$$
$$\overrightarrow{CA} = (-2,1) - (-1,6) = (-1,-5)$$
$$\text{so } |\overrightarrow{CA}| = \sqrt{(-1)^2 + (-5)^2} = \sqrt{26}$$

Therefore the perimeter of $\triangle ABC$ is $\sqrt{34} + 2\sqrt{5} + \sqrt{26} \doteq 15.4$ ⬡

EXERCISE 4.2

A 1. Perform the indicated operations.
(a) $(8, -2) + (-3, -5)$ (b) $(3, 5, -4) + (1, 0, -8)$
(c) $3(-4, 9)$ (d) $-5(2, -3, 1)$

B 2. Perform the indicated operations.
(a) $-4(2, -3) + 5(-1, -2)$
(b) $-(2, 3, -4) - 5(-1, 2, -3)$
(c) $3\vec{i} + 5\vec{j} - 7\vec{i} + 6\vec{j}$
(d) $-3\vec{i} - 6\vec{j} + 2\vec{k} - 3\vec{j} + 6\vec{i} - \vec{k}$
(e) $|(2, -5)|$
(f) $|-4\vec{i} + 3\vec{j} - 3\vec{k}|$

3. If $\vec{u} = (-3, 5)$ and $\vec{v} = (-1, -4)$ find
(a) $\vec{u} + \vec{v}$ (b) $5\vec{u} - \vec{v}$
(c) $-3\vec{u} + 4\vec{v}$ (d) $7\vec{v} + 6\vec{i} - 8\vec{j} - 3\vec{u}$
(e) $|\vec{v}|$ (f) $|-3\vec{v} - 2\vec{u}|$

4. If $\vec{u} = (5, -6, 3)$ and $\vec{v} = (-3, -4, 7)$ find
(a) $\vec{v} - \vec{u}$ (b) $8\vec{v} + 2\vec{u}$
(c) $8\vec{i} - 5\vec{u} - 3\vec{j} - \vec{k}$ (d) $|2\vec{u} - 3\vec{v}|$

5. If $\vec{u} = 2\vec{i} + 3\vec{j} - 4\vec{k}$ and $\vec{v} = -3\vec{i} - 5\vec{j} + 5\vec{k}$ find $|4\vec{u} - 3\vec{v}|$.

6. Given the points $P(-6, 1)$, $Q(-2, -1)$, and $R(-3, 4)$, find:
(a) $\overrightarrow{QP}$ (b) $|\overrightarrow{RP}|$
(c) the perimeter of $\triangle PQR$

7. Given the points $A(3, -1, -4)$, $B(-3, 1, 5)$, and $C(-7, -4, 0)$, find:
(a) $\overrightarrow{CA}$ (b) $|\overrightarrow{AB}|$
(c) the perimeter of $\triangle ABC$.

8. If $\vec{u} = (-1, 4)$ and $\vec{v} = (-2, 2, 5)$ find
   (a) a unit vector with the same direction as $\vec{u}$
   (b) a unit vector with the opposite direction to $\vec{v}$

9. If $\vec{u} = (u_1, u_2)$ and $\vec{v} = (v_1, v_2)$, prove that
   $\vec{u} + \vec{v} = (u_1 + v_1, u_2 + v_2)$.

10. If $\vec{u} = (u_1, u_2)$ and $k \in R$, prove that $k\vec{u} = (ku_1, ku_2)$.

11. If $\vec{u} = (u_1, u_2)$ and $\vec{v} = (v_1, v_2)$, prove that
    $\vec{u} - \vec{v} = (u_1 - v_1, u_2 - v_2)$.

12. Given the points $P_1(x_1, y_1)$ and $P_2(x_2, y_2)$, prove that
    $\overrightarrow{P_1P_2} = (x_2 - x_1, y_2 - y_1)$.

13. If $\vec{u} = (u_1, u_2)$, prove that $|\vec{u}| = \sqrt{u_1^2 + u_2^2}$.

C 14. If $\vec{u} = (u_1, u_2, u_3)$ and $k \in R$, prove that $|k\vec{u}| = |k||\vec{u}|$.

15. If $|(1, 2) + (a, b)| = |(1, 2)| + |(a, b)|$, show $b = 2a$ and $a \geq 0$.

4.3 DOT PRODUCT IN COMPONENT FORM

In Chapter 3, we defined the dot product of two geometric vectors $\vec{u}$ and $\vec{v}$ as

$$\vec{u} \cdot \vec{v} = |\vec{u}||\vec{v}| \cos \theta$$

where θ is the angle between $\vec{u}$ and $\vec{v}$. By substituting into the formula and using the definition of the unit basis vectors $\vec{i}$, $\vec{j}$, and $\vec{k}$, we can easily obtain the following results.

$\vec{i} \cdot \vec{i} = 1$	$\vec{i} \cdot \vec{j} = \vec{j} \cdot \vec{i} = 0$
$\vec{j} \cdot \vec{j} = 1$	$\vec{i} \cdot \vec{k} = \vec{k} \cdot \vec{i} = 0$
$\vec{k} \cdot \vec{k} = 1$	$\vec{j} \cdot \vec{k} = \vec{k} \cdot \vec{j} = 0$

The proofs of these results are left as an exercise.
Now suppose that $\vec{u} = (u_1, u_2)$ and $\vec{v} = (v_1, v_2)$. Then

$$\vec{u} \cdot \vec{v} = u_1 v_1 + u_2 v_2$$

Proof

$$\begin{aligned}
\vec{u} \cdot \vec{v} &= (u_1, u_2) \cdot (v_1, v_2) \\
&= (u_1\vec{i} + u_2\vec{j}) \cdot (v_1\vec{i} + v_2\vec{j}) \\
&= u_1\vec{i} \cdot (v_1\vec{i} + v_2\vec{j}) + u_2\vec{j} \cdot (v_1\vec{i} + v_2\vec{j}) \\
&= u_1\vec{i} \cdot v_1\vec{i} + u_1\vec{i} \cdot v_2\vec{j} + u_2\vec{j} \cdot v_1\vec{i} + u_1\vec{j} \cdot v_2\vec{j} \\
&= u_1 v_1(\vec{i} \cdot \vec{i}) + u_1 v_2(\vec{i} \cdot \vec{j}) + u_2 v_1(\vec{j} \cdot \vec{i}) + u_2 v_2(\vec{j} \cdot \vec{j}) \\
&= u_1 v_1(1) + u_1 v_2(0) + u_2 v_1(0) + u_2 v_2(1) \\
&= u_1 v_1 + u_2 v_2
\end{aligned}$$

Similarly, if $\vec{u} = (u_1, u_2, u_3)$ and $\vec{v} = (v_1, v_2, v_3)$, then

$$\vec{u} \cdot \vec{v} = u_1v_1 + u_2v_2 + u_3v_3$$

Example 1 Find the indicated dot products.
(a) $(2, -4) \cdot (-7, -5)$
(b) $(-2, 5, 9) \cdot (-1, 0, -4)$

Solution (a) $(2, -4) \cdot (-7, -5) = (2)(-7) + (-4)(-5)$
$$= -14 + 20$$
$$= 6$$
(b) $(-2, 5, 9) \cdot (-1, 0, -4) = (-2)(-1) + (5)(0) + (9)(-4)$
$$= 2 + 0 - 36$$
$$= -34$$

Isolating for $\cos \theta$ in the formula $\vec{u} \cdot \vec{v} = |\vec{u}||\vec{v}| \cos \theta$, we obtain

$$\cos \theta = \frac{\vec{u} \cdot \vec{v}}{|\vec{u}||\vec{v}|}$$

If the components of two vectors are given, then the angle θ between them can be obtained using this formula.

Example 2 Find the angle θ between each pair of vectors.
(a) $\vec{u} = (-3, 6)$ and $\vec{v} = (4, 2)$
(b) $\vec{u} = (1, 1, 1)$ and $\vec{v} = (1, -1, -1)$

Solution (a) $\cos \theta = \frac{\vec{u} \cdot \vec{v}}{|\vec{u}||\vec{v}|}$
$$= \frac{(-3, 6) \cdot (4, 2)}{|(-3, 6)||4, 2)|}$$
$$= \frac{(-3)(4) + (6)(2)}{\sqrt{(-3)^2 + 6^2}\sqrt{4^2 + 2^2}}$$
$$= 0$$

Since $\cos \theta = 0$, $\theta = \frac{\pi}{2}$.

(b) $\cos \theta = \frac{\vec{u} \cdot \vec{v}}{|\vec{u}||\vec{v}|}$
$$= \frac{(1, 1, 1) \cdot (1, -1, -1)}{|(1, 1, 1)||(1, -1, -1)|}$$
$$= \frac{(1)(1) + (1)(-1) + (1)(-1)}{\sqrt{1^2 + 1^2 + 1^2}\sqrt{1^2 + (-1)^2 + (-1)^2}}$$
$$= \frac{-1}{\sqrt{3}\sqrt{3}}$$
$$= -\frac{1}{3}$$
Since $\cos \theta = -\frac{1}{3}$, $\theta \doteq 122°$.

Recall that $\vec{u}$ and $\vec{v}$ are orthogonal if, and only if, $\vec{u} \cdot \vec{v} = 0$.

Example 3   If $\vec{u} = (2, -3, 5)$ and $\vec{v} = (-3, 8, c)$ and $\vec{u}$ and $\vec{v}$ are orthogonal, find c.

Solution   If $\vec{u}$ and $\vec{v}$ are orthogonal then

$$\vec{u} \cdot \vec{v} = 0$$
$$(2, -3, 5) \cdot (-3, 8, c) = 0$$
$$(2)(-3) + (-3)(8) + (5)(c) = 0$$
$$5c = 30$$
$$c = 6$$

EXERCISE 4.3

A **1.** Find the dot product of each pair of vectors.

(a) $\vec{u} = (-3, -2)$ $\vec{v} = (1, -7)$

(b) $\vec{u} = (7, -6)$ $\vec{v} = (-1, -4)$

(c) $\vec{u} = \left(-\frac{1}{3}, -\frac{1}{4}\right)$ $\vec{v} = (3, -4)$

(d) $\vec{u} = 8\vec{i} - 5\vec{j}$ $\vec{v} = -2\vec{i} - 3\vec{j}$

(e) $\vec{u} = (0, 1)$ $\vec{v} = (-1, 0)$

B **2.** Find the dot product of each pair of vectors.

(a) $\vec{u} = (-1, 2, -2)$ $\vec{v} = (-4, 1, -1)$

(b) $\vec{u} = (2, -1, -9)$ $\vec{v} = (-6, -1, 1)$

(c) $\vec{u} = (0, 0, 1)$ $\vec{v} = (1, 0, 0)$

(d) $\vec{u} = \frac{2}{5}\vec{i} + \frac{1}{5}\vec{j} - \frac{1}{5}\vec{k}$ $\vec{v} = \frac{1}{2}\vec{i} - \frac{1}{2}\vec{j} + \frac{1}{2}\vec{k}$

3. Use the definition of the dot product, $\vec{u} \cdot \vec{v} = |\vec{u}||\vec{v}| \cos \theta$, to show

(a) $\vec{i} \cdot \vec{i} = 1$ (b) $\vec{i} \cdot \vec{k} = 0$ (c) $\vec{k} \cdot \vec{j} = 0$

4. Find the angle θ between the two given vectors. Give your answer to the nearest degree.

(a) $\vec{u} = (5, -4)$ $\vec{v} = (3, -6)$

(b) $\vec{u} = -7\vec{i} - 8\vec{j}$ $\vec{v} = -\vec{i} + 2\vec{j}$

(c) $\vec{u} = \left(\frac{1}{2}, -\frac{1}{5}\right)$ $\vec{v} = \left(\frac{1}{3}, 4\right)$

(d) $\vec{u} = (1, -2, 3)$ $\vec{v} = (-1, 2, -3)$

(e) $\vec{u} = (8, -10, 12)$ $\vec{v} = (-4, -3, 12)$

(f) $\vec{u} = (1, 0, 0)$ $\vec{v} = (0, 1, 0)$

(g) $\vec{u} = \left(\frac{1}{2}, \frac{1}{2}, 0\right)$ $\vec{v} = \left(\frac{1}{3}, -\frac{1}{3}, \frac{1}{3}\right)$

(h) $\vec{u} = 3\vec{i} + 2\vec{j} - \vec{k}$ $\vec{v} = -\vec{i} + 4\vec{j} - 5\vec{k}$

5. In each of the following $\vec{u}$ and $\vec{v}$ are orthogonal. Find c.
    (a) $\vec{u} = (2, c)$ $\qquad\qquad\qquad$ $\vec{v} = (-3, 4)$
    (b) $\vec{u} = (-1, -3, 5)$ $\qquad\qquad$ $\vec{v} = (2, c, -6)$
    (c) $\vec{u} = (1, c, -2)$ $\qquad\qquad$ $\vec{v} = (-4, 5, c)$

6. If $\vec{u} = (2, 3)$ find a vector perpendicular to $\vec{u}$.

7. If $\vec{u} = (2, 3, 4)$ find two non-collinear vectors perpendicular to $\vec{u}$.

8. The points $A(-2, 1, 3)$, $B(-6, 4, 0)$, and $D(4, -3, 1)$ are three vertices of the parallelogram $ABCD$.
    (a) Find the coordinates of C.
    (b) Find the measures of the interior angles of the parallelogram (to the nearest degree).
    (c) Find the measures of the angles between the diagonals of the parallelogram (to the nearest degree).

9. Use the dot product to find the angles between a pair of interior diagonals of a unit cube.

10. If $\vec{u} = (u_1, u_2, u_3)$ and $\vec{v} = (v_1, v_2, v_3)$ prove that
    $\vec{u} \cdot \vec{v} = u_1 v_1 + u_2 v_2 + u_3 v_3$.

C 11. If $\vec{u} = (1, 2, -3)$ and $\vec{v} = (2, -1, 4)$, find a unit vector perpendicular to both $\vec{u}$ and $\vec{v}$.

4.4   THE CROSS PRODUCT IN COMPONENT FORM

In Chapter 3, we defined the cross product of two vectors in space as

$$\vec{u} \times \vec{v} = |\vec{u}||\vec{v}| \sin \theta \, \hat{n}$$

where θ is the angle between $\vec{u}$ and $\vec{v}$ and $\hat{n}$ is a unit vector perpendicular to both $\vec{u}$ and $\vec{v}$ whose direction is determined by the right-hand rule. By substituting into the formula and using the definition of the unit basis vectors, we can easily obtain the following results.

$\vec{i} \times \vec{i} = \vec{0}$	$\vec{i} \times \vec{j} = \vec{k}$	$\vec{j} \times \vec{i} = -\vec{k}$
$\vec{j} \times \vec{j} = \vec{0}$	$\vec{j} \times \vec{k} = \vec{i}$	$\vec{k} \times \vec{j} = -\vec{i}$
$\vec{k} \times \vec{k} = \vec{0}$	$\vec{k} \times \vec{i} = \vec{j}$	$\vec{i} \times \vec{k} = -\vec{j}$

The proofs of these results are left as an exercise.

Now suppose $\vec{u} = (u_1, u_2, u_3)$ and $\vec{v} = (v_1, v_2, v_3)$, then

$$\vec{u} \times \vec{v} = (u_2 v_3 - u_3 v_2, \; u_3 v_1 - u_1 v_3, \; u_1 v_2 - u_2 v_1)$$

Proof

$$\vec{u} \times \vec{v} = (u_1, u_2, u_3) \times (v_1, v_2, v_3)$$
$$= (u_1\vec{i} + u_2\vec{j} + u_3\vec{k}) \times (v_1\vec{i} + v_2\vec{j} + v_3\vec{k})$$
$$= u_1\vec{i} \times (v_1\vec{i} + v_2\vec{j} + v_3\vec{k}) + u_2\vec{j} \times (v_1\vec{i} + v_2\vec{j} + v_3\vec{k})$$
$$\quad + u_3\vec{k} \times (v_1\vec{i} + v_2\vec{j} + v_3\vec{k})$$
$$= u_1\vec{i} \times v_1\vec{i} + u_1\vec{i} \times v_2\vec{j} + u_1\vec{i} \times v_3\vec{k}$$
$$\quad + u_2\vec{j} \times v_1\vec{i} + u_2\vec{j} \times v_2\vec{j} + u_2\vec{j} \times v_3\vec{k}$$
$$\quad + u_3\vec{k} \times v_1\vec{i} + u_3\vec{k} \times v_2\vec{j} + u_3\vec{k} \times v_3\vec{k}$$
$$= u_1v_1(\vec{i} \times \vec{i}) + u_1v_2(\vec{i} \times \vec{j}) + u_1v_3(\vec{i} \times \vec{k})$$
$$\quad + u_2v_1(\vec{j} \times \vec{i}) + u_2v_2(\vec{j} \times \vec{j}) + u_2v_3(\vec{j} \times \vec{k})$$
$$\quad + u_3v_1(\vec{k} \times \vec{i}) + u_3v_2(\vec{k} \times \vec{j}) + u_3v_3(\vec{k} \times \vec{k})$$
$$= u_1v_2\vec{k} - u_1v_3\vec{j} - u_2v_1\vec{k} + u_2v_3\vec{i} + u_3v_1\vec{j} - u_3v_2\vec{i}$$
$$= (u_2v_3 - u_3v_2)\vec{i} + (u_3v_1 - u_1v_3)\vec{j} + (u_1v_2 - u_2v_1)\vec{k}$$
$$= (u_2v_3 - u_3v_2, \ u_3v_1 - u_1v_3, \ u_1v_2 - u_2v_1)$$

Example 1 Find $(6, -1, 3) \times (-2, 5, 4)$.

Solution 1 By substituting into the formula we get

$$(6, -1, 3) \times (-2, 5, 4) = ((-1)(4) - (3)(5), (3)(-2) - (6)(4), (6)(5) - (-1)(-2))$$
$$= (-19, -30, 28)$$

This expression for the cross product might be difficult to remember. We illustrate two other methods by repeating Example 1.

Solution 2 We write the first vector above the second vector in the following way. [Since the cross product is not commutative, the order in which we write the vectors is important.]

$$(\ \ 6, -1, 3)$$
$$(-2, \ \ 5, 4)$$

The first component is obtained by blocking out the first entries.

$$(\ \ \ , -1, 3)$$
$$(\ \ \ , \ \ 5, 4)$$
$$(-1)(4) - (3)(5) = -19$$

The second component is obtained by blocking out the second entries.

$$(\ \ 6, \ \ \ , 3)$$
$$(-2, \ \ \ , 4)$$
$$(3)(-2) - (6)(4) = -30$$

The third component is obtained by blocking out the third entries.

$$(\ 6 \ , -1 \ , \ )$$
$$(-2, \ \ 5, \ )$$
$$(6)(5) - (-1)(-2) = 28$$

So $(6, -1, 3) \times (-2, 5, 4) = (-19, -30, 28)$.

Solution 3   As in Solution 2 we write the first vector above the second vector. However, unlike the first solution, we write the components of the vectors twice.

$$\begin{array}{cccccc} 6 & -1 & 3 & 6 & -1 & 3 \\ -2 & 5 & 4 & -2 & 5 & 4 \end{array}$$

The components are obtained by taking *the down products minus the up products*. The down products are

$$\begin{array}{cccccc} 6 & -1 & 3 & 6 & -1 & 3 \\ -2 & 5 & 4 & -2 & 5 & 4 \end{array}$$
$$(-1)(4) = -4 \qquad (3)(-2) = -6 \qquad (6)(5) = 30$$

The up products are

$$\begin{array}{cccccc} 6 & -1 & 3 & 6 & -1 & 3 \\ -2 & 5 & 4 & -2 & 5 & 4 \end{array}$$
$$(5)(3) = 15 \qquad (4)(6) = 24 \qquad (-2)(-1) = 2$$

The down products minus the up products are
$$-4 - 15 = -19 \qquad -6 - 24 = -30 \qquad 30 - 2 = 28$$

Therefore $(6, -1, 3) \times (-2, 5, 4) = (-19, -30, 28)$.

Having found a cross product, there is a partial check that we can use. Since $\vec{u} \times \vec{v}$ is perpendicular to both $\vec{u}$ and $\vec{v}$, the dot product of $\vec{u} \times \vec{v}$ with both $\vec{u}$ and $\vec{v}$ should be 0. We use this to check the result from Example 1.

$$\begin{aligned} (-19, -30, 28) \cdot (6, -1, 3) &= (-19)(6) + (-30)(-1) + (28)(3) \\ &= -114 + 30 + 84 \\ &= 0 \end{aligned}$$

and

$$\begin{aligned} (-19, -30, 28) \cdot (-2, 5, 4) &= (-19)(-2) + (-30)(5) + (28)(4) \\ &= 38 - 150 + 112 \\ &= 0 \end{aligned}$$

Recall from Chapter 3, that $|\vec{u} \times \vec{v}|$ gives the area of the parallelogram with adjacent sides $\vec{u}$ and $\vec{v}$. We can use the cross product to determine the areas of geometric figures when the coordinates of their vertices are given.

Example 2 The points $A(1, 1, 1)$, $B(-2, 0, -4)$, $C(1, 2, -3)$, and $D(4, 3, 2)$ are the vertices of a parallelogram. Find the area of each of the following figures.

(a) *ABCD*

(b) triangle *ABC*

Solution (a) First we determine the vectors representing two adjacent sides.

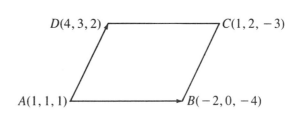

$$\overrightarrow{AB} = (-2, 0, -4) - (1, 1, 1) = (-3, -1, -5)$$
$$\overrightarrow{AD} = (4, 3, 2) - (1, 1, 1) = (3, 2, 1)$$

Now, Area $= |\overrightarrow{AB} \times \overrightarrow{AD}|$

$$= |(-3, -1, -5) \times (3, 2, 1)|$$
$$= |(9, -12, -3)|$$
$$= \sqrt{9^2 + (-12)^2 + (-3)^2}$$
$$= \sqrt{234}$$

Therefore the area of parallelogram *ABCD* is $\sqrt{234}$.

(b) The area of triangle *ABC* is one-half the area of parallelogram *ABCD*; that is $\frac{1}{2}\sqrt{234}$.

Example 3 If $\vec{u} = (-1, 2, 1)$, $\vec{v} = (1, -1, -1)$, and $\vec{w} = (1, 1, -2)$, evaluate

(a) $(\vec{u} \times \vec{v}) \cdot \vec{w}$

(b) $(\vec{u} \times \vec{v}) \times \vec{w}$

Solution (a) $(\vec{u} \times \vec{v}) \cdot \vec{w} = [(-1, 2, 1) \times (1, -1, -1)] \cdot (1, 1, -2)$

$$= (-1, 0, -1) \cdot (1, 1, -2)$$
$$= (-1)(1) + (0)(1) + (-1)(-2)$$
$$= 1$$

(b) $(\vec{u} \times \vec{v}) \times \vec{w} = [(-1, 2, 1) \times (1, -1, -1)] \times (1, 1, -2)$

$$= (-1, 0, -1) \times (1, 1, -2)$$
$$= (1, -3, -1)$$

The product $(\vec{u} \times \vec{v}) \cdot \vec{w}$ is called the **triple scalar product** because it is a scalar quantity. The product $(\vec{u} \times \vec{v}) \times \vec{w}$ is called the **triple vector product** because it is a vector quantity.

EXERCISE 4.4

B **1.** For each of the following pairs of vectors find $\vec{u} \times \vec{v}$.

(a) $\vec{u} = (1, -2, 2)$ $\vec{v} = (3, 4, -1)$

(b) $\vec{u} = (3, -1, -5)$ $\vec{v} = (7, -3, 0)$

(c) $\vec{u} = (2, -4, -6)$ $\vec{v} = (-1, 2, 3)$

(d) $\vec{u} = (1, -6, 9)$ $\vec{v} = (3, 3, -2)$

(e) $\vec{u} = -2\vec{i} + 3\vec{j} - \vec{k}$ $\vec{v} = 6\vec{i} - 9\vec{j} + 3\vec{k}$

(f) $\vec{u} = 5\vec{i} + 3\vec{j} + \vec{k}$ $\vec{v} = \vec{i} - 3\vec{j} - 5\vec{k}$

2. Use the definition of the cross product, $\vec{u} \times \vec{v} = |\vec{u}||\vec{v}| \sin \theta \, \hat{n}$, to show that

(a) $\vec{i} \times \vec{j} = \vec{k}$ (b) $\vec{j} \times \vec{i} = -\vec{k}$

(c) $\vec{i} \times \vec{k} = -\vec{j}$ (d) $\vec{k} \times \vec{i} = \vec{j}$

(e) $\vec{k} \times \vec{k} = \vec{0}$

3. Use the components of $\vec{i}$, $\vec{j}$, and $\vec{k}$ to show that

(a) $\vec{j} \times \vec{k} = \vec{i}$ (b) $\vec{k} \times \vec{j} = -\vec{i}$

(c) $\vec{i} \times \vec{i} = \vec{0}$ (d) $\vec{j} \times \vec{j} = \vec{0}$

4. Find a unit vector perpendicular to both $\vec{u} = (1, 1, 1)$ and $\vec{v} = (2, -1, -2)$. Check your answer using the dot product.

5. Determine which of the following quadrilaterals $PQRS$ are parallelograms. For those which are, find their area.

(a) $P(-1, 1, 1)$ $Q(3, 2, -2)$ $R(5, 3, -5)$ $S(1, 2, -2)$

(b) $P(1, 1, 1)$ $Q(-2, 3, -2)$ $R(-1, 0, 1)$ $S(2, -2, 2)$

(c) $P(2, -1, -1)$ $Q(-4, -2, 3)$ $R(2, 3, 2)$ $S(8, 4, -2)$

6. Find the area of each of the following triangles.

(a) $P(1, 1, 1)$ $Q(-1, 2, -2)$ $R(3, -1, -3)$

(b) $P(4, -1, 3)$ $Q(1, -5, 2)$ $R(1, 1, -6)$

(c) $P(0, 1, 0)$ $Q(1, 0, 0)$ $R(0, 0, -1)$

7. Use components to prove that if $\vec{u}$ and $\vec{v}$ are collinear then $\vec{u} \times \vec{v} = \vec{0}$.

8. Use components to prove that, for any vectors $\vec{u}$ and $\vec{v}$, $\vec{u} \times \vec{v} = -\vec{v} \times \vec{u}$.

9. If $\vec{u} = (1, -2, 1)$, $\vec{v} = (2, 1, -1)$, and $\vec{w} = (-1, -1, 3)$, evaluate each of the following.

(a) $(\vec{u} \times \vec{v}) \cdot \vec{w}$ (b) $(\vec{u} \times \vec{w}) \cdot \vec{v}$

(c) $(\vec{u} \times \vec{v}) \times \vec{w}$ (d) $(\vec{u} \times \vec{w}) \times \vec{v}$

10. If $\vec{u} = (3, 2, -1)$, $\vec{v} = (-1, 2, -3)$, and $\vec{w} = (1, -1, 4)$, evaluate each of the following.

(a) $(\vec{w} \times \vec{v}) \cdot \vec{u}$ (b) $(\vec{v} \times \vec{u}) \cdot \vec{w}$

(c) $(\vec{w} \times \vec{v}) \times \vec{u}$ (d) $(\vec{v} \times \vec{u}) \times \vec{w}$

C **11.** By choosing the components for three particular vectors show that the cross product is *not associative*. That is

$$\vec{u} \times (\vec{v} \times \vec{w}) \neq (\vec{u} \times \vec{v}) \times \vec{w}.$$

4.5 LINEAR COMBINATIONS OF ALGEBRAIC VECTORS

Recall that two non-zero vectors $\vec{u}$ and $\vec{v}$ are collinear if, and only if, $\vec{u} = k\vec{v}$ for some $k \in R$.

Example 1 Determine which of the following pairs of vectors are collinear.
(a) $\vec{u} = (3, -4)$, $\vec{v} = (-9, 12)$
(b) $\vec{u} = (4, -8, 10)$, $\vec{v} = (-1, 2, 5)$

Solution (a) By inspection $\vec{u} = -\frac{1}{3}\vec{v}$, so $\vec{u}$ and $\vec{v}$ are collinear.

(b) Suppose $\vec{u} = k\vec{v}$. Then

$$(4, -8, 10) = k(-1, 2, 5)$$

Equating the first components we obtain $k = -4$. Equating the second components we obtain $k = -4$. However from the third components we get $k = 2$. Therefore there is no real number k such that $\vec{u} = kv$, so $\vec{u}$ and $\vec{v}$ are not collinear.

Example 2 Find a and b such that $\vec{u} = (-3, 4, -7)$ and $\vec{v} = (a, -7, b)$ are collinear.

Solution Since $\vec{u}$ and $\vec{v}$ are collinear,

$$(-3, 4, -7) = k(a, -7, b)$$

Equating components we obtain

$$-3 = ka \quad \text{①}$$
$$4 = -7k \quad \text{②}$$
$$-7 = kb \quad \text{③}$$

From Equation 2, $k = -\frac{4}{7}$.

Substituting in Equations 1 and 3 we obtain $a = \frac{21}{4}$ and $b = \frac{49}{4}$.

Recall that any two non-collinear vectors form a basis for the plane in which they lie, and any other vector in this plane can be written as a linear combination of these basis vectors.

Example 3 (a) Show that $\vec{u} = (-1, 3)$ and $\vec{v} = (2, 4)$ form a basis for the plane.
(b) Write $\vec{w} = (5, 8)$ as a linear combination of $\vec{u}$ and $\vec{v}$.

Solution (a) Suppose $\vec{u} = k\vec{v}$ for some $k \in R$. Then

$$(-1, 3) = k(2, 4)$$

Equating the first components we obtain $k = -\frac{1}{2}$. Equating the second components we get $k = \frac{3}{4}$. Therefore there is no real number k such that $\vec{u} = k\vec{v}$, so $\vec{u}$ and $\vec{v}$ are non-collinear and hence form a basis for the plane.

(b) Because $\vec{u}$ and $\vec{v}$ form a basis for the plane, we know that $\vec{w}$ can be written as some linear combination of them. Let $\vec{w} = k\vec{u} + l\vec{v}$.

$$(5, 8) = k(-1, 3) + l(2, 4)$$
$$= (-k+2l, 3k+4l)$$

To find k and l we equate components.

$$-k + 2l = 5 \quad ①$$
$$3k + 4l = 8 \quad ②$$

$② - 2 \times ①$ gives $\qquad 5k = -2$

$$k = -\tfrac{2}{5}$$

Substituting in Equation 1 we obtain $l = \tfrac{23}{10}$.

Therefore $\vec{w} = -\tfrac{2}{5}\vec{u} + \tfrac{23}{10}\vec{v}$.

We now limit our discussion to vectors in space. Recall that three vectors are coplanar if at least one of them can be written as a linear combination of the other two.

Example 4   In each case determine if the vectors are coplanar or non-coplanar.
(a) $\vec{u} = (2, 1, -2)$, $\vec{v} = (-3, 3, 4)$, $\vec{w} = (-6, -3, 6)$
(b) $\vec{u} = (2, -1, -2)$, $\vec{v} = (1, 1, 1)$, $\vec{w} = (1, -5, -7)$
(c) $\vec{u} = (1, -1, -1)$, $\vec{v} = (2, 1, 4)$, $\vec{w} = (-1, -1, -1)$

Solution   (a) We see that $\vec{w} = -3\vec{u}$, so $\vec{u}$ and $\vec{w}$ are collinear and we can write

$$\vec{w} = -3\vec{u} + 0\vec{v}$$

Therefore the three vectors are coplanar.

(b) We see that no two of the vectors are collinear. Since $\vec{u}$ and $\vec{v}$ are not collinear, they determine a plane. Does $\vec{w}$ lie in this plane? It will, only if, $\vec{w} = k\vec{u} + l\vec{v}$ for some real numbers k and l.

$$(1, -5, -7) = k(2, -1, -2) + l(1, 1, 1)$$
$$= (2k+l, -k+l, -2k+l)$$

To obtain values for k and l we equate components.

$$2k + l = 1 \quad ①$$
$$-k + l = -5 \quad ②$$
$$-2k + l = -7 \quad ③$$

We solve Equations 1 and 2.

$① - ②$ gives $3k = 6$
$$k = 2$$

Substituting in $①$ we get $l = -3$.

We now check this solution in Equation 3.

$$-2(2) + (-3) = -7$$

Therefore $\vec{w} = 2\vec{u} - 3\vec{v}$; so $\vec{u}$, $\vec{v}$, and $\vec{w}$ are coplanar.

(c) No two vectors are collinear. Since $\vec{u}$ and $\vec{v}$ are not collinear, they determine a plane. Does $\vec{w}$ lie in this plane? It will only if $\vec{w} = k\vec{u} + l\vec{v}$ for some k and l.

$$\begin{aligned} (-1, -1, -1) &= k(1, -1, -1) + l(2, 1, 4) \\ &= (k+2l, -k+l, -k+4l) \end{aligned}$$

Equating components we obtain

$$\begin{array}{ll} k + 2l = -1 & ① \\ -k + l = -1 & ② \\ -k + 4l = -1 & ③ \end{array}$$

We solve Equations 1 and 2.

$$① + ② \text{ gives } 3l = 0$$
$$l = 0$$

Substituting in ① we get $k = -1$.

We now check this solution in Equation 3.

$$-(-1) + 4(0) = 1 \neq -7$$

Therefore $\vec{w}$ cannot be written as a linear combination of $\vec{u}$ and $\vec{v}$; so $\vec{u}$, $\vec{v}$, and $\vec{w}$ are non-coplanar.

Since the three vectors in part (c) of Example 4 are non-coplanar, they form a basis for space and any other vector can be written as a linear combination of them.

Example 5 The vectors $\vec{u} = (1, 1, 1)$, $\vec{v} = (1, -1, 1)$, and $\vec{w} = (1, 1, -1)$ are not coplanar.
(a) Write $\vec{x} = (1, 3, 1)$ as a linear combination of $\vec{u}$, $\vec{v}$, and $\vec{w}$.
(b) Interpret your result in part (a).

Solution (a) Because $\vec{u}$, $\vec{v}$, and $\vec{w}$ are not coplanar, they form a basis for space. We know that $\vec{x}$ can be written as some linear combination of them.

Let
$$\begin{aligned} (1, 3, 1) &= k(1, 1, 1) + l(1, -1, 1) + m(1, 1, -1) \\ &= (k+l+m, k-l+m, k+l-m) \end{aligned}$$

Equating components we obtain

$$\begin{array}{ll} k + l + m = 1 & ① \\ k - l + m = 3 & ② \\ k + l - m = 1 & ③ \end{array}$$

① + ③ gives

$$2k + 2l = 2 \quad ④$$

② + ③ gives

$$2k = 4$$
$$k = 2$$

Substituting in ④ we obtain $l = -1$.
Substituting these values for k and l in Equation 1, we get $m = 0$.
Therefore

$$\vec{x} = 2\vec{u} - \vec{v} + 0\vec{w}$$

(b) Since $m = 0$, $\vec{x} = 2\vec{u} - \vec{v}$ and $\vec{x}$ is coplanar with $\vec{u}$ and $\vec{v}$.⊗

Finally we consider sets of four vectors and discuss them with respect to their collinearity and coplanarity.

Example 6 Discuss the following vectors with respect to collinearity and coplanarity.
$$\vec{u} = (1, 1, 1) \qquad \vec{v} = (1, 2, 3) \qquad \vec{w} = (-1, -1, 1)$$
$$\vec{x} = (1, 0, -1)$$

Solution No two vectors are collinear. Since $\vec{u}$ and $\vec{v}$ are non-collinear, they determine a plane. Does $\vec{w}$ lie in this plane? It will only if $\vec{w} = k\vec{u} + l\vec{v}$ for some k and l.

$$(-1, -1, 1) = k(1, 1, 1) + l(1, 2, 3)$$
$$= (k+l, k+2l, k+3l)$$

To obtain values for k and l we equate components.

$$k + l = -1 \quad ①$$
$$k + 2l = -1 \quad ②$$
$$k + 3l = 1 \quad ③$$

We solve Equations 1 and 2.

② − ① gives $l = 0$

Substituting in ① we get $k = -1$.
We now check this solution in Equation 3.

$$-1 + 3(0) = -1 \neq 1$$

Therefore $\vec{w}$ does not lie in this plane and $\vec{u}$, $\vec{v}$, and $\vec{w}$ form a basis for space.
We now write $\vec{x}$ as a linear combination of $\vec{u}$, $\vec{v}$, and $\vec{w}$.

$$(1, 0, -1) = k(1, 1, 1) + l(1, 2, 3) + m(-1, -1, 1)$$
$$= (k+l-m, \ k+2l-m, \ k+3l+m)$$

Equating components we get

$$k + l - m = 1 \qquad ①$$
$$k + 2l - m = 0 \qquad ②$$
$$k + 3l + m = -1 \qquad ③$$

① + ③ gives

$$2k + 4l = 0 \qquad ④$$

② + ③ gives

$$2k + 5l = -1 \qquad ⑤$$

⑤ − ④ gives $l = -1$

Substituting in ④ we obtain $k = 2$.
Substituting these values for k and l in Equation 1, we get $m = 0$.
So $\vec{x} = 2\vec{u} - \vec{v} + 0\vec{w}$. This means that $\vec{x}$ can be written as a linear combination of $\vec{u}$ and $\vec{v}$, hence is coplanar with them. Therefore $\vec{u}$, $\vec{v}$, and $\vec{x}$ are coplanar and $\vec{w}$ does not lie in this plane.

The following theorem, involving the triple scalar product, provides an alternative method for answering some of the questions discussed in this section.

Theorem

> For vectors $\vec{u}$, $\vec{v}$, and $\vec{w}$,
> $(\vec{u} \times \vec{v}) \cdot \vec{w} = 0$ if, and only if, $\vec{u}$, $\vec{v}$, and $\vec{w}$ are coplanar.

The proof of this theorem is requested in the exercise.

Example 7 (a) In Example 4, the vectors $\vec{u} = (2, -1, -2)$, $\vec{v} = (1, 1, 1)$, and $\vec{w} = (1, -5, -7)$ were shown to be coplanar. Show that $(\vec{u} \times \vec{v}) \cdot \vec{w} = 0$.

(b) In Example 4, the vectors $\vec{u} = (1, -1, -1)$, $\vec{v} = (2, 1, 4)$, and $\vec{w} = (-1, -1, -1)$ were shown to be non-coplanar. Show that $(\vec{u} \times \vec{v}) \cdot \vec{w} \neq 0$.

Solution (a) $(\vec{u} \times \vec{v}) \cdot \vec{w} = [(2, -1, -2) \times (1, 1, 1)] \cdot (1, -5, -7)$
$$= (1, -4, 3) \cdot (1, -5, -7)$$
$$= (1)(1) + (-4)(-5) + (3)(-7)$$
$$= 0$$

(b) $(\vec{u} \times \vec{v}) \cdot \vec{w} = [(1, -1, -1) \times (2, 1, 4)] \cdot (-1, -1, -1)$
$$= (-3, -6, 3) \cdot (-1, -1, -1)$$
$$= (-3)(-1) + (-6)(-1) + (3)(-1)$$
$$= 6$$

Example 8   Use the triple scalar product to determine whether the following vectors are coplanar or non-coplanar.

$$\vec{u} = (1, 1, -2) \qquad \vec{v} = (2, -3, 1) \qquad \vec{w} = (-1, -2, 3)$$

Solution

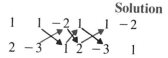

$$(\vec{u} \times \vec{v}) \cdot \vec{w} = [(1, 1, -2) \times (2, -3, 1)] \cdot (-1, -2, 3)$$
$$= (-5, -5, -5) \cdot (-1, -2, 3)$$
$$= (-5)(-1) + (-5)(-2) + (-5)(3)$$
$$= 0$$

Since $(\vec{u} \times \vec{v}) \cdot \vec{w} = 0$, $\vec{u}$, $\vec{v}$, and $\vec{w}$ are coplanar.

EXERCISE 4.5

A **1.** Determine which of the following pairs of vectors are collinear.
  (a) $\vec{u} = (-2, 5)$ $\qquad\qquad$ $\vec{v} = (4, -10)$
  (b) $\vec{u} = (6, -2)$ $\qquad\qquad$ $\vec{v} = (-2, 6)$
  (c) $\vec{u} = (5, -4)$ $\qquad\qquad$ $\vec{v} = (-15, -12)$
  (d) $\vec{u} = (1, -1, -1)$ $\qquad$ $\vec{v} = \left(-\frac{1}{2}, \frac{1}{2}, -\frac{1}{2}\right)$
  (e) $\vec{u} = 2\vec{i} + 4\vec{j} - 6\vec{k}$ $\qquad$ $\vec{v} = -\vec{i} - 2\vec{j} + 3\vec{k}$
  (f) $\vec{u} = \vec{i} - \vec{j} - \vec{k}$ $\qquad$ $\vec{v} = \vec{i} + \vec{j} - \vec{k}$

B **2.** Find a so that $\vec{u} = (-2, 5)$ and $\vec{v} = (5a, -8)$ are collinear.

  3. Find a and b so that $\vec{u} = (2, a, -6)$ and $\vec{v} = (-8, 3, b)$ are collinear.

  4. Determine if the following are coplanar or non-coplanar vectors.
  (a) $\vec{u} = (1, -1, 1)$ $\quad$ $\vec{v} = (0, 2, 6)$ $\quad$ $\vec{w} = (2, -3, -1)$
  (b) $\vec{u} = (-2, 4, 2)$ $\quad$ $\vec{v} = (-1, 3, 4)$ $\quad$ $\vec{w} = (3, -6, -3)$
  (c) $\vec{u} = (-1, 2, 3)$ $\quad$ $\vec{v} = (1, 2, 3)$ $\quad$ $\vec{w} = (1, -2, 3)$

  5. Determine which of the following sets of vectors form a basis for space.
  (a) $\vec{u} = (-2, 1, 1)$ $\quad$ $\vec{v} = (1, -1, -1)$ $\quad$ $\vec{w} = (-1, -1, -1)$
  (b) $\vec{u} = (2, -2, -1)$ $\quad$ $\vec{v} = (1, 1, 1)$ $\quad$ $\vec{w} = (1, 2, -1)$
  (c) $\vec{u} = (-1, -1, 1)$ $\quad$ $\vec{v} = (2, -2, -2)$ $\quad$ $\vec{w} = (3, 3, -3)$

  6. Discuss the following sets of vectors with respect to collinearity and coplanarity.
  (a) $\vec{u} = (3, -1, 3)$ $\qquad$ $\vec{v} = (1, -1, -1)$
  $\quad\;$ $\vec{w} = (-1, 1, 1)$ $\qquad$ $\vec{x} = (-6, 2, -6)$
  (b) $\vec{u} = (1, 1, -1)$ $\qquad$ $\vec{v} = (1, -1, 1)$
  $\quad\;$ $\vec{w} = (-1, 1, 1)$ $\qquad$ $\vec{x} = (1, 1, 1)$
  (c) $\vec{u} = (-1, 1, -1)$ $\qquad$ $\vec{v} = (2, 1, 0)$
  $\quad\;$ $\vec{w} = (1, -2, 1)$ $\qquad$ $\vec{x} = (0, 3, -2)$
  (d) $\vec{u} = (1, -1, 1)$ $\qquad$ $\vec{v} = (2, -2, -2)$
  $\quad\;$ $\vec{w} = (-1, 2, 3)$ $\qquad$ $\vec{x} = (0, 1, 1)$

7. In each of the following, determine (where possible) three vectors which form a basis for space and express the fourth vector as a linear combination of these basis vectors.

   (a) $\vec{u} = (2, 1, -1)$ $\vec{v} = (1, -1, -1)$
       $\vec{w} = (-2, -1, 1)$ $\vec{x} = (1, 1, 1)$

   (b) $\vec{u} = (1, 4, -5)$ $\vec{v} = (1, -1, 2)$
       $\vec{w} = (3, 2, -1)$ $\vec{x} = (1, -1, -1)$

   (c) $\vec{u} = (1, 1, 1)$ $\vec{v} = (2, -2, 1)$
       $\vec{w} = (1, -3, 0)$ $\vec{x} = (-2, 2, -1)$

   (d) $\vec{u} = (1, -1, -1)$ $\vec{v} = (1, 1, 1)$
       $\vec{w} = (-1, -1, 1)$ $\vec{x} = (-1, 1, -1)$

C 8. If $\vec{u} = (a, b)$ and $\vec{v} = (a^2, b^2)$, a and b non-zero, under what conditions will $\vec{u}$ and $\vec{v}$ be collinear?

9. For vectors $\vec{u}$, $\vec{v}$, and $\vec{w}$, prove that
$$(\vec{u} \times \vec{v}) \cdot \vec{w} = 0 \text{ if, and only if, } \vec{u}, \vec{v}, \text{ and } \vec{w} \text{ are coplanar.}$$

PROBLEMS PLUS

Victor's Computer Store uses vectors to do most of its inventory control and money management. For instance; it sells computers, monitors, keyboards, and printers and keeps track of the number sold in a given month. The vector $(33, 26, 25, 20)$ indicates the number of each type of machine sold in January. If $(28, 22, 20, 15)$ indicates the number of each type of machine sold in February, then vector addition can be used to find the total sold. Find situations where vector subtraction, scalar multiplication, and dot product can be used by Victor's store.

4.6 REVIEW EXERCISE

1. Draw each of the following vectors.
   (a) $(2, 1, 3)$ (b) $(-1, 2, 1)$ (c) $(-2, 2, -3)$

2. Give a geometric interpretation to each of the following sets of vectors.
   (a) $(0, 0, 1)$ $(0, 0, -4)$ $(0, 0, 3)$
   (b) $(2, 0, -1)$ $(-3, 0, 4)$ $(-1, 0, -1)$

3. If $\vec{u} = 2\vec{i} + a\vec{j} - 3\vec{k}$ and $\vec{v} = (-5, b, c)$ are collinear vectors, find c and a relationship between a and b.

4. Perform the indicated operations.
   (a) $-5(-2, 3, -4) - 2(5, -1, -3)$
   (b) $3\vec{i} - 7\vec{j} + 2\vec{k} - 6\vec{i} + 8\vec{k}$
   (c) $\left| -3\vec{i} + 2\vec{j} - 4\vec{k} \right|$
   (d) $\left| -6(2, -5) - 4(-4, 3) \right|$

5. If $\vec{u} = (-2, 3, 1)$ and $\vec{v} = 2\vec{i} - 3\vec{j} + 4\vec{k}$ find
    (a) $3\vec{u} - 4\vec{v}$ 　　　　　　　　　　(b) $|-2\vec{u} - \vec{v}|$

6. Given the points $A(-2, 3, 3)$, $B(-4, -2, 3)$, and $C(3, -1, 4)$, find the perimeter of $\triangle ABC$.

7. Find two unit vectors collinear with $(-2, 3, -3)$.

8. Use the definition of dot product, $\vec{u} \cdot \vec{v} = |\vec{u}| |\vec{v}| \cos \theta$, to show
    (a) $\vec{j} \cdot \vec{j} = 1$ 　　　　(b) $\vec{i} \cdot \vec{j} = 0$ 　　　　(c) $\vec{k} \cdot \vec{i} = 0$

9. Find the dot product of the following pairs of vectors.
    (a) $\vec{u} = (2, -5)$ 　　　　　　　　　$\vec{v} = (-4, -9)$
    (b) $\vec{u} = -4\vec{i} + 12\vec{j}$ 　　　　　$\vec{v} = 5\vec{i} - 6\vec{j}$
    (c) $\vec{u} = (-1, -2, 3)$ 　　　　　　$\vec{v} = (-6, 5, -5)$
    (d) $\vec{u} = 5\vec{i} + 3\vec{j} + 7\vec{k}$ 　　$\vec{v} = 8\vec{i} - 7\vec{k}$

10. Find the angle θ between the two given vectors. Give your answer to the nearest degree.
    (a) $\vec{u} = (-3, 6)$ 　　　　　　　　　$\vec{v} = (6, -12)$
    (b) $\vec{u} = 7\vec{i} - 10\vec{j}$ 　　　　　$\vec{v} = 8\vec{i} + 2\vec{j}$
    (c) $\vec{u} = (-1, 2, -3)$ 　　　　　　$\vec{v} = (-5, 10, -15)$
    (d) $\vec{u} = -3\vec{i} - 4\vec{j} - 6\vec{k}$ 　$\vec{v} = -4\vec{j} + 9\vec{k}$

11. If $\vec{u} = (-3, 6, a)$ and $\vec{v} = (b, -2, 4)$ are orthogonal, find a relationship between a and b.

12. Use the definition of the cross product, $\vec{u} \times \vec{v} = |\vec{u}| |\vec{v}| \sin \theta \hat{n}$, to show
    (a) $\vec{i} \times \vec{i} = \vec{0}$ 　　(b) $\vec{k} \times \vec{j} = -\vec{i}$ 　　(c) $\vec{j} \times \vec{k} = \vec{i}$

13. For each of the following pairs of vectors find $\vec{u} \times \vec{v}$.
    (a) $\vec{u} = (2, 7, -1)$ 　　　　　　　$\vec{v} = (-4, 5, 1)$
    (b) $\vec{u} = (1, 1, 1)$ 　　　　　　　$\vec{v} = (-2, -2, -2)$
    (c) $\vec{u} = 3\vec{i} - \vec{j} + 2\vec{k}$ 　　$\vec{v} = -\vec{i} + \vec{j} + 3\vec{k}$

14. Find a unit vector perpendicular to both $\vec{u} = (1, -1, 1)$ and $\vec{v} = (1, 1, 1)$. Check your answer using the dot product.

15. The points $P(1, 1, 1)$, $Q(3, -3, 4)$, and $S(-2, 4, 5)$ are three vertices of parallelogram $PQRS$.
    (a) Find the coordinates of R.
    (b) Find the measures of the interior angles.
    (c) Find the area of the parallelogram.

16. If $\vec{u} = (1, -3, 4)$, $\vec{v} = (-1, -2, 2)$, and $\vec{w} = (2, 1, -1)$, find
    (a) $(\vec{u} \times \vec{v}) \cdot \vec{w}$
    (b) $(\vec{u} \times \vec{v}) \times \vec{w}$
    (c) What conclusion can be made concerning the vectors $\vec{u}$, $\vec{v}$, and $\vec{w}$?

17. If $\vec{u} = (1, -1, 2)$, $\vec{v} = (2, -1, -1)$, and $\vec{w} = (1, -2, 6)$, find
    (a) $(\vec{u} \times \vec{v}) \cdot \vec{w}$
    (b) $(\vec{u} \times \vec{v}) \times \vec{w}$
    (c) What conclusion can be made concerning the vectors $\vec{u}$, $\vec{v}$, and $\vec{w}$?

18. Determine if the following are coplanar or non-coplanar vectors.
    (a) $\vec{u} = (2, -1, -3)$ $\vec{v} = (-1, 5, 1)$ $\vec{w} = (-1, -13, 3)$
    (b) $\vec{u} = (1, 4, -2)$ $\vec{v} = (-2, -3, 0)$ $\vec{w} = (-1, -3, 1)$
    (c) $\vec{u} = (-1, -1, 2)$ $\vec{v} = (-4, 1, 2)$ $\vec{w} = (-1, -2, 8)$

19. Determine which of the following sets of vectors form a basis for space.
    (a) $\vec{u} = (1, -1, 1)$ $\vec{v} = (-1, 4, -1)$ $\vec{w} = (-4, 7, -4)$
    (b) $\vec{u} = (-2, 3, -3)$ $\vec{v} = (2, 1, 0)$ $\vec{w} = (0, 4, -3)$
    (c) $\vec{u} = (1, 2, -2)$ $\vec{v} = (1, -1, 0)$ $\vec{w} = (0, 3, 1)$

20. Discuss the following sets of vectors with respect to collinearity and coplanarity.
    (a) $\vec{u} = (2, 2, -1)$ $\vec{v} = (-1, -1, 1)$
         $\vec{w} = (1, 1, 0)$ $\vec{x} = (-2, -2, 1)$
    (b) $\vec{u} = (-1, 1, -1)$ $\vec{v} = (-1, -1, 0)$
         $\vec{w} = (2, 1, 1)$ $\vec{x} = (-1, 4, -2)$
    (c) $\vec{u} = (-1, 1, 2)$ $\vec{v} = (1, -1, 1)$
         $\vec{w} = (1, 3, 1)$ $\vec{x} = (2, -1, 1)$

21. In each of the following, determine (where possible) three vectors that form a basis for space and express the fourth vector as a linear combination of these basis vectors.
    (a) $\vec{u} = (1, 1, -1)$ $\vec{v} = (-1, 1, 1)$
         $\vec{w} = (1, 3, -1)$ $\vec{x} = (1, 1, 0)$
    (b) $\vec{u} = (2, -1, 1)$ $\vec{v} = (-2, -1, 1)$
         $\vec{w} = (2, 2, 2)$ $\vec{x} = (4, 2, -2)$
    (c) $\vec{u} = (-1, -1, 1)$ $\vec{v} = (1, 1, 1)$
         $\vec{w} = (-1, 1, 1)$ $\vec{x} = (0, 0, 1)$

4.7 CHAPTER 4 TEST

1. Draw the vector $\vec{u} = (-2, -1, 3)$.
2. If $\vec{u} = (2, -3, -1)$ and $\vec{v} = -2\vec{i} - 3\vec{j} + \vec{k}$, find
   (a) $-2\vec{u} + 3\vec{v}$
   (b) $|3\vec{v} + 3\vec{i} - 2\vec{k}|$
   (c) a unit vector with the same direction as $\vec{u}$
   (d) $\vec{u} \cdot \vec{v}$
   (e) $\vec{v} \times \vec{u}$
3. The points $A(-1, 2, -1)$, $B(2, -1, 3)$, and $D(-3, 1, -3)$ are three vertices of parallelogram $ABCD$. Find
   (a) the coordinates of C,
   (b) the measures of the interior angles,
   (c) the area of the parallelogram.
4. Find a unit vector perpendicular to both $\vec{u} = (1, -1, -1)$ and $\vec{v} = (2, -2, 3)$. Check your answer by using the dot product.
5. If $\vec{u} = (u_1, u_2, u_3)$ and $\vec{v} = (v_1, v_2, v_3)$ prove that
   $\vec{u} \cdot \vec{v} = u_1 v_1 + u_2 v_2 + u_3 v_3$.
6. If $\vec{u} = (3, -1, -2)$, $\vec{v} = (1, -2, 3)$, and $\vec{w} = (3, 2, -1)$, find
   (a) $(\vec{u} \times \vec{v}) \cdot \vec{w}$
   (b) $(\vec{u} \times \vec{v}) \times \vec{w}$
7. Discuss the following set of vectors with respect to collinearity and coplanarity.
$$\vec{u} = (-3, 1, -1) \qquad \vec{v} = (1, -2, 4)$$
$$\vec{w} = (-1, -3, 7) \qquad \vec{x} = (1, 1, -1)$$
8. The vectors $\vec{u} = (1, 1, 0)$, $\vec{v} = (0, 1, 1)$, and $\vec{w} = (1, 0, 1)$ form a basis for space. Express $\vec{x} = (2, 1, -1)$ as a linear combination of these basis vectors. Interpret your answer geometrically.

TWENTIETH CENTURY MATHEMATICIANS

Jules Henri Poincaré was born in Nancy, France, 1854 and died a Professor at the University of Paris in 1912. He is often referred to as the 'last Universalist.' He was the last man to take practically all mathematics, both pure and applied, and master and develop its theories.

His studies ranged from the theory of differential equations, celestial mechanics, and mathematical physics to scientific philosophy and mathematical psychology. ''Poincaré was indeed the living brain of rational Science.''

One of Poincaré's important contributions to mathematical astronomy was his work on the ''problem of n-bodies.'' This problem is concerned with what the organization of the heavens will be a year from now, or a million years from now. Newton analysed this problem thoroughly for $n = 2$ which gave rise to Newton's laws of gravitation. Poincaré studied the 3-body problem, of which the sun-earth-moon is an important case, and received numerous awards and honours for his work. Stated mathematically, the problem reduces to solving a system of nine simultaneous differential equations; however, the solution of the system is not an elementary task!

Poincaré was keenly interested in promoting mathematics and to this end wrote popular essays to encourage its appreciation. ''A scientist worthy of the name, above all a mathematician, has the same feeling towards his work as an artist: the joy is as great and of the same nature.''

His passion for mathematics seized him during his adolescence. From the first, he exhibited a life-long peculiarity: his mathematics was done in his head as he paced restlessly about, and was committed to paper only when all had been thought through. When a mathematical difficulty was submitted to him by his colleagues, they would often exclaim, ''How does he do it? The reply comes like an arrow!''

Poincaré's profound ability in mathematics extended into scientific philosophy. ''What about the harmony which human intelligence believes to have discovered in Nature: does it exist outside of that intelligence? Definitely not; a reality independent of the mind which conceives it, sees it or feels it, is an impossibility. We shall understand this harmony better through mathematical laws.''

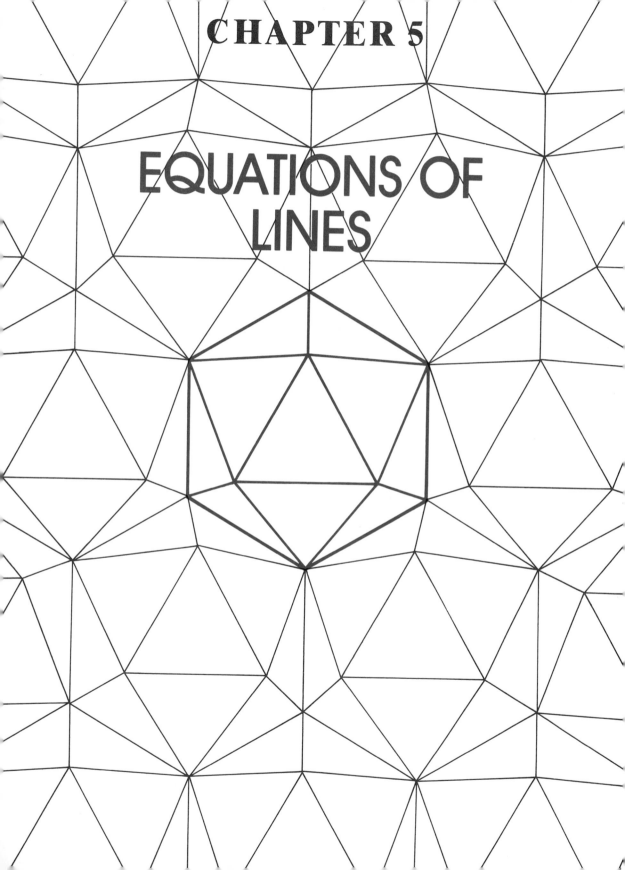

CHAPTER 5

EQUATIONS OF LINES

REVIEW AND PREVIEW TO
CHAPTER 5

Equation of a Line

Equation of a line: point-slope form

Given a point $P_0(x_0, y_0)$ on a line having slope m, an equation of the line is $y - y_0 = m(x - x_0)$.

Example   Find an equation of the line through points $Q(1, 4)$ and $R(5, -2)$.

Solution   We use the coordinates of the points Q and R to determine the slope of the line.

$$m = \frac{\Delta y}{\Delta x} = \frac{-2 - 4}{5 - 1} = \frac{-6}{4} = -\frac{3}{2}$$

Using the point Q which is on the line we obtain $y - 4 = -\frac{3}{2}(x - 1)$
as the equation of the line through Q and R.
This may be rewritten in the form $Ax + By + C = 0$.

$$2(y - 4) = -3(x - 1)$$
$$2y - 8 = -3x + 3$$

Thus $3x + 2y - 11 = 0$ is an equation of the line through Q and R.

EXERCISE 1

1. Determine an equation of the line through the point $(4, 5)$ and
   (a) having slope -2,
   (b) parallel to the x-axis,
   (c) also through the point $(2, -1)$.

2. Find an equation of the line through each pair of points. Write each equation in the form $Ax + By + C = 0$.
   (a) $(3, 4)$ and $(1, -1)$ (b) $(-4, -6)$ and $(5, -2)$
   (c) $(3, -7)$ and $(-2, 5)$ (d) $(1.2, -0.6)$ and $(-0.8, 0.4)$

3. (a) What is the slope of a vertical line?
   (b) Why is the point-slope form not a suitable form for the equation of a vertical line?
   (c) What form is used for the equation of a vertical line?

Intersections of Lines

We can find the intersection of two lines by solving the system of linear equations that describes the lines.

Example Find the intersection of the lines $3x + 4y - 9 = 0$ and $5x - 8y - 4 = 0$.

Solution We solve the following system.

$$3x + 4y = 9 \quad ①$$
$$5x - 8y = 4 \quad ②$$
$$5 × ① \qquad 15x + 20y = 45 \quad ③$$
$$3 × ② \qquad 15x - 24y = 12 \quad ④$$
$$③ - ④ \qquad 44y = 33$$
$$\text{So,} \qquad y = \tfrac{3}{4}$$

We substitute this in Equation 1 to obtain the value of x.

$$3x + 4\left(\tfrac{3}{4}\right) = 9$$
$$3x + 3 = 9$$
$$3x = 6$$
$$x = 2$$

So the lines $3x + 4y - 9 = 0$ and $5x - 8y - 4 = 0$ intersect at the point $\left(2, \tfrac{3}{4}\right)$.

EXERCISE 2

1. Find the intersection of each pair of lines.
    (a) $5x - 2y = -9$
          $3x + 7y = 11$
    (b) $2x - 3y + 10 = 0$
          $4x + y = 5$
    (c) $4x - 3y - 1 = 0$
          $8x + 15y - 9 = 0$
    (d) $3x - 8y + 7 = 0$
          $2x + 9y + 19 = 0$

Geometric Interpretations

An ordered pair of the form $(x, 2)$ describes any point in the plane that is two units above the x-axis. This set is a straight line in the plane.

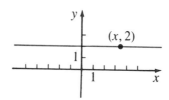

Similarly an ordered triple of the form $(x, 2, 3)$ describes any point that is both two units to the right of the xz-plane and three units above the xy-plane; this set is a straight line in space.

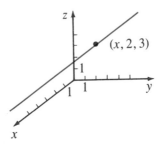

What is described by an ordered triple of the form $(x, y, 3)$ in space? This is any point that is three units above the xy-plane (but whose location relative to the x- and y-axes is unspecified). What is the set of such points? It is an entire plane.

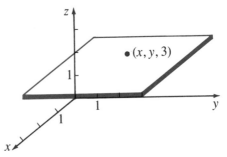

If we consider all points in the plane of the form (x, y) where $y > 0$ we describe the **upper half-plane** shown in the diagram.

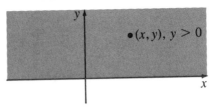

If we consider all points in space of the form (x, y, z) where $z > 0$ we describe the **upper half-space** shown in the diagram.

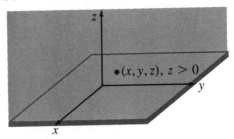

EXERCISE 3

1. What is described by each of the following?
   (a) $(x, -1)$ (b) $(2, y)$ (c) $(0, y)$
   (d) $(x, 2, -1)$ (e) $(2, y, 0)$ (f) $(-3, 4, z)$

2. What is described by each ordered triple?
   (a) $(2, y, z)$ (b) $(x, -3, z)$ (c) $(x, y, 0)$

3. Describe each by an ordered pair or triple.
   (a) any point in the plane two units below the x-axis
   (b) any point in the plane three units to the right of the y-axis
   (c) any point in space one unit below the xy-plane and 4.5 units to the right of the xz-plane

4. Graph each of the following:
   (a) the set of ordered pairs $(-3, y)$,
   (b) the set of ordered pairs $(x, 1)$,
   (c) the set of ordered pairs $(2, y)$,
   (d) the set of ordered triples $(2, y, z)$,
   (e) the set of ordered triples $(x, -2, z)$,
   (f) the set of ordered triples $(x, y, -3)$,
   (g) the set of ordered triples $(2, 5, z)$,
   (h) the set of ordered triples $(2, y, -1)$,
   (i) the set of ordered triples $(x, 3, -2)$,
   (j) the set of ordered triples $(0, y, 4)$.

INTRODUCTION

What is the equation of a graph? It is simply a mathematical statement that is true for every point on that graph, and for no other points.

In previous mathematical settings you have worked with equations of straight lines in the plane in the form $Ax + By + C = 0$. This is often referred to as the *standard form of the equation of a line*. In order to distinguish the form $Ax + By + C = 0$ from others that we introduce in this chapter, we call such an equation a *scalar equation of the line* or *a Cartesian equation of the line*.

In this chapter we explore alternative forms of equations of lines in the plane and then extend these approaches to develop equations of lines in space. The skill of recognition of various forms of equations for the same line is developed. Finally, the value of these approaches is seen in their application to finding intersections of lines and also distances between points and lines and between non-intersecting lines.

5.1 EQUATIONS OF LINES IN THE PLANE

In order to determine a straight line it is enough to specify either of the following sets of information:
1. two points on the line, or
2. one point on the line and its direction

> For a line l a fixed vector $\vec{d}$ is called a **direction vector for the line** if it is parallel to l.

Note that every line has an infinite number of direction vectors that can be represented as $t\vec{d}$ where $\vec{d}$ is one direction vector for the line and t is a non-zero real number.

Example 1   Find a direction vector for each line.
(a)   the line l_1 through points $A(4, -5)$ and $B(3, -7)$
(b)   the line l_2 with slope $\frac{4}{5}$

Solution   (a)   The vector $\overrightarrow{AB} = (3-4, -7-(-5)) = (-1, -2)$.
So, a direction vector for l_1 is given by the vector $(-1, -2)$.
Note that any scalar multiple of $(-1, -2)$ could also serve as a direction vector for l_1.

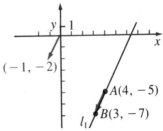

(b) A line with slope $\frac{4}{5}$ that passes through the origin would pass through the point $(5, 4)$. Thus as direction vector for l_2 we can use the position vector $(5, 4)$.

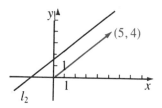

Using a direction vector for a line to specify the "slant" of the line and one point on the line to fix its location on the coordinate plane, we can develop a vector equation of the line.

Example 2   Develop a vector equation for the line through the point $P_0(-3, 5)$ with direction vector $\vec{d} = (1, 2)$.

Solution   We pick any point $P(x, y)$ on the line.

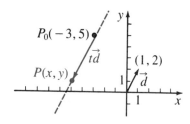

Because P is on the line the vector $\overrightarrow{P_0P}$, from P_0 to P, can be written as a scalar multiple of the direction vector $(1, 2)$; that is,

$$\overrightarrow{P_0P} = t\vec{d}$$

or $(x + 3, y - 5) = t(1, 2)$ for t any real number

is a vector equation of the line through $P_0(-3, 5)$ with direction vector $\vec{d} = (1, 2)$.

Note that use of a different point on the line or a different direction vector for the line may produce a different equation for the same line. For example, in Example 2 using point $(-3, 5)$ and direction vector $4(1, 2) = (4, 8)$ would produce the vector equation $(x + 3, y - 5) = t(4, 8)$. We investigate this situation later in this section.

The procedure of Example 2 can be followed to find the general form of a vector equation of the line through point $P_0(x_0, y_0)$ with direction vector $\vec{d} = (d_1, d_2)$.

For any point $P(x, y)$ on the line, the vector $\overrightarrow{P_0P}$, from P_0 to P, can be written as a scalar multiple of its direction vector $\vec{d}$. This produces a vector equation of the line.

A Vector Equation of the Line

through P_0 with direction vector $\vec{d}$ is
$\overrightarrow{P_0P} = t\vec{d}$ for any real number t.

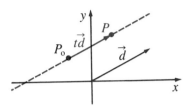

Using this form we can develop an alternative form of the vector equation. This could be called the *position vector form* of the equation of the line.

$$\overrightarrow{OP} = \overrightarrow{OP_0} + \overrightarrow{P_0P}$$

so $$\overrightarrow{OP} = \overrightarrow{OP_0} + t\vec{d}$$

or $$(x, y) = (x_0, y_0) + t(d_1, d_2)$$

Each real value of the scalar t in this equation corresponds to a point on the line. This scalar is called the **parameter** for the equation of the line. Another alternative form of an equation of a line that emphasizes how each coordinate is related to the parameter can be easily derived from the position vector form of a vector equation of the line by using equality of algebraic vectors.

Parametric Equations of the Line

through $P_0(x_0, y_0)$ with direction vector $\vec{d} = (d_1, d_2)$ are

$$x = x_0 + td_1 \qquad y = y_0 + td_2$$

The numbers d_1 and d_2 are called **direction numbers of the line**. Just as there are an infinite number of direction vectors for any line so there are an infinite number of pairs of direction numbers for any line in the plane.

Example 3   Find vector and parametric equations of the line through points $A(1, 7)$ and $B(4, 0)$.

Solution   A direction vector for this line is

$$\vec{d} = \overrightarrow{AB} = (4-1, 0-7) = (3, -7)$$

Thus, a vector equation of this line is given by

$$\overrightarrow{OP} = (1, 7) + t(3, -7)$$

From the vector equation we can obtain parametric equations. Because $\overrightarrow{OP} = (x, y) = (1, 7) + t(3, -7)$,

$$x = 1 + 3t$$
$$y = 7 - 7t$$

are parametric equations for the line through A and B.

$x = 1 + 3t$
$y = 7 - 7t$

Note that the coefficients of the parameter in parametric equations of the line are direction numbers for the line.

Example 4   Find three points on each line.
(a) the line with vector equation $\overrightarrow{OP} = (0, 4) + t(5, -2)$.
(b) the line with parametric equations
$$x = 1 + 4r \quad y = -3r$$

Solution   Each point on the line corresponds to a value of the parameter.
(a)

value of t	**point**
1	$(0, 4) + 1(5, -2) = (5, 2)$
0	$(0, 4) + 0(5, -2) = (0, 4)$
-0.5	$(0, 4) + (-0.5)(5, -2) = (-2.5, 5)$

(b)

value of r	x	y	**point**
1	$1 + 4(1) = 5$	$-3(1) = -3$	$(5, -3)$
0	$1 + 4(0) = 1$	$-3(0) = 0$	$(1, 0)$
2.5	$1 + 4(2.5) = 11$	$-3(2.5) = -7.5$	$(11, -7.5)$

Yet another form of equation of a line evolves from solving the parametric equations for the parameter.

Because $x = x_0 + td_1$, $t = \dfrac{x - x_0}{d_1}$ and because $y = y_0 + td_2$,

$t = \dfrac{y - y_0}{d_2}$.

A line that has zero as a direction number has no symmetric equations

---
A Symmetric Equation of the Line

through (x_0, y_0) with direction vector (d_1, d_2) is
$$\frac{x - x_0}{d_1} = \frac{y - y_0}{d_2}.$$

$\dfrac{x - x_0}{d_1} = \dfrac{y - y_0}{d_2}$

Note that the denominators in the symmetric equation are direction numbers for the line.

Example 5   Find a symmetric equation of the line through points $X(2, -3)$ and $Y(1, 0)$.

Solution   In this situation we choose the point $(x_0, y_0) = X(2, -3)$ and the direction vector $(d_1, d_2) = \overrightarrow{XY} = (-1, 3)$.

Then $\dfrac{x - 2}{-1} = \dfrac{y + 3}{3}$ is a symmetric equation for the line.

With so many variations of equations of a line it becomes useful to be able to distinguish between different equations of the same line and equations of different lines. By recognizing that each point on the line must correspond to a value of the parameter it is possible to compare such equations to decide whether they describe the same line.

Example 6   For each pair of equations determine whether or not they describe the same line.

(a)   (i) $(x-1, y-6) = r(3, -2)$ and (ii) $(x-4, y-4) = s(-6, 4)$

(b)   (i) $x = 2 - t$
$\qquad y = 5t$ and (ii) $x - 3 = \dfrac{1 - y}{5}$

(c)   (i) $(x-5, y+3) = s(2, 1)$ and (ii) $\dfrac{x + 5}{-2} = \dfrac{y - 3}{1}$

Solution   First we compare the direction vectors of the lines described; if they are parallel the equations may represent the same line so we investigate further by determining whether or not a point from one line is on the other line.

(a)   Because $-2(3, -2) = (-6, 4)$, the direction vectors are parallel; the equations may describe the same line.

Rewriting the equation $(x-4, y-4) = s(-6, 4)$ as $(x, y) = (4, 4) + s(-6, 4)$ we see that the point $(4, 4)$ is on this line. Is $(4, 4)$ on the line described by $(x-1, y-6) = r(3, -2)$ or

$(x, y) = (1, 6) + r(3, -2)$?

If so, $(4, 4) = (1, 6) + r(3, -2)$ for some value of r.

So, $4 = 1 + 3r$ and $4 = 6 - 2r$

Thus $3 = 3r$ $\qquad -2 = -2r$

So $1 = r$ $\qquad 1 = r$

These are equations for the same line.

(b)   Direction vectors for these lines are the parallel vectors $(-1, 5)$ and $(1, -5)$. The point $(2, 0)$ is on the line $x = 2 - t$ and $y = 5t$.

Is it on the line $x - 3 = \dfrac{1 - y}{5}$?

We rewrite this equation in parametric form

$$x = 3 + t, \ y = 1 - 5t$$

If $(2, 0)$ is on this line

$$2 = 3 + t \quad \text{and} \quad 0 = 1 - 5t$$

that is, $-1 = t$ $\qquad$ and $t = \frac{1}{5}$

Because such values for t (at the same time) are impossible, we conclude that $(2, 0)$ is not on this line and, thus, that these are not equations of the same line.

(c)   Direction vectors for these lines are $(2, 1)$ and $(-2, 1)$. Because these are not parallel, the lines cannot be identical.

EXERCISE 5.1

A 1. Find a direction vector for each line.
   (a) the line through $(2, 1)$ and $(7, 0)$
   (b) a line parallel to $(x-1, y-3) = r(-3, 4)$
   (c) a line with slope -0.25
   (d) a line parallel to $\dfrac{x-7}{5} = \dfrac{y-2}{3}$

2. Give direction numbers for each line.
   (a) a line parallel to $(x, y) = (3+5r, -1+r)$
   (b) a line perpendicular to $x = 3 - 4t$
      $$y = 2t$$

3. Give two points on each line.
   (a) $\overrightarrow{OP} = (2, 0) + t(5, 3)$ (b) $x = 3 - 4t$
      $$y = 2t$$
   (c) $(x-3, y+1) = r(5, 1)$ (d) $\dfrac{x-7}{5} = \dfrac{y-2}{3}$

B 4. Give parametric equations for each line.
   (a) $\overrightarrow{OP} = (2, 0) + t(3, 5)$ (b) $\dfrac{x-7}{5} = \dfrac{y-2}{3}$
   (c) $(x, y) = (3+5r, -1+r)$ (d) $(x-4, y+0.5) = s(0, 0.75)$

5. Give a vector equation for each line.
   (a) $\dfrac{x-7}{5} = \dfrac{y-2}{3}$ (b) $x = 3 - 4t$
      $$y = 2t$$

6. Give a symmetric equation for each line.
   (a) $\overrightarrow{OP} = (2, 0) + t(5, 3)$ (b) $x = 3 - 4t$
      $$y = 2t$$

7. Rewrite each equation of a line in the form $\overrightarrow{P_0P} = t\vec{d}$.
   (a) $\overrightarrow{OP} = (2, 0) + t(5, 3)$ (b) $x = 3 - 4t$
      $$y = 2t$$
   (c) $\dfrac{x-7}{5} = \dfrac{y-2}{3}$ (d) $(x, y) = (3+5r, -1+r)$

8. Equations in the form $\overrightarrow{P_0P} = t\vec{d}$ can be easily rewritten as symmetric equations;
   for example, if $(x-2, y+1) = t(5, 3)$, then $\dfrac{x-2}{5} = \dfrac{y+1}{3}$.

   Write a symmetric equation for each line.
   (a) $(x-3, y+7) = r(2, 5)$ (b) $(x+4, y) = r(-2, 3)$
   (c) $(x, y) = r(2, -5)$ (d) $(x, y) = (5, 6) + r(1, 9)$

9. For each equation determine whether or not it describes the line $\overrightarrow{OP} = (0, 3) + s(-1, 5)$.
   (a) $\overrightarrow{OP} = (0, 3) + r(1, 5)$ (b) $x = 1 + 2s$
      $$y = -2 - 10s$$

(c) $\dfrac{x}{-2} = \dfrac{y-3}{10}$

(d) $(x+1, y-5) = t(0, 3)$

10. Develop a vector equation for each line.
    (a) the line with slope 3 through the point $(2, 5)$
    (b) the line through points $A(1, -3)$ and $B(9, 2)$
    (c) the line parallel to the y-axis through $(3, -2)$
    (d) the line perpendicular to $x - 3 = 2 - y$, through the origin

11. Find parametric equations of each line.
    (a) the line through the origin with direction vector $(3, -2)$
    (b) the line parallel to $(x-2, y+1) = s(0, 4)$, through $(1, 7)$
    (c) the line through $(2, 5)$ and $(6, -1)$
    (d) the line perpendicular to $\dfrac{x-4}{2} = 3 - y$ with y-intercept 5

12. Find a symmetric equation of each line.
    (a) the line through points $(1, 6)$ and $(2, -1)$
    (b) the line with direction vector $(3, -4)$ and y-intercept -5
    (c) the line parallel to the x-axis through $(2, 7)$
    (d) the line parallel to $(x, y) = (1, -3) + t(4, 3)$ with the same x-intercept as $(x-1, y-1) = t(2, -3)$

13. (a) Why is there no symmetric equation of a line when the line has zero as a direction number?
    (b) What is the common feature of the graphs of such lines in the plane?

14. Develop vector, parametric, and symmetric equations of the line through $(3, -5)$ and perpendicular to the line
    $$x = 3t - 5 \quad y = 2 + t$$

15. Find vector, parametric, and symmetric equations for the line $3x + y = 5$.

C 16. (a) Rewrite the given symmetric equation of the line in the form $Ax + By + C = 0$; that is, obtain from a symmetric equation of a line a Cartesian equation of the line.
    $$\dfrac{x-2}{5} = \dfrac{2-y}{3}$$
    (b) Show that a Cartesian equation of the line through (x_0, y_0) with direction numbers (d_1, d_2) is
    $$d_2 x - d_1 y + k = 0 \qquad \text{where } k = -d_2 x_0 + d_1 y_0.$$

17. (a) Draw a diagram to illustrate that a vector equation of the line through points X and Y is given by
    $$\overrightarrow{XP} = r\overrightarrow{XY} \qquad \text{for } P \text{ any point on the line}$$
    (b) When the parameter r takes on the value $\frac{1}{2}$ what point P is obtained? What if the value of r is $\frac{3}{5}$? -2? 0?
    (c) Into what ratio does the point P divide the line segment XY if $\overrightarrow{XP} = \frac{2}{3}\overrightarrow{XY}$? if $\overrightarrow{XP} = -3\overrightarrow{XY}$? if $\overrightarrow{XP} = \frac{5}{4}\overrightarrow{XY}$?

18. For points $X(1, 3)$ and $Y(2, -4)$, find (a) the coordinates of the point P that divides the line segment XY (internally) in the ratio $3:2$,

    (b) the coordinates of the point Q that divides XY in the ratio $4:7$, and

    (c) the point R that divides XY (externally) in the ratio $-2:5$.

19. Using the methods of this section show that a vector equation of the line through points A and B is given by
$$\overrightarrow{OP} = a\overrightarrow{OA} + b\overrightarrow{OB}$$
    where P is any point on the line and $a + b = 1$.

    Note that this result (by a different method) was requested as Question 10 in Exercise 2.4.

5.2 EQUATIONS OF LINES IN SPACE

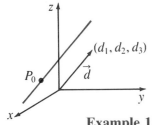

To specify a particular line in space it is sufficient, as it is for a line in the plane, to indicate either two points on the line or one point on the line and the line's direction as indicated by a direction vector. In space, however, points on lines and direction vectors are represented by ordered triples. We begin by considering direction vectors.

Example 1 Find a direction vector for each line in space.

(a) any line l_1 parallel to the line with direction vector $\vec{d} = (2, -1, 5)$

(b) the line l_2 through points $A(4, -5, 3)$ and $B(3, -7, 1)$

Solution (a) Any line has the same direction vectors as all lines parallel to it. Thus a direction vector for the line l_1 is the vector $\vec{d} = (2, -1, 5)$.

(b) $\overrightarrow{AB} = (3-4, -7-(-5), 1-3) = (-1, -2, -2)$

So, one direction vector for l_2 is the vector $(-1, -2, -2)$.

Of course any non-zero scalar multiple of $\overrightarrow{AB}$ is parallel to it and thus also serves as a direction vector for this line.   ⬡

Using a direction vector $\vec{d}$ for a line to specify the "slant" of the line and one point P_0 on the line to fix its location in space we can develop a vector equation of the line.

Example 2 Develop a vector equation for the line through the point $P_0(-3, 5, 2)$ with direction vector $\vec{d} = (1, 2, -1)$.

Solution We pick any point $P(x, y, z)$ on the line.

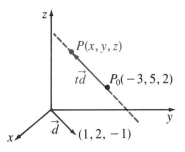

Because P is on the line the vector $\overrightarrow{P_0P}$, from P_0 to P, can be written as a scalar multiple of the direction vector $(1, 2, -1)$. Thus

$$\overrightarrow{P_0P} = t(1, 2, -1)$$

or

$$(x+3, y-5, z-2) = t(1, 2, -1)$$

for t any real number is a vector equation of the line through $P_0(-3, 5, 2)$ with direction vector $\vec{d} = (1, 2, -1)$.

The procedure of Example 2 can be followed to find the general form of a vector equation of the line in space through the point $P_0(x_0, y_0, z_0)$ with direction vector $\vec{d} = (d_1, d_2, d_3)$.

Just as in the plane, for any point $P(x, y, z)$ on the line the vector $\overrightarrow{P_0P}$, from P_0 to P, can be written as a scalar multiple of the direction vector $\vec{d}$.

A Vector Equation of the Line in Space

through P_0 with direction vector $\vec{d}$ is
$.\overrightarrow{P_0P} = t\vec{d}$ for any real number t.

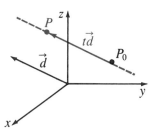

Again, as for a line in the plane, we can develop from this form of vector equation for the line three equations which together describe the line.

Parametric Equations for the Line in Space

through $P_0(x_0, y_0, z_0)$ with direction vector $\vec{d} = (d_1, d_2, d_3)$ are
$$x = x_0 + td_1$$
$$y = y_0 + td_2$$
$$z = z_0 + td_3$$

The numbers d_1, d_2 and d_3 are called **direction numbers of the line**. Just as there are an infinite number of direction vectors for any line, so there are an infinite number of triples of direction numbers for any line in space.

Example 3   Find vector and parametric equations of the line through the points $A(1, 7, -3)$ and $B(4, 0, 2)$.

Solution   A direction vector for this line is

$$\vec{d} = \overrightarrow{AB} = (4-1, 0-7, 2-(-3)) = (3, -7, 5)$$

Thus, a vector equation of this line is given by

$$\overrightarrow{OP} = (1, 7, -3) + t(3, -7, 5)$$

Because $\overrightarrow{OP} = (x, y, z) = (1, 7, -3) + t(3, -7, 5)$,

$$x = 1 + 3t$$
$$y = 7 - 7t$$
$$z = -3 + 5t$$

are parametric equations for the line through A and B.

$x = 1 + 3t$
$y = 7 - 7t$
$z = -3 + 5t$

Note that the coefficients of the parameter in parametric equations of the line are direction numbers for the line.

Example 4   Find three points on each line.
(a)   The line with vector equation $\overrightarrow{OP} = (0, 4, 1) + t(5, -2, 3)$,
(b)   the line with parametric equations
$$x = 1 + 4r \quad y = -3r \quad z = 9 + 2r$$

Solution   Each point on the line corresponds to a value of the parameter.

(a)

value of t	point
1	$(0, 4, 1) + 1(5, -2, 3) = (5, 2, 4)$
0	$(0, 4, 1) + 0(5, -2, 3) = (0, 4, 1)$
-0.5	$(0, 4, 1) + (-0.5)(5, -2, 3) = (-2.5, 5, -0.5)$

(b)

r	x	y	z	point
1	$1 + 4(1) = 5$	$-3(1) = -3$	$9 + 2(1) = 11$	$(5, -3, 11)$
0	$1 + 4(0) = 1$	$-3(0) = 0$	$9 + 2(0) = 9$	$(1, 0, 9)$
-7	$1 + 4(-7) = -27$	$-3(-7) = 21$	$9 + 2(-7) = -5$	$(-27, 21, -5)$

Again, as for lines in the plane, we can develop symmetric equations for lines in space by solving for the parameter in the parametric equations.

A line with zero as a direction number has no symmetric equations.

Symmetric Equations of the Line

through (x_0, y_0, z_0) with direction vector (d_1, d_2, d_3) are

$$\frac{x - x_0}{d_1} = \frac{y - y_0}{d_2} = \frac{z - z_0}{d_3}$$

$$\frac{x - x_0}{d_1} = \frac{y - y_0}{d_2} = \frac{z - z_0}{d_3}$$

Note that the denominators in the symmetric equations are direction numbers for the line.

Example 5   Find symmetric equations of the line through $X(2, 5, -3)$ and $Y(1, 0, 2)$.

Solution   We use the point $X(2, 5, -3)$ as a point on the line and
$\vec{d} = \overrightarrow{XY} = (-1, -5, 5)$ as a direction vector.

So, $\dfrac{x - 2}{-1} = \dfrac{y - 5}{-5} = \dfrac{z + 3}{5}$ are symmetric equations for the line.

By comparing direction vectors and points on the lines described by given equations we can determine whether two equations actually describe the same line.

Example 6   For each pair of equations, determine whether or not they describe the same line.
(a) (i) $(x - 1, y - 6, z - 2) = r(3, -2, 1)$ and
(ii) $(x - 4, y - 4, z - 3) = s(-6, 4, -2)$
(b) (i) $(x, y, z) = (2, 0, 9) + r(-1, 5, 2)$ and
(ii) $x - 3 = \dfrac{1 - y}{5} = \dfrac{1 - z}{2}$

Solution   (a) Because $-2(3, -2, 1) = (-6, 4, -2)$, the direction vectors are parallel; the equations may describe the same line.
The point $(4, 4, 3)$ is on the line given by
$(x - 4, y - 4, z - 3) = s(-6, 4, -2)$. Is $(4, 4, 3)$ on the line described by $(x - 1, y - 6, z - 2) = r(3, -2, 1)$?
If so, $(4, 4, 3) = (1, 6, 2) + r(3, -2, 1)$ for some value of r.
So, $4 = 1 + 3r$ and $4 = 6 - 2r$ and $3 = 2 + r$
$ 3 = 3r -2 = -2r 1 = r$
$ 1 = r 1 = r$
These are equations for the same line.

(b) Direction vectors for these lines are the parallel vectors $(-1, 5, 2)$ and $(1, -5, -2)$. The point $(2, 0, 9)$ is on the line

$$(x, y, z) = (2, 0, 9) + r(-1, 5, 2)$$

Is it on the line $x - 3 = \dfrac{1 - y}{5} = \dfrac{1 - z}{2}$?

We rewrite these symmetric equations in parametric form

$$x = 3 + s, \; y = 1 - 5s, \; z = 1 - 2s$$

If $(2, 0, 9)$ is on the line
$$2 = 3 + s \quad \text{and} \quad 0 = 1 - 5s \quad \text{and} \quad 9 = 1 - 2s$$
that is, $-1 = s$ and $s = \frac{1}{5}$ and $s = -4$

Because such values for s (at the same time) are impossible we conclude that $(2, 0, 9)$ is not on this line and, thus, that these are not equations of the same line.

EXERCISE 5.2

A **1.** Find a direction vector for each line.
  (a) the line through $(2, 1, 5)$ and $(7, 0, 2)$
  (b) a line parallel to $(x-1, y-3, z-6) = r(-3, 4, 0)$
  (c) a line parallel to $\dfrac{x-7}{5} = \dfrac{y-2}{3} = z + 1$

2. Give direction numbers for each line.
  (a) A line parallel to $(x, y, z) = (3+5r, -1+r, 2-3r)$
  (b) The line with parametric equations
    $x = 2 - t, \quad y = 2t, \quad z = 3t - 1$
  (c) The line with symmetric equations $\dfrac{x+5}{2} = \dfrac{y+2}{-3} = \dfrac{4-z}{2}$

3. Give two points on each line.
  (a) $\overrightarrow{OP} = (2, 0, -1) + t(5, 3, 4)$ (b) $x = 3 - 4t$
                                                             $y = 2t$
                                                             $z = 1 + 5t$
  (c) $(x, y, z) = (3+5r, -1+r, 4)$ (d) $\dfrac{x-7}{5} = \dfrac{y-2}{3} = \dfrac{z+1}{2}$

B **4.** Give parametric equations for each line.
  (a) $\overrightarrow{OP} = (2, 0, -2) + t(3, 5, 1)$
  (b) $\dfrac{x-7}{5} = \dfrac{y-2}{3} = \dfrac{z+1}{2}$
  (c) $(x, y, z) = (3+5r, -1 + r, 4)$
  (d) $(x-4, y+0.5, z-1) = s(0, 0.75, 2.0)$

5. Give a vector equation for each line.
  (a) $\dfrac{x-7}{5} = \dfrac{y-2}{3} = \dfrac{z+1}{2}$ (b) $x = 3 - 4t$
                                                                 $y = 2t$
                                                                 $z = 1 + 5t$

6. Give symmetric equations for each line.
  (a) $\overrightarrow{OP} = (2, 0, -2) + t(3, 5, 1)$ (b) $x = 3 - 4t$
                                                             $y = 2t$
                                                             $z = 1 + 5t$

7. Rewrite each equation in the form $\overrightarrow{P_0P} = t\vec{d}$.
  (a) $\overrightarrow{OP} = (2, 0, -2) + t(3, 5, 1)$ (b) $x = 3 - 4t$
                                                             $y = 2t$
                                                             $z = 1 + 5t$
  (c) $\dfrac{x-7}{5} = \dfrac{y-2}{3} = \dfrac{z+1}{2}$ (d) $(x, y, z) = (3+5r, -1+r, 4)$

8. Rewrite each equation in symmetric form.
  (a) $(x-3, y+2, z+1) = t(1, 5, -1)$
  (b) $(x, y+1, z-1) = t(2, 3, -1)$

9. For each equation determine whether or not it describes the line
    $\overrightarrow{OP} = (0, 3, 2) + s(-1, 5, 2)$.

    (a) $\overrightarrow{OP} = (0, 3, 2) + r(1, 5, 2)$　(b) $x = 2 + s$
    $$y = -7 - 5s$$
    $$z = -2 - 2s$$

    (c) $\dfrac{x}{-2} = \dfrac{y - 3}{10} = \dfrac{z - 2}{4}$

    (d) $(x + 1, y - 5, z - 2) = t(0, 3, 2)$

10. Find vector and parametric equations of each line
    (a) the line through the origin with direction vector $(3, -2, 7)$
    (b) the line through points $(1, -3, 2)$ and $(9, 2, 0)$
    (c) the line parallel to the y-axis through the point $(1, 3, 5)$
    (d) the line with z-intercept 4, parallel to the line
    $$x = 1, \quad y = 2 + s, \quad z = s$$

11. Find symmetric equations of each line.
    (a) the line through points $(1, 6, 2)$ and $(2, -1, 5)$
    (b) the line parallel to $(x - 1, y + 2, z) = r(1, -1, 1)$ through $(0, 0, 5)$.

12. (a) If any one of a triple of direction numbers for the line l is zero, there are no symmetric equations for the line. Why not?
    (b) Describe the set of lines in space with one or more direction numbers equal to zero.

13. Develop vector, parametric, and symmetric equations of the line through $(3, -5, 1)$ and parallel to the line
    $$x = 3t - 5, \quad y = 2 + t, \quad z = t - 5$$

C 14. For points $X(1, 3, 5)$ and $Y(2, -4, 6)$, find:
    (a) the coordinates of the point P that divides the line segment XY (internally) in the ratio $3:2$,
    (b) the coordinates of the point Q that divides XY in the ratio $4:7$, and
    (c) the point R that divides XY (externally) in the ratio $-2:5$.

5.3　DIRECTION NUMBERS, ANGLES AND COSINES

One alternative technique for describing the direction of a line focusses on the *direction angles of the line*.

α—alpha
β—beta

> The **direction angles of a line l in the plane** are the angles, α and β, $0 \le \alpha, \beta \le \pi$, between a direction vector of l in the upper half-plane (where $y \ge 0$) and the positive x- and y-axes.

direction angles
of a line in a plane

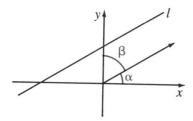 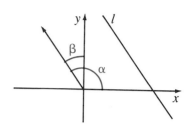

γ—gamma

> The **direction angles of a line l in space** are the angles, α, β, and γ, $0 \leq \alpha, \beta, \gamma \leq \pi$, between a direction vector of l in the upper half-space (where $z \geq 0$) and the positive x-, y-, and z-axes respectively.

direction angles
of a line in a plane

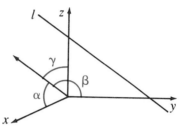

There are other ways of defining the term "direction angles" of a line. The advantage, however, of this definition is that the angles are unique for a particular line. Note that for this definition the last direction number of the direction vector used is always positive. Note also that the direction angles are between 0 and π.

What is the relationship between the direction numbers of a line and its direction angles? We can investigate this using the dot product operation.

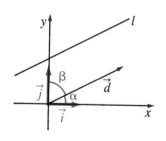

Consider a line l in the plane, $\vec{d} = (d_1, d_2)$ a direction vector for l with $d_2 > 0$ and the standard basis vectors $\vec{i}$, $\vec{j}$. Then the direction angles for l are the angles between $\vec{d}$ and $\vec{i}$, $\vec{d}$ and $\vec{j}$.

Then,
$$\vec{d} \cdot \vec{i} = |\vec{d}| |\vec{i}| \cos \alpha$$

Thus,
$$(d_1, d_2) \cdot (1, 0) = |\vec{d}| \times 1 \times \cos \alpha$$

so,
$$d_1 = |\vec{d}| \cos \alpha$$

and
$$\cos \alpha = \frac{d_1}{|\vec{d}|}$$

Similarly, $\cos \beta = \dfrac{d_2}{|\vec{d}|}$

A similar result holds in space; that is,

$$\cos \alpha = \frac{d_1}{|\vec{d}|}, \cos \beta = \frac{d_2}{|\vec{d}|}, \text{ and } \cos \gamma = \frac{d_3}{|\vec{d}|}$$

The proof of this result is left to the student as Question 8(a) in Exercise 5.3.

We summarize.

Direction Cosines of a Line

In the plane:
For a line l with direction vector $\vec{d} = (d_1, d_2)$, $d_2 \geqslant 0$

$$\cos \alpha = \frac{d_1}{|\vec{d}|} \qquad \cos \beta = \frac{d_2}{|\vec{d}|}$$

In space:
For a line l with direction vector $\vec{d} = (d_1, d_2, d_3)$, $d_3 \geqslant 0$

$$\cos \alpha = \frac{d_1}{|\vec{d}|} \qquad \cos \beta = \frac{d_2}{|\vec{d}|} \qquad \cos \gamma = \frac{d_3}{|\vec{d}|}$$

Looking at these relationships in the form

$$(\cos \alpha, \cos \beta) = \frac{1}{|\vec{d}|}(d_1, d_2) = \frac{1}{|\vec{d}|}\vec{d}$$

$$\left[\text{or } (\cos \alpha, \cos \beta, \cos \gamma) = \frac{1}{|\vec{d}|}(d_1, d_2, d_3) = \frac{1}{|\vec{d}|}\vec{d} \right]$$

we can see that the direction cosines of a line are the components of a unit vector in the direction of the line.

Example 1 (a) The line l_1 has direction vector $(-2, 1)$. Find its direction cosines.
(b) The line l_2 has direction vector $(1, 3, 5)$. Find its direction cosines and, thus, its direction angles.

Solution (a) Let $\vec{d} = (-2, 1)$. Then $|\vec{d}| = \sqrt{(-2)^2 + 1^2} = \sqrt{5}$.
So, the direction cosines for l_1 are

$$\cos \alpha = \frac{-2}{\sqrt{5}}$$

$$\cos \beta = \frac{1}{\sqrt{5}}$$

(b) Let $\vec{d} = (1, 3, 5)$. Then
$$|\vec{d}| = \sqrt{1^2 + 3^2 + 5^2} = \sqrt{1 + 9 + 25} = \sqrt{35}.$$

So, $$\cos \alpha = \frac{1}{\sqrt{35}}$$

$$\cos \beta = \frac{3}{\sqrt{35}}$$

$$\cos \gamma = \frac{5}{\sqrt{35}}$$

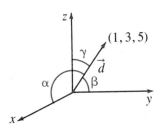

Thus, the direction angles for l_2 are

$$\alpha \doteq 80°$$
$$\beta \doteq 60°$$
$$\gamma \doteq 32°$$

It is possible to find direction cosines and/or angles for a line, given an equation of the line.

Example 2   (a) Find direction angles of the line

$$\frac{x-2}{1} = \frac{y-4}{-5} = \frac{z+3}{4}$$

(b) Find direction cosines of the line

$$x = 5 + t$$
$$y = 1 + 2t$$
$$z = 3 - t$$

Solution   (a) From the symmetric equations

$$\frac{x-2}{1} = \frac{y-4}{-5} = \frac{z+3}{4}$$

we identify $\vec{d} = (1, -5, 4)$ as a direction vector of the line that is in the upper half-space of the coordinate system because its last coordinate is greater than 0.

Because $|\vec{d}| = \sqrt{1^2 + (-5)^2 + 4^2} = \sqrt{42}$

$$\cos \alpha = \frac{1}{\sqrt{42}}$$

$$\cos \beta = \frac{-5}{\sqrt{42}}$$

$$\cos \gamma = \frac{4}{\sqrt{42}}$$

So, the direction angles for the line are

$$\alpha \doteq 81°$$
$$\beta \doteq 140°$$
$$\gamma \doteq 52°$$

(b) From the parametric equations of the line we identify a direction vector of the line as $(1, 2, -1)$. But this vector is not in the upper half-space because its last coordinate is not positive. We choose $\vec{d} = (-1, -2, 1)$ as a direction vector that is in this upper half-space.

Then, $|\vec{d}| = \sqrt{(-1)^2 + (-2)^2 + 1^2} = \sqrt{6}$

so, $\cos \alpha = \dfrac{-1}{\sqrt{6}}$

$\cos \beta = \dfrac{-2}{\sqrt{6}}$

$\cos \gamma = \dfrac{1}{\sqrt{6}}$

It is also possible to produce a direction vector for a line given its direction cosines.

Example 3   A line l through the point $(0, 3, 2)$ has direction cosines $\dfrac{1}{\sqrt{14}}, \dfrac{-3}{\sqrt{14}},$ and $\dfrac{2}{\sqrt{14}}$. Find parametric equations of the line.

Solution   As direction vector for the line we could use $(\cos \alpha, \cos \beta, \cos \gamma)$. However we multiply by $\sqrt{14}$ to obtain ''nicer'' numbers.

$$\vec{d} = \sqrt{14} (\cos \alpha, \cos \beta, \cos \gamma)$$
$$= \sqrt{14} \left(\dfrac{1}{\sqrt{14}}, \dfrac{-3}{\sqrt{14}}, \dfrac{2}{\sqrt{14}} \right)$$
$$= (1, -3, 2)$$

A vector equation of the line is given by
$$\overrightarrow{OP} = (0, 3, 2) + t(1, -3, 2)$$
Thus, parametric equations of the line are

$x = t$
$y = 3 - 3t$
$z = 2 + 2t$

EXERCISE 5.3

A **1.** Find direction cosines of each axis in space.
(a) the x-axis   (b) the y-axis   (c) the z-axis

2. Find direction cosines of each line.
(a) A line with direction vector $(2, 1)$,
(b) a line with direction numbers -2 and 5,
(c) a line parallel to vector $(2, -1, 5)$.

B **3.** Find direction cosines of each line.
(a) The line through $(2, 3)$ and $(4, -1)$,
(b) a line with direction vector $(-3, -2)$,
(c) a line parallel to the line $\overrightarrow{OP} = (2, 6, -1) + r(0, 3, 2)$,

(d) the line $x = 2 - 3t$, $y = 1 + t$

(e) the line $\dfrac{x + 1}{2} = \dfrac{y - 3}{5} = z - 1$

4. Find direction angles of each line.
    (a) A line parallel to $(x, y) = (7, 1) + s(3, 2)$,
    (b) the line through $(1, 7, -2)$ and $(0, 2, 5)$,
    (c) the line $x = 5 - 3s$, $y = s - 2$, $z = 4$

5. Find direction cosines and direction angles for each line.
    (a) The line $\overrightarrow{OP} = (-4, 1) + t(5, -2)$
    (b) the line $\dfrac{x - 4}{2} = \dfrac{2 - y}{3} = \dfrac{5 - z}{6}$

6. (a) Find vector and symmetric equations of the line through $(3, 0)$
         with direction cosines $\dfrac{2}{\sqrt{5}}$ and $\dfrac{1}{\sqrt{5}}$.
    (b) Find parametric and symmetric equations of the line with
         direction cosines $\dfrac{5}{\sqrt{30}}$, $\dfrac{-2}{\sqrt{30}}$, and $\dfrac{1}{\sqrt{30}}$ passing through the
         origin.

7. Prove, for a line in the plane with direction cosines $\cos \alpha$ and $\cos \beta$,
    that $\cos^2 \alpha + \cos^2 \beta = 1$.

8. (a) Prove that the direction cosines of a line in space with direction
         vector $\vec{d} = (d_1, d_2, d_3)$ are given by

    $$\cos \alpha = \frac{d_1}{|\vec{d}|}, \cos \beta = \frac{d_2}{|\vec{d}|}, \cos \gamma = \frac{d_3}{|\vec{d}|}$$

    (b) Prove that $\cos^2 \alpha + \cos^2 \beta + \cos^2 \gamma = 1$.

9. Consider a line in space for which $\cos \alpha = \dfrac{-2}{\sqrt{21}}$, $\cos \gamma = \dfrac{1}{\sqrt{21}}$,

    and $\dfrac{\pi}{2} < \beta < \pi$. If the line passes through the point $(0, 1, 5)$,

    develop parametric equations describing the line.

C 10. Using the relationship between the direction cosines of perpendicular
        lines in space, prove that, for lines l_1 and l_2 with direction angles α_1,
        β_1, γ_1 and α_2, β_2, γ_2,

        $$\cos \alpha_1 \cos \alpha_2 + \cos \beta_1 \cos \beta_2 + \cos \gamma_1 \cos \gamma_2 = 0.$$

11. (a) What is the relationship between the direction angles of a line in
          the plane if (i) the line has positive slope? or (ii) the line has
          negative slope?
     (b) For a line in the plane with direction angles α and β, express
          $\cos \beta$ in terms of α.
     (c) Show that the slope of the line is $\tan \alpha$.

5.4 SCALAR EQUATIONS OF LINES IN THE PLANE

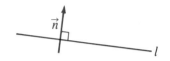

The *standard form* of the equation of a line in the plane, $Ax + By + C = 0$, can be developed using one point on the line and its slope as in Exercise 1 of the Review and Preview to this chapter. This form is also referred to as a **scalar equation of the line** or as a **Cartesian equation of the line**. An alternate development of such an equation makes use of vector concepts.

> A **normal (vector) to a line** l is a vector $\vec{n}$ which is perpendicular to the line.

Example 1 Develop a scalar equation of the line through the point $P_0(4, -1)$ with normal $\vec{n} = (3, 5)$.

Solution We pick any point $P(x, y)$ on the line.
Because points P_0 and P are both on the line, the vector $\overrightarrow{P_0P}$ is in the direction of the line. So, $\overrightarrow{P_0P}$ is perpendicular to $\vec{n}$.

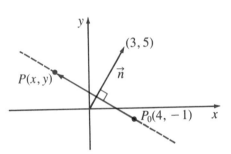

We call $\overrightarrow{P_0P} \cdot \vec{n} = 0$ *the normal form* of the line.

Thus, $$\overrightarrow{P_0P} \cdot \vec{n} = 0$$
But $$\overrightarrow{P_0P} = (x-4, y+1)$$
so $$(x-4, y+1) \cdot (3, 5) = 0$$
$$3(x - 4) + 5(y + 1) = 0$$
that is, $$3x - 12 + 5y + 5 = 0$$

So, $3x + 5y - 7 = 0$ is a scalar equation of the line through the point $P_0(4, -1)$ with normal $\vec{n} = (3, 5)$.

$3x + 5y - 7 = 0$

Note the location of the components of the normal, 3 and 5, in the scalar equation—as coefficients of the x- and y-terms. This is not a coincidence but a general result.

> A scalar equation of the line through the point $P_0(x_0, y_0)$ with normal $\vec{n} = (n_1, n_2)$ is given by
> $$n_1x + n_2y + C = 0$$

Proof

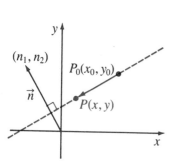

For point $P(x, y)$ on the line, vector $\overrightarrow{P_0P}$ is in the direction of the line. So,

$$\overrightarrow{P_0P} \cdot \vec{n} = 0$$
$$(x - x_0, y - y_0) \cdot (n_1, n_2) = 0$$
$$n_1(x - x_0) + n_2(y - y_0) = 0$$
$$n_1 x - n_1 x_0 + n_2 y - n_2 y_0 = 0$$
$$n_1 x + n_2 y - n_1 x_0 - n_2 y_0 = 0$$

The expression $-n_1 x_0 - n_2 y_0$ is a constant. Thus, $n_1 x + n_2 y + C = 0$ is a scalar equation of this line.

This general result allows us to obtain a scalar equation of a line more simply if we are given one point on the line and a normal to the line. We redo Example 1 with the benefit of this insight.

Example 2   Find a scalar equation of the line through the point $P_0(4, -1)$ with normal $\vec{n} = (3, 5)$.

Solution   Because $\vec{n} = (3, 5)$ is a normal to this line a scalar equation of the line could be of the form $3x + 5y + C = 0$.
To determine the constant C we substitute the coordinates of the point P_0 into the line's equation.

Then, $3(4) + 5(-1) + C = 0$
$$12 - 5 + C = 0$$
$$7 + C = 0$$
So, $$C = -7$$

Thus, $3x + 5y - 7 = 0$ is a scalar equation of the line.

On the other hand, from a scalar equation of a line it is always possible to identify a normal for the line.

For a line given by $Ax + By + C = 0$, the vector (A, B) is a normal for the line.

Proof

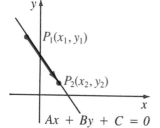

Consider two distinct points $P_1(x_1, y_1)$ and $P_2(x_2, y_2)$ on the line. Then the vector $\overrightarrow{P_1P_2}$ is in the direction of the line.

So $\overrightarrow{P_1P_2} \cdot (A, B) = (x_2 - x_1, y_2 - y_1) \cdot (A, B)$
$$= A(x_2 - x_1) + B(y_2 - y_1)$$
$$= Ax_2 - Ax_1 + By_2 - By_1$$

However, because points P_1 and P_2 are on the line,

$$Ax_1 + By_1 + C = 0 \quad ①$$

and $\quad Ax_2 + By_2 + C = 0 \quad ②$

Subtracting Equation 1 from Equation 2 we obtain

$$Ax_2 - Ax_1 + By_2 - By_1 = 0$$

So, $\qquad \overrightarrow{P_1P_2} \cdot (A, B) = 0$

that is, vector (A, B) is perpendicular to the line; in other words (A, B) is a normal to the line.

Identifying a normal vector for a line is useful in developing a scalar equation for the line or a related line.

Example 3   Find a normal vector for each line.
(a) $3x + 2y = 7$ (b) $(x-2, y+4) = r(3, -1)$

Solution   (a) Comparing the equation $3x + 2y = 7$ to the form $Ax + By + C = 0$, we obtain the normal $\vec{n} = (3, 2)$.

(b) $(3, -1)$ is a direction vector for the line $(x-2, y+4) = r(3, -1)$. A normal $\vec{n} = (n_1, n_2)$ must be perpendicular to $\vec{d}$,

that is, $\qquad \vec{d} \cdot \vec{n} = 0$

$$(3, -1) \cdot (n_1, n_2) = 0$$

$$3n_1 - n_2 = 0$$

To satisfy this equation we choose $n_1 = 1$ and $n_2 = 3$, so
$\vec{n} = (1, 3)$ is a normal for the line.

Once we identify a normal to a line we can rewrite other forms of the equation of a line in scalar form.

Example 4   Rewrite the equation $(x, y) = (2, -5) + t(2, -3)$ as a scalar equation for the line.

Solution 1   We rewrite the equation as a symmetric equation.

From $\qquad\qquad (x, y) = (2, -5) + t(2, -3)$

we obtain $\qquad (x-2, y+5) = t(2, -3)$

so $\qquad\qquad \dfrac{x - 2}{2} = \dfrac{y + 5}{-3}$

Thus, $\qquad\qquad -3(x - 2) = 2(y + 5)$

$$-3x + 6 = 2y + 10$$

so, $\qquad\qquad 3x + 2y + 4 = 0$ is a scalar equation for this line.

Solution 2   This method relies on selecting a normal to the line, then finding the dot product of the position vector of any point on the line with the normal. Because the normal is perpendicular to the direction vector, their dot product is 0, the parameter is eliminated, and we obtain a scalar equation.

Because $(2, -3)$ is a direction vector for the line, $(3, 2)$ is a normal for the line. For any point (x, y) on the line

$t(2, -3) \cdot (3, 2) = 0$

$$(x, y) = (2, -5) + t(2, -3)$$
$$(x, y) \cdot (3, 2) = (2, -5) \cdot (3, 2)$$

so $3x + 2y = 6 - 10 + 0$

thus $3x + 2y + 4 = 0$ is a scalar equation of the line.

What is the effect when we add a third unknown to a scalar equation; that is, what is described by an equation of the form $Ax + By + Cz + D = 0$? In general an equation of the form $Ax + By + Cz + D = 0$ describes a plane. We investigate scalar equations with three variables in Chapter 6, Equations of Planes.

EXERCISE 5.4

A **1.** Identify a normal for each line.
   (a) $3x + 2y + 5 = 0$ (b) $x + y = 7$
   (c) $y = 3x + 2$ (d) $x + 2 = 0$
   (e) $5x - 2y = 3$ (f) $y = 3$

2. For each line in Question 1, give a unit normal.

3. Describe the relationship between
   (a) normals of parallel lines
   (b) normals of perpendicular lines

B **4.** Find a scalar equation for each line.
   (a) the line through $(2, -1)$ with $\vec{n} = (5, 7)$
   (b) the line through the origin parallel to $2x - 3y + 6 = 0$
   (c) the line with direction numbers 1 and 5 through the point $(3, 4)$
   (d) the line parallel to the y-axis through $(4, -1)$
   (e) the line passing through the origin with direction cosines
   $-\dfrac{\sqrt{5}}{5}$ and $\dfrac{2\sqrt{5}}{5}$
   (f) the line through $(2, 7)$ and $(1, -3)$

5. In each situation develop a scalar equation for the line through the point A *parallel* to the line l.

	point A	**line l**
(a)	$(1, 2)$	$(x-2, y+3) = r(3, 0)$
(b)	$(0, -3)$	$x = 5s - 4$
		$y = 3s + 2$
(c)	$(-2, 5)$	$\dfrac{x-4}{3} = y + 5$
(d)	$(2, -4)$	$y = 3x + 5$
(e)	$(0, 0)$	$\overrightarrow{OP} = (3+5t, 2t)$
(f)	$(7, 0.5)$	$(x-2, y) \cdot (1, 6) = 0$

6. For each situation in Question 5 develop a scalar equation for the line through the point A *perpendicular* to the line l.

7. Rewrite each equation as a scalar equation of the line.
   (a) $(x, y) = (1, 0) + t(1, -1)$ (b) $\overrightarrow{OP} = (2 + 5t, 3 + t)$
   (c) $(x - 3, y + 1) = t(2, 5)$ (d) $x = 3 - 7t$
   $\qquad\qquad\qquad\qquad\qquad\qquad\qquad\qquad y = t - 1$

8. Find vector, parametric, and symmetric equations of each line.
   (a) $x + 2y + 3 = 0$ (b) $y + 5 = 0$
   (c) $y = 4x - 3$ (d) $(x - 3, y + 2) \cdot (3, 1) = 0$

C 9. (a) Prove that two lines are perpendicular if and only if their normals are perpendicular.
   (b) Prove that two lines are parallel if and only if their normals are parallel.

10. Prove that $(\cos \beta, -\cos \alpha)$ is a normal for a line with direction angles α and β.

11. Prove that a line that makes an angle α with the horizontal can be described by an equation of the form
   $$x \sin \alpha - y \cos \alpha + k = 0$$

12. Another normal form of a line is given by $\overrightarrow{OP} \cdot \vec{n} = c$ where P is any point on the line, $\vec{n}$ is a normal for the line, and c is a scalar.
   (a) Rewrite the equation $\overrightarrow{OP} \cdot (2, -1) = 6$ as a scalar equation of the line.
   (b) Rewrite the equation $\overrightarrow{OP} \cdot (2, -1) = -5$ as a scalar equation of the line.
   (c) Describe the relationship between the line $\overrightarrow{OP} \cdot (2, -1) = 6$ and the line $\overrightarrow{OP} \cdot (2, -1) = -5$.
   (d) Describe the family of lines with equations of the form $\overrightarrow{OP} \cdot \vec{n} = c$ for c any scalar.

PROBLEMS PLUS

Partitioning a Plane

(a) What is the maximum number of regions into which two lines can partition a plane?

(b) What is the maximum number of regions into which three lines can partition a plane?

(c) What is the maximum number of regions into which four lines can partition a plane?

(d) What is the maximum number of regions into which n lines can partition a plane?

5.5 INTERSECTIONS OF LINES

One method for determining the intersection, if any, of two lines in the plane involves solving a system of two scalar equations of lines as in Exercise 2 of the Review and Preview to this chapter. However, the other forms of equations of lines in the plane and in space suggest alternate techniques for investigating intersections.

Example 1   Investigate the intersection of the lines l_1 and l_2 in the plane.

$$l_1: \quad x = 2 - 3s \qquad\qquad l_2: \quad x = 1 + 3t$$
$$\quad\;\; y = 3 + 5s \qquad\qquad\qquad\; y = 4 - 2t$$

Solution   Because the direction vectors of l_1 and l_2 are $(-3, 5)$ and $(3, -2)$, we know that l_1 and l_2 are non-parallel lines in the plane and therefore do intersect. At the point where these lines intersect, the x-coordinates and y-coordinates must be the same.

So, $2 - 3s = 1 + 3t$
and $3 + 5s = 4 - 2t$

We rewrite these equations as

$$3s + 3t = 1 \;①$$
and
$$5s + 2t = 1 \;②$$

Then we solve for the parameter t.

Alternatively, we could solve for s to find $s = \frac{1}{9}$ then using s:

$$x = 2 - 3\left(\tfrac{1}{9}\right)$$
$$= 2 - \left(\tfrac{1}{3}\right)$$
$$= \tfrac{5}{3}$$
$$y = 3 + 5\left(\tfrac{1}{9}\right)$$
$$= 3 + \tfrac{5}{9}$$
$$= \tfrac{32}{9}$$

$5 \times ①$ $15s + 15t = 5\;③$
$3 \times ②$ $15s + 6t = 3\;④$
$③ - ④$ $9t = 2$

so, $t = \tfrac{2}{9}$

Using the value for t we find the point of intersection

$$x = 1 + 3t = 1 + 3\left(\tfrac{2}{9}\right) = 1 + \tfrac{2}{3} = \tfrac{5}{3}$$
and
$$y = 4 - 2t = 4 - 2\left(\tfrac{2}{9}\right) = 4 - \tfrac{4}{9} = \tfrac{32}{9}$$

So the lines l_1 and l_2 intersect at the point $\left(\tfrac{5}{3}, \tfrac{32}{9}\right)$.

The value of this approach is that it also works for lines in space.

Example 2   Investigate the intersection of the lines l_1 and l_2 for

$$l_1: \frac{x + 5}{3} = \frac{y - 2}{2} = \frac{z + 7}{6} \quad \text{and} \quad l_2: x = \frac{y + 6}{-5} = \frac{z + 3}{-1}$$

Solution   For each line we obtain its parametric equations.

$$l_1:\ \ x = -5 + 3s \qquad\qquad l_2:\ \ x = t$$
$$y = 2 + 2s \qquad\qquad\qquad y = -6 - 5t$$
$$z = -7 + 6s \qquad\qquad\qquad z = -3 - t$$

From these sets of equations we observe that $(3, 2, 6)$ is a direction vector for l_1 and $(1, -5, -1)$ is a direction vector for l_2; hence the lines are not parallel. At any point of intersection the values of the coordinates are equal.

$$-5 + 3s = t$$
$$2 + 2s = -6 - 5t$$
$$-7 + 6s = -3 - t$$

We rewrite these equations as

$$3s - t = 5 \qquad ①$$
$$2s + 5t = -8 \qquad ②$$
$$6s + t = 4 \qquad ③$$

Solving Equations 1 and 3 for the parameter s, we obtain

$$① + ③ \quad 9s = 9$$
$$\text{so,}\ \ s = 1$$

Substituting for s in Equation 1 we obtain

$$3(1) - t = 5$$
$$3 - t = 5$$
$$\text{So,} \qquad t = -2$$

We check these values of s and t in Equation 2.

$$2(1) + 5(-2) = 2 - 10 = -8$$

Because they satisfy this equation too we conclude that there is a point of intersection for l_1 and l_2.

To find this point we substitute for s in the equations for l_1.

Using t:
$$x = -2$$
$$y = -6 - 5(-2)$$
$$= -6 + 10$$
$$= 4$$
$$z = -3 - (-2)$$
$$= -3 + 2$$
$$= -1$$

$$x = -5 + 3s = -5 + 3(1) = -5 + 3 = -2$$
$$y = 2 + 2s\ \ \ = 2 + 2(1)\ \ \ = 2 + 2\ \ \ = 4$$
$$z = -7 + 6s = -7 + 6(1) = -7 + 6 = -1$$

Thus, the lines l_1 and l_2 intersect at the point $(-2, 4, -1)$.

This method allows us to deal with a situation involving the intersection of lines in space as is illustrated in the next example. In space it is possible to have lines that are not parallel but which do not intersect (because they lie on parallel planes). Such lines are called **skew lines**.

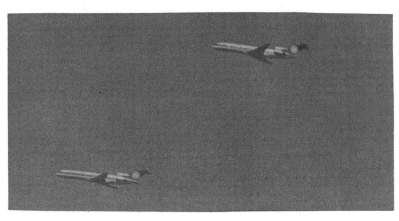

Example 3   Investigate the point of intersection of the lines l_1 and l_2 for

$$l_1: \overrightarrow{OP} = (-2, 1, 0) + s(1, 3, 7)$$

and $$l_2: \frac{x - 3}{5} = \frac{y + 3}{-4} = \frac{4 - z}{2}$$

Solution   The vector $(1, 3, 7)$ is a direction vector for l_1 and the vector $(5, -4, -2)$ is a direction vector for l_2; so, the lines are not parallel. We obtain parametric equations for the lines.

$$
\begin{array}{ll}
l_1: & x = -2 + s \\
& y = 1 + 3s \\
& z = 7s
\end{array}
\qquad
\begin{array}{ll}
l_2: & x = 3 + 5t \\
& y = -3 - 4t \\
& z = 4 - 2t
\end{array}
$$

At any intersection point

$$
\begin{aligned}
-2 + s &= 3 + 5t \\
1 + 3s &= -3 - 4t \\
7s &= 4 - 2t
\end{aligned}
$$

We rewrite these equations as

$$
\begin{aligned}
s - 5t &= 5 & \text{①} \\
3s + 4t &= -4 & \text{②} \\
7s + 2t &= 4 & \text{③}
\end{aligned}
$$

Then we solve for the parameter t using Equations 1 and 2.

$$
\begin{aligned}
3 \times \text{①} \qquad 3s - 15t &= 15 \qquad \text{④} \\
\text{④} - \text{②} \qquad -19t &= 19 \\
t &= -1
\end{aligned}
$$

so,

Substituting for t in Equation 1 we find

$$
\begin{aligned}
s - 5(-1) &= 5 \\
s + 5 &= 5
\end{aligned}
$$

So, $$s = 0$$

Next we check these values for s and t in Equation 3.

$$7(0) + 2(-1) = 0 - 2 = -2 \neq 4$$

Because these values do not satisfy all three equations we conclude that there is no point of intersection for these lines; that is, l_1 and l_2 are skew lines.

EXERCISE 5.5

A **1.** Which pairs of lines are parallel?

	line l_1	**line l_2**
(a)	$x = 3 - t$	$x = s + 2$
	$y = 5 - 3t$	$y = 3s - 1$

    (b) $(x-2, y+3, z) = t(1, 2, -3)$ $x = 2r,\ y = r,\ z = 1 - 3r$

    (c) $\dfrac{x+5}{2} = 2 - y = \dfrac{z+1}{5}$ $\overrightarrow{OP} = (2t-5, 2-t, 5t-1)$

B **2.** Identify any pair(s) of lines in Question 1 that are parallel but not identical.

3. Find the point of intersection of lines l_1 and l_2 where
$$l_1: (x-1, y) = r(3, 4) \quad \text{and} \quad l_2: (x-5, y+1) = s(-1, -1)$$

4. Investigate the intersection of the line $\overrightarrow{OP} = (1, 7) + t(3, 7)$ with each of the lines:

    (a) $(x-2, y+5) = r(3, 7)$ (b) $x = 5s$
                                             $y = 7s$

    (c) $x - 4 = \dfrac{1-y}{2}$ (d) $(x, y) \cdot (7, -1) = 5$

5. Find the point of intersection, if any exists, of the two lines.

    $x = 9 + 4t$ $x = 3r - 2$
    $y = 3$ $y = 6 - 3r$
    $z = 4 + 2t$ $z = r - 1$

6. Investigate the intersection of the line
$(x-7, y-12, z-17) = r(2, -4, 5)$ with each of the lines.

    (a) $\overrightarrow{OP} = (3, 1, -1) + s(2, 1, -3)$

    (b) $\dfrac{x+1}{2} = \dfrac{y-3}{-4} = \dfrac{z}{5}$

    (c) $x = 0$ (d) $x = 3 - t$
        $y = 4 + 3k$ $y = 2 - t$
        $z = 1 - 2k$ $z = t$

7. Prove that the lines described by $(x-1, y-4, z) = r(-4, 2, 6)$ and $(x+3, y-3, z) = s(0, 1, 2)$ lie in the same plane. [Hint: Show that the lines intersect.]

8. Find all values of k for which the lines do not intersect.

(a) $\dfrac{x-1}{2} = \dfrac{y}{4}$ and $\dfrac{x+2}{k} = \dfrac{y+3}{2}$

(b) $(x-2, y+1, z-3) = (r, 0, 3r)$ and
$\overrightarrow{OP} = (2, 1, 4) + s(2, k, 6)$

5.6 DISTANCES BETWEEN LINES

In the previous section, through investigating the intersection of lines, we realized that there are several possible relationships between two lines in space. Two lines in space may be:

1. parallel and identical,

2. parallel and non-identical,

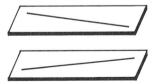

3. non-parallel and intersecting, or

4. non-parallel and non-intersecting (that is, skew lines).

In the first and third cases the distance between the lines is zero. In the other cases however, the distance is non-zero. In this section we develop methods for determining how far apart such lines are.

In preparation for finding distances between lines we find the distance from a point A to a line l. Our method involves vector techniques, specifically projections, from earlier chapters. We pick a point X on the line l. Next we find the magnitude P of the projection of $\overrightarrow{AX}$ on l. Combining this in the Pythagorean Theorem with the magnitude of $\overrightarrow{AX}$ gives us the distance from the point A to the line l.

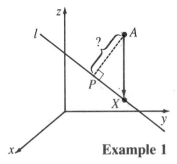

Example 1 Find the distance from the point $A(1, 2, 3)$ to the line l where l is given by l: $(x, y, z) = (0, 1, 5) + t(3, 4, 1)$.

Solution Consider any point X on the line l. We use the point $X(0, 1, 5)$. Next consider the vector $\overrightarrow{AX} = (0-1, 1-2, 5-3) = (-1, -1, 2)$ and $\vec{d} = (3, 4, 1)$ a direction vector for l.

We find the length p of the projection of $\overrightarrow{AX}$ on $\vec{d}$.

$$p = \left|\operatorname{proj}_{\vec{d}} \overrightarrow{AX}\right| = \frac{\left|\overrightarrow{AX} \cdot \vec{d}\right|}{\left|\vec{d}\right|}$$

$$= \frac{\left|(-1,-1,2) \cdot (3,4,1)\right|}{\sqrt{3^2 + 4^2 + 1^2}}$$

$$= \frac{\left|-3 - 4 + 2\right|}{\sqrt{9 + 16 + 1}}$$

$$= \frac{5}{\sqrt{26}}$$

We also require the length of $\overrightarrow{AX}$:

$$\left|\overrightarrow{AX}\right| = \sqrt{(-1)^2 + (-1)^2 + 2^2}$$
$$= \sqrt{6}$$

Then, if D is the distance between A and the line l

$$p^2 + D^2 = \left|\overrightarrow{AX}\right|^2$$

So $$\left(\frac{5}{\sqrt{26}}\right)^2 + D^2 = (\sqrt{6})^2$$

that is, $$\tfrac{25}{26} + D^2 = 6$$

So, $$D^2 = \frac{156 - 25}{26} = \frac{131}{26}$$

Thus, $$D = \sqrt{\tfrac{131}{26}} \doteq 2.2$$

So, the point A is about 2.2 units from the line l.

Note: The *distance between two lines* is understood to be the perpendicular distance between the lines.

The method for finding the distance from a point to a line can be adapted to find the distance between two parallel lines. We simply pick a point on one of the lines, then proceed as in the previous situation.

Example 2 Find the distance between the lines l_1 and l_2 where

$$l_1: \quad x = 4 + 3s \qquad\qquad l_2: \quad x = 1 + 3t$$
$$ \quad y = -7 \qquad\qquad\qquad \quad y = 4$$
$$ \quad z = 1 + 2s \qquad\qquad \quad z = 5 + 2t$$

Solution Both lines have direction vector $(3,0,2)$ and, thus, are parallel. Choose the point $A(4,-7,1)$ on the line l_1. We will find the distance from A to l_2.

We select the point $X(1,4,5)$ on l_2 and $\vec{d} = (3,0,2)$ a direction vector of the lines.

Then $\overrightarrow{AX} = (1-4, 4-(-7), 5-1) = (-3, 11, 4)$

We find the length p of the projection of $\overrightarrow{AX}$ on $\vec{d}$.

$$p = \left|\text{proj}_{\vec{d}}\, \overrightarrow{AX}\right| = \frac{\left|\overrightarrow{AX} \cdot \vec{d}\right|}{\left|\vec{d}\right|}$$

$$= \frac{\left|(-3, 11, 4) \cdot (3, 0, 2)\right|}{\sqrt{3^2 + 0^2 + 2^2}}$$

$$= \frac{\left|-9 + 0 + 8\right|}{\sqrt{9 + 0 + 4}}$$

$$= \frac{1}{\sqrt{13}}$$

Also, $\left|\overrightarrow{AX}\right| = \sqrt{(-3)^2 + 11^2 + 4^2}$

$$= \sqrt{9 + 121 + 16}$$

$$= \sqrt{146}$$

If D is the distance between the lines then

$$p^2 + D^2 = \left|\overrightarrow{AX}\right|^2$$

$$\tfrac{1}{13} + D^2 = 146$$

So, $\qquad D = \sqrt{\dfrac{1898 - 1}{13}} \doteq 12.1$

Thus, the distance between l_1 and l_2 is about 12.1.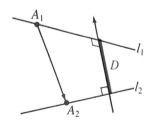

Finally, in order to find the distance between skew lines l_1 and l_2, we adapt the method slightly. We take the cross product $\vec{d}_1 \times \vec{d}_2$ of direction vectors of the lines to produce a vector perpendicular to both lines (a *normal to the lines*). Then we choose points A_1 and A_2 on each line and project the position vector $\overrightarrow{A_1A_2}$ onto the normal vector $\vec{d}_1 \times \vec{d}_2$. The length D of this projection is the distance between the lines.

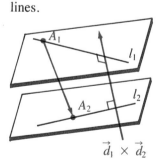

Example 3 For lines l_1 and l_2 given by the following equations

$$l_1: x - 1 = y = z \qquad\qquad l_2: \frac{x}{2} = 1 - y = z$$

(a) show that l_1 and l_2 are skew lines, and

(b) find the distance between l_1 and l_2.

Solution   (a) The direction vectors $\vec{d_1} = (1, 1, 1)$ and $\vec{d_2} = (2, -1, 1)$ are not parallel so the lines are not parallel.

In order to show that l_1 and l_2 are skew lines we attempt to find the intersection of these lines.

We rewrite the equations of both lines as parametric equations.

$$l_1: \quad x = 1 + t \qquad\qquad\qquad l_2: \quad x = 2s$$
$$y = t \qquad\qquad\qquad\qquad\qquad y = 1 - s$$
$$z = t \qquad\qquad\qquad\qquad\qquad z = s$$

At a point of intersection of l_1 and l_2

$$1 + t = 2s$$
$$t = 1 - s$$

and
$$t = s$$

that is,
$$2s - t = 1 \qquad ①$$
$$s + t = 1 \qquad ②$$
$$s - t = 0 \qquad ③$$

We solve ② and ③ for s and t.

$$② + ③ \qquad 2s = 1$$

so
$$s = \tfrac{1}{2}$$

and
$$t = \tfrac{1}{2} \qquad \text{(substitute for } s \text{ in ③)}$$

Substituting these values in Equation 1 we obtain

$$2(\tfrac{1}{2}) - \tfrac{1}{2} = \tfrac{1}{2} \neq 1$$

Thus there is no intersection for these lines; that is, l_1 and l_2 are skew lines.

(b) Direction vectors for the lines are $\vec{d_1} = (1, 1, 1)$ and $\vec{d_2} = (2, -1, 1)$.

So, $\vec{n} = (1, 1, 1) \times (2, -1, 1)$
$$= (2, 1, -3)$$

Point $A_1(1, 0, 0)$ is on l_1 and point $A_2(0, 1, 0)$ is on l_2.

We consider $\overrightarrow{A_1A_2} = (0 - 1, 1 - 0, 0 - 0) = (-1, 1, 0)$.

Then $\left| \text{proj}_{\vec{n}} \, \overrightarrow{A_1A_2} \right| = \dfrac{\left| \overrightarrow{A_1A_2} \cdot \vec{n} \right|}{\left| \vec{n} \right|}$

$$= \dfrac{\left| (-1, 1, 0) \cdot (2, 1, -3) \right|}{\sqrt{2^2 + 1^2 + (-3)^2}}$$

$$= \dfrac{1}{\sqrt{14}}$$

$$\doteq 0.3$$

So the distance between the lines is about 0.3.

EXERCISE 5.6

B **1.** Find a normal for each line.

(a) $2x - 5y = 1$

(b) $(x - 2, y) = r(3, -1)$

(c) $\overrightarrow{OP} = (1, 0, -1) + s(2, 0, 1)$

(d) $\dfrac{x - 2}{3} = 2 - y = \dfrac{z + 1}{5}$

2. Calculate the cross product $\vec{u} \times \vec{v}$ for the given vectors.

(a) $\vec{u} = (1, 0, 5)$, $\vec{v} = (-2, 7, 1)$

(b) $\vec{u} = (2, 3, -1)$, $\vec{v} = (0, 2, 5)$

3. Find the distance from the point $(0, 4, 1)$ to each of the following lines.

(a) the line $\overrightarrow{OP} = (1, 0, 5) + r(-1, 0, 1)$

(b) the line $x = 4 - 2s$, $y = 3 + s$, $z = 5s$

(c) the line $\dfrac{1 - x}{2} = \dfrac{y + 1}{3} = \dfrac{z - 1}{4}$

4. The method of Example 1 can be applied to find the distance from a point to a line in the plane.

(a) Give the coordinates of one point, call it point X, on the line $l: x = 3 + s$, $y = 1 - 3s$.

(b) For the point $A(1, -2)$ find the magnitude of the projection of $\overrightarrow{AX}$ on the direction vector $(1, -3)$ of the line l.

(c) Draw a graph showing points A and X, the line l, and the projection of $\overrightarrow{AX}$ on l.

(d) On the graph label the perpendicular distance from A to l as D.

(e) Use the Pythagorean Theorem to calculate D, the distance from the point A to the line l.

5. Using the method of Question 4, find the distance from the point $(-1, 5)$ to each line in the plane.

(a) the line $x = 2 - 5t$, $y = 3t$

(b) the line $\overrightarrow{OP} = (4, 2) + r(-1, 1)$

(c) the line $\dfrac{x - 2}{3} = 4 - y$

6. It is also possible to find the distance from a point to a line in the same plane using a normal to the line and a point on the line.

(a) Find a normal $\vec{n}$ to the line $2x - 3y = 5$.

(b) Choose one point, call it X, on the line $2x - 3y = 5$.

(c) Draw a graph showing the line $2x - 3y = 5$, its normal $\vec{n}$, the point X, and the point $A(3, 1)$.

(d) Find the magnitude of the projection of $\overrightarrow{AX}$ on $\vec{n}$.

(e) What is the connection between the quantity found in (d) and the perpendicular distance from the point A to the line l?

7. Using the method of Question 6 find the distance of the point $A(3, 5)$ from each line.
   (a) the line through $(1, 3)$ with normal $\vec{n} = (-2, 1)$
   (b) the line $3x - y = 2$
   (c) the line $x = 2 + 3s$, $y = 5$
   (d) the line $(x + 2, y - 1) = r(1, 0)$

8. Find the distance between the indicated parallel lines in space.
   (a) l_1: $(x - 2, y, z + 1) = r(3, 0, -2)$
      l_2: $x = 1 + 3s$, $y = 4$, $z = 5 - 2s$
   (b) l_1: $(x, y, z) = (0, 1, 2) + t(1, -1, 2)$
      l_2: $x - 2 = 2 - y = \dfrac{z - 3}{2}$
   (c) l_1: the x-axis l_2: $(x, y, z) = (1 + 2t, 3, 2)$

9. The method of Example 2, as used in Question 8, can be adapted to find the distance between parallel lines in the plane.
   (a) Select a point, X, on the line l_1: $(x, y) = (2, -1) + t(0, 3)$.
   (b) Find the distance from the point X to the line l_2: $x = 4$, $y = 2 +$ and, hence, the distance between the parallel lines l_1 and l_2.

10. For each pair of lines,
    (i)   verify that the lines are skew lines, and
    (ii) find the distance between the (skew) lines.
    (a) l_1: $(x, y, z) = (-2, 1, 0) + s(1, 3, 7)$
       l_2: $\dfrac{x - 1}{5} = \dfrac{y + 3}{-4} = \dfrac{4 - z}{2}$
    (b) l_1: $x = 2 + 2t$
           $y = -1 + 10t$
           $z = 7 + 5t$
       l_2: $\overrightarrow{OP} = (2, 1, 23) + s(-2, 22, 17)$

11. For each pair of lines in space, determine whether or not they are parallel, intersecting, or skew. Then, if they do not intersect, apply a suitable method to find the distance between them.
    (a) $x - 1 = \dfrac{2 - y}{3} = \dfrac{z + 3}{4}$
       and $x = -2t$, $y = 5 + 6t$, $z = -7 - 8t$
    (b) $\overrightarrow{OP} = (-1, 1, -7) + p(3, 4, -7)$
       and $(x - 16, y - 19, z + 12) = q(2, -2, 23)$
    (c) $\dfrac{x - 3}{3} = 1 - y = \dfrac{z - 7}{2}$
       and $\dfrac{x - 1}{2} = \dfrac{y + 3}{4} = \dfrac{4 - z}{3}$
    (d) $(x, y, z) = (2, 3, 1) + r(2, 1, -1)$
       and $x = -3 + s$, $y = 2$, $z = 5$

C 12. Using the technique of Question 6, develop a formula for the distance from a point A to a line in the plane given its normal $\vec{n} = (n_1, n_2)$ and one point X on the line.

13. (a) Find the distance from the origin to the line $x + 2y = 5$.

  (b) Write the equation of the line in (a) in the form $\overrightarrow{OP} \cdot \vec{n} = c$ (the normal form of the line).

  (c) Repeat (a) and (b) for the line $3x - 7y = 2$.

  (d) If an equation of the form $\overrightarrow{OP} \cdot \vec{n} = c$ is a scalar equation of a line in the plane, what is the significance of the constant c?

  (e) For each set of information given produce equations for two different lines that have the specified normal and are c units from the origin.

  (i) $\vec{n} = (3, 5)$, $c = 2$ (ii) $\vec{n} = (1, -6)$, $c = 5$

5.7 REVIEW EXERCISE

1. Find a direction vector of each line.

  (a) the line through $P(2, 5)$ and $Q(3, -4)$

  (b) a line with slope $\frac{3}{7}$

  (c) a line parallel to $\overrightarrow{OP} = (2 + 3s, 1 - 5s, 9s)$

2. Find vector and symmetric equations of each line.

  (a) the line through $(2, 0, 5)$ and $(3, 6, -1)$

  (b) the line with x-intercept -5, perpendicular to the line

$$x = 1 + s$$
$$y = 2s - 5$$

3. Find parametric equations of each line.

  (a) the line passing through $(2, -7, 1)$ parallel to

$$\frac{x - 2}{5} = \frac{y - 4}{3} = \frac{1 - z}{2},$$

  (b) the line $2x - y + 9 = 0$

4. Find a normal for each line.

  (a) the line $3x = 2y - 7$

  (b) the line $(x, y) = (1, 0) + r(2, -5)$

5. Develop a scalar equation for each line.

  (a) the line through the origin with normal $\vec{n} = (6, -1)$

  (b) the line with same y-intercept as $4x + 10y = 3$, direction numbers -4 and 1

  (c) the line $x = 2 + s$, $y = 1 - 3s$

6. Develop vector and scalar equations for each line.

  (a) the line through $(2, -4)$ perpendicular to the line $2x - y = 5$

  (b) the line $\dfrac{x - 2}{3} = \dfrac{7 - y}{5}$

7. Fine two (additional) points on each line.
   (a) the line $(x-2, y+3, z+4) = t(1, -2, 7)$
   (b) the line $3x + 5y = 2$
   (c) the line $x = 2 + s$
   $$y = -1$$
   $$z = 5s - 3$$
   (d) The line through $(1, 0, 5)$ and $(3, -1, 2)$

8. Determine whether the two equations describe the same line.
   (a) l_1: $(x-8, y-1) = t(3, -4)$ l_2: $\dfrac{x-1}{3} = \dfrac{2-y}{4}$

   (b) l_1: $\dfrac{x-4}{2} = y + 1 = 2 - z$ l_2: $x = 6 - 2r$
   $$y = -4 - r$$
   $$z = 3 + r$$

   (c) l_1: $x - 2 = \dfrac{y}{2} = \dfrac{z+1}{3}$
   l_2: $(x, y, z) = (2, 0, -1) + t(-1, 2, 3)$

   (d) l_1: $x = 1 + 3t$ l_2: $\dfrac{x+2}{3} = y + 2 = \dfrac{z-1}{4}$
   $$y = -2$$
   $$z = 5 + 4t$$

9. Find direction cosines and angles of each line.
   (a) the line $\overrightarrow{OP} = (2, -1, 4) + r(3, 1, 0)$
   (b) the line $\dfrac{2-x}{3} = \dfrac{y+1}{5} = \dfrac{6-z}{2}$
   (c) the line $3x + 5y + 2 = 0$.

10. A line in space has direction angles $\alpha = \dfrac{2\pi}{3}$, β where $0 \leqslant \beta \leqslant \dfrac{\pi}{2}$,

    and $\gamma = \dfrac{\pi}{4}$. If the line passes through the point $(2, -1, 5)$ give

    parametric equations for the line.

11. Determine the intersection of each pair of lines, if it exists.
    (a) $(x, y) = (2, 5) + r(1, -2)$ and $(x, y) = (1, 0) + s(3, 1)$
    (b) $x = 1 + 3s$ and $x = -t$
    $$y = 5s \qquad\qquad y = 2t - 9$$
    $$z = 4s - 3 \qquad\quad z = -1 - 3t$$
    (c) $\overrightarrow{OP} = (-2, 1, 0) + s(1, 3, 7)$ and $x = 1 + 5t$,
    $$y = -3 - 4t,$$
    $$z = 4 - 2t$$

12. Show that the lines $\dfrac{x+5}{3} = \dfrac{y-2}{2} = \dfrac{z+7}{6}$ and

    $(x, y, z) = (0, -6, -3) + r(-1, 5, 1)$ lie in the same plane.
    [Hint: Are they parallel? Investigate their intersection.]

13. Find the distance from the point A to the line l.

   (a) $A(0, 2)$ $l: (x, y) = \left(\frac{1}{2}, \frac{1}{2}\right) + t(4, -3)$

   (b) $A(1, -2, -3)$ $l: x = y = z - 2$

   (c) $A(8, 3, -2)$ $l: \dfrac{x - 4}{2} = y + 1 = 2 - z$

14. Find the distance between each pair of lines.

   (a) $l_1: (x, y) = (2 + r, 5 - r)$

        $l_2: (x, y) = \left(\frac{3}{2}, 6\right) + s(1, -1)$

   (b) $l_1: \dfrac{x - 2}{3} = \dfrac{y + 4}{5} = z - 3$

        $l_2: x = 5t, \ y = t - 6, \ z = 5$

   (c) $l_1: (x + 2, y - 2, z - 1) = r(7, 3, -4)$

        $l_2: x = 2 + 7t, \ y = 3t - 1, \ z = -4t - 2$

5.8 CHAPTER 5 TEST

1. Find vector and scalar equations of the line through the point $(4, 1)$ and parallel to the line $\dfrac{x-3}{2} = \dfrac{y}{7}$.

2. Find parametric equations of the line through the points $R(3, -1, 0)$ and $S(2, 11, -5)$.

3. Determine whether or not both equations describe the same line.
   (i) $(x-2, y+3, z+4) = r(1, -2, 7)$
   (ii) $\overrightarrow{OP} = (1, -1, 0) + s(-1, 2, 7)$

4. Develop a scalar equation for the line perpendicular to the line $2x - 3y = 5$, with the same x-intercept as the line $(x, y) = (0, 1) + t(-3, 4)$.

5. Find the direction angles of the line
   $$x = 2 - 3t,\ y = 4t,\ z = 2t - .5$$

6. Investigate the intersection of the pair of lines.
   $$l_1:\ (x, y, z) = (1, 2, 1) + r(1, -1, -1)$$
   $$l_2:\ (x, y, z) = (0, 2, -5) + s(0, 1, -1)$$

7. Find the distances:
   (a) from the point $A(5, 4, 2)$ to the line $x = s$
   $$y = 5 + 2s$$
   $$z = 3 + 3s$$

   (b) between the (parallel) lines
   $$l_1:\ \overrightarrow{OP} = (1, 1, -1) + r(2, -3, 6)$$
   $$l_2:\ \overrightarrow{OP} = (9, 0, 4) + s(2, -3, 6)$$

8. Prove that, if a, b, and c are direction numbers for the line l, $c \geqslant 0$ then the direction cosines of l are given by
   $$\cos \alpha = \frac{a}{d},\ \cos \beta = \frac{b}{d},\ \cos \gamma = \frac{c}{d}\quad \text{where}$$
   $$d = \sqrt{a^2 + b^2 + c^2}.$$

PROBLEMS PLUS

Distance from a point to a line

Show that the distance from the point A to the line through points B and C is

$$\frac{\left| \overrightarrow{OA} \times \overrightarrow{OB} + \overrightarrow{OB} \times \overrightarrow{OC} + \overrightarrow{OC} \times \overrightarrow{OA} \right|}{\left| \overrightarrow{OB} - \overrightarrow{OC} \right|} \qquad \text{for origin } O.$$

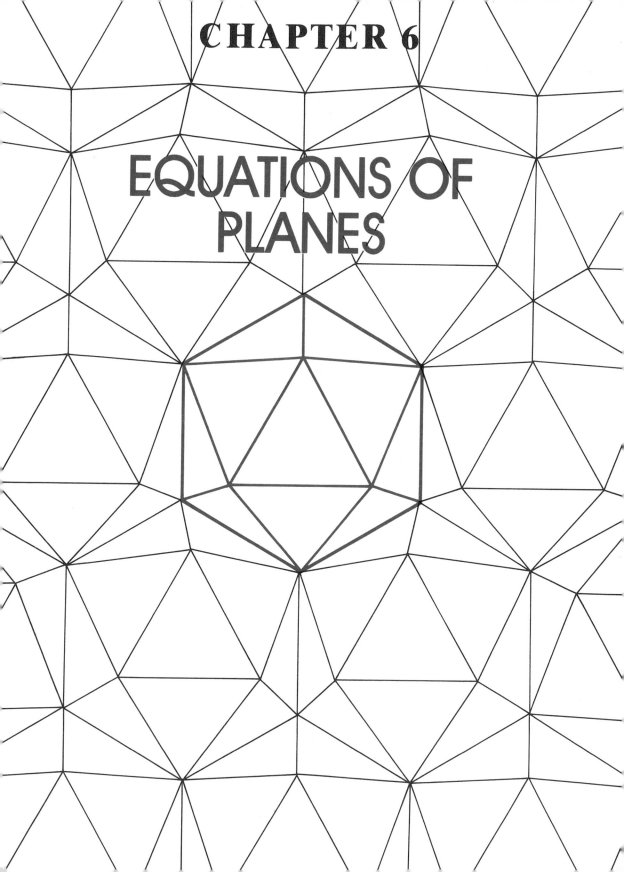

CHAPTER 6

EQUATIONS OF PLANES

REVIEW AND PREVIEW TO
CHAPTER 6

EXERCISE 1 　　　　**Satisfying an Equation**

---

1. Is the point P on the given line?
   (a) $(x-7, y+1) = r(3,0)$; $P(10, -1)$
   (b) $\dfrac{x-4}{2} = y + 1 = 2 - z$; $P(14, 4, -3)$
   (c) $x = 1 + 3r$, $y = -5r$, $z = r + 1$; $P(-5, 5, -1)$
   (d) $(x, y, z) = (1, 3, -5) + s(0, 0, 1)$; $P(1, 3, -1)$

2. Is the ordered triple (x, y, z) a solution of the equation?
   (a) $3x + y + 2z = 6$; $(1, 1, 1)$
   (b) $2x + 3y - z = 10$; $(3, 2, 1)$
   (c) $4x - 2y + 3z = -9$; $(0, 3, -1)$
   (d) $2x - 3y - z = -5$; $(-2, 1, -2)$

EXERCISE 2 　　　　**Collinear and Coplanar Vectors**

---

1. Determine whether the vectors are collinear.
   (a) $\vec{u} = (3, -2)$ 　　　　　　$\vec{v} = (4, 6)$
   (b) $\vec{u} = (1, -2, 5)$ 　　　　$\vec{v} = (-1, 2, -5)$
   (c) $\vec{u} = (0, 0, 5)$ 　　　　　$\vec{v} = (0, 0, 2)$
   (d) $\vec{u} = (12, 15, -3)$ 　　　$\vec{v} = (-8, -10, 2)$

2. Determine whether the vectors are coplanar by attempting to write one vector as a linear combination of the other two.
   (a) $\vec{u} = (3, 5)$ 　　　　$\vec{v} = (1, 0)$ 　　　$\vec{w} = (0, -1)$
   (b) $\vec{u} = (2, 2, -5)$ 　$\vec{v} = (1, 1, 0)$ 　$\vec{w} = (0, 0, 1)$
   (c) $\vec{u} = (3, 1, 1)$ 　　$\vec{v} = (0, 1, 1)$ 　$\vec{w} = (1, 1, 0)$
   (d) $\vec{u} = (10, -3, 1)$ $\vec{v} = (1, 3, -2)$ $\vec{w} = (4, 1, -1)$

3. Determine whether the vectors are coplanar by calculating $(\vec{u} \times \vec{v}) \cdot \vec{w}$. Recall: Vectors $\vec{u}, \vec{v},$ and $\vec{w}$ are coplanar if and only if $(\vec{u} \times \vec{v}) \cdot \vec{w} = 0$.]
   (a) $\vec{u} = (2, 3, -5)$ 　　$\vec{v} = (1, 0, 0)$ 　　$\vec{w} = (0, 1, 0)$
   (b) $\vec{u} = (-3, 11, -16)$ $\vec{v} = (1, 3, -4)$ $\vec{w} = (2, 1, -1)$

INTRODUCTION

In this chapter we extend the ideas from Chapter 5 as we explore several forms of equations of planes. The skill of recognition of various forms of equations for the same plane is developed, as is a technique for finding the distance from a point to a plane. The main thrust of the chapter is an investigation of the possibilities for the intersection of lines with planes and planes with each other. After considering geometric interpretations of these situations, we give an algebraic scheme for the classification of systems of linear equations based on the nature of the solution of the system.

6.1 EQUATIONS OF PLANES

In order to determine a plane it is enough to specify either of the following sets of information:

1.   three non-collinear points on the plane

or

2.   one point on the plane and two non-collinear direction vectors.

Using two independent direction vectors $\vec{d_1}$ and $\vec{d_2}$ for a plane to specify its "slant" and one point P_0 on the plane to fix its location in space we can develop a vector equation describing any point P on the plane.

Example 1   Develop a vector equation for the plane through the point $P_0(-3, 5, 0)$ with direction vectors $\vec{d_1} = (1, 2, -1)$ and $\vec{d_2} = (3, -1, 4)$.

Solution   We pick any point $P(x, y, z)$ on the plane.

Because P is on the plane the vector $\overrightarrow{P_0P}$, from P_0 to P, can be written as a linear combination of the independent direction vectors $(1, 2, -1)$ and $(3, -1, 4)$. Thus

$$\overrightarrow{P_0P} = s\vec{d_1} + t\vec{d_2}$$

or $(x+3, y-5, z-0) = s(1, 2, -1) + t(3, -1, 4)$ $s, t \in R$

is a vector equation of the plane through point $(-3, 5, 0)$ with direction vectors $(1, 2, -1)$ and $(3, -1, 4)$.

Note that use of a different point on the plane or different direction vectors for the plane may produce a different equation for the same plane. For instance, in Example 1, use of direction vectors $(2, 4, -2)$ and $(-3, 1, -4)$ which are parallel to the original direction vectors would produce the equation

$$(x+3, y-5, z-0) = s(2, 4, -2) + t(-3, 1, -4)$$

We investigate this situation later in this section.

The technique of Example 1 can be followed to find the general form of a vector equation of the plane through the point $P_0(x_0, y_0, z_0)$ with independent direction vectors $\vec{d} = (d_1, d_2, d_3)$ and $\vec{e} = (e_1, e_2, e_3)$.

For any point $P(x, y, z)$ on the plane, the vector $\overrightarrow{P_0P}$, from P_0 to P, is on the plane and can be written as a linear combination of its two independent direction vectors $\vec{d}$ and $\vec{e}$.

A Vector Equation of the Plane

through P_0 with direction vectors $\vec{d}$ and $\vec{e}$ is
$$\overrightarrow{P_0P} = s\vec{d} + t\vec{e}$$
for real numbers s and t.

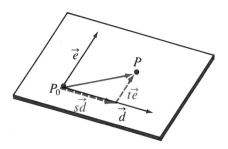

Using this form we can develop an alternative form of the vector equation. This could be called the *position vector form* of the equation of the plane.

$$\overrightarrow{OP} = \overrightarrow{OP}_0 + \overrightarrow{P_0P}$$

so
$$\overrightarrow{OP} = \overrightarrow{OP}_0 + s\vec{d} + t\vec{e}$$

or
$$(x, y, z) = (x_0, y_0, z_0) + s(d_1, d_2, d_3) + t(e_1, e_2, e_3)$$

Each pair (s, t) of real values of the scalars in this equation corresponds to a point on the plane. There scalars are called the **parameters** for the equation of the plane. Another alternative form of an equation of a plane that emphasizes how each coordinate is related to the parameters can be easily derived from the position vector form of a vector equation of the plane by using equality of algebraic vectors.

Parametric Equations of the Plane

through $P_0(x_0, y_0, z_0)$ with direction vectors $\vec{d} = (d_1, d_2, d_3)$ and $\vec{e} = (e_1, e_2, e_3)$ are

$$x = x_0 + sd_1 + te_1$$
$$y = y_0 + sd_2 + te_2$$
$$z = z_0 + sd_3 + te_3$$

Example 2   Find vector and parametric equations of the plane through points $A(1,7,2)$, $B(4,0,-1)$, and $C(1,2,3)$.

Solution   One direction vector for this plane is

$$\vec{d} = \overrightarrow{AB} = (4-1, 0-7, -1-2) = (3, -7, -3)$$

Another is given by

$$\vec{e} = \overrightarrow{AC} = (1-1, 2-7, 3-2) = (0, -5, 1)$$

Using A as a point on the plane we obtain a vector equation of the plane

$$\overrightarrow{OP} = (1,7,2) + s(3, -7, -3) + t(0, -5, 1)$$

From the vector equation we can obtain parametric equations. Because $\overrightarrow{OP} = (x, y, z) = (1,7,2) + s(3, -7, -3) + t(0, -5, 1)$,

$$x = 1 + 3s$$
$$y = 7 - 7s - 5t$$
$$z = 2 - 3s + t$$

are parametric equations for the plane through A, B, and C.

Example 3   Find three points on each plane.
(a)   The plane with vector equation
$$\overrightarrow{OP} = (0,4,2) + s(5, -2, 3) + t(1,0,1)$$
(b)   The plane with parametric equations
$$x = 1 + 4r + 3s \quad y = -3r + s \quad z = 1 - 2r$$

Solution   Each point on the plane corresponds to a pair of values for the two parameters.

(a)

value of s	value of t	point
1	1	$(0,4,2) + 1(5, -2, 3) + 1(1,0,1) = (6,2,6)$
1	0	$(0,4,2) + 1(5, -2, 3) + 0(1,0,1) = (5,2,5)$
-1	3	$(0,4,2) + (-1)(5, -2, 3) + 3(1,0,1) = (-2,6,2)$

(b)

r	s	x	y	z	point
0	1	$1 + 4(0) + 3(1) = 4$	$-3(0) + (1) = 1$	$1 - 2(0) = 1$	$(4,1,1)$
1	1	$1 + 4(1) + 3(1) = 8$	$-3(1) + (1) = -2$	$1 - 2(1) = -1$	$(8, -2, -1)$
-1	0	$1 + 4(-1) + 3(0) = -3$	$-3(-1) + (0) = 3$	$1 - 2(-1) = 3$	$(-3,3,3)$

With so many variations of equations of planes it becomes useful to be able to distinguish between different equations of the same plane and equations of different planes. By recognizing that each point on the plane must correspond to a value of the parameter, it is possible to compare such equations to decide whether they describe the same plane. We first determine whether or not the planes are parallel. In order to do this we introduce the concept of a normal to a plane.

> A **normal (vector) to a plane** π is a vector $\vec{n}$ that is perpendicular to every vector in the plane.

It is not as difficult as it might at first appear to check that a given vector is normal to a specified plane. In fact, if a vector $\vec{n}$ is perpendicular to any two independent vectors in a plane then it is a normal to the plane.

Proof

Consider a vector $\vec{n}$. We choose any vector $\vec{v}$ in a plane π and two independent vectors $\vec{u}$ and $\vec{w}$ that are perpendicular to $\vec{n}$ and lie on the plane π. Then $\vec{u}$ and $\vec{w}$ form a basis for π;

so $\qquad \vec{v} = a\vec{u} + b\vec{w} \qquad$ for some scalars a and b.

To determine whether or not $\vec{n}$ is perpendicular to $\vec{v}$ we calculate their dot product.

$$
\begin{aligned}
\vec{n} \cdot \vec{v} &= \vec{n} \cdot (a\vec{u} + b\vec{w}) \\
&= \vec{n} \cdot a\vec{u} + \vec{n} \cdot b\vec{w} \\
&= a(\vec{n} \cdot \vec{u}) + b(\vec{n} \cdot \vec{w}) \\
&= a \cdot 0 + b \cdot 0 \\
&= 0
\end{aligned}
$$

Thus $\vec{n}$ is perpendicular to $\vec{v}$ and, therefore, to the plane π.

If planes are not parallel, then they are not identical. Parallel planes have collinear normals. If they are parallel we consider whether or not they have one point in common. If they do have a common point then they are identical planes.

Example 4   Determine whether or not both equations describe the same plane.

$\qquad \pi_1$: $(x-1, y-6, z) = r(3, -2, 1) + s(1, 0, 1)$ and

$\qquad \pi_2$: $x = 5 + 3p + 4q$

$\qquad\qquad y = 4 - 2p - 2q$

$\qquad\qquad z = 2 + p + 2q$

Solution   To decide whether planes π_1 and π_2 are parallel, we consider $\vec{n}_1$, a normal to π_1, and $\vec{n}_2$, a normal to π_2. We obtain these normals by finding the cross product of the direction vectors of each plane.

$\qquad \vec{n}_1 = (3, -2, 1) \times (1, 0, 1) \qquad \vec{n}_2 = (3, -2, 1) \times (4, -2, 2)$

$\qquad\quad = (-2, -2, 2) \qquad\qquad\qquad = (-2, -2, 2)$

Because these normals are collinear, the planes π_1 and π_2 may be identical. Setting $r = s = 0$ in the vector equation for π_1 we find that the point $(1, 6, 0)$ is on π_1. Is this point also on π_2? If so,

$$1 = 5 + 3p + 4q$$
$$6 = 4 - 2p - 2q$$
$$0 = 2 + p + 2q$$

We rewrite these equations as

$$-4 = 3p + 4q \qquad ①$$
$$2 = -2p - 2q \qquad ②$$
$$-2 = p + 2q \qquad ③$$

We solve Equations 2 and 3 for p and q.

$$② + ③ \qquad 0 = -p$$
so, $\qquad\qquad p = 0$

Substituting for p in ③ we obtain $-2 = 0 + 2q$.

Thus, $q = -1$

These values check in Equation 1:

$$-4 = 3(0) + 4(-1)$$

so $(1, 6, 0)$ is a point on the plane π_2. Thus π_1 and π_2 are identical planes although their equations look different.

EXERCISE 6.1

A **1.** Find two direction vectors for each plane.
 (a) The plane through $(2, 1, 5)$, $(1, 0, 1)$, and $(7, 0, 2)$
 (b) A plane parallel to
  $$(x-1, y-3, z-6) = r(-3, 4, 0) + s(2, -1, 3)$$
 (c) A plane parallel to the plane
  $$x = 3s + t$$
  $$y = 2 - s - 5t$$
  $$z = 1 + 2s + 3t$$
 (d) The plane through $(2, 1, 0)$, containing the line $x = t$,
  $y = 1 - 2t, z = 3t + 1$
 (e) The xz-plane

 2. Give two points on each plane.
 (a) $\overrightarrow{OP} = (2, 0, -1) + s(0, 2, -1) + t(5, 3, 4)$
 (b) $x = 3 - 2s + 4t$
  $$y = s + 2t$$
  $$z = 1 + s - 5t$$
 (c) $(x, y, z) = (3 + 5r + s, -1 + r - 2s, 4)$

3. Identify which equations describe lines in space and which describe planes.
   (a) $(x, y, z) = (1, 2, 7) + r(2, 0, 1)$
   (b) $(x-2, y, z-3) = s(1, 1, 1) + t(0, 3, 5)$
   (c) $x = 3s, \ y = 2r + s, \ z = r + s$
   (d) $\dfrac{x-1}{4} = \dfrac{2-y}{5} = 1 - z$
   (e) $x + 2 = t, \ y = t, \ z - 4 = 5t$

B 4. Give parametric equations for each plane.
   (a) $\overrightarrow{OP} = (2, 0, -2) + s(0, 1, -2) + t(3, 5, 1)$
   (b) $(x, y, z) = (3+5r+s, -1+r, 4+3s)$
   (c) $(x-4, y+0.5, z-1) = s(0, 0.75, 2) + t(1, 2.5, -1)$

5. Give a vector equation for the plane described by
$$x = 3 - s + 4t$$
$$y = 2t$$
$$z = 1 + 4s - 5t$$

6. Rewrite each equation in the form $\overrightarrow{P_0P} = s\vec{d_1} + t\vec{d_2}$.
   (a) $\overrightarrow{OP} = (2, 0, -2) + s(0, 3, -1) + t(3, 5, 1)$
   (b) $x = 3 - 2s + 4t$
   $y = 2t$
   $z = 1 + 5s$
   (c) $(x, y, z) = (3+5r-s, -1+r+2s, 4+3s)$

7. For each vector $\vec{v}$ show that it is a normal to the given plane:
   (a) $\vec{v} = (1, -5, 7)$;
   $(x, y, z) = (1, 0, 1) + r(1, 3, 2) + s(5, 1, 0)$
   (b) $\vec{v} = (-5, 2, 13)$;
   the plane through points $(0, 4, 0), (1, 0, 1), (4, 1, 2)$
   (c) $\vec{v} = (5, -1, -11)$;
   $x = 3r + 2s, \ y = 1 + 4r - s, \ z = 5 + r + s$

8. Find a normal to each plane.
   (a) $\overrightarrow{OP} = (3, 1, -6) + s(0, 1, 1) + t(-1, 2, 1)$
   (b) $x = 2 - 3r + s$
   $y = 5 + 4r$
   $z = r - 2s$

9. For each equation determine whether or not it describes the plane
$\overrightarrow{OP} = (0, 3, 2) + s(-1, 5, 2) + t(2, 4, 2)$
   (a) $\overrightarrow{OP} = (0, 3, 2) + r(1, 5, 2) + s(1, 2, 1)$
   (b) $x = 2 + s - t$
   $y = -7 - 5s - 2t$
   $z = -2 - 2s - t$
   (c) $(x+1, y-5, z-2) = s(2, 4, 2) + t(0, 3, 2)$
   (d) $\overrightarrow{OP} = (-2, 6, 3) + r(1, 2, 1) + s(1, -5, -2)$

10. Find vector and parametric equations of each plane.
    (a) The plane through the origin with direction vectors $(3, -2, 7)$ and $(0, 1, -2)$.
    (b) The plane through the points $(1, -3, 2)$, $(0, 1, -2)$, and $(9, 2, 0)$.
    (c) The plane parallel to the xy-plane through the point $(1, 3, 5)$.
    (d) The plane with z-intercept 4, parallel to the plane
    $$x = 1 + r, \; y = 2 + 3r - s, \; z = s$$

A *z-intercept* is the
z coordinate of the
point where the plane
intersects the z-axis.

11. Develop vector and parametric equations of the plane through $(3, -5, 1)$ and parallel to the plane given by
    $$x = s + 3t - 5, \quad y = 2 + s - t, \quad z = s + t - 5$$

12. Find vector and parametric equations of the plane through the point $(4, 1, -1)$ and
    (a) the points $(0, 1, 2)$ and $(1, 1, -1)$,
    (b) parallel to the plane
    $$(x-1, y-3, z+4) = r(1, 0, 1) + s(2, 1, 0),$$
    (c) containing the z-axis,
    (d) parallel to the plane $x = r + s$
    $$y = 3$$
    $$z = 1 + r + 3s$$

C 13. Show that the points $P(1, 1, 1)$, $Q(2, 3, 2)$, $R(3, -2, 5)$, and $S(4, 0, 6)$ are coplanar.

14. Using the methods of this section show that an equation of the plane through points A, B, and C is given by
    $$\overrightarrow{OP} = a\overrightarrow{OA} + b\overrightarrow{OB} + c\overrightarrow{OC}$$
    where P is any point on the plane and $a + b + c = 1$
    Note that this result (by a different method) was requested as Question 12 in Exercise 2.4.

PROBLEMS PLUS

Using one vertex of a tetrahedron as the origin, the position vectors of the other three vertices are $\vec{u}$, $\vec{v}$, and $\vec{w}$. Through each vertex a plane is drawn parallel to the opposite face. Express the position vectors of the vertices of the tetrahedron formed by these planes in terms of $\vec{u}$, $\vec{v}$, and $\vec{w}$.

6.2 SCALAR EQUATIONS OF PLANES

At the conclusion of Section 5.4 we noted that an equation of the form $Ax + By + Cz + D = 0$ describes a plane. This form of the equation of a plane is referred to as a **scalar equation of the plane** or as a **Cartesian equation of the plane**. One example of this is the equation with $A = B = D = 0$ and $C = 1$, that is, $z = 0$. This equation describes all points of the form $(x, y, 0)$; that is, the xy-plane.

A development of such an equation makes use of vector concepts.

Example 1   Develop a scalar equation of the plane through the point $P_0(4, -1, 3)$ with normal $\vec{n} = (3, 5, 2)$.

Solution   We pick any point $P(x, y, z)$ on the plane.

Because points P_0 and P are both on the plane, the vector $\overrightarrow{P_0P}$ is a vector in the direction of the plane. So, $\overrightarrow{P_0P}$ is perpendicular to $\vec{n}$.

We call $\overrightarrow{P_0P} \cdot \vec{n} = 0$ the *normal form* of the plane.

Thus, $\overrightarrow{P_0P} \cdot \vec{n} = 0$

But $\overrightarrow{P_0P} = (x-4, y+1, z-3)$

so $(x-4, y+1, x-3) \cdot (3, 5, 2) = 0$

$$3(x - 4) + 5(y + 1) + 2(z - 3) = 0$$

that is, $3x - 12 + 5y + 5 + 2z - 6 = 0$

So, $3x + 5y + 2z - 13 = 0$ is a scalar equation of the plane through the point $A(4, -1, 3)$ with normal $\vec{n} = (3, 5, 2)$.

$3x + 5y + 2z - 13 = 0$

Note the location of the components of the normal, 3, 5, and 2, in the scalar equation—as coefficients of the x-, y-, and z-terms. This is not a coincidence but a general result.

A scalar equation of the plane through the point $P_0(x_0, y_0, z_0)$ with normal $\vec{n} = (n_1, n_2, n_3)$ is given by

$$n_1x + n_2y + n_3z + D = 0$$

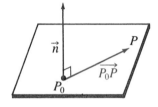

Proof

For any point $P(x, y, z)$ on the plane, vector $\overrightarrow{P_0P}$ is in the direction of the plane.

So, $\overrightarrow{P_0P} \cdot \vec{n} = 0$

$$(x - x_0, y - y_0, z - z_0) \cdot (n_1, n_2, n_3) = 0$$

$$n_1(x - x_0) + n_2(y - y_0) + n_3(z - z_0) = 0$$

$$n_1x - n_1x_0 + n_2y - n_2y_0 + n_3z - n_3z_0 = 0$$

$$n_1x + n_2y + n_3z - n_1x_0 - n_1y_0 - n_1z_0 = 0$$

The expression $-n_1x_0 - n_2y_0 - n_3z_0$ is a constant. Thus, $n_1x + n_2y + n_3z + D = 0$ is a scalar equation of this plane.

This general result allows us to obtain a scalar equation of a plane more simply given one point on the plane and a normal to the plane. We redo Example 1 with the benefit of this insight.

Example 2   Find a scalar equation of the plane through the point $P_0(4, -1, 3)$ with normal $\vec{n} = (3, 5, 2)$.

Solution   Because $\vec{n} = (3, 5, 2)$ is normal to this plane, a scalar equation of the plane can be written in the form $3x + 5y + 2z + D = 0$.
To determine the constant D we substitute the coordinates of the point P_0 into the plane's equation.

Then, $3(4) + 5(-1) + 2(3) + D = 0$
$$12 - 5 + 6 + D = 0$$
$$13 + D = 0$$
So, $$D = -13$$

Thus, $3x + 5y + 2z - 13 = 0$ is a scalar equation of the plane. ⬡

On the other hand, from a scalar equation of a plane it is always possible to identify a normal for the plane.

For a plane given by $Ax + By + Cz + D = 0$, the vector (A, B, C) is a normal for the plane.

Because the proof follows the same procedure as for the scalar equation of a line (Section 5.4) we leave it as a question in Exercise 6.2.
Once we have identified a normal vector for the plane we can rewrite the equation of a plane in scalar form.

Example 3   Rewrite the equation
$(x, y, z) = (2, -5, 1) + s(2, -3, 0) + t(1, 1, -1)$
as a scalar equation for the plane.

Solution 1   We find a normal (A, B, C) for the plane then substitute the coordinates of a point on the plane to find the value of the constant D for the scalar equation $Ax + By + Cz + D = 0$.
To find a normal we use the cross product of two non-collinear direction vectors.

$$\vec{n} = (2, -3, 0) \times (1, 1, -1)$$
$$= (3, 2, 5)$$

Thus a scalar equation of the plane is of the form
$$3x + 2y + 5z + D = 0$$

We use the point $(2, -5, 1)$ on the plane to find the value of D.

$$3(2) + 2(-5) + 5(1) + D = 0$$
$$6 - 10 + 5 + D = 0$$
$$1 + D = 0$$

So

$$D = -1$$

Thus a scalar equation of the plane is $3x + 2y + 5z - 1 = 0$.

Solution 2   This solution also relies on selecting a normal to the plane, then finding the dot product of the position vector of any point on the plane with the normal. Because the normal is perpendicular to both direction vectors their dot product is 0, the parameters are eliminated, and we obtain a scalar equation.

We use the normal $(3, 2, 5)$ as found in Solution 1. For any point (x, y, z) on the plane

$s(2, -3, 0) \cdot (3, 2, 5)$
$= t(1, 1, -1) \cdot (3, 2, 5)$
$= 0$

$$(x, y, z) = (2, -5, 1) + s(2, -3, 0) + t(1, 1, -1)$$
$$(x, y, z) \cdot (3, 2, 5) = (2, -5, 1) \cdot (3, 2, 5)$$
$$3x + 2y + 5z = 6 - 10 + 5 + 0 + 0$$

Thus $3x + 2y + 5z = 1$ is a scalar equation of the plane.

One use for the scalar equation of a plane is in finding the distance from a point to a plane.

Example 4   Find the distance from the point $A(3, -1, 1)$ to the plane $4x - 8y - z = -41$

Solution   Consider $\vec{n} = (4, -8, -1)$ a normal to the plane and one point, say $X(4, 7, 1)$, on the plane.

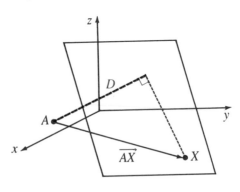

From the diagram we see that the (perpendicular) distance, D, from A to the plane is the magnitude of the projection of $\overrightarrow{AX}$ onto a vector perpendicular to the plane. For this perpendicular vector we use the normal $\vec{n}$.

$$\overrightarrow{AX} = (1, 8, 0)$$

so $\left| \text{proj}_{\vec{n}} \overrightarrow{AX} \right| = \dfrac{\left| \overrightarrow{AX} \cdot \vec{n} \right|}{\left| \vec{n} \right|}$

$$= \frac{\left| (1, 8, 0) \cdot (4, -8, -1) \right|}{\sqrt{4^2 + (-8)^2 + (-1)^2}}$$

$$= \frac{\left| 4 - 64 + 0 \right|}{\sqrt{16 + 64 + 1}}$$

$$= \frac{60}{\sqrt{81}}$$

$$= \frac{60}{9}$$

$$\doteq 6.7$$

Thus the distance from the point A to the plane is about 6.7.

EXERCISE 6.2

A **1.** Identify a normal for each plane.
   (a) $3x + 2y + z - 5 = 0$ (b) $x + y + z = 7$
   (c) $y = 3x + 2$ (d) $x + 2z = 0$
   (e) $5x - 2y - 3z = 3$ (f) $z = 3$

2. Describe the relationship between;
   (a) normals of parallel planes,
   (b) normals of perpendicular planes.

B **3.** Identify pairs of planes that are
             (i) parallel   or   (ii) perpendicular.
   (a) $2x + y - z = 4$
       $6x + 3y - 3z - 12 = 0$
   (b) $x + y = 5$
       $y = x - 6z + 3$
   (c) $(x-1, y+1, z+4) \cdot (2, -1, 5) = 0$
       $2x - y - z = 6$
   (d) $x = 3, x + 2 = 0$

4. Find a scalar equation for each plane.
   (a) The plane through $(2, -1, 1)$ with $\vec{n} = (5, 7, 0)$.
   (b) The plane through the origin parallel to $2x - 3y + z - 6 = 0$.
   (c) The plane with direction vectors $(1, 5, -2)$ and $(0, 0, 1)$ through the point $(3, 4, 1)$.
   (d) The plane parallel to the xy-plane through $(4, -1, 5)$.
   (e) The plane through points $(2, 7, 1)$, $(1, 1, 1)$, and $(1, -3, 0)$.

(f) The plane containing the line $(x, y, z) = (1, 3, -1) + r(3, 2, 2)$ and parallel to the line $x = 2 + 3s$, $y = -2s$, $z = 4$.

(g) The plane through the point $(0, 2, -1)$ and perpendicular to the line $(x, y, z) = t(3, -2, 4)$.

5. In each situation develop a scalar equation for the plane through the point A *parallel* to the plane π.

	point A	plane π
(a)	$(1, 2, 3)$	$(x-2, y+3, z) = r(3, 0, -1) + s(1, 0, 2)$
(b)	$(0, -3, 4)$	$x = 5s + 2t - 4$
		$y = 3s + 2$
		$z = 2s + t - 1$
(c)	$(2, -4, 1)$	$y = 3x - z + 5$
(d)	$(0, 0, 0)$	$\overrightarrow{OP} = (3+2s-5t, 2t, 1-3s+t)$
(e)	$(7, 0.5, 1)$	$(x-2, y, z+1) \cdot (1, 6, 2) = 0$

6. Rewrite each equation as a scalar equation of the plane.
    (a) $(x, y, z) = (1, 0, -1) + r(1, -1, 3) + s(0, 0, 1)$
    (b) $\overrightarrow{OP} = (2+3s-5t, 3+t, s+t)$
    (c) $(x-3, y+1, z-4) = r(2, 4, 0) + s(1, 2, -1)$
    (d) $x = 3 - s + 7t$
        $y = 2s + t - 1$
        $z = s - t$

7. Find vector and parametric equations of each plane.
    (a) $x + 2y + 7z - 3 = 0$
    (b) $y - z + 5 = 0$
    (c) $y = 4x + 9z - 3$
    (d) $(x-3, y+2, z) \cdot (3, 1, -5) = 0$

8. Prove that the vector (A, B, C) is a normal for the plane
$$Ax + By + Cz + D = 0$$

9. Find the distance from the point $A(1, 2, 3)$ to each plane.
    (a) $3x + y - z = 5$ (b) $2x - 3y + 6z = 5$
    (c) $x + 4y - 3z = 0$ (d) $9x + y + z + 7 = 0$

10. Find the distance from the origin to the plane through the points $(0, 1, 5)$, $(2, -1, 4)$, and $(3, 0, 7)$.

C 11. Prove that two distinct planes do not intersect if and only if their normals are parallel.

12. What is described by the scalar equation $Ax + By + Cz + D = 0$,
    (a) if $A = B = C = D = 0$?
    (b) if $A = B = C = 0$ and $D \neq 0$?

13. The *angle between two planes* is defined as the smaller angle between their normals.
    (a) Find the angle between the planes
$$x + y + z = 4 \quad \text{and} \quad 2x - y + 3z = 5$$

(b) Develop a formula for the angle between planes π_1 and π_2
for $\pi_1: A_1x + B_1y + C_1z = D_1$
and $\pi_2: A_2x + B_2y + C_2z = D_2$

14. (a) Show that the distance from the origin to the plane
$Ax + By + Cz + D = 0$ is given by $\dfrac{|D|}{\sqrt{A^2 + B^2 + C^2}}$

(b) Show that the distance from the point (x_1, y_1, z_1) to the plane
$Ax + By + Cz + D = 0$ is given by $\dfrac{|Ax_1 + By_1 + Cz_1 + D|}{\sqrt{A^2 + B^2 + C^2}}$

15. Another normal form of a plane is given by $\overrightarrow{OP} \cdot \vec{n} = c$ where P is any point on the plane, $\vec{n}$ is a normal for the plane, and c is a scalar.

(a) Rewrite the equation $\overrightarrow{OP} \cdot (2, -1, 5) = 6$ as a scalar equation of the plane then find the distance from the origin to the plane.

(b) Rewrite the equation $\overrightarrow{OP} \cdot (2, -1, 5) = -5$ as a scalar equation of the plane then find the distance from the origin to the plane.

(c) Describe the relationship between the plane $\overrightarrow{OP} \cdot (2, -1, 5) = 6$ and the plane $\overrightarrow{OP} \cdot (2, -1, 5) = -5$.

(d) Describe the family of planes with equations of the form
$\overrightarrow{OP} \cdot \vec{n} = c$ for c any scalar.

(e) Write the equations of two different planes with normal $(2, -3, 6)$ that are two units from the origin.

6.3   INTERSECTION OF A LINE AND A PLANE

It is clear geometrically that a line and a plane have exactly one point in common, except when the line is parallel to the plane. We examine this situation algebraically by means of equations for lines and planes.

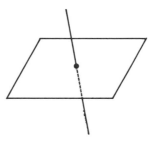

Example 1   Find the point of intersection of the line

$$l: \quad \frac{x - 3}{4} = \frac{y - 2}{3} = \frac{z + 1}{2}$$

and the plane

$$\pi: \quad x - y - 2z = 0$$

Solution   We rewrite the symmetric equations for l as parametric equations:

$$x = 3 + 4t$$
$$y = 2 + 3t$$
$$z = -1 + 2t$$

If (x, y, z) lies on the plane π, these values for x, y, and z must satisfy the equation for the plane, so

$$(3 + 4t) - (2 + 3t) - 2(-1 + 2t) = 0$$
$$3 - 3t = 0$$
$$t = 1$$

Hence $x = 3 + 4(1) = 7$
$\quad\quad\quad y = 2 + 3(1) = 5$
$\quad\quad\quad z = -1 + 2(1) = 1$

The point of intersection of the line and the plane is $(7, 5, 1)$.

Each of the other ways of presenting equations for lines and planes gives opportunities for different methods of solution.

Example 2   A line is given by

$$(x, y, z) = (1, 0, -1) + t(3, 1, -7)$$

The equation of the plane is in normal form.

and a plane by

$$(1, 3, 1) \cdot (x, y, z) = 2$$

Find the point of intersection.

Solution   Suppose (x, y, z) is the point of intersection. Then

$$(x, y, z) = (1, 0, -1) + t(3, 1, -7) \quad\quad ①$$
$$\text{and} \quad (1, 3, 1) \cdot (x, y, z) = 2 \quad\quad ②$$

Substituting into Equation 2, we get

$$(1, 3, 1) \cdot ((1, 0, -1) + t(3, 1, -7)) = 2$$
$$(1, 3, 1) \cdot (1, 0, -1) + t(1, 3, 1) \cdot (3, 1, -7) = 2$$
$$1(1) + 3(0) + 1(-1) + t(1(3) + 3(1) + 1(-7)) = 2$$
$$0 + (-1)t = 2$$
$$t = -2$$

Hence $(x, y, z) = (1, 0, -1) - 2(3, 1, -7)$
$\quad\quad\quad\quad\quad = (-5, -2, 13)$

So the point of intersection is $(-5, -2, 13)$.

Example 3   Show that there is no point of intersection of the line

$$\frac{x - 2}{3} = \frac{y + 5}{1} = \frac{z - 6}{8}$$

and the plane

$$5x + y - 2z + 2 = 0$$

Solution   We rewrite the symmetric equations for the line in parametric form:

$$x = 2 + 3t$$
$$y = -5 + t$$
$$z = 6 + 8t$$

If (x, y, z) lies on the line and on the plane then

$$5(2 + 3t) + (-5 + t) - 2(6 + 8t) + 2 = 0$$
$$10 + 15t - 5 + t - 12 - 16t + 2 = 0$$
$$-5 = 0$$

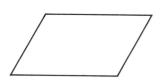

Since this is absurd, we deduce that there is no point in common to the line and the plane.

We now illustrate algebraically the third possibility that can occur: the given line lies entirely in the given plane.

Example 4   Find the point(s) of intersection (if any) of the line

$$l: \frac{x - 2}{1} = \frac{y + 1}{-2} = \frac{z + 3}{-5}$$

and the plane

$$\pi: 3x + 19y - 7z - 8 = 0$$

Solution   We rewrite the symmetric equations for l in parametric form:

$$x = 2 + t$$
$$y = -1 - 2t$$
$$z = -3 - 5t$$

If (x, y, z) belongs to both l and π then

$$3(2 + t) + 19(-1 - 2t) - 7(-3 - 5t) - 8 = 0$$
$$6 + 3t - 19 - 38t + 21 + 35t - 8 = 0$$
$$0 = 0$$

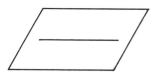

Since this is true for each value of the parameter t, the line l lies in the plane π. So every point of l is a point of π.

EXERCISE 6.3

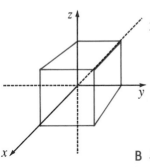

A 1. State the point of intersection of the following.
   (a) The xy-plane and the z-axis.
   (b) The yz-plane and the x-axis.

2. A unit cube is placed so that its vertices are $(0,0,0)$, $(1,0,0)$, $(0,1,0)$, $(0,0,1)$, $(1,1,0)$, $(0,1,1)$, $(1,0,1)$, and $(1,1,1)$.
   (a) Find a vector equation of the line l joining $(0,0,0)$ and $(1,1,1)$.
   (b) Find a vector equation of the plane π containing $(1,0,0)$, $(0,1,0)$, $(0,1,1)$, and $(1,0,1)$.
   (c) What is the point of intersection of l and π? Do you need to know the equations for l and π to answer this?

B 3. The line l is given by
$$\frac{x-3}{4} = \frac{y-2}{3} = \frac{z+1}{2}$$
   Find its point of intersection with the given plane.
   (a) $3x - 5y + 2z + 7 = 0$
   (b) $2x - 5y - 3z - 1 = 0$

4. The plane π is given by
$$2x + 3y + 5z + 1 = 0$$
   Find the point of intersection of π with the given line.
   (a) $\dfrac{x-5}{2} = \dfrac{y-1}{6} = \dfrac{z}{-5}$
   (b) $\dfrac{x+4}{4} = \dfrac{y+5}{5} = \dfrac{z-6}{-6}$

5. The line l is given by
$$(x,y,z) = (2,-3,1) + t(3,-1,2)$$
   Find its point of intersection with each plane.
   (a) $(4,1,-5) \cdot (x,y,z) = 0$
   (b) $(3,-1,-5) \cdot (x,y,z) = 6$
   (c) $(2,4,-1) \cdot (x,y,z) = -9$

6. Find the point(s) of intersection if any.
   (a) $\dfrac{x+7}{-2} = \dfrac{y-3}{5} = \dfrac{z-2}{3}$ and $13x + 7y - 3z - 14 = 0$
   (b) $\dfrac{x-3}{4} = \dfrac{y+1}{2} = \dfrac{z-2}{3}$ and $3x - 4y - 7z + 83 = 0$
   (c) $(x,y,z) = (-3,2,1) + t(-1,3,2)$ and $(4,13,-77) \cdot (x,y,z) = 43$

7. Find the point(s) of intersection if any.
   (a) $\dfrac{x-3}{5} = \dfrac{y+2}{4} = \dfrac{z-6}{7}$ and $5x - y - 3z + 1 = 0$
   (b) $\dfrac{x-3}{5} = \dfrac{y+7}{-2} = \dfrac{z-2}{3}$ and $x + y - z + 2 = 0$

(c) $\dfrac{x + 1}{2} = \dfrac{y - 3}{4} = \dfrac{z - 2}{3}$ and $x - y + z - 12 = 0$

8. Find the point(s) of intersection if any.

(a) $(-2, -1, 3) \cdot (x, y, z) = -4$ and
$(x, y, z) = (2, -3, 1) + t(3, -1, 2)$

(b) $(1, 3, 5) \cdot (x, y, z) = -7$ and
$(x, y, z) = (47, -31, 73) + t(-17, -11, 10)$

(c) $(x, y, z) = (1, -3, 2) + t(2, -1, 3)$ and
$(3, -1, -2) \cdot (x, y, z) = -4$

(d) $(x, y, z) = (-3, -8, 0) + t(13, 20, -1)$ and
$(3, -2, -1) \cdot (x, y, z) = 7$

C **9.** Suppose l is given by
$$l: (x, y, z) = (a, b, c) + t(d, e, f)$$
and π is given by
$$\pi: (m, n, p) \cdot (x, y, z) = k$$
where $a, b, c, d, e, f, m, n, p$ and k are constants and, as usual, t is a parameter.

(a) Suppose $(m, n, p) \cdot (d, e, f) \ne 0$. Find the point of intersection of l and π.

(b) Suppose $(m, n, p) \cdot (d, e, f) = 0$ but $(m, n, p) \cdot (a, b, c) \ne k$. Show that l and π do not intersect; they have no points in common.

(c) Suppose $(m, n, p) \cdot (d, e, f) = 0$ and $(m, n, p) \cdot (a, b, c) = k$. Show that l is contained in (lies on) π.

6.4   INTERSECTION OF TWO PLANES

If two distinct planes meet, their intersection is a line, as the diagram shows. Let us verify this algebraically by finding parametric equations for the line of intersection.

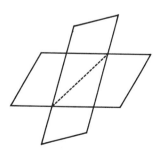

Example 1   Find the parametric form of the line of intersection of the planes
$$\pi_1: 4x - 5y - 2z - 1 = 0 \quad \text{and} \quad \pi_2: x - y - 2z = 0$$

Solution A normal to π_1 is $\vec{n}_1 = (4, -5, -2)$ and a normal to π_2 is $\vec{n}_2 = (1, -1, -2)$. Since $\vec{n}_1$ is not parallel to $\vec{n}_2$ the planes π_1 and π_2 are not parallel.

We use the technique of elimination to solve for their intersection.

$$4x - 5y - 2z - 1 = 0 \quad \textcircled{1}$$
$$x - y - 2z = 0 \quad \textcircled{2}$$

We eliminate x by considering $\textcircled{1} - 4 \times \textcircled{2}$:

$$-y + 6z - 1 = 0$$
$$y = 6z - 1$$

We eliminate y by considering $\textcircled{1} - 5 \times \textcircled{2}$:

$$-x + 8z - 1 = 0$$
$$x = 8z - 1$$

We let $z = t$, a parameter, to see that

$$x = -1 + 8t$$
$$y = -1 + 6t$$
$$z = 0 + t$$

This is the desired parametric form of the line.

We can see that a direction vector of the line is

$$\vec{d} = (8, 6, 1)$$

We could have found a direction vector for the line using normals. Let $\vec{n}_1$ and $\vec{n}_2$ be the normals to the planes in Example 1.

Then $\vec{n}_1 \times \vec{n}_2 = (4, -5, -2) \times (1, -1, -2)$

$$= (8, 6, 1)$$

So

$$\vec{n}_1 \times \vec{n}_2 = \vec{d}$$

The reason for this is that the line of intersection of the planes lies in each plane, so the direction $\vec{d}$ of the line is perpendicular to both $\vec{n}_1$ and $\vec{n}_2$. Hence $\vec{d}$ is a multiple of $\vec{n}_1 \times \vec{n}_2$.

Example 2 Find the parametric form of the line of intersection of the planes π_1 and π_2.

$$\pi_1: x = -4 + s \qquad\qquad \pi_2: x = 8 + 6u + 2v$$
$$y = \quad\ s + 3t \qquad\qquad\quad y = \quad\ 3u + 5v$$
$$z = \quad -s - 2t \qquad\qquad\quad z = \quad\ u - v$$

Solution We obtain the scalar equations of π_1 and π_2, and then use them to find the line of intersection by the technique of elimination.

As we saw in Section 6.1, a normal for π_1 is

$$(1, 1, -1) \times (0, 3, -2) = (1, 2, 3)$$

Note that $(-4, 0, 0)$ is on the plane.
So a scalar equation for π_1 is given by

$$(x+4, y, z) \cdot (1, 2, 3) = 0$$
$$x + 2y + 3z + 4 = 0$$

We repeat this process for π_2. A normal for π_2 is

$$(6, 3, 1) \times (2, 5, -1) = (-8, 8, 24)$$

Note that $(8, 0, 0)$ is on the plane.
Hence a scalar equation for π_2 is

$$(x-8, y, z) \cdot (-8, 8, 24) = 0$$
$$-8x + 8y + 24z + 64 = 0$$

This is not obvious from the given parametric forms of the planes.

We see that the normals $(1, 2, 3)$ and $(-8, 8, 24)$ are not parallel, so the planes are not parallel.
We have

$$x + 2y + 3z + 4 = 0 \qquad ①$$
$$-8x + 8y + 24z + 64 = 0 \qquad ②$$

We eliminate x by considering $8 \times ① + ②$:

$$24y + 48z + 96 = 0$$
$$y + 2z + 4 = 0$$
$$y = -4 - 2z$$

We eliminate y by considering $4 \times ① - ②$:

$$12x - 12z - 48 = 0$$
$$x - z - 4 = 0$$
$$x = 4 + z$$

We let $z = t$. Then we have

$$x = 4 + t$$
$$y = -4 - 2t$$
$$z = t$$

This is a parametric form of the line of intersection of π_1 and π_2.
We can see that a direction vector for the line is $\vec{d} = (1, -2, 1)$.
Again we could have found a direction vector for the line using normals.

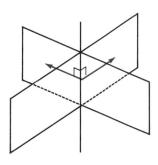

The normals are $\vec{n}_1 = (1, 2, 3)$ and $\vec{n}_2 = (-8, 8, 24)$.

$$\vec{n}_1 \times \vec{n}_2 = (1, 2, 3) \times (-8, 8, 24)$$
$$= (24, -48, 24)$$
$$= 24(1, -2, 1)$$
$$= 24\vec{d}$$

So $\qquad \vec{d} = \frac{1}{24}\vec{n}_1 \times \vec{n}_2$

Thus the direction of the line of intersection is a multiple of the cross product of the normals to the planes.

Example 3 Show that the planes

$$\pi_1: x + 2y + 3z - 6 = 0 \quad \text{and}$$
$$\pi_2: 4x + 8y + 12z - 25 = 0$$

are parallel and distinct.

Solution 1 A normal $\vec{n}_1$ of π_1 is $(1, 2, 3)$ and a normal $\vec{n}_2$ of π_2 is $(4, 8, 12)$. Since $\vec{n}_2 = 4\vec{n}_1$, these normals are parallel, so the planes are parallel. The planes are distinct since, for example, $(6, 0, 0)$ is on π_1 but not on π_2:

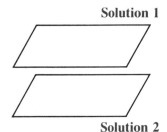

$$4(6) + 8(0) + 12(0) - 25 = -1 \neq 0$$

Solution 2 If we did not notice this but proceeded with elimination, here is what happens. Our equations are

$$x + 2y + 3z - 6 = 0 \qquad \text{①}$$
$$4x + 8y + 12z - 25 = 0 \qquad \text{②}$$

We eliminate x by considering $4 \times$ ① $-$ ②:

$$-24 + 25 = 0$$
$$1 = 0$$

We have arrived at a contradiction. This shows that there cannot be any point in common to π_1 and π_2. The planes are distinct and parallel.

EXERCISE 6.4

A 1. Identify the line of intersection of the following pairs of planes.
  (a) The xy-plane and the yz-plane,
  (b) the xz-plane and the xy-plane,
  (c) the yz-plane and the xz-plane.

2. State equations for a pair of planes, parallel to the coordinate planes, whose line of intersection is
  (a) $\{(1, 2, t) \,|\, t \in R\}$ \qquad\qquad (b) $\{(t, 3, -2) \,|\, t \in R\}$

B **3.** Find symmetric equations for the line of intersection of the plane
$$x - y - z - 12 = 0$$
and each of the following planes.
(a) $3x - 2y - 4z - 8 = 0$
(b) $3x - 5y + 2z + 7 = 0$

4. (a) Find parametric equations for the line of intersection of the planes
$$\pi_1\colon 2x + 3y + 5z + 1 = 0 \quad \text{and}$$
$$\pi_2\colon 4x + y + 4z - 4 = 0$$
(b) Show that the direction vector of the line of intersection of π_1 and π_2 is a multiple of the cross product of the normals.

5. Repeat Question 4 using the planes
$$\pi_1\colon 3x - 7y - 4z + 83 = 0 \quad \text{and}$$
$$\pi_2\colon x - y - z - 12 = 0$$

6. Find the intersection of π_1 and π_2.
(a) $\pi_1\colon 3x - 4y + 2z - 5 = 0 \quad \text{and}$
$\pi_2\colon 6x - 8y + 4z - 9 = 0$
(b) $\pi_1\colon 5x + 2y + 5z = 0 \quad \text{and}$
$\pi_2\colon 2x + 3y + 5z + 1 = 0$
(c) $\pi_1\colon x - y + 2 = 0 \quad \text{and}$
$\pi_2\colon 5x - 5y + 10 = 0$

7. (a) The plane π_1 is given in parametric form and π_2 in scalar form. Find the parametric form of their line of intersection.
$$\pi_1\colon \quad x = 2 + 3s - 3t \qquad \pi_2\colon \quad 4x + y - 5z = 0$$
$$y = -3 - s - 23t$$
$$z = 1 + 2s - 7t$$
(b) Find a normal $\vec{n}_1$ for π_1, and a direction $\vec{d}$ for the line of intersection.
(c) Compute $\vec{n}_1 \times (4, 1, -5)$ and find $k \in R$ such that
$$\vec{d} = k(\vec{n}_1 \times (4, 1, -5))$$

C **8.** Suppose $\vec{m} = (m_1, m_2, m_3)$ and $\vec{n} = (n_1, n_2, n_3)$ are not collinear. Show that the planes
$$m_1x + m_2y + m_3z = 0 \quad \text{and} \quad n_1x + n_2y + n_3z = 0$$
intersect in the line
$$x = (m_2n_3 - m_3n_2)t$$
$$y = (m_3n_1 - m_1n_3)t$$
$$z = (m_1n_2 - m_2n_1)t$$

9. Suppose $\vec{m} = (m_1, m_2, m_3)$ and $\vec{n} = (n_1, n_2, n_3)$ satisfy $\vec{m} \times \vec{n} \neq 0$. Show that the planes
$$m_1x + m_2y + m_3z + d = 0 \quad \text{and}$$
$$n_1x + n_2y + n_3z + e = 0$$
intersect in a line whose direction is $\vec{m} \times \vec{n}$.
[Hint: $\vec{m}, \vec{n}, \vec{m} \times \vec{n}$ is a basis for space so
$(x, y, z) = r\vec{m} + s\vec{n} + t\,\vec{m} \times \vec{n}$. Now use the fact that (x, y, z) is on both planes.

10. In this question we use $\vec{r} = \overrightarrow{OP}$, the position vector of P, to denote a point in space. A plane, π_1, is given by $\vec{m} \cdot \vec{r} = c$ and a second plane, π_2, is given by $\vec{n} \cdot \vec{r} = d$, where $\vec{m}$, $\vec{n}$ are given non-zero vectors, and $c, d \in R$. Prove:

    (a) If $\vec{m} \times \vec{n} \neq \vec{0}$ then π_1 and π_2 have a unique line of intersection whose direction is a multiple of $\vec{m} \times \vec{n}$.
    [Hint: $\vec{m}, \vec{n}, \vec{m} \times \vec{n}$ is a basis for space. So write $\vec{r} = t\vec{m} + u\vec{n} + v\vec{m} \times \vec{n}$.]

    (b) If $\vec{m} \times \vec{n} = \vec{0}$ but $d\vec{m} \neq c\vec{n}$ then the planes are parallel and distinct.

    (c) If $\vec{m} \times \vec{n} = \vec{0}$ and $d\vec{m} = c\vec{n}$ the planes are identical.

6.5 INTERSECTION OF THREE PLANES: ANALYSIS

In Section 6.4 we saw that two distinct planes either intersected in a line or were parallel. We then used elimination to actually find the intersection. In this section we consider the configurations that can arise when three distinct planes are intersected. In the next section we use elimination to find the intersection.

We use the normals to planes to analyse their intersection. Let π_1, π_2, π_3 be the planes with normals $\vec{n}_1$, $\vec{n}_2$, and $\vec{n}_3$ respectively. If, by examination of their equations we realize the planes are not distinct, then we have only one or two distinct planes. These situations have been considered already.

Type I

If $\vec{n}_1$, $\vec{n}_2$, and $\vec{n}_3$, are collinear, the planes are parallel, and, being distinct, do not intersect.

Type I
All planes are parallel.

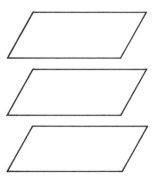

Example 1   Using normals, identify the intersection of the distinct planes

$$\pi_1: 3x - 2y + 5z - 8 = 0$$
$$\pi_2: 6x - 4y + 10z + 7 = 0$$
$$\pi_3: 24x - 16y + 40z + 1 = 0$$

Solution   The normals are $\vec{n}_1 = (3, -2, 5)$, $\vec{n}_2 = (6, -4, 10)$, and $\vec{n}_3 = (24, -16, 40)$. Since $\vec{n}_2 = 2\vec{n}_1$ and $\vec{n}_3 = 8\vec{n}_1$ we see that $\vec{n}_1$, $\vec{n}_2$, and $\vec{n}_3$ are collinear. Hence the planes are parallel. Since the planes are distinct, they have no point in common. There is no intersection point of these three planes.

Type II

If only one pair of $\vec{n}_1$, $\vec{n}_2$, and $\vec{n}_3$ is collinear then there is a pair of parallel planes.

Type II
Only two planes are parallel.

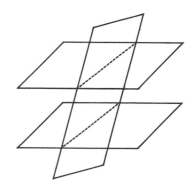

Example 2   Use normals to identify the intersection of the distinct planes

$$\pi_1: \quad 3x + 5y - 2z - 4 = 0$$
$$\pi_2: \quad 4x - 7y + 6z + 11 = 0$$
$$\pi_3: \quad 6x + 10y - 4z + 1 = 0$$

Solution   The normals are $\vec{n}_1 = (3, 5, -2)$, $\vec{n}_2 = (4, -7, 6)$ and $\vec{n}_3 = (6, 10, -4)$. Since $\vec{n}_3 = 2\vec{n}_1$ but $\vec{n}_2$ is not collinear with $\vec{n}_1$ or $\vec{n}_3$ we see that π_1 and π_3 are parallel. Since π_1 and π_3 are distinct there is no point in common to the planes. There is no point of intersection of these three planes.

> ## Type III
>
> If the normals $\vec{n}_1$, $\vec{n}_2$, and $\vec{n}_3$ are coplanar but no pair is collinear then either the planes have no point in common, or they have a line in common.

Type III
No planes are parallel
but normals are
coplanar

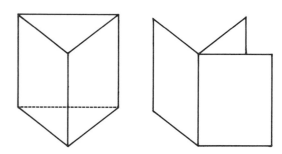

Since $\vec{n}_1$ and $\vec{n}_2$ are not collinear the planes π_1 and π_2 are not parallel. So π_1 and π_2 meet in a line with direction $\vec{n}_1 \times \vec{n}_2$, by the results of Section 6.4. Since $\vec{n}_1$, $\vec{n}_2$, and $\vec{n}_3$ are coplanar

$$\vec{n}_3 = a\vec{n}_1 + b\vec{n}_2$$

$$
\begin{aligned}
&(\vec{n}_1 \times \vec{n}_2) \cdot \vec{n}_3 \\
&= (\vec{n}_1 \times \vec{n}_2) \cdot a\vec{n}_1 \\
&+ (\vec{n}_1 \times \vec{n}_2) \cdot b\vec{n}_1 \\
&= 0 + 0 \\
&= 0
\end{aligned}
$$

for some $a, b \in R$. Now $\vec{n}_1 \times \vec{n}_2$ is perpendicular to the plane containing $\vec{n}_1$ and $\vec{n}_2$ so it must be perpendicular to $\vec{n}_3$. Every vector lying in π_3 is perpendicular to $\vec{n}_3$, so every vector in π_3 is parallel to $\vec{n}_1 \times \vec{n}_2$ and hence to the line of intersection of π_1 and π_2.

Example 3   Show, using normals, that the distinct planes either intersect in a line or have no point in common.

$$
\begin{aligned}
\pi_1 &: & x + 2y + 3z - 4 &= 0 \\
\pi_2 &: & 2x - y + 4z + 7 &= 0 \\
\pi_3 &: & 3x - 14y + z - 31 &= 0
\end{aligned}
$$

Solution   The normals are $\vec{n}_1 = (1, 2, 3)$, $\vec{n}_2 = (2, -1, 4)$, and $\vec{n}_3 = (3, -14, 1)$. We see that no pair is collinear, so we check for coplanarity by evaluating $(\vec{n}_1 \times \vec{n}_2) \cdot \vec{n}_3$.

$$
\begin{aligned}
(\vec{n}_1 \times \vec{n}_2) \cdot \vec{n}_3 &= ((1, 2, 3) \times (2, -1, 4)) \cdot (3, -14, 1) \\
&= (11, 2, -5) \cdot (3, -14, 1) \\
&= 0
\end{aligned}
$$

So $\vec{n}_1$, $\vec{n}_2$, and $\vec{n}_3$ are coplanar. We conclude that either the planes have a line in common or they have no point in common.

The fourth type of intersection arises when the normals are not coplanar.

Type IV

If $\vec{n}_1$, $\vec{n}_2$, and $\vec{n}_3$ are not coplanar then the planes intersect in a single point.

Type IV
Normals not coplanar

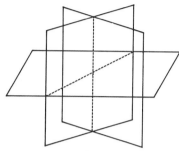

The direction of the line of intersection of π_1 and π_2 is $\vec{n}_1 \times \vec{n}_2$. The plane π_3 is parallel to this line if and only if $\vec{n}_1 \times \vec{n}_2 \cdot \vec{n}_3 = 0$. Since $\vec{n}_1 \times \vec{n}_2 \cdot \vec{n}_3 \neq 0$ (because the vectors $\vec{n}_1$, $\vec{n}_2$, and $\vec{n}_3$ are not coplanar) it follows that the plane π_3 intersects the line of intersection of π_1 and π_2 in a single point.

Example 4 Using normals, prove that the distinct planes have a unique point of intersection.

$$\pi_1: \quad x + y - 3 = 0$$
$$\pi_2: \quad y + z + 5 = 0$$
$$\pi_3: \quad x + z + 2 = 0$$

Solution We show that the normals $\vec{n}_1$, $\vec{n}_2$, and $\vec{n}_3$ are not coplanar by evaluating $(\vec{n}_1 \times \vec{n}_2) \cdot \vec{n}_3$. The normals are $\vec{n}_1 = (1, 1, 0)$, $\vec{n}_2 = (0, 1, 1)$ and $\vec{n}_3 = (1, 0, 1)$.
Now

$$(\vec{n}_1 \times \vec{n}_2) \cdot \vec{n}_3 = ((1, 1, 0) \times (0, 1, 1)) \cdot (1, 0, 1)$$
$$= (1, -1, 1) \cdot (1, 0, 1)$$
$$= 2$$

Since $(\vec{n}_1 \times \vec{n}_2) \cdot \vec{n}_3 \neq 0$ the normal vectors are not coplanar and the planes intersect in a point. ⬡

To apply what has been proved above in Types I, II, III, and IV we have to be able to decide when planes are distinct, when normals are collinear, and when normals are coplanar. The first two steps are relatively straightforward, and the third requires only the evaluation of $(\vec{n}_1 \times \vec{n}_2) \cdot \vec{n}_3$.
We illustrate the general procedure in our final example.

Example 5 Decide on the type of intersection of the sets of distinct planes.

(a) $3x - 2y + 5z + 1 = 0$
$\quad\ x + 5y + 2z - 3 = 0$
$\quad\ 6x - 4y + 10z - 2 = 0$

(b) $\quad x - 2y + 3z - 4 = 0$
$\quad\ 2x - 4y + 6z - 7 = 0$
$\quad\ 3x - 6y + 9z - 10 = 0$

(c) $\quad 2x + 5y + z - 3 = 0$
$\quad\ 3x - 2y + 5z + 1 = 0$
$\quad\ x + 31y - 10z + 7 = 0$

(d) $x - 2y + 3z - 4 = 0$
$\quad\ 2x + 5y + z + 8 = 0$
$\quad\ x + 5y + 2z - 3 = 0$

Solution (a) The normals are $\vec{n}_1 = (3, -2, 5)$, $\vec{n}_2 = (1, 5, 2)$, and $\vec{n}_3 = (6, -4, 10)$. We see that $\vec{n}_3 = 2\vec{n}_1$, but $\vec{n}_2$ and $\vec{n}_1$ are not collinear. So this gives us a Type II configuration.

(b) Here the normals are $\vec{n}_1 = (1, -2, 3)$, $\vec{n}_2 = (2, -4, 6) = 2\vec{n}_1$, and $\vec{n}_3 = (3, -6, 9) = 3\vec{n}_1$. So all normals are collinear. This is a Type I configuration.

(c) The normals are $\vec{n}_1 = (2, 5, 1)$, $\vec{n}_2 = (3, -2, 5)$, and $\vec{n}_3 = (1, 31, -10)$. No pair is collinear, so we evaluate $(\vec{n}_1 \times \vec{n}_2) \cdot \vec{n}_3$:

$$
\begin{aligned}
(\vec{n}_1 \times \vec{n}_2) \cdot \vec{n}_3 &= ((2, 5, 1) \times (3, -2, 5)) \cdot (1, 31, -10) \\
&= (27, -7, -19) \cdot (1, 31, -10) \\
&= 27(1) - 7(31) - 19(-10) \\
&= 0
\end{aligned}
$$

So $\vec{n}_1$, $\vec{n}_2$, and $\vec{n}_3$ are coplanar but no pair is collinear: this is a Type III configuration.

(d) Here the normals are $(1, -2, 3)$, $(2, 5, 1)$, and $(1, 5, 2)$. Since no pair is collinear we evaluate

$$
\begin{aligned}
(\vec{n}_1 \times \vec{n}_2) \cdot \vec{n}_3 &= ((1, -2, 3) \times (2, 5, 1)) \cdot (1, 5, 2) \\
&= (-17, 5, 9) \cdot (1, 5, 2) \\
&= -17(1) + 5(5) + 2(9) \\
&= 26 \neq 0
\end{aligned}
$$

So the normals are not coplanar: this is a Type IV configuration.

EXERCISE 6.5

A **1.** State the point of intersection of the three planes.

(a) $x = 0$
$\quad\ y = 0$
$\quad\ z = 0$

(b) $x - 1 = 0$
$\quad\ y - 2 = 0$
$\quad\ z + 1 = 0$

(c) $\quad\quad x = 0$
$\quad\quad\quad y = 0$
$\quad\ x + y + z - 1 = 0$

(d) $\quad\quad x = 0$
$\quad\quad\quad y - 1 = 0$
$\quad\ x + y + z - 1 = 0$

2. Classify the normals to the planes as collinear or not collinear.

(a) $x + y - 2 = 0$
$2x + 2y - 3 = 0$
$3x + 3y - 4 = 0$

(b) $2x - 4y + 5 = 0$
$3x - 10y - 7 = 0$
$5x - 14y + 3 = 0$

(c) $3x + y + 7 = 0$
$6x + 2y - 3 = 0$
$9x - 3y + 4 = 0$

(d) $2x + 4y + 6z = 0$
$3x + 6y + 9z = 0$
$5x + 10y + 10z = 0$

3. How many distinct planes are represented by each set of equations?

(a) $2x - y + 3z - 5 = 0$
$4x - 2y + 6z - 6 = 0$
$6x - 3y + 9z - 15 = 0$

(b) $3x + 4y - 5z + 6 = 0$
$x + y + z = 0$
$4x + 5y - 4z + 6 = 0$

(c) $x + 2y + 3z + 4 = 0$
$2x + 4y + 7z - 1 = 0$
$2x + 4y + 6z + 8 = 0$

(d) $3x - 2y + 5z = 0$
$6x - 4y + 10z = 0$
$9x - 6y + 15z = 0$

B 4. Classify the intersections of the planes as Type I, II, III, or IV.

(a) $3x + z + 11 = 0$
$2x + y - z + 4 = 0$
$x + y + z - 3 = 0$

(b) $3x - 2y + z - 5 = 0$
$4x - y + z + 4 = 0$
$9x - y + 4z = 0$

(c) $2x - 6y + 4z - 11 = 0$
$x - 3y + 2z + 7 = 0$
$8x + 18y - 2z + 1 = 0$

(d) $3x - 2y + 5z - 1 = 0$
$5x + y - 3z + 4 = 0$
$6x - 17y + 44z - 31 = 0$

(e) $3x + 4y + 6z + 18 = 0$
$2x + 7y + 7z - 1 = 0$
$7x + 6y + 2z + 7 = 0$

(f) $x + y + z + 3 = 0$
$2x + 2y + 2z + 7 = 0$
$3x + 3y + 3z + 11 = 0$

(g) $x + y + z + 3 = 0$
$2x + 2y + 3z + 1 = 0$
$3x + 3y + 2z - 4 = 0$

(h) $2x - 4y + 2z + 1 = 0$
$3x - 6y + 3z - 2 = 0$
$x - 2y + z + 17 = 0$

5. Classify the intersection of the planes. The answer may depend on the value of k.

(a) $3x + z + 11 = 0$
$2x + y - z + 4 = 0$
$5x + y + kz = 0$

(b) $3x - 2y + z - 5 = 0$
$4x - ky + z + 4 = 0$
$9x - y + 4z = 0$

(c) $2x - 6y + 4z - 11 = 0$
$x - 3y + 2z + 7 = 0$
$(3+k)x - 9y + 6z + 2 = 0$

(d) $5x + 3y + 7z - 2 = 0$
$10x + 5y + 14z - 3 = 0$
$15x + 8y + 21kz - 5 = 0$

C 6. For which values of the constant k is the intersection of the planes a line?

(a) $x + y + z = 0$
$x + 2y + 3z = 0$
$x + 4y + kz = 0$

(b) $2x + y + 3z = 0$
$3x - 4y + 5z = 0$
$kx + 6y + z = 0$

6.6 ELIMINATION: SOLVING THREE EQUATIONS IN THREE UNKNOWNS

We learned in Section 6.5, using analysis of normals, what types of geometric situations arise when three planes intersect. In this section we show how to determine the intersection, if there is one.

Example 1   Solve the system of equations.

$$x + y - 3 = 0 \quad \textcircled{1}$$
$$y + z + 5 = 0 \quad \textcircled{2}$$
$$x + z + 2 = 0 \quad \textcircled{3}$$

[We know from Example 4 in Section 6.5 that this system has a unique solution.]

Solution   Using Equation 1 we eliminate x from Equation 3:
$\textcircled{3} - \textcircled{1}$ gives

$$-y + z + 5 = 0 \quad \textcircled{4}$$

Next using Equation 2 we eliminate y from Equation 4:
$\textcircled{4} + \textcircled{2}$ gives

$$2z + 10 = 0$$
$$z = -5$$

Substituting $z = -5$ in Equation 4 gives $y = 0$ and substituting in Equation 3 gives $x = 3$.
Hence the unique solution is

$$x = 3, y = 0, z = -5 \quad \text{or} \quad (x, y, z) = (3, 0, -5)$$

In intersections of Type III, such as Example 3 of Section 6.5, an analysis of normals yields the conclusion that the intersection is either a line or empty. Here we see how this occurs algebraically.

Example 2   Solve
(a) $x + 2y + 3z - 4 = 0 \quad \textcircled{1}$
    $2x - y + 4z + 7 = 0 \quad \textcircled{2}$
    $3x - 14y + z + 48 = 0 \quad \textcircled{3}$

(b) $x + 2y + 3z - 4 = 0 \quad \textcircled{1}$
    $2x - y + 4z + 7 = 0 \quad \textcircled{2}$
    $3x - 14y + z - 20 = 0 \quad \textcircled{3}$

Solution   (a)   We use Equation 1 to eliminate x from Equations 2 and 3.
$\textcircled{2} - 2 \times \textcircled{1}$ gives

$$-5y - 2z + 15 = 0 \quad \textcircled{4}$$

③ − 3 × ① gives

$$-20y - 8z + 60 = 0 \qquad ⑤$$

Now we observe that Equation 5 is four times Equation 4. So we have no way of eliminating y from Equation 5 using Equation 4 without, at the same time, eliminating z.

We let $z = t$, a parameter, and see from Equation 4 that

$$5y = 15 - 2t$$
$$y = 3 - \tfrac{2}{5}t$$

Using this value for y in Equation 1 gives

$$x + 6 - \tfrac{4}{5}t + 3t - 4 = 0$$
$$x = -2 - \tfrac{11}{5}t$$

Hence the solution is

$$x = -2 - \tfrac{11}{5}t$$
$$y = 3 - \tfrac{2}{5}t$$
$$z = t$$

These are the parametric equations of a line.

(b) We use Equation 1 to eliminate x from Equations 2 and 3.

② − 2 × ① gives

$$-5y - 2z + 15 = 0 \qquad ④$$

③ − 3 × ① gives

$$-20y - 8z + 8 = 0 \qquad ⑤$$

Next we use Equation 4 to eliminate y from Equation 5:

⑤ − 4 × ④ gives

$$-8 - 60 = 0$$

This is absurd, so there are no values of x, y, and z that satisfy these equations. There is no solution to the system.

EXERCISE 6.6

A **1.** Solve the following systems of three equations in three unknowns.

(a) $x = 0$ (b) $x = 0$ (c) $x = 0$
$\ x = 0$ $x = 0$ $y = 0$
$\ x = 0$ $y = 0$ $z = 0$

2. Give a system of three equations whose solution is

(a) $(1, 0, 0)$ (b) $(2, -1, 3)$

B **3.** Solve by elimination.

(a) $3x + + z + 11 = 0$
$2x + y + z + 4 = 0$
$x + y + z - 3 = 0$

(b) $3x - 2y + z - 5 = 0$
$4x - y + z + 4 = 0$
$9x - y + 2z = 0$

(c) $2x - 6y + 4z - 11 = 0$
$x - 3y + 4z + 7 = 0$
$8x + 18y - 2z + 1 = 0$

(d) $3x - 2y + 5z - 1 = 0$
$5x + y - 3z + 4 = 0$
$6x - 17y + 44z - 31 = 0$

(e) $3x + 4y + 6z + 8 = 0$
$2x + 7y + 7z - 1 = 0$
$7x + 2y + 9z - 7 = 0$

(f) $2x + 2y + 2z + 1 = 0$
$5x + 5y + 5z + 2 = 0$
$9x + 9y + 9z - 3 = 0$

(g) $x + y + z + 3 = 0$
$2x + 2y - 3z - 4 = 0$
$3x + 3y + 7z - 4 = 0$

(h) $x + 2y + 3z + 4 = 0$
$2x + 3y + 4z + 5 = 0$
$3x + 4y + 5z + 6 = 0$

4. For which values of k do the systems have infinitely many solutions?

(a) $x + y + z + 3 = 0$
$2x + 2y - 3z - 4 = 0$
$3x + 3y - 2z + k = 0$

(b) $x + 2y + 3z + 4 = 0$
$2x + 3y + 4z + 5 = 0$
$x + 4y + 7z + k = 0$

(c) $3x - 2y + 5z - 1 = 0$
$5x + y - 3z + 4 = 0$
$x - 5y + 13z + k = 0$

(d) $3x - 2y + 5z - 1 = 0$
$5x + y - 3z + 4 = 0$
$x - 18y + 47z + k = 0$

C **5.** Solve giving your answers in terms of k, l, m, and n.

(a) $x + y + z + k = 0$
$x + 2y + 3z + l = 0$
$x + 4y + 8z + m = 0$

(b) $x + y + z + k = 0$
$x + 2y + 3z + l = 0$
$x + 4y + 7z + m = 0$

(c) $x + y + z + k = 0$
$x + 2y + 3z + l = 0$
$x + 4y + 6z + m = 0$

(d) $x + y + z + k = 0$
$x + 2y + 3z + l = 0$
$x + 4y + nz + m = 0$

PROBLEMS PLUS

Consider the system of equations

$$ax + by + cz = 0$$
$$dx + ey + fz = 0$$
$$gx + hy + kz = 0$$

with unknowns x, y, and z. The coefficients satisfy

(a) a, e, k are positive numbers,

(b) b, c, d, f, g, h are negative numbers,

(c) in each equation, the sum of the coefficients is positive.

Prove that the only solution of the system is $x = 0$, $y = 0$, and $z = 0$.

6.7 CLASSIFYING SYSTEMS OF LINEAR EQUATIONS

In Section 6.5 we gave a geometrical classification of the types of intersection three distinct planes could have. In this section we shift to a more algebraic viewpoint, initiated in Section 6.6, and classify systems of linear equations by the number of solutions they have.

A **linear equation** in n variables is an equation of the form

$$a_1x_1 + a_2x_2 + \ldots + a_nx_n = b$$

where $a_1, a_2, \ldots, a_n$, b are given constants and $x_1, x_2, \ldots x_n$ are the n variables. Since we are interested mainly in the two cases $n = 2$ and $n = 3$ we write x, y for x_1, x_2 and x, y, z for x_1, x_2, x_3.

A **system of linear equations** is a set of one or more linear equations. If there are $m \geqslant 1$ equations in n unknowns we say there are **m equations in n unknowns**.

Example 1   Each of the following systems consists of two equations in two unknowns. Solve them.

(a) $x + 2y = 4$ (b) $x + 2y = 4$ (c) $x + 2y = 4$
     $3x + 5y = 11$ $3x + 6y = 11$ $3x + 6y = 12$

Solution   (a)   To eliminate x we subtract three times the first equation from the second.

It follows that $-y = -1$

So $y = 1$, and thus $x = 2$. Hence $(2, 1)$ is the solution of the system (a).

(b)   We use the first equation to eliminate x from the second:

It follows that $0 = -1$

But this is impossible: so system (b) has no solution.

(c)   We again use the first equation to eliminate x from the second:

It follows that $0 = 0$

We deduce (if we did not see it instantly) that the second equation is merely a multiple (in this case three) of the first equation, so it brings no further information about the values of x and y. The solution to $x + 2y = 4$ may be written in parametric form as $(x, y) = (4 - 2t, t)$ for $t \in R$. So system (c) has an infinite number of solutions.

This example was chosen to illustrate the full range of possibilities for solutions of two equations in two unknowns. If there is no solution (case (b) above) we say the system is **inconsistent**. If there is at least one solution (cases (a) and (c) above) we say the system is **consistent**.

If a system is consistent it can be further described as **independent** if it has a unique solution, and **dependent** if it has more than one solution.

Schematically we have

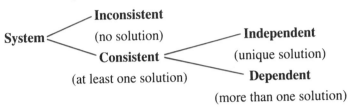

Example 2   Solve and classify the following systems of three equations in three unknowns.

(a)
$$x + y + z = 1$$
$$x + 2y + 3z = 3$$
$$x + 4y + 6z = 5$$

(b)
$$x + y + z = 1$$
$$x + 2y + 3z = 3$$
$$x + 4y + 7z = 5$$

(c)
$$x + y + z = 1$$
$$x + 2y + 3z = 3$$
$$x + 4y + 7z = 7$$

Solution   (a)
$$x + y + z = 1 \quad ①$$
$$x + 2y + 3z = 3 \quad ②$$
$$x + 4y + 6z = 5 \quad ③$$

We eliminate x from Equations 2 and 3.

$$② - ① \quad \text{gives} \quad y + 2z = 2 \quad ④$$
$$③ - ① \quad \text{gives} \quad 3y + 5z = 4 \quad ⑤$$

We now use Equation 4 to eliminate y from Equation 5.

$$⑤ - 3 \times ④ \text{ gives } \quad -z = -2$$

So $z = 2$. Hence, from Equation 4, $y = -2$, and from Equation 1 $x = 1$. Thus system (a) has a unique solution $(1, -2, 2)$, and so is consistent and independent.

(b)
$$x + y + z = 1 \quad ①$$
$$x + 2y + 3z = 3 \quad ②$$
$$x + 4y + 7z = 5 \quad ③$$
$$② - ① \text{ gives} \quad y + 2z = 2 \quad ④$$
$$③ - ① \text{ gives} \quad 3y + 6z = 4 \quad ⑤$$

Now $⑤ - 3 \times ④$ (to eliminate y) gives

$$0 = -2$$

This is impossible, so system (b) is inconsistent.

(c)
$$x + y + z = 1 \quad ①$$
$$x + 2y + 3z = 3 \quad ②$$
$$x + 4y + 7z = 7 \quad ③$$

Elimination gives, as above,

$$y + 2z = 2 \quad ④$$
$$3y + 6z = 6 \quad ⑤$$

$$⑤ - 3 \times ④ \text{ gives} \quad 0 = 0$$

Hence Equation 5 is a multiple of Equation 4.

Let $z = t$. Then $y = 2 - 2t$ from Equation 4, and
$x + 2 - 2t + t = 1$ from Equation 1, so $x = -1 + t$.
Hence, $x = -1 + t$
$$y = 2 - 2t$$
$$z = t$$

or equivalently $(x, y, z) = (-1 + t, 2 - 2t, t)$ is a solution to (c) for each value of the parameter t. Hence system (c) is consistent and dependent.

We can look at this example from the point of view of the normals involved. We let $\vec{n}_1 = (1, 1, 1)$, $\vec{n}_2 = (1, 2, 3)$, and $\vec{n}_3 = (1, 4, k)$. Then

$$(\vec{n}_1 \times \vec{n}_2) \cdot \vec{n}_3 = (1, 1, 1) \times (1, 2, 3) \cdot (1, 4, k)$$
$$= (1, -2, 1) \cdot (1, 4, k)$$
$$= k - 7$$

So if $k \neq 7$ (system (a)) then the normals $\vec{n}_1$, $\vec{n}_2$, and $\vec{n}_3$ are not coplanar and there is a unique solution. If $k = 7$ (systems (b) and (c)) the normals are coplanar but the system may be consistent or inconsistent.

PROBLEMS PLUS

Analysis of an Electrical Current

Determine the currents for the network shown.

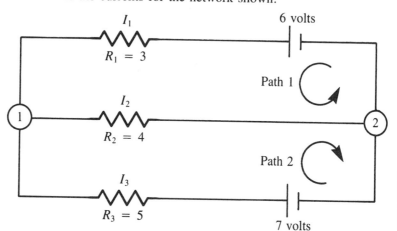

To solve this problem use *Kirchoff's Laws*:

1. All the current flowing into a junction must flow out of it.

2. The sum of the products *IR* (*I* is *current* and *R* is *resistance*) around a closed path is equal to the total voltage in the path.

EXERCISE 6.7

A **1.** State whether the given equation in x, y, and z is linear or not.

(a) $3x + 2y + 5z = 4$

(b) $3x^2 + 2y + 5z = 4$

(c) $3x + 2y + 5\sqrt{z} = 4$

(d) $\dfrac{3}{x} + \dfrac{4}{y} - \dfrac{5}{z} = 2$

2. (a) If the equation $2x = 3$ is interpreted as one equation in one unknown, what is the geometric interpretation?

(b) If $2x = 3$ is interpreted as one equation in two unknowns (x, y), what is the geometric interpretation?

(c) Finally, if $2x = 3$ is interpreted as one equation in three unknowns (x, y, z), what is the geometric interpretation?

B **3.** Where possible, find the solutions to the following systems of two linear equations in two unknowns. Classify them as inconsistent or consistent, and, if consistent as dependent or independent.

(a) $2x + 5y = -3$
$3x + 7y = 4$

(b) $2x + 5y = 7$
$4x + 10y = 14$

(c) $2x + 5y = 0$
$4x + 10y = -3$

(d) $3x - 7y = -11$
$10x - 23y = 14$

4. Solve and classify the following systems of three linear equations in three unknowns as consistent or inconsistent, dependent or independent.

(a) $x + y = 2$
$2x + 2y = 3$
$3x + 3y = 4$

(b) $3x + z = -11$
$2x + y - z = -4$
$x + y + z = 3$

(c) $3x - 2y + z = 5$
$4x - y + z = -4$
$9x - y + 4z = 0$

(d) $3x - 2y + 5z = 1$
$5x + y - 3z = -4$
$6x - 17y + 44z = 31$

(e) $3x + 4y + 6z = -8$
$2x + 7y + 7z = 1$
$7x + 6y + 2z = -7$

(f) $x + y + z = -3$
$2x + 2y + 2z = -7$
$3x + 3y + 3z = -11$

(g) $x + y + z = -3$
$2x + 2y + 3z = -1$
$3x + 3y + 2z = 4$

(h) $2x - 3y + 2z = -1$
$3x - 6y + 3z = 12$
$x - 2y + z = 4$

5. Classify these systems. The answer may depend on the constant k.

(a) $3x + z = -11$
$2x + y - z = -4$
$5x + y + kz = 0$

(b) $3x - 2y + z = 5$
$4x + ky + z = -4$
$9x - y + 4z = 0$

(c) $2x - 6y + 4z = 11$
$x - 3y + 2z = -7$
$(8+k)x + 5y - z = 4$

(d) $5x + 3y - 7z = -2$
$10x + 6y - 14z = -4$
$15x + ky - 21z = 5$

6.8 REVIEW EXERCISE

1. Give a vector equation, parametric equations, and a scalar equation for the plane through the point $P_0(-1, -3, 7)$ with direction vectors $\vec{d_1} = (-1, -2, 1)$ and $\vec{d_2} = (-3, 1, -4)$.

2. Give parametric equations for the plane $3x - y - z - 1 = 0$.

3. Is the plane $\overrightarrow{OP} = (0, 3, 2) + s(1, 2, 1) + t(-1, 5, 2)$ parallel to the plane $x + 3y - 7z + 15 = 0$? Are the planes identical?

4. Find the distance from the origin to each plane.
    (a) $x + y + 4z + 8 = 0$

    (b) $(x-1, y+4, z-7) = s(1, 0, 1) + t(-2, 1, 2)$

    (c) $x = 3 + 5s - 4t$
    $y = -1 - s + t$
    $z = 3s + 8t$

5. Find the distance between the planes.
    (a) $\pi_1:$ $x = 1$ and $\pi_2:$ $2x = 3$

    (b) $\pi_1:$ $3x + 6y - 2z = 0$ and
    $\pi_2:$ $3x + 6y - 2z - 7 = 0$

    (c) $\pi_1:$ $x + y + z - 3 = 0$ and
    $\pi_2:$ $2x + 2y + 2z + 3 = 0$

    (d) $\pi_1:$ $x + 2y + 3z - 6 = 0$ and
    $\pi_2:$ the plane through $P_0(0, 3, -5)$ parallel to π_1

6. Find the intersection (if any) of the line l and the plane π.
    $$l: \frac{x-2}{3} = \frac{y+1}{2} = \frac{z-3}{4}$$
    $$\pi: 5x - 2y - 3z - 7 = 0$$

7. Find the intersection of
    $(-1, 3, -2) \cdot (x, y, z) = -4$ and
    $(x, y, z) = (-3, 1, 2) + t(-1, 2, 3)$

8. Find symmetric equations for the line of intersection of the planes
    $x + y - z + 12 = 0$ and $2x + 4y - 3z + 8 = 0$

9. Draw diagrams illustrating the possible intersections of three distinct planes.

10. Using normals, classify the intersection of the planes as Type I, II, III, or IV.
    (a) $2x + y - 3z + 5 = 0$ (b) $3x - y - 2z + 8 = 0$
    $x + y + z - 6 = 0$ $x - 5y + 4z - 2 = 0$
    $4x - 5y + z + 3 = 0$ $x + 79y - 80z + 82 = 0$

    (c) $79x - 80y + z = 0$ (d) $x + y + z + 3 = 0$
    $5x - 4y - z + 2 = 0$ $2x + 3y - 6z - 1 = 0$
    $x + 2y - 3z - 8 = 0$ $4x + 6y - 12z + 11 = 0$

(e) $3x - 2y + 6z + 7 = 0$
$3x - 2y + 6z + 8 = 0$
$3x - 2y + 6z + 9 = 0$

11. For each part in Question 10, solve the system by elimination and classify it as consistent/inconsistent, dependent/independent.

12. Solve by elimination.
$$2x + y + z = 5$$
$$4x - y - 3z = 12$$
$$3x + 5y + z = 21$$

13. For which value(s) of k is the system (i) consistent, (ii) dependent?

(a) $x + y + z = 0$ (b) $x + y + z = 0$
$2x + 2y - 3z = 0$ $2x + 2y - 3z = 0$
$3x - 3y + kz = 0$ $3x + 3y + kz = 0$

PROBLEMS PLUS

Prove that a necessary condition that the three planes

$$-x + ay + bz = 0$$
$$ax - y + cz = 0$$
$$bx + cy - z = 0$$

have a line in common is that

$$a^2 + b^2 + c^2 + 2abc = 1$$

PROBLEMS PLUS

Into how many regions is space separated by n planes in general position? For $n = 1$, the answer is 2 regions, and for $n = 2$ it is 4 regions. What is the answer for $n = 3$? $n = 4$? Find the general result.

6.9 CHAPTER 6 TEST

1. The parametric equations for a plane π are
$$x = -1 + 2s - 3t$$
$$y = 4 - 5s + 6t$$
$$z = 2 + s + t$$
   (a) Identify two independent direction vectors for the plane π.
   (b) Find a normal to the plane π.
   (c) Find a scalar equation for the plane π.
   (d) Find a scalar equation for a plane parallel to π that passes through the origin.

2. (a) Find the point (x, y, z) of intersection of the line l and the plane π where
$$l: \frac{x + 1}{2} = \frac{y - 2}{3} = \frac{z - 3}{4} \quad \text{and} \quad \pi: 2x + y - z = 0$$
   (b) Show that the line l' and the plane π' do not meet.
$$l': \frac{x - 6}{8} = \frac{y + 5}{1} = \frac{z - 2}{3} \quad \text{and} \quad \pi': 2x - y - 5z - 2 = 0$$
   (c) Find the distance between l' and π'.

3. (a) By analysing normals show that, no matter what a, b, and c are, the planes
$$x + y + z + a = 0$$
$$x + 2y + 3z + b = 0$$
$$x + 4y + 9z + c = 0$$
   always intersect in a point.
   (b) Find k such that the intersection of the planes
$$x + y + z + a = 0$$
$$x + 2y + 3z + b = 0$$
$$x + 4y + kz + c = 0$$
   is never a point.

4. Solve the system, and classify it using the categories: consistent, inconsistent, dependent, and independent.
$$x + 2y + 3z - 4 = 0$$
$$3x - 14y + z + 48 = 0$$
$$2x - y + 4z + 7 = 0$$

CUMULATIVE REVIEW FOR CHAPTERS 4 TO 6

1. Draw the following vectors.
   (a) $(2, -1, -3)$ (b) $(-1, 2, 1)$

2. For the vector given in the diagram, position it so that its tail is at the origin and find its components.

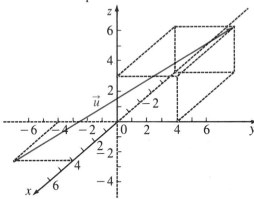

3. If the vectors $\vec{u} = 2\vec{i} - a\vec{j} + b\vec{k}$ and $\vec{v} = -5\vec{i} + c\vec{j} + 4\vec{k}$ are collinear, find b and a relationship between a and c.

4. If $\vec{u} = (-2, 1, 3)$, $\vec{v} = (1, -1, 1)$, and $\vec{w} = 4\vec{i} - 3\vec{j} + \vec{k}$, find
   (a) $2\vec{u} - 3\vec{v} + 5\vec{w}$
   (b) $\left| 2\vec{v} + 4\vec{w} \right|$
   (c) two unit vectors collinear with $\vec{u}$
   (d) $(\vec{u} \cdot \vec{v})\vec{w}$
   (e) $(\vec{v} \times \vec{w}) \cdot \vec{u}$
   (f) $(\vec{w} \times \vec{u}) \times \vec{v}$

5. If $\vec{u} = (2, 1, -4)$, $\vec{v} = (5, -1, 0)$, and $\vec{w} = (-2, -2, 1)$, find
   (a) $3\vec{u} - 4\vec{v} + \vec{w}$
   (b) $\left| \vec{v} - \vec{u} \right|$
   (c) $(\vec{u} + \vec{v}) \cdot \vec{w}$
   (d) $(\vec{v} + \vec{w}) \times \vec{u}$
   (e) $(\vec{u} \times \vec{v}) \times \vec{w}$

6. Find the angle between the following pairs of vectors. Give your answers to the nearest degree.
   (a) $\vec{u} = (2, -4)$ $\vec{v} = 3\vec{i} + 4\vec{j}$
   (b) $\vec{u} = (-2, 1, 3)$ $\vec{v} = (-1, 1, -1)$
   (c) $\vec{u} = 4\vec{i} - \vec{j} - 3\vec{k}$ $\vec{v} = (1, -4, 5)$

7. Given the points $P(-2, 1, 3)$, $Q(1, 3, 4)$, and $R(3, -2, 0)$, find
   (a) $\overrightarrow{PQ}$
   (b) $\left| \overrightarrow{QR} \right|$
   (c) the perimeter of $\triangle PQR$
   (d) the area of $\triangle PQR$

8. The points $A(-6, 1, 4)$, $B(-2, -3, 7)$, and $D(2, 4, -1)$ are three vertices of parallelogram $ABCD$.
   (a) Find the coordinates of C.
   (b) Find the measures of the interior angles of the parallelogram to the nearest degree.
   (c) Find the measures of the angles between the diagonals of the parallelogram to the nearest degree.
   (d) Find the area of $ABCD$.

9. If the vectors $\vec{u} = (1, -2, 3)$ and $\vec{v} = (3, -4, k)$ are orthogonal, find k.

10. Determine if the following vectors are coplanar or non-coplanar.
    (a) $\vec{u} = (4, -2, 1)$ $\vec{v} = (-3, 0, -2)$ $\vec{w} = (-13, 3, -1)$
    (b) $\vec{u} = (-1, -2, 1)$ $\vec{v} = (-1, 7, -1)$ $\vec{w} = (3, -3, -1)$

11. Determine which of the following sets of vectors form a basis for space.
    (a) $\vec{u} = (1, -1, -1)$ $\vec{v} = (3, -2, -1)$ $\vec{w} = (-2, 0, -2)$
    (b) $\vec{u} = (-1, -1, 4)$ $\vec{v} = (3, 1, -5)$ $\vec{w} = (10, 3, -8)$

12. Discuss the following sets of vectors with respect to collinearity and coplanarity.
    (a) $\vec{u} = (1, 2, 0)$ $\vec{v} = (0, -1, 1)$
        $\vec{w} = (1, -1, -1)$ $\vec{x} = (-2, -4, 0)$
    (b) $\vec{u} = (-2, -1, 1)$ $\vec{v} = (1, 1, 1)$
        $\vec{w} = (0, 1, -1)$ $\vec{x} = (-4, 0, -4)$
    (c) $\vec{u} = (-3, -1, 1)$ $\vec{v} = (2, 1, -4)$
        $\vec{w} = (0, 5, -2)$ $\vec{x} = (6, -3, 0)$

13. In each of the following, determine (where possible) three vectors that form a basis for space and express the fourth vector as a linear combination of these basis vectors.
    (a) $\vec{u} = (1, 1, 0)$ $\vec{v} = (1, 0, 1)$
        $\vec{w} = (0, 1, 1)$ $\vec{x} = (1, 1, 1)$
    (b) $\vec{u} = (3, 4, -5)$ $\vec{v} = (-1, -2, 3)$
        $\vec{w} = (1, -2, 5)$ $\vec{x} = (-2, 1, -1)$
    (c) $\vec{u} = (3, 1, 2)$ $\vec{v} = (-1, -1, 6)$
        $\vec{w} = (1, 1, 1)$ $\vec{x} = (2, 1, -8)$

14. Find a direction vector for each line.
    (a) The line through the points $(-2, 3)$ and $(4, -4)$.
    (b) A line parallel to $\dfrac{x + 2}{-4} = \dfrac{y - 1}{3} = \dfrac{z - 4}{-5}$
    (c) A line perpendicular to $\begin{array}{l} x = -1 + 2t \\ y = 3 - 5t \end{array}$

15. Give two points on each line.

(a) $(x+5, y+1) = r(-1, 2)$

(b) $x = -1 + t$
$y = 2$
$z = -3t$

(c) $\overrightarrow{OP} = (-2, -3, 1) + t(1, -5, 3)$

16. Give parametric equations for each line.

(a) $\overrightarrow{OP} = (-1, 2) + t(3, -1)$

(b) $(x+3, y-2, z) = r(-3, -4, 5)$

(c) $\dfrac{x+10}{6} = \dfrac{y-12}{-7} = \dfrac{z+2}{-3}$

17. Give a symmetric equation for each line.

(a) $(x-2, y-3) = s(-1, 2)$ (b) $x = 2 - 3t$
$y = 2t$
$z = -1 + t$

18. Find a vector equation for each line.

(a) The line through the points $(2, -5, -2)$ and $(3, 6, 4)$

(b) The line through $(-3, -5)$ perpendicular to the line
$\dfrac{x+1}{-2} = \dfrac{y}{3}$

(c) The line, in space, parallel to the x-axis with y-intercept -4

19. Find parametric equations of each line.

(a) The line through the points $(-4, 7)$ and $(1, -4)$

(b.) The line parallel to $(x+3, y+1, z) = t(1, 6, -1)$ through the point $(2, -5, 4)$

(c) The line parallel to $\dfrac{x}{-5} = y - 3 = \dfrac{z+2}{2}$ with x-intercept 7

20. Find vector, parametric, and symmetric equations for the line $2x + 3y = 6$.

21. Develop vector, parametric, and symmetric equations of the line through $(-1, 2, -1)$ and parallel to line $x = 3s + 1$
$y = 5 - s$
$z = -3s + 1$

22. Find direction numbers, direction cosines, and direction angles of each line.

(a) The line through the points $(1, -2)$ and $(3, -2)$

(b) A line parallel to the line $\overrightarrow{OP} = (2, -1) + t(1, -3)$

(c) The line $\dfrac{x+2}{-1} = \dfrac{y-2}{3}$

(d) The line $x = 3 + 2s$
$y = -2 - 5s$

23. Find direction numbers, direction cosines, and direction angles of each line.
   (a) The line through the points $(3, -1, -4)$ and $(-1, 2, 0)$
   (b) A line parallel to the line $(x-1, y+3, z+2) = t(-1, 0, 5)$
   (c) The line $\dfrac{x}{3} = \dfrac{y+4}{5} = z - 3$
   (d) The line $\begin{aligned} x &= -5 + 4t \\ y &= 1 - 2t \\ z &= -8 - 2t \end{aligned}$

24. Find vector and symmetric equations of the line through $(2, -1)$ with direction cosines $\dfrac{-3}{\sqrt{10}}$ and $\dfrac{1}{\sqrt{10}}$.

25. Find parametric and symmetric equations of the line through $(-1, -1, 1)$ with directions cosines $\frac{2}{3}, -\frac{1}{3}$, and $\frac{2}{3}$.

26. Find a unit normal for each line.
   (a) $2x - 3y + 3 = 0$ (b) $y = 3x - 4$

27. Find a scalar equation for each line.
   (a) The line through $(-1, 3)$ with $\vec{n} = (7, -2)$.
   (b) The line parallel to $x + 2y - 1 = 0$ with y-intercept -3.
   (c) The line through the points $(8, 1)$ and $(-1, 4)$.
   (d) The line passing through the origin with direction cosines $\dfrac{-1}{\sqrt{2}}$ and $\dfrac{1}{\sqrt{2}}$.
   (e) The line through $(2, -3)$ parallel to $\dfrac{x+4}{-1} = y - 1$.
   (f) The line through $(-1, -4)$ perpendicular to $(x+1, y-2) \cdot (2, -3) = 0$.
   (g) The line with x-intercept 2 parallel to $\begin{aligned} x &= 2 + 3t \\ y &= -4 - t \end{aligned}$

28. Rewrite each equation as a scalar equation.
   (a) $\overrightarrow{OP} = (-1 - 2s, 5s)$ (b) $\dfrac{x-2}{3} = \dfrac{y}{-3}$
   (c) $\begin{aligned} x &= 3 \\ y &= 1 + 3r \end{aligned}$

29. Find vector, parametric, and symmetric equations of each line.
   (a) $3x + 4y - 1 = 0$ (b) $y = \frac{1}{2}x + 4$

30. Find direction numbers, direction cosines, and direction angles for the line $2x + 5y + 10 = 0$.

31. Which pairs of lines are parallel?

(a) l_1: $\dfrac{x+3}{-4} = \dfrac{y-1}{2}$ $\qquad$ l_2: $(x+4, y+1) = t(2, -1)$

(b) l_1: $\begin{array}{l} x = 3 - 2r \\ y = -4 + 5r \end{array}$ $\qquad$ l_2: $\overrightarrow{OP} = (5t-1, -2t)$

32. Find the point of intersection, if any, of the following pairs of lines.

(a) l_1: $(x+1, y+4) = t(1, -1)$ $\quad$ l_2: $\begin{array}{l} x = 3 - 2s \\ y = -1 + 3s \end{array}$

(b) l_1: $(x, y) \cdot (6, -5) = 10$ $\qquad$ l_2: $\dfrac{x-1}{3} = \dfrac{y+1}{-2}$

(c) l_1: $\dfrac{x-1}{-3} = \dfrac{y+1}{2}$ $\qquad$ l_2: $2x + 3y + 1 = 0$

33. Investigate the intersection of the following pairs of lines.

(a) $\qquad$ l_1: $\begin{array}{l} x = 3 - r \\ y = -2 + r \\ z = 3 + 2r \end{array}$ $\qquad$ l_2: $\begin{array}{l} x = 1 + t \\ y = -1 + t \\ z = 4 + 4t \end{array}$

(b) l_1: $\dfrac{x-1}{3} = \dfrac{y+3}{-1} = \dfrac{z}{2}$ $\quad$ l_2: $\dfrac{x-2}{-2} = \dfrac{y}{2} = \dfrac{z-1}{4}$

(c) l_1: $\overrightarrow{OP} = (3, 2, 0) + r(-1, -1, 1)$

$\qquad$ l_2: $\dfrac{x+1}{2} = \dfrac{y-3}{-4} = \dfrac{z}{5}$

34. Find all values of k for which the following lines do not intersect.

l_1: $\begin{array}{l} x = -1 + 2r \\ y = 3 \\ z = 1 + 3r \end{array}$ $\qquad$ l_2: $\dfrac{x-1}{3} = \dfrac{y}{k} = z + 2$

35. Find the distance from the given point P to the given line l.

(a) $P(1, -1)$ $\qquad$ l: $2x + 3y = 3$

(b) $P(3, -2)$ $\qquad$ l: $\dfrac{x-4}{6} = \dfrac{y+8}{-5}$

(c) $P(2, -4, 1)$ $\qquad$ l: $\begin{array}{l} x = 2 - 3r \\ y = -1 + r \\ z = 5 + 3r \end{array}$

(d) $P(-5, 0, 2)$ $\qquad$ l: $\overrightarrow{OP} = (1, 1, 1) + t(2, 3, -4)$

36. Find the distance between the indicated parallel lines.

(a) l_1: $(x+1, y-2) = r(-3, 5)$

$\qquad\qquad$ $x = 6 + x$

$\qquad$ l_2: $\dfrac{x}{6} = \dfrac{y+2}{-10}$

(b) l_1: $\begin{array}{l} y = -3 - 2s \\ z = 5s \end{array}$

$\qquad$ l_2: $(x, y, z) = (1, -2, -3) + t(-1, 2, -5)$

37. For each pair of lines, verify that the lines are skew and find the distance between them.

(a) l_1: $(x, y, z) = (1 - 2r, -3, 5 + r)$

l_2: $\begin{aligned} x &= 2 - 3s \\ y &= 5 + s \\ z &= -1 - 3s \end{aligned}$

(b) l_1: $\dfrac{x}{-4} = \dfrac{y + 3}{3} = \dfrac{z - 1}{2}$

l_2: $\overrightarrow{OP} = (5, -1, 2) + r(1, 1, 1)$

38. For each pair of lines in space, determine whether or not they are parallel, intersecting, or skew, then apply a suitable method to find the distance between them.

(a) l_1: $(x, y, z) = (1, 1, 1) + r(2, -4, 6)$

l_2: $\begin{aligned} x &= 2 - s \\ y &= -3 - 2s \\ z &= 6 + s \end{aligned}$

(b) l_1: $\dfrac{x + 1}{-7} = \dfrac{3 - y}{3} = z$

l_2: $(x + 3, y, z - 2) = r(1, -1, 2)$

(c) l_1: $\overrightarrow{OP} = (5, -4, 3) + s(2, 3, -4)$

l_2: $\dfrac{x + 6}{-2} = \dfrac{y}{-3} = \dfrac{1 - z}{-4}$

39. Give parametric equations for each plane.

(a) $\overrightarrow{OP} = (1, -1, -1) + s(2, 0, -3) + t(1, -4, -2)$

(b) $(x - 2, y + 3, z) = (2s - t, -2t, -3s + 4t)$

40. Rewrite the following equation in the form $\overrightarrow{P_0P} = s\vec{d_1} + t\vec{d_2}$.

$\begin{aligned} x &= -2 + 5s - 3t \\ y &= 1 - 2s - t \\ z &= 3 + 4s + 2t \end{aligned}$

41. Find vector and parametric equations of each plane.

(a) The plane through $(1, -2, 1)$ with direction vectors $(6, -2, 1)$ and $(-3, -1, 0)$.

(b) The plane parallel to the xz-plane through the point $(1, -2, 3)$.

(c) The plane through $(1, -1, -6)$, $(3, 4, 0)$, and $(-1, -8, 2)$.

(d) The plane through $(0, -4, -1)$ containing the line

$\begin{aligned} x &= 2 - t \\ y &= -1 + 4t \\ z &= 5t - 2 \end{aligned}$

42. Find a scalar equation for each plane.

(a) The plane through $(2, -1, -1)$ parallel to $3x - y + 2z - 3 = 0$.

(b) The plane through the points $(1, 2, 3)$, $(2, 3, 4)$, and $(4, 5, 5)$.

(c) The plane through the point $(-3, 2, -4)$ perpendicular to the line $(x - 1, y, z + 2) = s(2, -1, 3)$.

(d) The plane through the point $(1, -1, -1)$ parallel to the plane
$$x = 2 - 3s + t$$
$$y = -1 - s + 4t$$
$$z = 4 + s$$

43. Rewrite each equation as a scalar equation of the plane.
(a) $\overrightarrow{OP} = (2 + s + t, 1 - 2t, 3s - 3t)$
(b) $(x, y, z) = (1, 0, -1) + s(2, 0, 1) + t(1, -2, -5)$

44. Find vector and parametric equations of each plane.
(a) $x + 2y + 3z = 1$
(b) $(x + 1, y - 2, z) \cdot (2, -1, 6) = 0$

45. Find the point of intersection of the given line and the given plane.
(a) $l: \dfrac{x - 2}{3} = \dfrac{y}{2} = \dfrac{z + 1}{-1}$ $\pi: 2x - 3y + 3z - 1 = 0$

(b) $l: \dfrac{x + 2}{5} = y - 1 = \dfrac{z}{-2}$ $\pi: 2x + 3y - z + 2 = 0$

(c) $l: (x, y, z) = (1, 1, -1) + t(1, 0, -4)$
$\pi: (2, 1, -1) \cdot (x, y, z) = 3$

46. Find the intersection, if any, of the given line with the given plane.
(a) $l: \dfrac{x - 2}{2} = \dfrac{y}{-3} = \dfrac{z + 1}{4}$ $\pi: 2x - 3y + z - 4 = 0$

(b) $x = 1 + 3t$
$l: y = -2 - t$ $\pi: x - 2y - z + 5 = 0$
$z = 4 + 3t$

(c) $l: (x, y, z) = (2, -1, 0) + t(0, 1, -1)$
$\pi: (3, 1, -2) \cdot (x, y, z) = 4$

(d) $l: \dfrac{x - 1}{3} = \dfrac{y + 1}{-2} = z$ $\pi: 2x + 2y - 2z + 5 = 0$

(e) $l: (x, y, z) = (2, -2, 2) + r(-1, -1, -3)$
$\pi: (2, 1, -1) \cdot (x, y, z) = -2$

(f) $l: \dfrac{x - 1}{2} = \dfrac{y + 1}{-3} = \dfrac{z}{-3}$ $\pi: 3x - 2y + 4z - 10 = 0$

47. (a) Find the parametric equations of the line of intersection of the following planes.
$\pi_1: 2x - y + z - 3 = 0$ $\pi_2: 3x + 2y + z - 4 = 0$
(b) Show that the direction vector of the line of intersection is a multiple of the cross product of the normals.

48. Find the intersection, if any, of the following pairs of planes.
(a) $\pi_1: 3x + y - z - 4 = 0$ $\pi_2: 2x - 3y + z - 6 = 0$
(b) $\pi_1: 2x - y + 3z - 4 = 0$
$x = 2 + s - t$
$\pi_2: 4x - 2y + 6z - 12 = 0$
(c) $\pi_1: y = 1 - s + t$
$z = -3 + 2s - 3t$ $\pi_2: 5x - y - 9 = 0$

(d)

$$\pi_1: 3x - 4z + 2 = 0 \qquad \begin{array}{l} x = 1 - 2s + 3t \\ \pi_2: y = 2 + s - 4t \\ z = t \end{array}$$

49. Classify, using normals, the intersections of the planes.

(a) $\begin{array}{l} 2x - y + z + 1 = 0 \\ x + 2y - z + 2 = 0 \\ 3x + 6y - 3z + 9 = 0 \end{array}$ (b) $\begin{array}{l} 3x + 2y - z + 10 = 0 \\ 2x - y + 3z - 4 = 0 \\ 4x + 3y - 2z + 3 = 0 \end{array}$

(c) $\begin{array}{l} 5x + 2y + z - 3 = 0 \\ x + 3y - 2z + 1 = 0 \\ 2x - 7y + 7z + 8 = 0 \end{array}$ (d) $\begin{array}{l} x - y + z + 3 = 0 \\ 2x - 2y + 2z + 7 = 0 \\ -3x + 3y - 3z + 1 = 0 \end{array}$

(e) $\begin{array}{l} 3x + y - z = 0 \\ 2x + 4y - 4z + 3 = 0 \\ x + 7y - 7z + 2 = 0 \end{array}$

50. Classify the intersection of the planes using normals. The answer may depend on the value of k.

$$\begin{array}{l} 4x - 2y + z - 15 = 0 \\ 3x + y - z + 10 = 0 \\ x - 3y + kz + 4 = 0 \end{array}$$

51. For each of the systems of equations in Question 49, solve the system by elimination and classify it as consistent or inconsistent, dependent or independent.

TWENTIETH CENTURY MATHEMATICIANS

D r. Garrett Birkhoff of Harvard University came to the study of mathematics through the example of his father, Dr. George David Birkhoff, one of the first Americans to be ranked among the world's greatest mathematicians. Although as a boy the younger Birkhoff embraced a wide range of interests, on his father's caution that he would have to make a living when he graduated, he prepared in college for a career as a mathematical physicist.

The discoveries of scientists are often pre-dated by the theoretical work of mathematicians. In his post-graduate work at Cambridge, Birkhoff was lead to the edge of knowledge in mathematical physics and beyond into the world of abstract algebra. It is in this area that he has made monumental contributions to mathematics. At first, in the early 1930s, he began work on a new branch of mathematics which he termed *lattice theory*. Work in this field was being carried out at the same time in Germany under Dedekind, but Birkhoff's efforts were significant enough to earn the young mathematician a laudable reputation. It is his continuing work in this field that has given him the most satisfaction.

In collaboration with Dr. Saunders MacLane, he wrote the classic text *A Survey of Modern Algebra*. He "found it most unfortunate that one studied algebra and geometry exclusively in high school, followed by three years of calculus in college, with little visible connection between them." So in this text they "tried not to lose sight of the fact that, for many students, the value of algebra lies in its applications to other fields: higher analysis, geometry, physics, and philosophy." The book remains a standard reference for scores of students of mathematics, both applied and pure.

Dr. Birkhoff himself never lost interest in the applications of abstract algebra. During the Second World War he applied his mathematical skills to the problems of fluid mechanics as an aid to both the Army and the Navy. In this work and in discussions with John von Neumann he "realized that the computer was going to influence profoundly the nature of applied mathematics." Accordingly he worked in the field of scientific computing. In work at Westinghouse in the 1950s he and a colleague related the theory of vector lattices to nuclear reactors.

This man who joined the faculty of Harvard in 1936 on the occasion of that institution's tricentennial is himself an institution among mathematicians. Although he claims that at Harvard "we always felt that inbreeding was a weakness" he followed his father to Harvard as a student and later a faculty member. From this post he has, on his own and in collaboration with scores of worthy colleagues, influenced immeasurably the development of modern algebra.

CHAPTER 7

TRANSLATIONS

REVIEW AND PREVIEW TO CHAPTER 7

Completing The Square

Completing the square in an equation enables us to identify its graph geometrically. For example:

$$x^2 + y^2 + 6x - 2y = -6$$
$$x^2 + 6x \qquad\qquad + y^2 - 2y = -6$$
$$x^2 + 6x + 3^2 + y^2 - 2y + (-1)^2 = -6 + 3^2 + (-1)^2$$
$$(x + 3)^2 + (y - 1)^2 = 4$$

From this we deduce that the graph is a circle with centre $C(-3, 1)$ and radius 2.

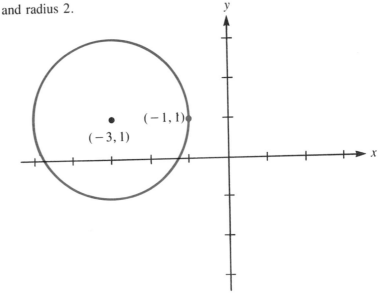

EXERCISE 1

1. Complete the square in each of the following.
   (a) $x^2 + 10x = 0$
   (b) $x^2 - 3x = 0$
   (c) $4x^2 + 4x = 0$
   (d) $4y^2 - 3y = 0$

2. Complete the square and identify the graph.
   (a) $x^2 + 10x + y^2 + 4y = 0$
   (b) $x^2 - 3x + y^2 - 3y = 0$
   (c) $x^2 + 2x - 4y + 9 = 0$
   (d) $x^2 + y^2 - 6x + 8y = 0$
   (e) $2x^2 + 5x + 2y^2 - 11y = 0$
   (f) $6x^2 - 11x + 6y^2 + 5y = 0$

Conics

The types of conics are circles, ellipses, parabolas, and hyperbolas. These curves have a geometric definition and meaning coming from their appearance as sections of a cone by a plane.

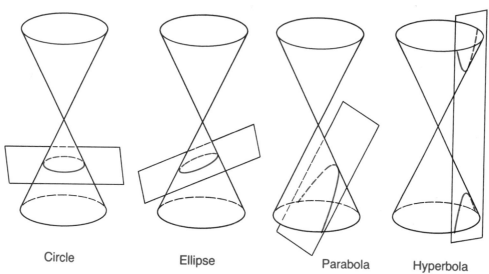

Circle   Ellipse   Parabola   Hyperbola

The extreme cases where we slice the cone and obtain a single point, a line, or a pair of intersecting lines are called degenerate conic sections.

INTRODUCTION

We introduce Cartesian coordinates for the purpose of treating geometric objects algebraically. We saw this process in action in Chapters 4, 5, and 6 where we applied it to vectors, lines, and planes.

In this chapter (and in Chapters 8 and 9) we need to examine, more closely, what happens when a transformation is applied. For this we require a notation for a geometric point and its image, as well as a notation that keeps track of the coordinates associated with the point and its image.

7.1 COORDINATES

To introduce Cartesian coordinates into the geometric plane we choose an origin, an x-axis, and a y-axis. In this way to each geometric point P in the plane there corresponds a unique pair (x_P, y_P) of numbers. Using the subscript notation (x_P, y_P) allows us to keep track of the point P whose coordinates we have determined. When no confusion is likely we write (x, y) for the coordinates of a general point P.

Let us see how this notation can be used to link the geometry and the algebra of a line in the plane.

Example 1 Given the line l whose equation is $x + 2y - 4 = 0$:
(a) State a condition that determines whether a point P lies on l.
(b) Suppose Q is a point such that $x_Q = 2$ and $y_Q = 5$. Does Q lie on l?
(c) Suppose R is a point on l and $y_R = 1$. Find x_R.

Solution (a) If P lies on l, its coordinates satisfy the equation; that is,

$$x_P + 2y_P - 4 = 0$$

(b) If Q lies on l, its coordinates satisfy the equation. We test Q using this criterion.

$$x_Q + 2y_Q - 4 = 2 + 2(5) - 4$$
$$= 8$$

Since this is not 0, Q does not lie on l.

(c) Since R does lie on l

$$x_R + 2y_R - 4 = 0$$

Since $y_R = 1$, $x_R + 2(1) - 4 = 0$

$$x_R = 2$$

In general, if a curve $\mathscr{C}$ in the plane is given by an equation, then a point P lies on $\mathscr{C}$ if, and only if, the coordinates x_P and y_P satisfy the equation.

Example 2 Suppose a curve $\mathscr{C}$ is given by the equation

$$x^2 + y^2 + 6x - 8y = 0$$

Describe this curve geometrically.

Solution We complete the square

$$x^2 + y^2 + 6x - 8y = 0$$
$$x^2 + 6x \qquad + y^2 - 8y \qquad = 0$$
$$x^2 + 6x + 3^2 + y^2 - 8y + (-4)^2 = 3^2 + (-4)^2$$
$$(x + 3)^2 + (y - 4)^2 = 25$$

So a point $P(x_P, y_P)$ lies on this curve if, and only if,

$$(x_P + 3)^2 + (y_P - 4)^2 = 25$$

We recognize this as the equation of a circle with centre $C(-3, 4)$ and radius 5.

We can reverse this process and set up links from geometry to algebra.

Example 3 Find an equation for the curve $\mathscr{C}$ that is the set of all points equidistant from the points $A(1, 2)$ and $B(-1, 3)$.

Solution Let P be a point equidistant from A and B.

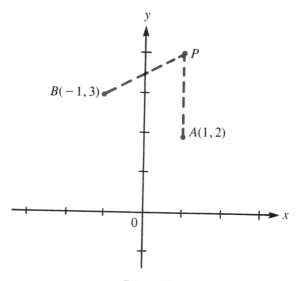

Then

$$PA = PB$$
$$\sqrt{(x_P - 1)^2 + (y_P - 2)^2} = \sqrt{(x_P + 1)^2 + (y_P - 3)^2}$$

Hence an equation for $\mathscr{C}$ is

$$\sqrt{(x - 1)^2 + (y - 2)^2} = \sqrt{(x + 1)^2 + (y - 3)^2}$$

We can simplify this equation as follows.

$$(x - 1)^2 + (y - 2)^2 = (x + 1)^2 + (y - 3)^2$$
$$x^2 - 2x + 1 + y^2 - 4y + 4 = x^2 + 2x + 1 + y^2 - 6y + 9$$
$$- 2x - 4y + 5 = 2x - 6y + 10$$
$$- 4x + 2y - 5 = 0$$

Hence the set of all points equidistant from A to B is the line with the equation $4x - 2y + 5 = 0$

EXERCISE 7.1

A 1. Let a point P be given. State a geometric meaning for each of the quantities listed.

(a) $|x_P|$ (b) $\sqrt{x_P^2 + y_P^2}$

(c) $|y_P - 1|$ (d) $|x_P| + |y_P|$

(e) $\dfrac{y_P}{x_P}$ (f) $|x_P y_P|$

2. Let points P and Q be given. State a geometric meaning for the following quantities.

(a) $\sqrt{(x_P - x_Q)^2 + (y_P - y_Q)^2}$ (b) $\dfrac{y_P - y_Q}{x_P - x_Q}$

(c) $\frac{1}{2}|x_P y_Q - x_Q y_P|$ (d) $\dfrac{x_P x_Q + y_P y_Q}{\sqrt{x_P^2 + y_P^2} \sqrt{x_Q^2 + y_Q^2}}$

B 3. Given the line l whose equation is $4x - 2y + 5 = 0$:

(a) State a condition which determines whether a point P lies on l.

(b) Suppose Q is a point such that $x_Q = 3$ and $y_Q = 4$. Does Q lie on l?

(c) Suppose R is a point on l and $x_R = y_R$. Find the coordinates of R.

4. Identify, geometrically, the curves whose equations are given.

(a) $x^2 + y^2 - 4 = 0$ (b) $x^2 + y^2 + 10x + 4y = 0$

(c) $2x^2 + 2y^2 + 3x + 3y = 0$

(d) $x^2 + y^2 - 4x + 6y - 8 = 0$

5. Find the equation of the set of all points equidistant from the given points A and B.

(a) $A(0, 0), B(2, -2)$ (b) $A(5, 3), B(-7, 3)$

(c) $A(5, 1), B(5, -3)$ (d) $A(0, 1), B(0, -1)$

C 6. Identify, geometrically, the curves whose equations are given.

(a) $|x| = 1$ (b) $|x| + |y| = 1$

(c) $|x| - |y| = 0$ (d) $x^2 + y^2 = 0$

7. Find an equation for the set $\mathscr{C}$ of all points P equidistant from the line $x + 1 = 0$ and the point $F(1, 0)$, as follows.
   (a) Find the distance from P to l.
   (b) Evaluate PF.
   (c) Equate the results from parts (a) and (b) and simplify.
   (d) Identify the curve.

8. Find an equation for the set $\mathscr{C}$ of all points P that satisfy the product of the slopes of the lines joining P to $F(-1, 0)$ and $G(1, 0)$ respectively is 1, as follows.
   (a) Find the slope of the line joining P and F.
   (b) Repeat part (a) but for P and G.
   (c) Multiply the results of parts (a) and (b) and equate to 1.
   (d) Simplify and identify the curve.

9. Find an equation for the curve $\mathscr{C}$ consisting of the points P satisfying: the sum of the distances from P to $F(-1, 0)$ and $G(1, 0)$ is equal to 3. Identify the curve.

7.2 TRANSLATIONS OF LINES AND CIRCLES

A *transformation* is defined whenever the image P' of an arbitrary point P is given.

> A **translation** is a transformation in which the relationship between P and P' is
>
> $$\overrightarrow{PP'} = \vec{w}$$
>
> where $\vec{w}$ is a given vector.

We can reformulate this by saying: a point is translated to its image by $\vec{w}$.

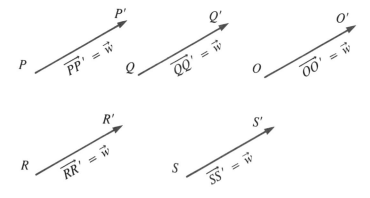

We can restate the definition using position vectors with respect to the origin 0.

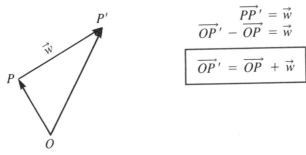

$$\overrightarrow{PP'} = \vec{w}$$
$$\overrightarrow{OP'} - \overrightarrow{OP} = \vec{w}$$

$$\boxed{\overrightarrow{OP'} = \overrightarrow{OP} + \vec{w}}$$

In terms of coordinates, letting $\vec{w} = r\vec{i} + s\vec{j}$, we have

$$(x_{P'}, y_{P'}) = (x_P, x_P + r(1,0) + s(0,1)) = (x_P + r, y_P + s)$$

$$\boxed{\begin{aligned} x_{P'} &= x_P + r \\ y_{P'} &= y_P + s \end{aligned}}$$

We know that distances and angles and, hence, shapes are preserved by translations. In particular, if we translate a line l, then its image l' is also a line; moreover l' is parallel to l.

Example 1 Find an equation of the image l' of the line l: $x + 2y - 4 = 0$, under the translation

$$\begin{cases} x_{P'} = x_P + 3 \\ y_{P'} = y_P + 2 \end{cases}$$

Solution 1 We sketch a graphical solution.

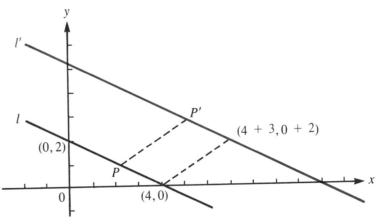

The image of $(4, 0)$ is $(4+3, 0+2) = (7, 2)$. So $(7, 2)$ is on l'. Since l' is parallel to l its equation is of the form $x + 2y + c = 0$. We

substitute $(7, 2)$ to obtain

$$7 + 2(2) + c = 0$$
$$c = -11$$

So an equation for l' is $x + 2y - 11 = 0$.

Solution 2 We can proceed algebraically with no need for sketches or pictures.

We are looking for a relation between $x_{P'}$ and $y_{P'}$ where P' is an arbitrary point of l'. We are given the relationship between x_P and y_P $(x_P + 2y_P - 4 = 0)$ and through the translation we can relate $x_{P'}$ to x_P and $y_{P'}$ to y_P. This enables us to find an equation relating $x_{P'}$ to $y_{P'}$.

$$\begin{cases} x_{P'} = x_P + 3 \\ y_{P'} = y_P + 2 \end{cases} \quad \text{so} \quad \begin{cases} x_P = x_{P'} - 3 \\ y_P = y_{P'} - 2 \end{cases}$$

We know that $\qquad\qquad x_P + 2y_P - 4 = 0$

By substituting we obtain

$$x_{P'} - 3 + 2(y_{P'} - 2) - 4 = 0$$

Dropping the subscripts, an equation for l' is

$$x - 3 + 2(y - 2) - 4 = 0$$
$$x + 2y - 11 = 0$$

Example 2 Find an equation of the image $\mathscr{C}'$ of the circle $\mathscr{C}: x^2 + y^2 = 5^2$ under the translation which maps the origin to $(-3, 4)$.

Solution 1 We give the solution with the geometrical flavour first.

$\mathscr{C}'$ is also a circle of radius 5 but its centre is at $(-3, 4)$ which is the image of the centre of $\mathscr{C}$.

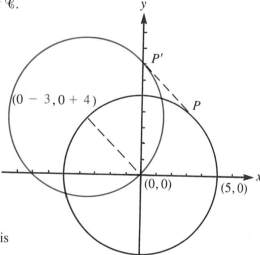

So an equation for $\mathscr{C}'$ is

$$(x + 3)^2 + (y - 4)^2 = 5^2$$
$$x^2 + 6x + 9 + y^2 - 8y + 16 = 25$$
$$x^2 + y^2 + 6x - 8y = 0$$

Solution 2 We now give a purely algebraic solution.

Let P' be an arbitrary point on $\mathscr{C}'$. Then P' is the image of P on $\mathscr{C}$ under the translation which maps $(0, 0)$ to $(-3, 4)$. This translation is

$$\begin{cases} x_{P'} = x_P - 3 \\ y_{P'} = y_P + 4 \end{cases}$$

Solving this system for x_P and y_P we have

$$\begin{cases} x_P = x_{P'} + 3 \\ y_P = y_{P'} - 4 \end{cases}$$

Since P is on $\mathscr{C}$, $\qquad\qquad\qquad x_P^2 + y_P^2 = 5^2$

so $\qquad\qquad\qquad (x_{P'} + 3)^2 + (y_{P'} - 4)^2 = 5^2$

Dropping the subscripts, an equation for $\mathscr{C}'$ is

$$(x + 3)^2 + (y - 4)^2 = 5^2$$

As in Solution 1, we can expand this to obtain

$$x^2 + y^2 + 6x - 8y = 0$$

Let us consider a more general situation.

Example 3 Using algebra find an equation of the image $\mathscr{C}'$ of the circle $\mathscr{C}$: $x^2 + y^2 = r^2$ under the translation given by

$$\begin{cases} x_{P'} = x_P - g \\ y_{P'} = y_P - f \end{cases}$$

Solution We let P' denote an arbitrary point on $\mathscr{C}'$ and P the corresponding point on $\mathscr{C}$. Solving for x_P and y_P we obtain

$$\begin{cases} x_P = x_{P'} + g \\ y_P = y_{P'} + f \end{cases}$$

Since P is on $\mathscr{C}$ $\qquad\qquad\qquad x_P^2 + y_P^2 = r^2$

so $\qquad\qquad\qquad (x_{P'} + g)^2 + (y_{P'} + f)^2 = r^2$

Hence an equation for $\mathscr{C}'$ is

$$(x + g)^2 + (y + f)^2 = r^2$$

We expand and simplify this to obtain

$$x^2 + 2gx + g^2 + y^2 + 2fy + f^2 - r^2 = 0$$
$$x^2 + y^2 + 2gx + 2fy + g^2 + f^2 - r^2 = 0$$

This is another form of the equation for $\mathscr{C}'$.

EXERCISE 7.2

A **1.** Suppose A' and B' are the images of the distinct points A and B under a translation. What can be said about the quadrilateral $AA'B'B$?

B **2.** Find the equation for the image l' of the given l, under the translation
$$\begin{cases} x_{P'} = x_P + 3 \\ y_{P'} = y_P + 2 \end{cases}$$
(a) $x - y + 3 = 0$ (b) $2x + 3y - 6 = 0$
(c) $x = 0$ (d) $y = 0$
(e) $x + y + 1 = 0$ (f) $3x - y + 6 = 0$

3. Using the algebraic method, find an equation for the image l' of the given line l, under the translation
$$\begin{cases} x_{P'} = x_P - 3 \\ y_{P'} = y_P + 1 \end{cases}$$
(a) $x = 0$ (b) $y = 0$
(c) $x + y - 2 = 0$ (d) $2x + 3y + 6 = 0$
(e) $15x - 43y + 78 = 0$ (f) $197x + 831y - 347 = 0$

4. Find r and s such that the translation
$$\begin{cases} x_{P'} = x_P + r \\ y_{P'} = y_P + s \end{cases}$$
maps A to A'.
(a) $A(1, 2)$, $A'(3, -3)$ (b) $A(0, 4)$, $A'(-1, 0)$
(c) $A(3, -2)$, $A'(0, 0)$ (d) $A(0, 0)$, $A'(-4, 2)$
(e) $A(-1, 4)$, $A'(17, 11)$ (f) $A(13, 46)$, $A'(-181, 473)$

5. Find the equation of the image $\mathscr{C}'$ of the circle $\mathscr{C}: x^2 + y^2 = 1$ under the translation that maps $(0, 0)$ to the given point. Sketch $\mathscr{C}$ and $\mathscr{C}'$.
(a) $(3, 0)$ (b) $(0, 4)$
(c) $(3, 4)$ (d) $(-1, 2)$
(e) $(-1, -2)$ (f) $(3, -1)$

6. Using the algebraic method, find an equation for the image l' of the line $l: ax + by + c = 0$ under the translation
$$\begin{cases} x_{P'} = x_P + r \\ y_{P'} = y_P + s \end{cases}$$

7. (a) Find all pairs (r, s) such that under the translation
$$\begin{cases} x_{P'} = x_P + r \\ y_{P'} = y_P + s \end{cases}$$
the line $l: ax + by + c = 0$ and its image has the same equation.
(b) Explain this result geometrically.

7.3 TRANSLATIONS OF CONICS IN STANDARD POSITION

For our purposes in this section we must accept the fact that the image of an ellipse under a translation is a congruent ellipse, and similarly for parabolas and hyperbolas. The geometric way of defining conics, which uses only properties of length and distance, makes it evident that translations do not change the shape of conics.

By choosing a coordinate system that takes into account the geometry of the conics we arrive at **standard forms** for their equations. A conic whose equation has standard form is said to be in **standard position**.

STANDARD FORMS

	Ellipse	Parabola	Hyperbola
Equation	$\dfrac{x^2}{a^2} + \dfrac{y^2}{b^2} = 1$ $(a > b > 0)$	$y^2 = ax$	$\dfrac{x^2}{a^2} - \dfrac{y^2}{b^2} = 1$ $(a, b > 0)$
Vertices	$(-a, 0), (a, 0)$	$(0, 0)$	$(-a, 0), (a, 0)$
Centre	$(0, 0)$	none	$(0, 0)$

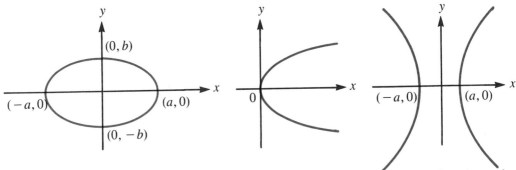

Let us now consider what happens to the equations of conics under a translation.

Example 1 (a) Find the equation of the image $\mathscr{C}'$ of the ellipse $\mathscr{C}: \dfrac{x^2}{16} + \dfrac{y^2}{4} = 1$

under the translation

$$\begin{cases} x_{P'} = x_P + 1 \\ y_{P'} = y_P - 1 \end{cases}$$

(b) Find the coordinates of the centre and vertices of the ellipse $\mathscr{C}'$.

Solution (a) We can make a sketch of $\mathscr{C}$ and then one of $\mathscr{C}'$, but unlike what happened in the case of lines and circles, the equation of $\mathscr{C}'$ is not immediately obvious.

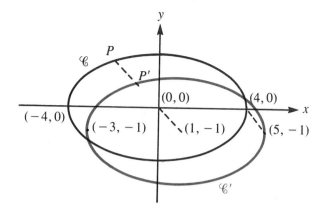

We continue algebraically. Let P' be any point on $\mathscr{C}'$, and P the corresponding point on $\mathscr{C}$. Now

$$\begin{cases} x_{P'} = x_P + 1 \\ y_{P'} = y_P - 1 \end{cases} \qquad \text{so} \qquad \begin{cases} x_P = x_{P'} - 1 \\ y_P = y_{P'} + 1 \end{cases}$$

Since P is on $\mathscr{C}$

$$\frac{x_P{}^2}{16} + \frac{y_P{}^2}{4} = 1$$

so

$$\frac{(x_{P'} - 1)^2}{16} + \frac{(y_{P'} + 1)^2}{4} = 1$$

Hence an equation for $\mathscr{C}'$ is

$$\frac{(x - 1)^2}{16} + \frac{(y + 1)^2}{4} = 1$$

We can expand this and remove fractions as follows.

$$(x - 1)^2 + 4(y + 1)^2 = 16$$
$$x^2 - 2x + 1 + 4(y^2 + 2y + 1) = 0$$
$$x^2 + 4y^2 - 2x + 8y - 11 = 0$$

This is another, equivalent, equation for $\mathscr{C}'$.

(b) The vertices of $\mathscr{C}$ are $(-4, 0)$ and $(4, 0)$ and its centre is $(0, 0)$. The vertices of $\mathscr{C}'$ are

$$(-4 + 1, 0 + 1) = (-3, 1)$$

and

$$(4 + 1, 0 - 1) = (5, -1)$$

and its centre is

$$(0 + 1, 0 - 1) = (1, -1)$$

We notice that the equation given for $\mathscr{C}$ (in standard form) may be written

$$x^2 + 4y^2 - 16 = 0$$

Therefore both $\mathscr{C}$ and $\mathscr{C}'$ have equations of the form

$$ax^2 + by^2 + 2gx + 2fy + c = 0$$

with $a = 1$ and $b = 4$ in both cases.

Next we examine a parabola under translation.

Example 2 (a) Find the equation of the image $\mathscr{C}'$ of the parabola $\mathscr{C}: y^2 = 4x$ under the translation that maps $(0,0)$ to $(-2,3)$.

(b) Find the coordinates of the vertex of $\mathscr{C}'$.

Solution Once again a sketch is useful to keep clear what is happening.

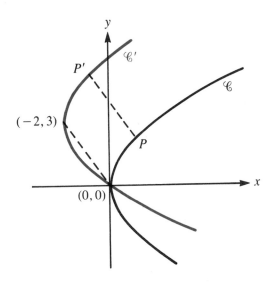

To find an equation of $\mathscr{C}'$ first let P' denote any point on $\mathscr{C}'$ and P the corresponding point on $\mathscr{C}$. Since the translation maps $(0,0)$ to $(-2,3)$ we have, in general,

$$\begin{cases} x_{P'} = x_P - 2 \\ y_{P'} = y_P + 3 \end{cases} \quad \text{so} \quad \begin{cases} x_P = x_{P'} + 2 \\ y_P = y_{P'} - 3 \end{cases}$$

Since P is on $\mathscr{C}$ $y_P^2 = 4x_P$

so $(y_{P'} - 3)^2 = 4(x_{P'} + 2)$

Hence an equation for $\mathscr{C}'$ is

$$(y - 3)^2 = 4(x + 2)$$

We can expand this to obtain

$$y^2 - 6y + 9 = 4x + 8$$
$$y^2 - 4x - 6y + 1 = 0$$

(b) The vertex of $\mathscr{C}$ is $(0,0)$ so the vertex of $\mathscr{C}'$ is
$(0-2, 0+3) = (-2, 3)$.

The equation for $\mathscr{C}'$ is more complicated than the equation for $\mathscr{C}$. However the equation for $\mathscr{C}'$ still fits the pattern

$$ax^2 + by^2 + 2gx + 2fy + c = 0$$

with $a = 0$ and $b = 1$.

For the sake of completeness we see what happens to the equation of a standard hyperbola under translation.

Example 3   Let $\mathscr{C}$ be the hyperbola whose equation is $x^2 - y^2 = 1$. Let $\mathscr{C}'$ denote the image of $\mathscr{C}$ under the translation

$$\begin{cases} x_{P'} = x_P + r \\ y_{P'} = y_P + s \end{cases}$$

Find an equation for $\mathscr{C}'$.

Solution   Let P' be any point on $\mathscr{C}'$ and P be the corresponding point on $\mathscr{C}$.

$$\text{Now} \quad \begin{cases} x_{P'} = x_P + r \\ y_{P'} = y_P + s \end{cases} \quad \text{so} \quad \begin{cases} x_P = x_{P'} - r \\ y_P = y_{P'} - s \end{cases}$$

Since P is on $\mathscr{C}$, $\qquad x_P^2 - y_P^2 = 1$

so $\qquad (x_{P'} - r)^2 - (y_{P'} - s)^2 = 1$

Hence an equation for $\mathscr{C}'$ is

$$(x - r)^2 - (y - s)^2 = 1$$

We can expand this to obtain

$$x^2 - y^2 - 2rx + 2sy + r^2 - s^2 - 1 = 0$$

This, too, is an equation for $\mathscr{C}'$.

We see that in translating circles (Section 7.2), ellipses, parabolas, and hyperbolas in standard position, the equations of the images become more complicated by the presence of terms in x and y. However all fit the pattern

$$ax^2 + by^2 + 2gx + 2fy + c = 0$$

PROBLEMS PLUS

Let R be a point on the conic $ax^2 + by^2 = 1$. Prove that the tangent line to the conic at R is given by

$$ax_R x + by_R y = 1.$$

EXERCISE 7.3

B **1.** Find the equation of the image $\mathscr{C}'$ of the ellipse $\mathscr{C}$ under the translation

$$\begin{cases} x_{P'} = x_P + 2 \\ y_{P'} = y_P + 3 \end{cases}$$

Sketch $\mathscr{C}$ and $\mathscr{C}'$, labelling the vertices and the centre of each.

(a) $\dfrac{x^2}{9} + \dfrac{y^2}{4} = 1$ (b) $\dfrac{x^2}{16} + \dfrac{y^2}{9} = 1$

(c) $\dfrac{x^2}{4} + y^2 = 1$ (d) $\dfrac{x^2}{25} + \dfrac{y^2}{9} = 1$

2. Find the equation of the image $\mathscr{C}'$ of the parabola $\mathscr{C}$ under the translation which maps the origin to $(1, -2)$. Sketch $\mathscr{C}$ and $\mathscr{C}'$ labelling the vertex of each.

(a) $y^2 = 4x$ (b) $y^2 = x$

(c) $y^2 - 2x = 0$ (d) $3y^2 - x = 0$

3. Find the equation of the image $\mathscr{C}'$ of the hyperbola $\mathscr{C}$ under the translation.

$$\begin{cases} x_{P'} = x_P - 2 \\ y_{P'} = y_P + 1 \end{cases}$$

Sketch $\mathscr{C}$ and $\mathscr{C}'$ labelling the vertices and centre of each.

(a) $\dfrac{x^2}{4} - \dfrac{y^2}{9} = 1$ (b) $\dfrac{x^2}{16} - \dfrac{y^2}{16} = 1$

(c) $\dfrac{x^2}{4} - \dfrac{y^2}{4} = 1$ (d) $x^2 - \dfrac{y^2}{25} = 1$

C **4.** Let $\mathscr{C}$ denote the ellipse $b^2x^2 + a^2y^2 - a^2b^2 = 0$. Let $\mathscr{C}'$ denote the image of $\mathscr{C}$ under the general translation

$$\begin{cases} x_{P'} = x_P + r \\ y_{P'} = y_P + s \end{cases}$$

Find g, f, and c such that

$$b^2x^2 + a^2y^2 + 2gx + 2fy + c = 0$$

is an equation for $\mathscr{C}'$.

5. Let $\mathscr{C}$ denote the parabola $y^2 - 4ax = 0$. Let $\mathscr{C}'$ be the image of $\mathscr{C}$ under the translation that maps the origin to (r, s). Find g, f, and c such that

$$y^2 + 2gx + 2fy + c = 0$$

is an equation for $\mathscr{C}'$.

6. Let $\mathscr{C}$ be the hyperbola $b^2x^2 - a^2y^2 - a^2b^2 = 0$. Let $\mathscr{C}'$ be the image of $\mathscr{C}$ under the translation that maps the origin to (r, s). Find g, f, and c such that

$$b^2x^2 - a^2y^2 + 2gx + 2fy + c = 0$$

is an equation for $\mathscr{C}'$.

7.4   TRANSLATIONS THAT ELIMINATE FIRST-DEGREE TERMS

We have seen that the image of a translation of a conic in standard position has an equation of the form

$$ax^2 + by^2 + 2gx + 2fy + c = 0$$

In this section we begin with instances of this equation, for particular values of a, b, g, h, and c, and show how to translate the associated curves to standard position. This process has the effect of simplifying the equation by eliminating **first-degree terms**, that is, the x-term or the y-term or both. Initially our main technique for doing this is completing the square.

Example 1   (a)   By completing the square, identify the curve whose equation is

$$x^2 + y^2 + 6x - 8y = 0$$

(b)   Identify a translation that eliminates the first-degree terms from this equation.

Solution   (a)
$$x^2 + 6x + y^2 - 8y = 0$$
$$x^2 + 6x + 3^2 + y^2 - 8y + (-4)^2 = 3^2 + (-4)^2$$
$$(x + 3)^2 + (y - 4)^2 = 25$$

So the curve is a circle whose centre is at $(-3, 4)$ and whose radius is 5.

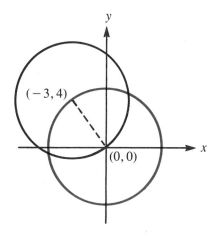

(b)   The translation that maps $(-3, 4)$ to $(0, 0)$, or equivalently maps $(0, 0)$ to $(3, -4)$, maps the given circle into a circle whose centre is at the origin, and so has the equation $x^2 + y^2 - 25 = 0$. This equation has no first degree terms. So the desired translation is given by

$$\begin{cases} x_{P'} = x_P + 3 \\ y_{P'} = y_P - 4 \end{cases}$$

Example 2 (a) By completing the square, identify a translation that eliminates the first degree terms from the equation

$$16x^2 + 25y^2 - 160x - 200y + 400 = 0$$

(b) Identify the graph of this equation.

Solution (a)

$$16x^2 - 160x + 25y^2 - 200y = -400$$
$$16(x^2 - 10x) + 25(y^2 - 8y) = -400$$
$$16\ x^2 - 10x + (-5)^2 + 25\ y^2 - 8y + (-4)^2 = -400 + 16(-5)^2 + 25(-4^2)$$
$$16(x - 5)^2 + 25(y - 4)^2 = 400$$
$$\frac{(x - 5)^2}{25} + \frac{(y - 4)^2}{16} = 1$$

The translation that maps $(5, 4)$ to $(0, 0)$, given by

$$\begin{cases} x_{P'} = x_P - 5 \\ y_{P'} = y_P - 4 \end{cases}$$

eliminates the first degree terms.

(b) The image of the given curve under the translation we just found is the ellipse

$$\frac{x^2}{25} + \frac{y^2}{16} = 1$$

So the given curve is an ellipse.

We now consider an example where completing the square is not feasible, yet a translation can be found to eliminate the first degree terms.

Example 3 The curve $\mathscr{C}$ has the equation

$$x^2 - xy + y^2 + 7x - 8y + 18 = 0$$

Find a translation such that the image curve $\mathscr{C}'$ has an equation

$$x^2 - xy + y^2 + c = 0$$

and determine the number c.

Solution We have to find r and s such that the translation

$$\begin{cases} x_{P'} = x_P + r \\ y_{P'} = y_P + s \end{cases}$$

maps $\mathscr{C}$ to $\mathscr{C}'$, and $\mathscr{C}'$ has the equation $x^2 - xy + y^2 + c = 0$.

Let P' be any point on $\mathscr{C}'$, and P the corresponding point on $\mathscr{C}$. Then

$$\begin{cases} x_P = x_{P'} - r \\ y_P = y_{P'} - s \end{cases}$$

so

$$(x_{P'} - r)^2 - (x_{P'} - r)(y_{P'} - s) + (y_{P'} - s)^2$$
$$+ 7(x_{P'} - r) - 8(y_{P'} - s) + 18 = 0$$

Hence an equation for $\mathscr{C}'$ is

$$(x - r)^2 - (x - r)(y - s) + (y - s)^2$$
$$+ 7(x - r) - 8(y - s) + 18 = 0$$

Collecting like terms we obtain

$$x^2 - xy + y^2 - (2r - s - 7)x - (-r + 2s + 8)y + c = 0$$

where $c = r^2 - rs + s^2 - 7r + 8s + 18$.

We require this equation for $\mathscr{C}'$ to have no first-degree terms, so we choose r and s to satisfy

$$2r - s - 7 = 0 \quad \text{①} \quad \text{and} \quad -r + 2s + 8 = 0 \quad \text{②}$$

Equation 1 gives $s = 2r - 7$. Substituting in Equation 2 we obtain

$$-r + 2(2r - 7) + 8 = 0$$
$$r = 2$$

Substituting in Equation 1 we get $s = -3$.
For this choice of r and s we have

$$c = 2^2 - 2(-3)^3 - 7(2) + 8(-3) + 18 = -1$$

The translation

$$\begin{cases} x_{P'} = x_P + 2 \\ y_{P'} = y_P - 3 \end{cases}$$

has the required property. The image $\mathscr{C}'$ of the given curve $\mathscr{C}$ under this translation satisfies the equation

$$x^2 - xy + y^2 + c = 0$$

where $c = -1$.

It is no harder to do this sort of algebra in general.

Theorem

If the curve $\mathscr{C}$ has the equation

$$ax^2 + 2hxy + by^2 + 2gx + 2fy + c = 0$$

where $ab - h^2 \neq 0$, then there is a translation such that the image curve $\mathscr{C}'$ satisfies the equation

$$ax^2 + 2hxy + by^2 + d = 0$$

for a unique number d.

The proof of this is requested in the exercise. The condition $ab - h^2 \neq 0$ assumed in this theorem is critical. If $ab - h^2 = 0$, it is *not possible* to eliminate the first-degree terms using a translation. We see this in the next example.

Example 4   An equation for the curve $\mathscr{C}$ is $y^2 - x - 2y = 0$.
(a) Show that the image $\mathscr{C}'$ of $\mathscr{C}$ under any translation has an equation that has a non-zero x-term.
(b) Find a translation that eliminates the y-term, and hence identify $\mathscr{C}$.

Solution   (a) Consider the translation given by

$$\begin{cases} x_{P'} = x_P + r \\ y_{P'} = y_P + s \end{cases}$$

Let P' by any point on $\mathscr{C}'$, and P the corresponding point on $\mathscr{C}$. Since

$$\begin{cases} x_P = x_{P'} - r \\ y_P = y_{P'} - s \end{cases}$$

an equation for $\mathscr{C}'$ is

$$(y_{P'} - s)^2 - (x_{P'} - r) - 2(y_{P'} - s) = 0$$

Expanding and dropping subscripts we get

$$y^2 - x - (2s + 2)y + s^2 + r + 2s = 0$$

Since the coefficient of x is -1, no matter what r and s are, there is no translation that eliminates the x-term.

(b) We see that choosing $s = -1$ gives an image curve $\mathscr{C}'$ that satisfies

$$y^2 - x + r - 1 = 0$$

A further choice of $r = 1$ gives the curve

$$y^2 - x = 0$$
$$y^2 = x$$

So $\mathscr{C}'$ is a parabola, and thus $\mathscr{C}$ is a parabola. The translation is

$$\begin{cases} x_{P'} = x_P + 1 \\ y_{P'} = y_P - 1 \end{cases}$$

EXERCISE 7.4

B **1.** By completing the square, identify a translation that eliminates the first degree terms from the given equation and so identify the corresponding curve.
(a) $x^2 + 4y^2 + 4x - 24y + 36 = 0$
(b) $4x^2 + 9y^2 - 8x - 3 = 0$
(c) $x^2 - y^2 - 6x - 4y + 4 = 0$
(d) $3x^2 - 2y^2 + 6x + 4y = 0$

2. Find a translation that eliminates the first degree terms from the given equation
   (a) $x^2 - xy + 2y^2 + 3x - 5y + 3 = 0$
   (b) $xy + x + y = 0$
   (c) $2x^2 + 2xy - 3y^2 + 10x - 2y + 8 = 0$
   (d) $3x^2 + 4xy + 5y^2 - 4x - 10y = 0$

3. Find a translation for which the image curve has the standard equation for a parabola. Locate the vertex of each given parabola.
   (a) $y^2 - 4x - 4y + 8 = 0$
   (b) $y^2 - 4x + 2y + 9 = 0$
   (c) $y^2 - 3x + 4y + 1 = 0$
   (d) $5y^2 - x - 10y = 0$

C 4. Using a suitable translation, show that the curve $y^2 = px + qx^2$ is an ellipse or circle if $q < 0$ and a hyperbola if $q > 0$.

5. Prove the theorem stated in Section 7.4.

7.5 REVIEW EXERCISE

1. Find the images of the points $A(3, 1)$, $B(-4, 3)$, $C(-1, -2)$, and $D(1, -3)$ under the following translations. Sketch $ABCD$ and $A'B'C'D'$.

   (a) $\begin{cases} x_{P'} = x_P + 1 \\ y_{P'} = y_P - 1 \end{cases}$

   (b) $\begin{cases} x_{P'} = x_P - 2 \\ y_{P'} = y_P + 3 \end{cases}$

   (c) $\begin{cases} x_{P'} = x_P + 1 \\ y_{P'} = y_P + 2 \end{cases}$

   (d) $\begin{cases} x_{P'} = x_P - 4 \\ y_{P'} = y_P - 3 \end{cases}$

2. Find a translation of the form $x_{P'} = x_P + r$ and $y_{P'} = y_P + r$ that maps the line l: $2x - y = 5$ to the line l': $2x - y = 11$.

3. For the given line l and given point P, find r such that under the translation
   $$\begin{cases} x_{P'} = x_P + r \\ y_{P'} = y_P \end{cases}$$
   the image l' or l passes through P.
   (a) $3x + y + 2 = 0$, $P(2, 1)$
   (b) $x + y - 3 = 0$, $P(-1, 0)$
   (c) $2x - y + 4 = 0$, $P(0, 0)$
   (d) $-3x + 4y - 7 = 0$, $P(6, -5)$

4. Under what conditions is l': $y = 3x - 5$ the image of l: $y = 3x + 7$ under the translation $x_{P'} = x_P + r$, $y_{P'} = y_P + s$?

5. Find the equation of the image $\mathscr{C}'$ of the circle $\mathscr{C}: x^2 + y^2 = 5^2$ under the translation that maps $(0, 0)$ to the given point. Sketch $\mathscr{C}$ and $\mathscr{C}'$.

(a) $(3, 4)$

(b) $(-4, 3)$

(c) $\left(\dfrac{5}{\sqrt{2}}, -\dfrac{5}{\sqrt{2}}\right)$

(d) $\left(-\dfrac{5}{2}, -\dfrac{5\sqrt{3}}{2}\right)$

6. For each of the following circles find a translation that maps the centre to the origin and find the equation of the image circle.

(a) $x^2 + y^2 - 4x + 6y + 12 = 0$

(b) $x^2 + y^2 + 4x + 6y - 18 = 0$

(c) $x^2 + y^2 + 24x + 10y = 0$

(d) $x^2 + y^2 - 10x - 24y = 0$

7. Find equations for the images $\mathscr{C}'$ of the given curves $\mathscr{C}$ under the translation

$$\begin{cases} x_{P'} = x_P - 2 \\ y_{P'} = y_P - 1 \end{cases}$$

(a) $y^2 - 4x + 12 = 0$

(b) $y^2 - 2x^2 - 2y + 6x - 12 = 0$

(c) $4x^2 + 9y^2 + 24x + 36y + 36 = 0$

(d) $2x^2 + 3y^2 - 12x + 12y + 24 = 0$

(e) $3x^2 - y^2 - 6x - 4y - 1 = 0$

(f) $x^2 + y = 0$

8. Find (r, s) such that the translation

$$\begin{cases} x_{P'} = x_P + r \\ y_{P'} = y_P + s \end{cases}$$

will eliminate the first degree terms from the following. Identify the image curve as an ellipse or hyperbola.

(a) $y^2 - 2x^2 - 2y + 6x - 12 = 0$

(b) $2x^2 + 3y^2 - 12x + 12y + 24 = 0$

(c) $3x^2 - y^2 - 6x - 4y - 2 = 0$

(d) $4x^2 + 9y^2 + 24x + 36y + 36 = 0$

9. For each of the following curves find a translation that reduces the equation to the form

$$ax^2 + 2hxy + by^2 + c = 0$$

(a) $3x^2 + 2xy + 5y^2 + 6x - 26y + 44 = 0$

(b) $x^2 + 2xy - y^2 + 2x + 10y = 0$

(c) $x^2 + xy + y^2 - 14x - 13y + 60 = 0$

(d) $2xy - 18x + 20y - 181 = 0$

10. For each of the following parabolas find a translation that reduces the equation of the image to standard form. Find the vertex of the given parabola.

(a) $y^2 - 4x + 14y + 1 = 0$

(b) $y^2 - 4x + 10y + 1 = 0$

(c) $y^2 - 8x + 14y + 1 = 0$

(d) $y^2 - 8x - 8y = 0$

7.6 CHAPTER 7 TEST

1. Find an equation for the line with the property that every point R on the line satisfies $3x_R + 5y_R - 8 = 0$.

2. Find r such that under the translation
    $$\begin{cases} x_{P'} = x_P + r \\ y_{P'} = y_P \end{cases}$$
    the image of l' of the line l: $3x + y + 2 = 0$ passes through the point $P(1, 2)$.

3. What is the centre of the image $\mathscr{C}'$ of the circle $\mathscr{C}$: $x^2 + y^2 = 25$ under the translation
    $$\begin{cases} x_{P'} = x_P - 3 \\ y_{P'} = y_P + 4 \end{cases}$$

4. There is a translation that maps the ellipse given by
    $$4x^2 + 16y^2 - 24x + 32y + 36 = 0$$
    to standard position. What are the vertices of the image ellipse in standard position?

5. Find (r, s) such that the translation
    $$\begin{cases} x_{P'} = x_P + r \\ y_{P'} = y_P + s \end{cases}$$
    eliminates the first-degree terms from
    $$2x^2 + 3y^2 + 12x + 12y + 24 = 0.$$

6. Find c such that a translated image of
    $$\mathscr{C}: x^2 - 2xy - y^2 - 2x + 10y = 0$$
    satisfies the equation $x^2 - 2xy - y^2 + c = 0$.

7. (a) Find all pairs (r, s) such that under the translation
    $$\begin{cases} x_{P'} = x_P + r \\ y_{P'} = y_P + s \end{cases}$$
    the image of the circle $x^2 + y^2 = 1$ passes through the origin.
    (b) Explain this result geometrically.

PROBLEMS PLUS

Find $k > 0$, given that the line $x + y = \sqrt{2k}$ is tangent to the circle $x^2 + y^2 = k$.

PROBLEMS PLUS

Let R be a point on the parabola $y^2 = 4ax$. Prove that the tangent line to the parabola at R is given by
$$y_R y = 2a(x + x_R).$$

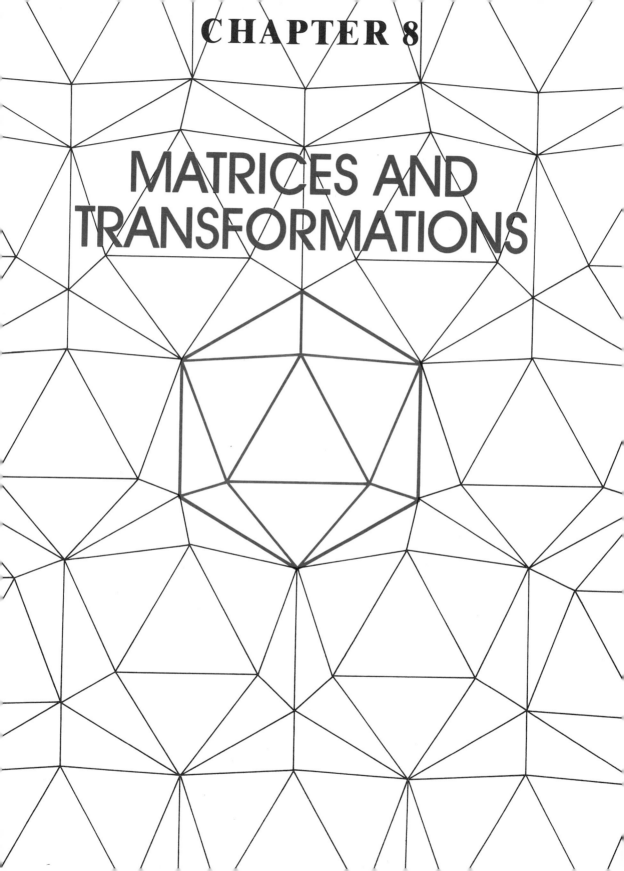

CHAPTER 8

MATRICES AND TRANSFORMATIONS

REVIEW AND PREVIEW TO CHAPTER 8

EXERCISE 1   **Transformations**

1. Draw the image of each figure under *reflection* in the indicated line.

   (a) F   (i)   reflected in the line l_1

   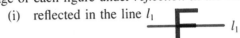

   (ii) and in the line l_2.

   (b) G   (i)   reflected in the line l_1

   (ii) and in the line l_2.

2. Draw the image of each figure under *rotation* about the point O through the given angle.

   (a) $\theta = \dfrac{\pi}{4}$ (b) $\theta = 90°$ (c) $\theta = 150°$

   A   B

   • 0   • 0

3. Draw the image of each figure under *projection* onto the given line.

   (a)   W   (b)

4. Draw the image of each figure under *dilatation* of the given factor *k* with the centre *O*.

(a) $k = 2$ (b) $k = \frac{3}{4}$

Addition Formulas For Sine and Cosine

For angles θ_1 and θ_2,

$$\sin (\theta_1 + \theta_2) = \sin \theta_1 \cos \theta_2 + \cos \theta_1 \sin \theta_2$$
$$\cos (\theta_1 + \theta_2) = \cos \theta_1 \cos \theta_2 - \sin \theta_1 \sin \theta_2$$

Example 1   Using the addition formulas for sine and cosine, develop formulas for (a) $\sin (\pi + \theta)$ and (b) $\cos (\pi + \theta)$.

Solution   Recall that $\sin \pi = 0$ and $\cos \pi = -1$.

(a) $\sin(\pi + \theta) = \sin \pi \cos \theta + \cos \pi \sin \theta$
$$= 0 \cos \theta + (-1) \sin \theta$$
$$= -\sin \theta$$

(b) $\cos(\pi + \theta) = \cos \pi \cos \theta - \sin \pi \sin \theta$
$$= (-1) \cos \theta - 0 \sin \theta$$
$$= -\cos \theta$$

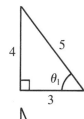

Example 2   If $\cos \theta_1 = \frac{3}{5}$ and $\sin \theta_2 = \frac{12}{13}$, and both θ_1 and θ_2 are acute angles, find $\sin (\theta_1 + \theta_2)$.

Solution   Because $0 < \theta_1 < 90°$ and $\cos \theta_1 = \frac{3}{5}$, $\sin \theta_1 = \frac{4}{5}$.

Because $0 < \theta_2 < 90°$ and $\sin \theta_2 = \frac{12}{13}$, $\cos \theta_2 = \frac{5}{13}$.

So, $\sin(\theta_1 + \theta_2) = \sin \theta_1 \cos \theta_2 + \cos \theta_1 \sin \theta_2$.

$$= \left(\tfrac{4}{5}\right)\left(\tfrac{5}{13}\right) + \left(\tfrac{3}{5}\right)\left(\tfrac{12}{13}\right)$$
$$= \tfrac{20}{65} + \tfrac{36}{65}$$
$$= \tfrac{56}{65}$$

EXERCISE 2

1. Using the addition formulas for sine and cosine, develop formulas for (a) $\sin(90° + \theta)$ and (b) $\cos(90° + \theta)$.

2. Recall that, for an angle θ, $\sin(-\theta) = -\sin\theta$ and $\cos(-\theta) = \cos\theta$. Develop the *difference formulas for sine and cosine*; that is, formulas for (a) $\sin(\theta_1 - \theta_2)$ and (b) $\cos(\theta_1 - \theta_2)$.
   formulas for (a) $\sin(\theta_1 - \theta_2)$ and (b) $\cos(\theta_1 - \theta_2)$.

3. Using the difference formulas for sine and cosine, develop formulas for (a) $\sin(\pi - \theta)$ and (b) $\cos(\pi - \theta)$.

4. Simplify each expression.
   (a) $\sin(\theta + 30°) + \cos(\theta + 60°)$
   (b) $\sin\left(\theta + \dfrac{\pi}{3}\right) - \cos\left(\theta + \dfrac{\pi}{6}\right)$
   (c) $\cos(30° - \theta) - \cos(30° + \theta)$

5. Given that $\sin\theta_1 = \frac{5}{13}$ and $\sin\theta_2 = \frac{4}{5}$, and both θ_1 and θ_2 are acute angles, find
   (a) $\sin(\theta_1 + \theta_2)$ (b) $\cos(\theta_1 + \theta_2)$
   (c) $\sin(\theta_1 - \theta_2)$ (d) $\cos(\theta_2 - \theta_1)$
   (e) $\sin(90° + \theta_1)$ (f) $\cos\left(\theta_2 - \dfrac{\pi}{2}\right)$

INTRODUCTION

In Chapter 7, using translations, we simplified the equations of second degree relations whose graphs were originally not centred at the origin of the specified coordinate system. In Chapter 9, we use rotations to put second degree equations into standard form and their graphs into standard position. In this chapter we prepare for the work of Chapter 9 by developing an approach to transformations based on matrices.

8.1   TRANSFORMATIONS USING MATRICES

Recall from Chapter 7 that a **transformation** is a mapping of the plane to itself; that is, a correspondence assigning points of a plane to other points of the same plane. In this chapter we focus on transformations for which the image P' of the point P is given by a pair of linear equations defining P'.

$$\begin{cases} x_{P'} = ax_P + by_P \\ y_{P'} = cx_P + dy_P \text{ for real numbers } a, b, c, d \end{cases}$$

Example 1   Find the image P' of the point $P(3, 2)$ under the transformation given by the following pair of equations:

$$\begin{cases} x_{P'} = x_P - 2y_P \\ y_{P'} = -x_P + 4y_P \end{cases}$$

Solution   We determine the coordinates of P'.

$$x_{P'} = 3 - 2(2) = 3 - 4 = -1$$
$$y_{P'} = -(3) + 4(2) = -3 + 8 = 5$$

The image of $P(3, 2)$ under this transformation is the point $P'(-1, 5)$. ⬡

Algebraic vectors (or points in the plane) can be represented as *column vectors*; for example the vector

$(3, 2)$ can be written as $\begin{bmatrix} 3 \\ 2 \end{bmatrix}$

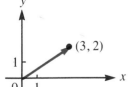

We usually denote column vectors by capital letters, X, Y ... . The column vector associated with a point P is denoted by X_P where

$$X_P = \begin{bmatrix} x_P \\ y_P \end{bmatrix}$$

We extend this form by arranging the coefficients from the equations defining a transformation in an array of 2 rows and 2 columns, known as a **2 × 2 matrix** (read as 'a two-by-two matrix'):

$$\text{transformation} \qquad 2 \times 2 \ matrix$$

$$\begin{cases} x_{P'} = x_P - 2y_P \\ y_{P'} = -x_P + 4y_P \end{cases} \qquad \begin{bmatrix} 1 & -2 \\ -1 & 4 \end{bmatrix}$$

The procedure of finding the image P' of the point $P(3, 2)$ is represented by

$$\begin{bmatrix} 1 & -2 \\ -1 & 4 \end{bmatrix}\begin{bmatrix} 3 \\ 2 \end{bmatrix}$$

To obtain the first entry of the column vector XP', we
  (i) multiply the first element in the first row of the first matrix by the first entry in the column vector, then
  (ii) multiply the second element in the first row of the first matrix by the second entry in the column vector, and, finally,
  (iii) add the products.

$$\begin{bmatrix} 1 & -2 \\ -1 & 4 \end{bmatrix}\begin{bmatrix} 3 \\ 2 \end{bmatrix} = \begin{bmatrix} (1)(3) + (-2)(2) \end{bmatrix} = \begin{bmatrix} -1 \end{bmatrix}$$

To obtain the second entry in the column vector we repeat these steps using the second row of the first matrix with the column vector.

$$\begin{bmatrix} 1 & -2 \\ -1 & 4 \end{bmatrix}\begin{bmatrix} 3 \\ 2 \end{bmatrix} = \begin{bmatrix} -1 \\ (-1)(3) + (4)(2) \end{bmatrix} = \begin{bmatrix} -1 \\ 5 \end{bmatrix}$$

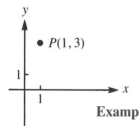

Example 2 Find the image P' of the point $P(1, 3)$ under the transformation represented by each matrix. In each case graph the point and its image.

(a) $\begin{bmatrix} 2 & 1 \\ 4 & -3 \end{bmatrix}$ (b) $\begin{bmatrix} 4 & 1 \\ 0 & 2 \end{bmatrix}$

Solution (a)
$$X_{P'} = \begin{bmatrix} 2 & 1 \\ 4 & -3 \end{bmatrix} X_P = \begin{bmatrix} 2 & 1 \\ 4 & -3 \end{bmatrix}\begin{bmatrix} 1 \\ 3 \end{bmatrix} = \begin{bmatrix} (2)(1) + (1)(3) \\ (4)(1) + (-3)(3) \end{bmatrix} = \begin{bmatrix} 5 \\ -5 \end{bmatrix}$$
So, the image of $P(1, 3)$ under the transformation represented by the matrix $\begin{bmatrix} 2 & 1 \\ 4 & -3 \end{bmatrix}$ is $P'(5, -5)$.

(b) $X_{P'} = \begin{bmatrix} 4 & 1 \\ 0 & 2 \end{bmatrix}\begin{bmatrix} 1 \\ 3 \end{bmatrix} = \begin{bmatrix} (4)(1) + (1)(3) \\ (0)(1) + (2)(3) \end{bmatrix} = \begin{bmatrix} 7 \\ 6 \end{bmatrix}$
So, the image of $P(1, 3)$ under the transformation represented by the matrix $\begin{bmatrix} 4 & 1 \\ 0 & 2 \end{bmatrix}$ is $P'(7, 6)$.

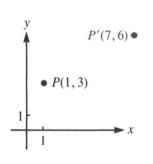

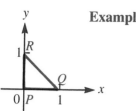

Example 3 Find the image of the figure shown in the diagram under the transformation given by (a) $\begin{bmatrix} 0 & -3 \\ 2 & 5 \end{bmatrix}$ and (b) $\begin{bmatrix} 1 & 3 \\ 0 & 1 \end{bmatrix}$

In each case draw a graph showing the original figure and its image.

Solution (a) We find the image of each vertex of the figure.

$$X_{P'} = \begin{bmatrix} 0 & -3 \\ 2 & 5 \end{bmatrix}\begin{bmatrix} 0 \\ 0 \end{bmatrix} = \begin{bmatrix} (0)(0) + (-3)(0) \\ (2)(0) + (5)(0) \end{bmatrix} = \begin{bmatrix} 0 \\ 0 \end{bmatrix}$$

$$X_{Q'} = \begin{bmatrix} 0 & -3 \\ 2 & 5 \end{bmatrix}\begin{bmatrix} 1 \\ 0 \end{bmatrix} = \begin{bmatrix} (0)(1) + (-3)(0) \\ (2)(1) + (5)(0) \end{bmatrix} = \begin{bmatrix} 0 \\ 2 \end{bmatrix}$$

$$X_{R'} = \begin{bmatrix} 0 & -3 \\ 2 & 5 \end{bmatrix}\begin{bmatrix} 0 \\ 1 \end{bmatrix} = \begin{bmatrix} (0)(0) + (-3)(1) \\ (2)(0) + (5)(1) \end{bmatrix} = \begin{bmatrix} -3 \\ 5 \end{bmatrix}$$

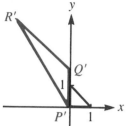

(b) We find the image of each vertex of the figure.

$$X_{P'} = \begin{bmatrix} 1 & 3 \\ 0 & 1 \end{bmatrix}\begin{bmatrix} 0 \\ 0 \end{bmatrix} = \begin{bmatrix} (1)(0) + (3)(0) \\ (0)(0) + (1)(0) \end{bmatrix} = \begin{bmatrix} 0 \\ 0 \end{bmatrix}$$

$$X_{Q'} = \begin{bmatrix} 1 & 3 \\ 0 & 1 \end{bmatrix}\begin{bmatrix} 1 \\ 0 \end{bmatrix} = \begin{bmatrix} (1)(1) + (3)(0) \\ (0)(1) + (1)(0) \end{bmatrix} = \begin{bmatrix} 1 \\ 0 \end{bmatrix}$$

$$X_{R'} = \begin{bmatrix} 1 & 3 \\ 0 & 1 \end{bmatrix}\begin{bmatrix} 0 \\ 1 \end{bmatrix} = \begin{bmatrix} (1)(0) + (3)(1) \\ (0)(0) + (1)(1) \end{bmatrix} = \begin{bmatrix} 3 \\ 1 \end{bmatrix}$$

The procedure followed to find the image of a point suggests a technique for multiplying a 2 × 2 matrix by a 2 × 1 matrix.

For 2 × 2 matrix $M = \begin{bmatrix} a & b \\ c & d \end{bmatrix}$ and column matrix $X = \begin{bmatrix} x \\ y \end{bmatrix}$, the **product MX** is given by

$$MX = \begin{bmatrix} ax + by \\ cx + dy \end{bmatrix}$$

Example 4 Multiply: (a) $\begin{bmatrix} 1 & -2 \\ 0 & 3 \end{bmatrix}\begin{bmatrix} 4 \\ 7 \end{bmatrix}$ (b) $\begin{bmatrix} 7 & 2 \\ 5 & -3 \end{bmatrix}\begin{bmatrix} 4 \\ -1 \end{bmatrix}$

Solution (a) $\begin{bmatrix} 1 & -2 \\ 0 & 3 \end{bmatrix}\begin{bmatrix} 4 \\ 7 \end{bmatrix} = \begin{bmatrix} (1)(4) + (-2)(7) \\ (0)(4) + (3)(7) \end{bmatrix} = \begin{bmatrix} 4 + (-14) \\ 0 + 21 \end{bmatrix} = \begin{bmatrix} -10 \\ 21 \end{bmatrix}$

(b) $\begin{bmatrix} 7 & 2 \\ 5 & -3 \end{bmatrix}\begin{bmatrix} 4 \\ -1 \end{bmatrix} = \begin{bmatrix} (7)(4) + (2)(-1) \\ (5)(4) + (-3)(-1) \end{bmatrix} = \begin{bmatrix} 28 - 2 \\ 20 + 3 \end{bmatrix} = \begin{bmatrix} 26 \\ 23 \end{bmatrix}$

EXERCISE 8.1

A **1.** Multiply.

(a) $\begin{bmatrix} 3 & -2 \\ 4 & 1 \end{bmatrix} \begin{bmatrix} x \\ y \end{bmatrix}$

(b) $\begin{bmatrix} -1 & 5 \\ 7 & 0 \end{bmatrix} \begin{bmatrix} x \\ y \end{bmatrix}$

B **2.** Multiply.

(a) $\begin{bmatrix} 5 & 0 \\ 2 & 3 \end{bmatrix} \begin{bmatrix} 1 \\ -1 \end{bmatrix}$

(b) $\begin{bmatrix} 3 & 8 \\ -2 & 1 \end{bmatrix} \begin{bmatrix} 5 \\ 0 \end{bmatrix}$

(c) $\begin{bmatrix} 2 & 3 \\ -1 & 7 \end{bmatrix} \begin{bmatrix} 0 \\ 2 \end{bmatrix}$

(d) $\begin{bmatrix} 0 & 1 \\ 1 & 0 \end{bmatrix} \begin{bmatrix} 4 \\ -2 \end{bmatrix}$

(e) $\begin{bmatrix} 5 & -3 \\ 4 & 0 \end{bmatrix} \begin{bmatrix} 2 \\ 3 \end{bmatrix}$

(f) $\begin{bmatrix} 1 & 1 \\ 1 & 1 \end{bmatrix} \begin{bmatrix} 3 \\ 5 \end{bmatrix}$

3. Find the image P' of the point P under the transformation defined by the given matrix M. Graph P and P' in each case.

(a) $P(1,5); M = \begin{bmatrix} 0 & -1 \\ 2 & 3 \end{bmatrix}$

(b) $P(2,0); M = \begin{bmatrix} 2 & 7 \\ 1 & 1 \end{bmatrix}$

(c) $P(0,0); M = \begin{bmatrix} 5 & -2 \\ -2 & 3 \end{bmatrix}$

4. (a) Find the image of a point $P(x_P, y_P)$ under the transformation represented by the 2×2 *zero matrix*; that is, the 2×2 matrix with all entries 0. Based on your results explain why such a transformation is called the *zero transformation*.

(b) Find the image of a point P under the transformation represented by the matrix $I = \begin{bmatrix} 1 & 0 \\ 0 & 1 \end{bmatrix}$. Based on your results explain why such a transformation is called the *identity transformation*.

5. Find the image of the figure shown in the diagram under the transformation represented by each matrix. In each case, draw a graph to show the original figure and its image.

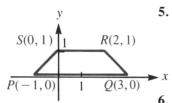

(a) $\begin{bmatrix} 4 & 1 \\ 0 & -1 \end{bmatrix}$

(b) $\begin{bmatrix} 2 & -2 \\ 3 & 1 \end{bmatrix}$

6. (a) Graph the unit square whose vertices are $(0,0)$, $(1,0)$, $(1,1)$, and $(0,1)$.

(b) By finding and graphing the image of each of the vertices of this square under each transformation, graph the image of the square under that transformation.

(i) $\begin{bmatrix} 1 & 0 \\ 0 & -1 \end{bmatrix}$

(ii) $\begin{bmatrix} 4 & 0 \\ 0 & 4 \end{bmatrix}$

(iii) $\begin{bmatrix} 0 & 1 \\ 1 & 0 \end{bmatrix}$ 　　　　　(iv) $\begin{bmatrix} 5 & 0 \\ 0 & 1 \end{bmatrix}$

(v) $\begin{bmatrix} 1 & 0 \\ 0 & 0 \end{bmatrix}$ 　　　　　(vi) $\begin{bmatrix} \frac{\sqrt{3}}{2} & -\frac{1}{2} \\ \frac{1}{2} & \frac{\sqrt{3}}{2} \end{bmatrix}$

(c) After examining the images of the unit square under the transformations of part (b), describe in your own words the effect of each transformation.

7. (a) Find the image P' of $P(4, 2)$ under the transformation given by the matrix $M = \begin{bmatrix} -1 & 3 \\ 0 & 5 \end{bmatrix}$.

　 (b) Find the image P'' of P' under the transformation defined by M.

8. Repeat Question 7 for the general point P given by $X_P = \begin{bmatrix} x_P \\ y_P \end{bmatrix}$.

C 9. A transformation is a *linear transformation* if and only if it satisfies two conditions:
　 (i) It maps the origin to itself.
　 (ii) It maps straight lines to straight lines.
　 Show that any transformation of the plane represented by a non-zero 2×2 matrix is linear.

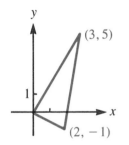

10. The diagram shows the image under a transformation of the triangle whose vertices are $(0, 0)$, $(1, 0)$, and $(0, 1)$. Give two possible matrices of the transformation.

8.2 REFLECTIONS

We are all familiar with real-life examples of reflections. If you look into a mirror you see a reflection or image of yourself that appears to be located on the other side of the mirror at an equal distance from the mirror. It also appears as if an imaginary line joining the original object to its image would intersect the reflecting surface at right angles. We use this as the defining property of a reflection.

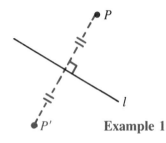

A **reflection in a line** l is a transformation that maps any point P to the point P' such that l is the perpendicular bisector of PP'.

We use this definition to develop the matrices which represent certain special reflections.

Example 1   (a) Develop the matrix of the reflection in the x-axis.

(b) Develop the matrix of the reflection in the line $x - y = 0$.

Solution   (a) We note that, for a general point $P(x_P, y_P)'$ its image point P' under reflection in the x-axis is given by

$$x_{P'} = x_P = 1\, x_P + 0\, y_P$$
$$y_{P'} = -y_P = 0\, x_P + (-1)\, y_P$$

Thus, $T = \begin{bmatrix} 1 & 0 \\ 0 & -1 \end{bmatrix}$ is the matrix of reflection in the x-axis.

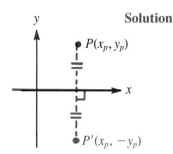

(b) We note that, for a general point $P(x_P, y_P)'$ its image point P' under reflection in the line $x - y = 0$ is given by

$$x_{P'} = y_P = 0\, x_P + 1\, y_P$$
$$y_{P'} = x_P = 1\, x_P + 0\, y_P$$

Thus, $T = \begin{bmatrix} 0 & 1 \\ 1 & 0 \end{bmatrix}$ is the matrix of reflection in the line $x - y = 0$.

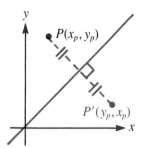

The development of two other standard reflections (in the y-axis and in the line $x + y = 0$) is left to Exercise 8.2. The results however are included here in a summary chart.

Matrices of Reflections	
line of reflection	**matrix of reflection**
x-axis	$\begin{bmatrix} 1 & 0 \\ 0 & -1 \end{bmatrix}$
y-axis	$\begin{bmatrix} -1 & 0 \\ 0 & 1 \end{bmatrix}$
$x - y = 0$ ($y = x$)	$\begin{bmatrix} 0 & 1 \\ 1 & 0 \end{bmatrix}$
$x + y = 0$ ($y = -x$)	$\begin{bmatrix} 0 & -1 \\ -1 & 0 \end{bmatrix}$

It is obvious from the geometry of the situation that a reflection maps any straight line to another straight line. We use this fact in the following example to check our graph of the image of a polygon under a reflection.

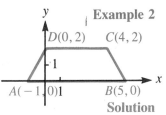

Example 2   (a) Using the definition of a reflection, draw the image of the figure shown under reflection in the y-axis.

(b) Using the appropriate reflection matrix, find the image of each vertex of the figure shown under this reflection, thus checking your graph for (a).

Solution   (a) We draw the image by plotting the image of each vertex, then joining these image points.

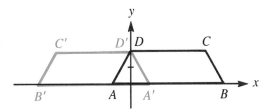

(b) We find the image of each vertex by applying the matrix of a reflection in the y-axis, $\begin{bmatrix} -1 & 0 \\ 0 & 1 \end{bmatrix}$.

$$X_{A'} = \begin{bmatrix} -1 & 0 \\ 0 & 1 \end{bmatrix} \begin{bmatrix} -1 \\ 0 \end{bmatrix} = \begin{bmatrix} 1 \\ 0 \end{bmatrix}$$

$$X_{B'} = \begin{bmatrix} -1 & 0 \\ 0 & 1 \end{bmatrix} \begin{bmatrix} 5 \\ 0 \end{bmatrix} = \begin{bmatrix} -5 \\ 0 \end{bmatrix}$$

$$X_{C'} = \begin{bmatrix} -1 & 0 \\ 0 & 1 \end{bmatrix} \begin{bmatrix} 4 \\ 2 \end{bmatrix} = \begin{bmatrix} -4 \\ 2 \end{bmatrix}$$

$$X_{D'} = \begin{bmatrix} -1 & 0 \\ 0 & 1 \end{bmatrix} \begin{bmatrix} 0 \\ 2 \end{bmatrix} = \begin{bmatrix} 0 \\ 2 \end{bmatrix}$$

The images of the vertices of the original figure as determined using the transformation matrix correspond to those in the graph drawn for (a).

Where a curve is described by an equation it is possible also to find the equation of the image of the curve under a reflection.

Example 3   Find the equation of the image of the line l given by $2x + y = 3$ under reflection in the line $y = -x$.

Solution   The image equated of a reflected line can be determined in at least three ways. *The first two methods use the fact that the image of a line under a reflection is still a line.*

Method 1 *We find the images of two points on the original line, then find the equation of the line through these two image points.*

Consider the points $P(0, 3)$ and $Q(1, 1)$ on the line l.
Because the matrix of the reflection in the line $y = -x$ is

$$T = \begin{bmatrix} 0 & -1 \\ -1 & 0 \end{bmatrix}$$

the image of P is given by

$$X_{P'} = \begin{bmatrix} 0 & -1 \\ -1 & 0 \end{bmatrix} \begin{bmatrix} 0 \\ 3 \end{bmatrix} = \begin{bmatrix} -3 \\ 0 \end{bmatrix}$$

and the image of Q is given by

$$X_{Q'} = \begin{bmatrix} 0 & -1 \\ -1 & 0 \end{bmatrix} \begin{bmatrix} 1 \\ 1 \end{bmatrix} = \begin{bmatrix} -1 \\ -1 \end{bmatrix}$$

The slope m of the line through $P'(3, 0)$ and $Q'(-1, -1)$ is

$$m = \frac{(-1 - 0)}{-1 - (-3)} = -\frac{1}{2}$$

So the line is of the form

$$y = -\tfrac{1}{2}x + b$$

Substituting the coordinates of P' we obtain

$$0 = -\tfrac{1}{2}(3) + b$$

So, $b = -\tfrac{3}{2}$

Thus the equation of the image of the line $2x + y = 3$ is the line

$$y = -\tfrac{1}{2}x - \tfrac{3}{2} \quad \text{or} \quad x + 2y = -3$$

Method 2 *We find the image $\vec{n}'$ of the normal vector $\vec{n}$ to l and of one point on l, then determine the equation of the line l' with normal $\vec{n}'$ through the image point.*
Because the matrix of the reflection in the line $y = -x$ is

$$T = \begin{bmatrix} 0 & -1 \\ -1 & 0 \end{bmatrix}$$

the image of the normal $\vec{n} = (2, 1)$ is given by

$$\vec{n}' = \begin{bmatrix} 0 & -1 \\ -1 & 0 \end{bmatrix} \begin{bmatrix} 2 \\ 1 \end{bmatrix} = \begin{bmatrix} -1 \\ -2 \end{bmatrix}$$

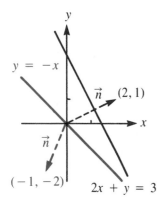

So, the equation of the image line l' is of the form $-x - 2y = c$.

Consider the point P on the line l determined by its x-intercept.
This is given by $X_P = \begin{bmatrix} 1.5 \\ 0 \end{bmatrix}$.

Then $\qquad X_{P'} = \begin{bmatrix} 0 & -1 \\ -1 & 0 \end{bmatrix} \begin{bmatrix} 1.5 \\ 0 \end{bmatrix} = \begin{bmatrix} 0 \\ -1.5 \end{bmatrix}$

Because P' is on the image line,

$$-(0) - 2(-1.5) = c$$
$$3 = c$$

Thus the equation of the image of the line $2x + y = 3$ under reflection in the y-axis is $-x - 2y = 3$ or $x + 2y = -3$.

Method 3 Consider a point P' on the image line l'.

Then, $X_{P'} = TX_P$ for $T = \begin{bmatrix} 0 & -1 \\ -1 & 0 \end{bmatrix}$ and P some point on l.

That is, $\begin{bmatrix} x_{P'} \\ y_{P'} \end{bmatrix} = \begin{bmatrix} 0 & -1 \\ -1 & 0 \end{bmatrix} \begin{bmatrix} x_P \\ y_P \end{bmatrix} = \begin{bmatrix} -y_P \\ -x_P \end{bmatrix}$ where $2x_P + y_P = 3$

$\qquad x_{P'} = -y_P$ so, $\quad y_P = -x_{P'}$

Similarly, $\quad y_{P'} = -x_P$ so, $\quad x_P = -y_{P'}$

Since $\qquad\qquad 2x_P + y_P = 3$

$$2(-y_{P'}) + (-x_{P'}) = 3$$

that is, the image line l' is given by

$$-2y_{P'} - x_{P'} = 3 \quad \text{or} \quad x + 2y = -3$$

EXERCISE 8.2

A 1. What point (or points) do not move (that is, *remain invariant*) under reflection in a given line?

B 2. Find the image of the point $P(1, -2)$ under reflection in each of the lines indicated. For each case, draw a graph showing both P and its image.
   (a) the y-axis (b) the line $x - y = 0$

3. Find the images, P' and Q', of the points $P(5, 0)$ and $Q(2, 3)$ under reflection in each of the lines specified.
   (a) the line $x + y = 0$ (b) the x-axis

4. Develop the matrix of the reflection in each of the following lines.
   (a) the y-axis (b) the line $y = -x$

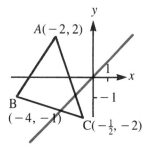

5. (a) Find the distance between points P and Q of Question 3.
   (b) Find the distance between the image points P' and Q' of Question 3(a).
   (c) Repeat part (b) for the image points P' and Q' of Question 3(b).
   (d) By comparing the results of parts (a) and (b) and the results of parts (a) and (c), form a conclusion about the effect of a reflection on distances.

6. (a) Graph the image of the triangle shown under reflection in the line $y = x$ *using the definition of a reflection.*
   (b) By applying the appropriate reflection matrix, find the image of each vertex under the reflection in $y = x$, thus checking your graph for part (a).

7. (a) Find the image P' of the point $P(2, 3)$ under reflection in the x-axis.
   (b) Find the image P'' of P' under reflection in the line $y = x$.
   (c) Find the image $P*$ of $P(2, 3)$ under reflection in the line $y = x$.
   (d) Finally, find the image $P**$ of $P*$ under reflection in the x-axis.

8. (a) Find the image P' of the point $P(1, -4)$ under reflection in the y-axis.
   (b) Find the image P'' of P' under reflection in the line $x + y = 0$.
   (c) Find the image $P*$ of $P(1, -4)$ under reflection in the line $x + y = 0$.
   (d) Finally, find the image $P**$ of $P*$ under reflection in the y-axis.

9. By comparing the results of parts (b) and (d) from Questions 7 and 8, form a conclusion about the significance of the order of performing reflections.

10. Find the equation of the image of each line under the indicated reflection.

	line	**line of reflection**
(a)	$y = x - 4$	x-axis
(b)	$3x + 5y - 2 = 0$	$x - y = 0$

11. (a) Using the definition of a reflection, draw the image of the given figure under reflection in the x-axis, followed by reflection in the y-axis.
    (b) Again using the definition of a reflection, draw the image of the same figure under reflection in the line $x + y = 0$ followed by reflection in the line $x - y = 0$.
    (c) What appears to be the relationship between the double reflection in part (a) and the double reflection in part (b)?
    (d) Verify the answer to part (c) by applying suitable reflection matrices to the point P given by $X_P = \begin{bmatrix} x_P \\ y_P \end{bmatrix}$.

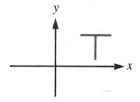

C **12.** For each figure find the equation of its image under the reflection in the given line. In each case draw a graph showing the original figure and its image under the reflection.

figure	reflection in line
(a) $y = 3x^2$	x-axis
(b) $x^2 + 9y^2 = 16$	$y = x$
(c) $25x^2 - 3y^2 = 1$	y-axis
(d) $y^2 = 4x$	$x + y = 0$

8.3 ROTATIONS

Each hand on the face of a clock turns about a fixed point. This action suggests a transformation called a rotation.

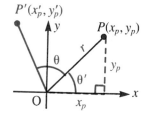

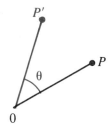

> A **rotation about a point** O **through an angle** θ is a transformation that maps any point P to the image point P' such that
>
> $$\angle POP' = \theta \quad \text{and} \quad OP = OP'$$

In Chapter 9 we apply rotations to second-degree relations as necessary to put them into standard position. For this reason we develop the *matrix of a general rotation* (through an angle θ about the origin). To do this we consider the effect of such a rotation on a point P by seeking the image point $P'(x_{P'}, y_{P'})$.

Consider θ', the angle between the positive x-axis and OP.

Let the length of OP (and OP') be represented by r.
Then

$$r \cos \theta' = x_P \qquad \text{①}$$

and $\qquad r \sin \theta' = y_P \qquad \text{②}$

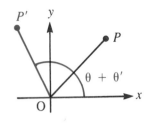

Because $\angle POP' = \theta$, the angle between OP' and the positive x-axis is $\theta + \theta'$, so

$$r\cos(\theta + \theta') = x_{P'} \qquad ③$$

and $\qquad r\sin(\theta + \theta') = y_{P'} \qquad ④$

Expanding the left-hand side of Equation 3 using the addition formula for cosine, we obtain

$$r(\cos\theta\cos\theta' - \sin\theta\sin\theta') = x_{P'}$$
$$r\cos\theta\cos\theta' - r\sin\theta\sin\theta' = x_{P'} \qquad ⑤$$

Substituting into ⑤ the expressions for $r\cos\theta'$ and $r\sin\theta'$ given in ① and ②, we have

$$(\cos\theta)\,x_P - (\sin\theta)\,y_P = x_{P'}$$

Expanding the left-hand side of Equation 4 using the addition formula for sine, we obtain

$$r(\cos\theta\sin\theta' + \sin\theta\cos\theta') = y_{P'}$$
$$r\cos\theta\sin\theta' + r\sin\theta\cos\theta' = y_{P'} \qquad ⑥$$

Substituting in ⑥ the expressions for $r\cos\theta'$ and $r\sin\theta'$ given in ① and ②, we obtain

$$(\cos\theta)\,y_P + (\sin\theta)\,x_P = y_{P'}$$

We now have a system of equations for $X_{P'}$:

$$x_{P'} = (\cos\theta)\,x_P - (\sin\theta)\,y_P$$
$$y_{P'} = (\sin\theta)\,x_P + (\cos\theta)\,y_P$$

Thus the matrix of the rotation through an angle of θ about the origin is

$$\begin{bmatrix} \cos\theta & -\sin\theta \\ \sin\theta & \cos\theta \end{bmatrix}$$

We summarize:

The image P' of the point P under the rotation about the origin through the angle θ is given by the matrix equation

$$X_{P'} = RX_P$$

where $\quad R = \begin{bmatrix} \cos\theta & -\sin\theta \\ \sin\theta & \cos\theta \end{bmatrix}$

Note that the matrix of a rotation through the angle $0°$ is given by

$$R = \begin{bmatrix} 1 & 0 \\ 0 & 1 \end{bmatrix}$$

because $\cos 0° = 1$ and $\sin 0° = 0$. This transformation is called the **identity transformation**.

As with reflections, it is obvious that the image of a straight line under a rotation is itself a straight line.

Example 1 Find the image of the specified point under rotation about the origin through the angle θ. Draw a graph showing the original point and the image point in each case.

	point	angle θ
(a)	$P(3,4)$	$\dfrac{\pi}{2}$
(b)	$P(-1,5)$	$120°$

Solution (a) Using $\cos \dfrac{\pi}{2} = 0$ and $\sin \dfrac{\pi}{2} = 1$, we have the rotation matrix

$$R = \begin{bmatrix} 0 & -1 \\ 1 & 0 \end{bmatrix}$$

so, $X_{P'} = \begin{bmatrix} 0 & -1 \\ 1 & 0 \end{bmatrix} \begin{bmatrix} 3 \\ 4 \end{bmatrix} = \begin{bmatrix} -4 \\ 3 \end{bmatrix}$

Thus, the image of $P(3,4)$ under the rotation through $\dfrac{\pi}{2}$ is $P'(-4,3)$.

(b) Because $\cos 120° = \cos (180° - 60°) = -\cos 60°$, we have

$$\cos 120° = -\tfrac{1}{2}$$

Also, $\sin 120° = \sin (180° - 60°) = \sin 60°$,

so, $\sin 120° = \dfrac{\sqrt{3}}{2}$

The matrix of rotation is $R = \begin{bmatrix} -\tfrac{1}{2} & -\tfrac{\sqrt{3}}{2} \\ \tfrac{\sqrt{3}}{2} & -\tfrac{1}{2} \end{bmatrix}$

So, $X_{P'} = \begin{bmatrix} -\tfrac{1}{2} & -\tfrac{\sqrt{3}}{2} \\ \tfrac{\sqrt{3}}{2} & -\tfrac{1}{2} \end{bmatrix} \begin{bmatrix} -1 \\ 5 \end{bmatrix} = \begin{bmatrix} \tfrac{1 - 5\sqrt{3}}{2} \\ \tfrac{-\sqrt{3} - 5}{2} \end{bmatrix}$

The image of $P(-1,5)$ under rotation of $120°$ is

$$P'\left(\frac{1 - 5\sqrt{3}}{2}, \frac{-\sqrt{3} - 5}{2}\right).$$

From our knowledge of the form of the matrix of a rotation, it is possible to determine an angle of rotation if we are given the rotation matrix.

Example 2 Find an angle of rotation for the rotation given by the matrix.

$$R = \begin{bmatrix} \frac{\sqrt{2}}{2} & \frac{\sqrt{2}}{2} \\ -\frac{\sqrt{2}}{2} & \frac{\sqrt{2}}{2} \end{bmatrix}$$

Solution We seek an angle θ for which $\cos \theta = \frac{\sqrt{2}}{2}$ and $\sin \theta = -\frac{\sqrt{2}}{2}$. This angle is in the fourth quadrant and is related to $45°$. Thus, an angle θ of rotation is $-45°$ or $315°$.

EXERCISE 8.3

A **1.** What point(s) remain invariant under every rotation about a point O?

2. What transformation is given by rotation through the angle θ_1 followed by rotation through the angle θ_2?

3. Why is the rotation given by the matrix $R = \begin{bmatrix} 1 & 0 \\ 0 & 1 \end{bmatrix}$ called the identity transformation?

B **4.** Using the general form of a rotation matrix find the matrix of rotation through each of the angles.

(a) $60°$ (b) $135°$ (c) $\frac{5\pi}{6}$ (d) $-\frac{\pi}{3}$

5. Find the image of the point $P(1, 3)$ under rotation about the origin through each angle θ. In each case, draw a graph showing both P and its image.

(a) $\theta = 30°$ (b) $\theta = \pi$ (c) $\theta = \frac{7\pi}{6}$ (d) $\theta = 45°$

6. Find the images, P', Q', R', and S' of the points $P(0, 2)$, $Q(-1, 5)$, $R(1, 0)$, and $S(0, 1)$ under rotation about the origin through the angle θ.

(a) $\theta = 30°$ (b) $\theta = \frac{3\pi}{4}$

7. From first principles, develop the matrix of the rotation through each angle.

   (a) 90°   (b) $\dfrac{\pi}{3}$

8. (a) Find the distance between points P and Q of Question 6.
   (b) Find the distance between the image points P' and Q' of Question 6(a).
   (c) Find the distance between the image points P' and Q' of Question 6(b).
   (d) By comparing the results of parts (a) and (b) and the results of parts (a) and (c), form a conclusion about the effect of a rotation on distances.

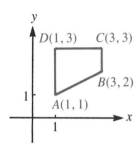

9. (a) Using the definition of a rotation, graph the image of the quadrilateral shown under a rotation of $\dfrac{3\pi}{2}$ about the origin.
   (b) By applying the appropriate rotation matrix, find the image of each vertex under the rotation of $\dfrac{3\pi}{2}$ about the origin, thus checking your graph for part (a).

10. Give two different transformations for which the transformation matrix is $\begin{bmatrix} -1 & 0 \\ 0 & -1 \end{bmatrix}$.

11. (a) Find the image P' of $P(x_P, y_P)$ under rotation through θ.
    (b) Find the image P'' of P' under rotation through $-\theta$.

12. (a) Find the image P' of the point $P(2, -1)$ under the rotation through 90° about the origin.
    (b) Find the image P'' of P' under the rotation through 45° about the origin.
    (c) Find the image $P*$ of P under the rotation through 45° about the origin.
    (d) Find the image $P**$ of $P*$ under the rotation through 90° about the origin.

13. (a) Find the image P' of the point $P(0, 3)$ under the rotation through $\dfrac{\pi}{3}$ about the origin.
    (b) Find the image P'' of P' under the rotation through π about the origin.
    (c) Find the image $P*$ of P under the rotation through π about the origin.
    (d) Find the image $P**$ of $P*$ under the rotation through $\dfrac{\pi}{3}$ about the origin.

14. By comparing the results of part (b) and (d) from Questions 12 and 13, form a conclusion about the significance of the order of performing rotations about the origin.

15. Using the matrix representation of a rotation about the origin, prove that such a transformation is a *rigid motion*; that is,
Given: Points P and Q and their images P' and Q' under rotation through an angle θ about the origin
Prove: the length of PQ = the length of $P'Q'$.

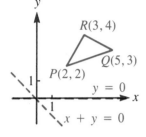

16. (a) Find the images P', Q', and R' of points P, Q, and R on the graph under the reflection in the line $x + y = 0$. Graph $\triangle P'Q'R'$.

   (b) Find the images P'', Q'', and R'' of P', Q', and R' under the reflection in the line $y = 0$. Graph $\triangle P''Q''R''$.

   (c) Describe, in your own words, the effect of this double reflection.

17. For each line l, find the equation of its image under rotation through the angle θ.

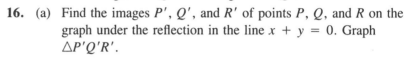

line l	θ
(a) $3x - y = 0$	$\dfrac{\pi}{6}$
(b) $x + 4y = -1$	$45°$
(c) $y = 3x - 2$	$-90°$

18. Each of the following is the matrix of a rotation. By comparing it to the general form of the matrix of a rotation, determine a possible angle of the rotation.

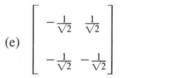

(a) $\begin{bmatrix} 0 & 1 \\ -1 & 0 \end{bmatrix}$ (b) $\begin{bmatrix} 0 & -1 \\ 1 & 0 \end{bmatrix}$

(c) $\begin{bmatrix} \frac{3}{5} & -\frac{4}{5} \\ \frac{4}{5} & \frac{3}{5} \end{bmatrix}$ (d) $\begin{bmatrix} \frac{1}{2} & \frac{\sqrt{3}}{2} \\ -\frac{\sqrt{3}}{2} & \frac{1}{2} \end{bmatrix}$

(e) $\begin{bmatrix} -\frac{1}{\sqrt{2}} & \frac{1}{\sqrt{2}} \\ -\frac{1}{\sqrt{2}} & -\frac{1}{\sqrt{2}} \end{bmatrix}$ (f) $\begin{bmatrix} -1 & 0 \\ 0 & -1 \end{bmatrix}$

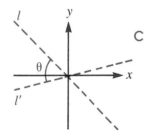

C **19.** Given: lines l and l' which intersect at the origin.
Prove geometrically that the reflection in line l followed by the reflection in the line l' has the same effect as the rotation about the origin through the angle 2θ where θ is the smaller angle between l and l'.

20. Prove that the order of performing rotations is of no consequence.

8.4   PROJECTIONS, DILATATIONS, STRETCHES, AND SHEARS

The transformations investigated in this section share a common property; they do not preserve distances between points, that is, in general the distance between two image points is not the same as the distance between the original points. Such a transformation is referred to as a **non-isometry**.

Projections

During a rainfall, the dry patch on the ground under a tree is the projection of the tree onto the ground. Such a situation (in which the rain falls straight down and is not blown at an angle by a wind) suggests a transformation which we define as follows.

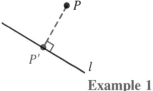

> A **projection onto a line** l is a transformation that maps any point P to the image point P' on l such that
>
> PP' is perpendicular to l

As for reflections and rotations, we develop a matrix which defines a projection.

Example 1   Develop the matrix of the projection onto the x-axis.

Solution   For the point $P(x_P, y_P)$, its image point P' is given by

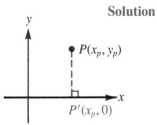

$$x_{P'} = x_P = 1\, x_P + 0\, y_P$$
and
$$y_{P'} = 0 = 0\, x_P + 0\, y_P$$

So, $T = \begin{bmatrix} 1 & 0 \\ 0 & 0 \end{bmatrix}$ is the matrix of the projection onto the x-axis.

The matrix of another special projection, onto the y-axis, is left to be developed in Question 4 of Exercise 8.4.

Dilatations

When a pebble is thrown into a pond, the ripples in the water are circles of ever-increasing diameter. This effect suggests a transformation that causes a change in the size of a figure but not in its shape.

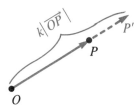

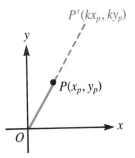

For a positive real number k, a **dilatation of factor k (with centre the origin O)** is a transformation that maps any point P to the image point P' such that

$$|\overrightarrow{OP'}| = k|\overrightarrow{OP}|$$

We investigate the effect of a dilatation of factor k with centre O on a point P. The image point is denoted by $P'(x_{P'}, y_{P'})$ and is given by

$$x_{P'} = kx_P = k\,x_P + 0\,y_P$$
$$y_{P'} = ky_P = 0\,x_P + k\,y_P$$

Thus, $T = \begin{bmatrix} k & 0 \\ 0 & k \end{bmatrix}$ is the matrix of the dilatation by a factor k.

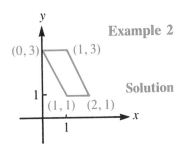

Example 2   Find the image of the figure shown in the diagram under a dilatation of factor 2.5.

Solution   The matrix of this transformation is $T = \begin{bmatrix} 2.5 & 0 \\ 0 & 2.5 \end{bmatrix}$

Thus for $X_P = (1, 1)$,

$$X_{P'} = TX_P = \begin{bmatrix} 2.5 & 0 \\ 0 & 2.5 \end{bmatrix}\begin{bmatrix} 1 \\ 1 \end{bmatrix} = \begin{bmatrix} 2.5 \\ 2.5 \end{bmatrix}$$

For $X_P = (2, 1)$,

$$X_{P'} = TX_P = \begin{bmatrix} 2.5 & 0 \\ 0 & 2.5 \end{bmatrix}\begin{bmatrix} 2 \\ 1 \end{bmatrix} = \begin{bmatrix} 5 \\ 2.5 \end{bmatrix}$$

For $X_P = (0, 3)$,

$$X_{P'} = TX_P = \begin{bmatrix} 2.5 & 0 \\ 0 & 2.5 \end{bmatrix}\begin{bmatrix} 0 \\ 3 \end{bmatrix} = \begin{bmatrix} 0 \\ 7.5 \end{bmatrix}$$

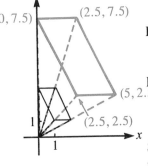

For $X_P = (1, 3)$,

$$X_{P'} = TX_P = \begin{bmatrix} 2.5 & 0 \\ 0 & 2.5 \end{bmatrix}\begin{bmatrix} 1 \\ 3 \end{bmatrix} = \begin{bmatrix} 2.5 \\ 7.5 \end{bmatrix}$$

So, the image of the original figure is, as shown on the diagram, a parallelogram.

Note that the sides of the image parallelogram in Example 2 are 2.5 times as long as those of the original parallelogram.

Stretches

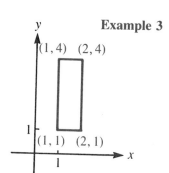

Example 3   (a) Find the image of the figure shown under the transformation defined by the matrix

$$T = \begin{bmatrix} 3 & 0 \\ 0 & 1 \end{bmatrix}$$

(b) Repeat (a) using the matrix

$$T = \begin{bmatrix} 1 & 0 \\ 0 & \frac{1}{2} \end{bmatrix}$$

Solution   (a) For $X_P = (1, 1)$,

$$X_{P'} = \begin{bmatrix} 3 & 0 \\ 0 & 1 \end{bmatrix}\begin{bmatrix} 1 \\ 1 \end{bmatrix} = \begin{bmatrix} 3 \\ 1 \end{bmatrix}$$

For $X_P = (2, 1)$,

$$X_{P'} = \begin{bmatrix} 3 & 0 \\ 0 & 1 \end{bmatrix}\begin{bmatrix} 2 \\ 1 \end{bmatrix} = \begin{bmatrix} 6 \\ 1 \end{bmatrix}$$

For $X_P = (1, 4)$,

$$X_{P'} = \begin{bmatrix} 3 & 0 \\ 0 & 1 \end{bmatrix}\begin{bmatrix} 1 \\ 4 \end{bmatrix} = \begin{bmatrix} 3 \\ 4 \end{bmatrix}$$

For $X_P = (2, 4)$,

$$X_{P'} = \begin{bmatrix} 3 & 0 \\ 0 & 1 \end{bmatrix}\begin{bmatrix} 2 \\ 4 \end{bmatrix} = \begin{bmatrix} 6 \\ 4 \end{bmatrix}$$

So, the image of the original figure is, as shown on the diagram, a rectangle "stretched" horizontally by a factor of 3.

(b) For $X_P = (1, 1)$,

$$X_{P'} = \begin{bmatrix} 1 & 0 \\ 0 & \frac{1}{2} \end{bmatrix}\begin{bmatrix} 1 \\ 1 \end{bmatrix} = \begin{bmatrix} 1 \\ \frac{1}{2} \end{bmatrix}$$

For $X_P = (3, 1)$,

$$X_{P'} = \begin{bmatrix} 1 & 0 \\ 0 & \frac{1}{2} \end{bmatrix}\begin{bmatrix} 2 \\ 1 \end{bmatrix} = \begin{bmatrix} 2 \\ \frac{1}{2} \end{bmatrix}$$

For $X_P = (1, 4)$,

$$X_{P'} = \begin{bmatrix} 1 & 0 \\ 0 & \frac{1}{2} \end{bmatrix}\begin{bmatrix} 1 \\ 4 \end{bmatrix} = \begin{bmatrix} 1 \\ 2 \end{bmatrix}$$

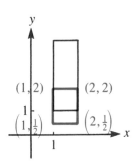

For $X_P = (3, 4)$,

$$X_{P'} = \begin{bmatrix} 1 & 0 \\ 0 & \frac{1}{2} \end{bmatrix} \begin{bmatrix} 2 \\ 4 \end{bmatrix} = \begin{bmatrix} 2 \\ 2 \end{bmatrix}$$

So, the image of the original figure is, as shown on the diagram, a rectangle "stretched" vertically by a factor of $\frac{1}{2}$.

Both of the transformations applied in Example 3 are **one-way stretches**.

Shears

Example 4 (a) Find the image of the figure shown under the transformation defined by the matrix

$$T = \begin{bmatrix} 1 & 2 \\ 0 & 1 \end{bmatrix}$$

(b) Repeat (a) using the matrix

$$T = \begin{bmatrix} 1 & 0 \\ \frac{2}{3} & 1 \end{bmatrix}$$

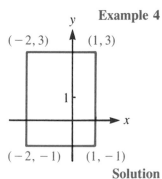

Solution (a) For $X_P = (1, -1)$,

$$X_{P'} = \begin{bmatrix} 1 & 2 \\ 0 & 1 \end{bmatrix} \begin{bmatrix} 1 \\ -1 \end{bmatrix} = \begin{bmatrix} -1 \\ -1 \end{bmatrix}$$

For $X_P = (-2, -1)$,

$$X_{P'} = \begin{bmatrix} 1 & 2 \\ 0 & 1 \end{bmatrix} \begin{bmatrix} -2 \\ -1 \end{bmatrix} = \begin{bmatrix} -4 \\ -1 \end{bmatrix}$$

For $X_P = (1, 3)$,

$$X_{P'} = \begin{bmatrix} 1 & 2 \\ 0 & 1 \end{bmatrix} \begin{bmatrix} 1 \\ 3 \end{bmatrix} = \begin{bmatrix} 7 \\ 3 \end{bmatrix}$$

For $X_P = (-2, 3)$,

$$X_{P'} = \begin{bmatrix} 1 & 2 \\ 0 & 1 \end{bmatrix} \begin{bmatrix} -2 \\ 3 \end{bmatrix} = \begin{bmatrix} 4 \\ 3 \end{bmatrix}$$

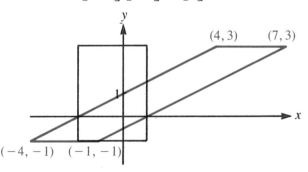

The image of the rectangle is a parallelogram; only the points on the x-axis have not moved under this transformation.

(b) For $X_P = (1, -1)$,

$$X_{P'} = \begin{bmatrix} 1 & 0 \\ \frac{2}{3} & 1 \end{bmatrix} \begin{bmatrix} 1 \\ -1 \end{bmatrix} = \begin{bmatrix} 1 \\ -\frac{1}{3} \end{bmatrix}$$

Fpr $X_P = (-2, -1)$,

$$X_{P'} = \begin{bmatrix} 1 & 0 \\ \frac{2}{3} & 1 \end{bmatrix} \begin{bmatrix} -2 \\ -1 \end{bmatrix} = \begin{bmatrix} -2 \\ -\frac{7}{3} \end{bmatrix}$$

For $X_P = (1, 3)$,

$$X_{P'} = \begin{bmatrix} 1 & 0 \\ \frac{2}{3} & 1 \end{bmatrix} \begin{bmatrix} 1 \\ 3 \end{bmatrix} = \begin{bmatrix} 1 \\ \frac{11}{3} \end{bmatrix}$$

For $X_P = (-2, 3)$,

$$X_{P'} = \begin{bmatrix} 1 & 0 \\ \frac{2}{3} & 1 \end{bmatrix} \begin{bmatrix} -2 \\ 3 \end{bmatrix} = \begin{bmatrix} -2 \\ \frac{5}{3} \end{bmatrix}$$

The image of the rectangle is a parallelogram; only the points on the y-axis have not moved under this transformation.

Both of the transformations applied in Example 4 are **shears**. Note that in each case the lengths of the base and height of the original figures are preserved so that their area remains the same.

We summarize by listing the results of this section.

Matrices of Non-isometries	
Matrix	**Type of transformation**
$\begin{bmatrix} 1 & 0 \\ 0 & 0 \end{bmatrix}$	projection onto the x-axis
$\begin{bmatrix} 0 & 0 \\ 0 & 1 \end{bmatrix}$	projection onto the y-axis
$\begin{bmatrix} k & 0 \\ 0 & k \end{bmatrix}$	dilatation of factor k, $k \neq 1$
$\begin{bmatrix} k & 0 \\ 0 & 1 \end{bmatrix}$	horizontal stretch by factor of k, $k \neq 1$
$\begin{bmatrix} 1 & 0 \\ 0 & k \end{bmatrix}$	vertical stretch by factor of k, $k \neq 1$
$\begin{bmatrix} 1 & k \\ 0 & 1 \end{bmatrix}$	horizontal shear by factor of k, $k \neq 0$
$\begin{bmatrix} 1 & 0 \\ k & 1 \end{bmatrix}$	vertical shear by factor of k, $k \neq 0$

EXERCISE 8.4

A 1. What point(s) remain(s) invariant under
   (a) a projection onto the line l?
   (b) a dilatation?
   (c) a (one-way) stretch?
   (d) a shear?

  2. For each matrix, determine whether it is the matrix of a dilatation, a stretch (horizontal or vertical), a shear (horizontal or vertical), or none of these.

   (a) $\begin{bmatrix} 5 & 0 \\ 0 & 5 \end{bmatrix}$
   (b) $\begin{bmatrix} 3 & 0 \\ 0 & -1 \end{bmatrix}$

   (c) $\begin{bmatrix} 0 & 1 \\ 1 & 4 \end{bmatrix}$
   (d) $\begin{bmatrix} 1 & 5 \\ 0 & 1 \end{bmatrix}$

   (e) $\begin{bmatrix} 1 & 0 \\ 3 & 1 \end{bmatrix}$
   (f) $\begin{bmatrix} 2 & 1 \\ 1 & 0 \end{bmatrix}$

  3. Find the matrix of the transformation of the specified type by the factor k.

	type of transformation	factor k
(a)	dilatation	3
(b)	vertical stretch	2.5
(c)	horizontal shear	1.4
(d)	horizontal stretch	4
(e)	dilatation	$\frac{1}{4}$
(f)	vertical shear	1.5

B 4. Develop, from first principles, the matrix of the projection onto the y-axis.

  5. Find the images, P', Q', R', and S' of the points $P(-1,2)$, $Q(0,5)$, $R(1,0)$, and $S(0, 1)$ under projection onto each line l.
   (a) l: the x-axis
   (b) l: the y-axis

  6. (a) Find the distance between points P and Q of Question 5.
   (b) Find the distance between the image points P' and Q' of Question 5(a).
   (c) Find the distance between the image points P' and Q' of Question 5(b).
   (d) By comparing the results of parts (a) and (b) and the results of parts (a) and (c), form a conclusion about the effect of a projection on distances.

  7. (a) Using the definition of a projection, graph the image of the figure shown under a projection onto the x-axis.
   (b) By applying the appropriate projection matrix, find the image of each vertex under the projection onto the x-axis, thus checking your graph for part (a).

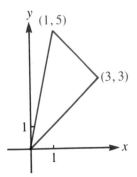

8. Find the vertices of the image of the figure shown under a dilatation by the factor indicated, then draw a graph showing the original and its image.

   (a) factor of 5

   (b) factor of $\frac{2}{3}$

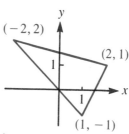

9. Find the vertices of the image of the figure shown under the transformation indicated, then draw a graph showing the original and its image.

   (a) a horizontal stretch by a factor of $\frac{4}{5}$

   (b) a vertical stretch by a factor of 3.4

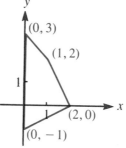

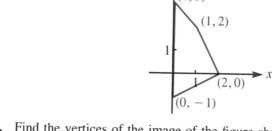

10. Find the vertices of the image of the figure shown under the transformation indicated, then draw a graph showing the original and its image.

    (a) a vertical shear by a factor of 2.5

    (b) a horizontal shear by a factor of 4

11. Find the images P', Q', R', and S' of $P(0, 3)$, $Q(1, -2)$, $R(1, 0)$, and $S(0, 1)$ under each dilatation.

    (a) factor of 2

    (b) factor of $\frac{2}{3}$

12. (a) Find the distance between points P and Q of Question 11.

    (b) Find the distance between image points P' and Q' of Question 11(a).

    (c) Find the distance between image points P' and Q' of Question 11(b).

    (d) Form a conclusion about the effect of a dilatation on distances.

13. Find the images P', Q', R', S' of $P(0, 3)$, $Q(0, -2)$, $R(1, 0)$, and $S(0, 1)$ under each stretch.

    (a) horizontal, factor of 2

    (b) vertical, factor of $\frac{2}{3}$

14. (a) Find the distance between points P and Q of Question 13.
    (b) Find the distance between image points P' and Q' of Question 13(a).
    (c) Find the distance between image points P' and Q' of Question 13(b).
    (d) Form a conclusion about the effect of a horizontal stretch on vertical distances.
    (e) Form a conclusion about the effect of a vertical stretch on vertical distances.

15. Find the images P', Q', R', and S' of $P(3,0)$, $Q(-5,0)$, $R(1,0)$, and $S(0, 1)$ under each shear.

    (a) vertical, factor of 3   (b) horizontal, factor of $\frac{3}{5}$

16. (a) Find the distance between points P and Q of Question 15.
    (b) Find the distance between image points P' and Q' of Question 15(a).
    (c) Find the distance between image points P' and Q' of Question 15(b).
    (d) Form a conclusion about the effect of a vertical shear on horizontal distances.
    (e) Form a conclusion about the effect of a horizontal shear on horizontal distances.

17. Prove that a dilatation has the same effect as two successive one-way stretches.

8.5 MATRIX MULTIPLICATION

Up to this stage we have defined and used the operation of matrix multiplication only in a very limited sense: multiplication of a matrix with two rows and two columns by a matrix with two rows and one column (a column vector). However the notion of compound transformations described by matrices suggests a procedure for multiplying two matrices each with two rows and two columns.

Example 1 (a) Find the image P' of the general point $P(x_P, y_P)$ under the transformation defined by the matrix

$$R = \begin{bmatrix} 1 & 3 \\ -2 & 4 \end{bmatrix}$$

(b) Find the image P'' of the image point P' under the transformation defined by the matrix

$$S = \begin{bmatrix} 0 & 2 \\ 5 & -3 \end{bmatrix}$$

(c)   Find the image P^* of the general point P under the transformation defined by the matrix

$$T = \begin{bmatrix} -4 & 8 \\ 11 & 3 \end{bmatrix}$$

Solution   (a) $\quad X_{P'} = RX_P = \begin{bmatrix} 1 & 3 \\ -2 & 4 \end{bmatrix} \begin{bmatrix} x_P \\ y_P \end{bmatrix} = \begin{bmatrix} x_P + 3y_P \\ -2x_P + 4y_P \end{bmatrix}$

(b) $\quad X_{P''} = SX_{P'} = SRX_P$

$$= \begin{bmatrix} 0 & 2 \\ 5 & -3 \end{bmatrix} \begin{bmatrix} x_P + 3y_P \\ -2x_P + 4y_P \end{bmatrix}$$

$$= \begin{bmatrix} 0(x_P + 3y_P) + 2(-2x_P + 4y_P) \\ 5(x_P + 3y_P) + (-3)(-2x_P + 4y_P) \end{bmatrix}$$

$$= \begin{bmatrix} -4x_P + 8y_P \\ 11x_P + 3y_P \end{bmatrix}$$

(c) $\quad X_{P^*} = TX_P = \begin{bmatrix} -4 & 8 \\ 11 & 3 \end{bmatrix} \begin{bmatrix} x_P \\ y_P \end{bmatrix} = \begin{bmatrix} -4x_P + 8y_P \\ 11x_P + 3y_P \end{bmatrix}$

Note that the transformation SR (by $\begin{bmatrix} 1 & 3 \\ -2 & 4 \end{bmatrix}$, then by $\begin{bmatrix} 0 & 2 \\ 5 & -3 \end{bmatrix}$) produced the same result as a transformation by T (defined by matrix $\begin{bmatrix} -4 & 8 \\ 11 & 3 \end{bmatrix}$). Thus the transformation T has the same effect as the transformation SR. We can obtain the matrix T from the matrices R and S if we extend our definition of matrix multiplication as follows:

"Row by column" multiplication

For matrices A and B, their **product** AB is given by

$$AB = \begin{bmatrix} a_1 & a_2 \\ a_3 & a_4 \end{bmatrix} \begin{bmatrix} b_1 & b_2 \\ b_3 & b_4 \end{bmatrix}$$

$$= \begin{bmatrix} a_1b_1 + a_2b_3 & a_1b_2 + a_2b_4 \\ a_3b_1 + a_4b_3 & a_3b_2 + a_4b_4 \end{bmatrix}$$

Example 2   Verify, using the extended definition of matrix multiplication, that

$$SR = T$$

Solution   To find the entry in the first row, first column:

$$SR = \begin{bmatrix} 0 & 2 \\ 5 & -3 \end{bmatrix} \begin{bmatrix} 1 & 3 \\ -2 & 4 \end{bmatrix} = \begin{bmatrix} (0)(1) + (2)(-2) & \\ & \end{bmatrix} = \begin{bmatrix} -4 & \\ & \end{bmatrix}$$

To find the entry in the first row, second column:

$$SR = \begin{bmatrix} 0 & 2 \\ 5 & -3 \end{bmatrix} \begin{bmatrix} 1 & 3 \\ -2 & 4 \end{bmatrix} = \begin{bmatrix} -4 & (0)(3) + (2)(4) \end{bmatrix} = \begin{bmatrix} -4 & 8 \end{bmatrix}$$

To find the entry in the second row, first column:

$$SR = \begin{bmatrix} 0 & 2 \\ 5 & -3 \end{bmatrix} \begin{bmatrix} 1 & 3 \\ -2 & 4 \end{bmatrix} = \begin{bmatrix} -4 & 8 \\ (5)(1) + (-3)(-2) & \end{bmatrix} = \begin{bmatrix} -4 & 8 \\ 11 & \end{bmatrix}$$

To find the entry in the second row, second column:

$$SR = \begin{bmatrix} 0 & 2 \\ 5 & -3 \end{bmatrix} \begin{bmatrix} 1 & 3 \\ -2 & 4 \end{bmatrix} = \begin{bmatrix} -4 & 8 \\ 11 & (5)(3) + (-3)(4) \end{bmatrix} = \begin{bmatrix} -4 & 8 \\ 11 & 3 \end{bmatrix}$$

So, $SR = T$

This is true for any pair of transformations; if transformation T_1 is followed by transformation T_2 the matrix of the compound transformation is given by T_2T_1.

Example 3   For matrices $M = \begin{bmatrix} 1 & 3 \\ -2 & 5 \end{bmatrix}$ and $N = \begin{bmatrix} 4 & 0 \\ 2 & 7 \end{bmatrix}$,

(a) find the product MN by considering the compound transformation given by transformation N followed by transformation M, then

(b) find the product MN using the definition of matrix multiplication.

Solution   (a) Consider the transformations defined by the matrices M and N. We look at a point P and determine its image P' under the transformation determined by N.

$$X_{P'} = NX_p$$

So, $$\begin{bmatrix} x_{P'} \\ y_{P'} \end{bmatrix} = \begin{bmatrix} 4 & 0 \\ 2 & 7 \end{bmatrix} \begin{bmatrix} x_P \\ y_P \end{bmatrix} = \begin{bmatrix} 4x_P + 0y_P \\ 2x_P + 7y_P \end{bmatrix} = \begin{bmatrix} 4x_P \\ 2x_P + 7y_P \end{bmatrix}$$

Next we find the image P'' of P' under the transformation defined by M.

$$X_{P''} = MX_{P'} = MNX_P$$

So, $$\begin{bmatrix} x_{P''} \\ y_{P''} \end{bmatrix} = \begin{bmatrix} 1 & 3 \\ -2 & 5 \end{bmatrix} \begin{bmatrix} 4x_P \\ 2x_P + 7y_P \end{bmatrix}$$

$$= \begin{bmatrix} 1(4x_P) + 3(2x_P + 7y_P) \\ -2(4x_P) + 5(2x_P + 7y_P) \end{bmatrix}$$

$$= \begin{bmatrix} 4x_P + 6x_P + 21y_P \\ -8x_P + 10x_P + 35y_P \end{bmatrix}$$

$$= \begin{bmatrix} 10x_P + 21y_P \\ 2x_P + 35y_P \end{bmatrix}$$

We note that this result is the same as that obtained by applying the transformation defined by the matrix $\begin{bmatrix} 10 & 21 \\ 2 & 35 \end{bmatrix}$.

This is the product MN.

Thus, $MN = \begin{bmatrix} 10 & 21 \\ 2 & 35 \end{bmatrix}$.

(b) We apply the definition of matrix multiplication.

To find the entry in the first row, first column:

$$\begin{bmatrix} 1 & 3 \\ -2 & 5 \end{bmatrix}\begin{bmatrix} 4 & 0 \\ 2 & 7 \end{bmatrix} = \begin{bmatrix} (1)(4) + (3)(2) \end{bmatrix} = \begin{bmatrix} 10 \end{bmatrix}$$

To find the entry in the first row, second column:

$$\begin{bmatrix} 1 & 3 \\ -2 & 5 \end{bmatrix}\begin{bmatrix} 4 & 0 \\ 2 & 7 \end{bmatrix} = \begin{bmatrix} 10 & (1)(0) + (3)(7) \end{bmatrix} = \begin{bmatrix} 10 & 21 \end{bmatrix}$$

To find the entry in the second row, first column:

$$\begin{bmatrix} 1 & 3 \\ -2 & 5 \end{bmatrix}\begin{bmatrix} 4 & 0 \\ 2 & 7 \end{bmatrix} = \begin{bmatrix} 10 & 21 \\ (-2)(4) + (5)(2) \end{bmatrix} = \begin{bmatrix} 10 & 21 \\ 2 \end{bmatrix}$$

To find the entry in the second row, second column:

$$\begin{bmatrix} 1 & 3 \\ -2 & 5 \end{bmatrix}\begin{bmatrix} 4 & 0 \\ 2 & 7 \end{bmatrix} = \begin{bmatrix} 10 & 21 \\ 2 & (-2)(0) + (5)(7) \end{bmatrix} = \begin{bmatrix} 10 & 21 \\ 2 & 35 \end{bmatrix}$$

So, $MN = \begin{bmatrix} 1 & 3 \\ -2 & 5 \end{bmatrix}\begin{bmatrix} 4 & 0 \\ 2 & 7 \end{bmatrix} = \begin{bmatrix} 10 & 21 \\ 2 & 35 \end{bmatrix}$

Example 4   Multiply each pair of matrices.

(a) $\begin{bmatrix} 3 & 1 \\ 2 & 4 \end{bmatrix}\begin{bmatrix} 1 & 0 \\ 5 & 6 \end{bmatrix}$

(b) $\begin{bmatrix} 2 & 5 \\ -1 & 7 \end{bmatrix}\begin{bmatrix} -4 & -3 \\ 6 & -2 \end{bmatrix}$

Solution   (a) $\begin{bmatrix} 3 & 1 \\ 2 & 4 \end{bmatrix}\begin{bmatrix} 1 & 0 \\ 5 & 6 \end{bmatrix} = \begin{bmatrix} (3)(1) + (1)(5) & (3)(0) + (1)(6) \\ (2)(1) + (4)(5) & (2)(0) + (4)(6) \end{bmatrix}$

$$= \begin{bmatrix} 8 & 6 \\ 22 & 24 \end{bmatrix}$$

(b) $\begin{bmatrix} 2 & 5 \\ -1 & 7 \end{bmatrix}\begin{bmatrix} -4 & -3 \\ 6 & -2 \end{bmatrix} = \begin{bmatrix} (2)(-4) + (5)(6) & (2)(-3) + (5)(-2) \\ (-1)(-4) + (7)(6) & (-1)(-3) + (7)(-2) \end{bmatrix}$

$$= \begin{bmatrix} 22 & -16 \\ 46 & 11 \end{bmatrix}$$

The notion of one transformation being followed by another (**compound transformation**) led us to a definition of matrix multiplication (for 2×2 matrices). In turn, that definition can reduce the work involved to find the image of a point under a compound transformation.

Example 5   For each compound transformation, find its matrix then find the image of the point $P(3, -2)$.
(a) reflection in the y-axis followed by a horizontal stretch by a factor of 3,
(b) rotation through $30°$ followed by projection onto the x-axis

Solution   (a) The matrix of reflection in the y-axis is

$$T_1 = \begin{bmatrix} -1 & 0 \\ 0 & 1 \end{bmatrix}$$

The matrix of horizontal stretch by a factor of 3 is

$$T_2 = \begin{bmatrix} 3 & 0 \\ 0 & 1 \end{bmatrix}$$

So, the compound transformation is that defined by the matrix T_2T_1

given by $T_2T_1 = \begin{bmatrix} 3 & 0 \\ 0 & 1 \end{bmatrix}\begin{bmatrix} -1 & 0 \\ 0 & 1 \end{bmatrix}$

$$= \begin{bmatrix} -3 & 0 \\ 0 & 1 \end{bmatrix}$$

Thus, the image of $P(3, -2)$ is given by

$$X_{P'} = \begin{bmatrix} -3 & 0 \\ 0 & 1 \end{bmatrix}\begin{bmatrix} 3 \\ -2 \end{bmatrix} = \begin{bmatrix} -9 + 0 \\ 0 + (-2) \end{bmatrix} = \begin{bmatrix} -9 \\ -2 \end{bmatrix}$$

(b) The matrix of rotation through $30°$ is

$$T_1 = \begin{bmatrix} \frac{1}{2} & -\frac{\sqrt{3}}{2} \\ \frac{\sqrt{3}}{2} & \frac{1}{2} \end{bmatrix}$$

The matrix of projection onto the x-axis is

$$T_2 = \begin{bmatrix} 1 & 0 \\ 0 & 0 \end{bmatrix}$$

So, the compound transformation is that defined by the matrix T_2T_1

given by $T_2T_1 = \begin{bmatrix} 1 & 0 \\ 0 & 0 \end{bmatrix}\begin{bmatrix} \frac{1}{2} & -\frac{\sqrt{3}}{2} \\ \frac{\sqrt{3}}{2} & \frac{1}{2} \end{bmatrix} = \begin{bmatrix} \frac{1}{2} & \frac{-\sqrt{3}}{2} \\ 0 & 0 \end{bmatrix}$

Thus, the image of $P(3, -2)$ is given by

$$X_{P'} = \begin{bmatrix} \frac{1}{2} & -\frac{\sqrt{3}}{2} \\ 0 & 0 \end{bmatrix}\begin{bmatrix} 3 \\ -2 \end{bmatrix} = \begin{bmatrix} \frac{1}{2}(3) - \frac{\sqrt{3}}{2}(-2) \\ 0(3) + 0(-2) \end{bmatrix} = \begin{bmatrix} \frac{3 + 2\sqrt{3}}{2} \\ 0 \end{bmatrix}$$

EXERCISE 8.5

B **1.** Multiply each pair of matrices.

(a) $\begin{bmatrix} 1 & 3 \\ 2 & 1 \end{bmatrix}\begin{bmatrix} 0 & 0 \\ 1 & 4 \end{bmatrix}$

(b) $\begin{bmatrix} 1 & 2 \\ 4 & -3 \end{bmatrix}\begin{bmatrix} 2 & 0 \\ -1 & 1 \end{bmatrix}$

(c) $\begin{bmatrix} 5 & 2 \\ 1 & 3 \end{bmatrix}\begin{bmatrix} 1 & 0 \\ 0 & 1 \end{bmatrix}$

(d) $\begin{bmatrix} 7 & 2 \\ 4 & 1 \end{bmatrix}\begin{bmatrix} -1 & -2 \\ 0 & 5 \end{bmatrix}$

2. For matrices A and B as specified, find the product AB in two ways,
   (i) by applying the transformation defined by B followed by the transformation defined by A to the point P given by $X_P = \begin{bmatrix} x_P \\ y_P \end{bmatrix}$ and
   (ii) by using the definition of the product of two matrices.

(a) $A = \begin{bmatrix} 1 & 3 \\ 0 & 4 \end{bmatrix}$, $B = \begin{bmatrix} 6 & 0.5 \\ 2 & 3 \end{bmatrix}$

(b) $A = \begin{bmatrix} 2 & 5 \\ 0 & -1 \end{bmatrix}$, $B = \begin{bmatrix} -3 & 8 \\ 2 & -1 \end{bmatrix}$

3. For the matrices A and B as specified,
   (i) find the product AB, then
   (ii) find the product BA

(a) $A = \begin{bmatrix} 3 & 0 \\ 0 & 4 \end{bmatrix}$, $B = \begin{bmatrix} 2 & -1 \\ 5 & 1 \end{bmatrix}$

(b) $A = \begin{bmatrix} 6 & 3 \\ 2 & -1 \end{bmatrix}$, $B = \begin{bmatrix} 2 & -5 \\ 2 & 1 \end{bmatrix}$

(c) $A = \begin{bmatrix} 1 & 0 \\ 0 & -1 \end{bmatrix}$, $B = \begin{bmatrix} 4 & 4 \\ 3 & 7 \end{bmatrix}$

4. By comparing the results for parts (i) and (ii) of Question 3, form a conclusion about the commutativity of multiplication of 2×2 matrices.

5. Using three specific 2×2 matrices, illustrate the associativity of multiplication of 2×2 matrices.

6. Why is the matrix $I_{2 \times 2} = \begin{bmatrix} 1 & 0 \\ 0 & 1 \end{bmatrix}$ referred to as the identity matrix for multiplication of 2×2 matrices?

7. Find the matrix that represents the rotation through $\dfrac{\pi}{4}$ followed by a horizontal stretch of factor 2.5.

8. Prove that the product of two rotations is a rotation.

9. Find the matrix of the transformation that has the same effect as projection onto the x-axis followed by projection onto the y-axis.

10. Find the image of the point $P(4, -3)$ under a dilatation of factor 3 followed by reflection in the line $y = x$.

11. Find the matrix of the transformation that has the same effect as a vertical shear by a factor of a followed by a reflection in the line $x + y = 0$ followed by a dilatation of factor b.

C 12. (a) For matrix $A = \begin{bmatrix} 1 & 1 \\ 0 & 1 \end{bmatrix}$, under what conditions on the entries of a matrix B will the product AB be the same as the product BA?

(b) For matrix $A = \begin{bmatrix} 0 & -1 \\ 1 & 0 \end{bmatrix}$, under what conditions on the entries of a matrix B will the product AB be the same as the product BA?

13. (a) Suggest a technique for multiplying 3×3 matrices which follows a similar procedure to that used for 2×2 matrices.

(b) Suggest a technique for multiplying a 3×4 matrix by a 4×5 matrix.

(c) Discuss the generalization of this technique to multiplication of $m \times n$ matrices by $p \times r$ matrices.

14. Discuss the effect of the compound transformation given by
$$\begin{bmatrix} d & -b \\ -c & a \end{bmatrix} \begin{bmatrix} a & b \\ c & d \end{bmatrix}$$

PROBLEMS PLUS

Inverse of a Matrix I

The *inverse of a matrix A* is a matrix B for which $AB = BA = \begin{bmatrix} 1 & 0 \\ 0 & 1 \end{bmatrix}$, the identity matrix.

(a) By identifying the reflection corresponding to the given matrix find the inverse of the matrix $\begin{bmatrix} -1 & 0 \\ 0 & 1 \end{bmatrix}$.

(b) By identifying the rotation corresponding to the given matrix find the inverse of the matrix $\begin{bmatrix} -\frac{\sqrt{2}}{2} & -\frac{\sqrt{2}}{2} \\ \frac{\sqrt{2}}{2} & -\frac{\sqrt{2}}{2} \end{bmatrix}$

(c) Find the inverse of the matrix $\begin{bmatrix} -2 & 3 \\ 1 & 5 \end{bmatrix}$ using the definition of matrix multiplication.

**8.6 GENERAL TRANSFORMATIONS

For reflections and projections, it is possible to determine the matrix of the transformation in more general cases than those that we developed in earlier sections. It is, in fact, possible to identify the type of transformation from its matrix.

Reflections

Example 1 Develop the matrix of the reflection in the line l through the origin given by $ax + by = 0$ where $a^2 + b^2 = 1$.

Solution The image of P under the reflection is denoted by P'.

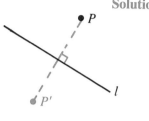

Because PP' is perpendicular to the line l given by $ax + by = 0$, both P and P' are on the line l' perpendicular to l. This line l' is given by $-bx + ay = d$ for some real number d. Because both P and P' are on the line $-bx + ay = d$,

$$-bx_{P'} + ay_{P'} = -bx_P + ay_P \; [= d] \qquad ①$$

Also, the distance from P to l is the same as the distance from P' to l; that is, Q, the midpoint of PP', is on the line l,

so, $$ax_Q + by_Q = 0$$

but $$X_Q = \frac{X_P + X_{P'}}{2}$$

So, $$a\left(\frac{x_P + x_{P'}}{2}\right) + b\left(\frac{y_P + y_{P'}}{2}\right) = 0$$

$$ax_P + by_P + ax_{P'} + by_{P'} = 0$$

and, thus, $$ax_{P'} + by_{P'} = -ax_P - by_P \qquad ②$$

We now solve Equations 1 and 2 for $x_{P'}$ and $y_{P'}$ using the method of elimination.

If we multiply Equation 2 by a and Equation 1 by b, then subtract, we obtain

$$a^2 x_{P'} + ab y_{P'} = -a^2 x_P - ab y_P$$

subtract $$\underline{-b^2 x_{P'} + ab y_{P'} = -b^2 x_P + ab y_P}$$

$$a^2 x_{P'} + b^2 x_{P'} = -a^2 x_P + b^2 x_P - 2ab y_P$$

$$(a^2 + b^2)x_{P'} = (b^2 - a^2)x_P - 2ab y_P$$

Recalling that $a^2 + b^2 = 1$ we have

$$x_{P'} = (b^2 - a^2)x_P - 2ab y_P$$

Then we multiply Equation 2 by b and Equation 1 by a and add.

$$abx_{P'} + b^2y_{P'} = -abx_P - b^2y_P$$

$$-abx_{P'} + a^2y_{P'} = -abx_P + a^2y_P$$

$$b^2y_{P'} + a^2y_{P'} = -2abx_P - b^2y_P + a^2y_P$$

$$(a^2 + b^2)y_{P'} = -2abx_P + (a^2 - b^2)y_P$$

So, $$y_{P'} = -2abx_P + (a^2 - b^2)y_P$$

This solution can be expressed in matrix form as

$$\begin{bmatrix} x_{P'} \\ y_{P'} \end{bmatrix} = \begin{bmatrix} b^2 - a^2 & -2ab \\ -2ab & a^2 - b^2 \end{bmatrix} \begin{bmatrix} x_P \\ y_P \end{bmatrix}$$

We summarize:

The image P' of point P under the reflection in the line l given by $ax + by = 0$, where $a^2 + b^2 = 1$, is given by the matrix equation

$$X_{P'} = TX_P$$

where $$T = \begin{bmatrix} b^2 - a^2 & -2ab \\ -2ab & a^2 - b^2 \end{bmatrix}$$

Example 2 Find the image of the point $P(3, 2)$ under the reflection in the line $\frac{1}{\sqrt{5}}x + \frac{2}{\sqrt{5}}y = 0$. Draw a graph showing the original point, the line of reflection, and the image point.

Solution The line of reflection has $a^2 + b^2 = 1$ so from it we can obtain the values of a and b in order to construct the reflection matrix.

Using $a = \frac{1}{\sqrt{5}}$ and $b = \frac{2}{\sqrt{5}}$, we have

$$b^2 - a^2 = \left(\frac{2}{\sqrt{5}}\right)^2 - \left(\frac{1}{\sqrt{5}}\right) = \frac{4}{5} - \frac{1}{5} = \frac{4-1}{5} = \frac{3}{5}$$

So, $a^2 - b^2 = -\frac{3}{5}$ and $-2ab = -2\left(\frac{1}{\sqrt{5}}\right)\left(\frac{2}{\sqrt{5}}\right) = -\frac{4}{5}$

Thus, $$T = \begin{bmatrix} \frac{3}{5} & -\frac{4}{5} \\ -\frac{4}{5} & -\frac{3}{5} \end{bmatrix}$$

So, $X_{P'} = \begin{bmatrix} \frac{3}{5} & -\frac{4}{5} \\ -\frac{4}{5} & -\frac{3}{5} \end{bmatrix} \begin{bmatrix} 3 \\ 2 \end{bmatrix}$

$= \begin{bmatrix} \frac{9}{5} - \frac{8}{5} \\ -\frac{12}{5} - \frac{6}{5} \end{bmatrix}$

$= \begin{bmatrix} \frac{1}{5} \\ -\frac{18}{5} \end{bmatrix}$

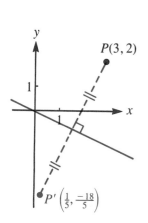

Therefore, the image of $P(3, 2)$ under the reflection in the given line is $P'(\frac{1}{5}, -\frac{18}{5})$.

By studying the general matrix of a reflection we can identify a matrix as the matrix of a reflection and find the line of reflection. Note that any matrix M of a reflection is of the form

$$M = \begin{bmatrix} p & q \\ r & s \end{bmatrix}, \text{ where } p + s = 0, q = r, \text{ and } p^2 + q^2 = 1.$$

(Verification of this is left as an exercise, Question 13 of Exercise 8.6).

Example 3   For the matrix $M = \begin{bmatrix} \frac{1}{2} & \frac{\sqrt{3}}{2} \\ \frac{\sqrt{3}}{2} & -\frac{1}{2} \end{bmatrix}$

(a) check whether it is the matrix of a reflection and, if so,
(b) give an equation of the line of reflection.

Solution   (a) Naming the entries as $\begin{bmatrix} p & q \\ r & s \end{bmatrix}$, we note that

$$q = r = \frac{\sqrt{3}}{2} \text{ and that } p + s = \frac{1}{2} + \left(-\frac{1}{2}\right) = 0$$

Also, $p^2 + q^2 = \left(\frac{1}{2}\right)^2 + \left(\frac{\sqrt{3}}{2}\right)^2 = \frac{1}{4} + \frac{3}{4} = 1$

So, this is the matrix of a reflection.

(b) To determine the line of reflection we must find the coefficients of x and y in $ax + by = 0$. We use the fact that the matrix of a reflection is of the form

$$T = \begin{bmatrix} b^2 - a^2 & -2ab \\ -2ab & a^2 - b^2 \end{bmatrix}$$

to say that $b^2 - a^2 = \frac{1}{2}$ ①

$-2ab = \frac{\sqrt{3}}{2}$ ②

From Equation 2 we obtain $b = -\frac{\sqrt{3}}{4a}$, which we substitute in Equation 1, to obtain

$$\left(-\frac{\sqrt{3}}{4a}\right)^2 - a^2 = \frac{1}{2}$$

Thus,

$$\frac{3}{16a^2} - a^2 = \frac{1}{2}$$

$$3 - 16a^4 = 8a^2$$

$$16a^4 + 8a^2 - 3 = 0$$

$$(4a^2 - 1)(4a^2 + 3) = 0$$

So, $4a^2 - 1 = 0$ or $4a^2 + 3 = 0$

The only real solutions for this equation are $a = \pm\frac{1}{2}$.

To find the value for b, we substitute for a in Equation 2.

If $a = \frac{1}{2}$, then $-2\left(\frac{1}{2}\right)b = \frac{\sqrt{3}}{2}$ so $b = -\frac{\sqrt{3}}{2}$.

If $a = -\frac{1}{2}$, then $-2\left(-\frac{1}{2}\right)b = \frac{\sqrt{3}}{2}$ so $b = \frac{\sqrt{3}}{2}$.

So, the line of reflection is $\frac{1}{2}x - \frac{\sqrt{3}}{2}y = 0$, or $-\frac{1}{2}x + \frac{\sqrt{3}}{2}y = 0$;

that is,

$$x - \sqrt{3}y = 0$$

Projections

The development of the matrix of a projection onto a line through the origin is left as an exercise, Question 10 in Exercise 8.6; however we summarize the result here in order to apply it.

The image P' of the point P under the projection onto the line l given by $ax + by = 0$, where $a^2 + b^2 = 1$, is given by the matrix equation

$$X_{P'} = TX_P$$

where

$$T = \begin{bmatrix} b^2 & -ab \\ -ab & a^2 \end{bmatrix}$$

Example 4   Find the image of the point $P(4, 1)$ under the projection onto the line $2x + 3y = 0$. Draw a graph showing the original point and the image point.

Solution   In order to use the standard form of a matrix for a projection onto a line through the origin we must write the equation of the line so that the normal is a unit vector.

The normal of $2x + 3y = 0$ is $(2, 3)$. Normalized, $(2, 3)$ is

$$\frac{(2, 3)}{\sqrt{2^2 + 3^2}} = \left(\frac{2}{\sqrt{13}}, \frac{3}{\sqrt{13}}\right)$$

So the line of projection is given by $\frac{2}{\sqrt{13}}x + \frac{3}{\sqrt{13}}y = 0$.

Using $a = \frac{2}{\sqrt{13}}$ and $b = \frac{3}{\sqrt{13}}$, we calculate

$$b^2 = \left(\frac{3}{\sqrt{13}}\right)^2 = \frac{9}{13}, \quad -ab = -\left(\frac{2}{\sqrt{13}}\right)\left(\frac{3}{\sqrt{13}}\right) = -\frac{6}{13}, \quad a^2 = \left(\frac{2}{\sqrt{13}}\right)^2 = \frac{4}{13}$$

Thus, $T = \begin{bmatrix} \frac{9}{13} & -\frac{6}{13} \\ -\frac{6}{13} & \frac{4}{13} \end{bmatrix}$

So, $X_{P'} = \begin{bmatrix} \frac{9}{13} & -\frac{6}{13} \\ -\frac{6}{13} & \frac{4}{13} \end{bmatrix}\begin{bmatrix} 4 \\ 1 \end{bmatrix} = \begin{bmatrix} \frac{36-6}{13} \\ \frac{-24+4}{13} \end{bmatrix} = \begin{bmatrix} \frac{30}{13} \\ -\frac{20}{13} \end{bmatrix}$

Thus, the image of $P(4, 1)$ under the projection onto the line $2x + 3y = 0$ is $P'\left(\frac{30}{13}, -\frac{20}{13}\right)$.

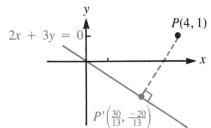

By studying the general matrix of a projection onto a line, we can identify a matrix as the matrix of a projection and find the line onto which each point is projected. Note that any matrix M of a projection is of the form

$$M = \begin{bmatrix} p & q \\ r & s \end{bmatrix} \text{ where } q = r, p + s = 1, \text{ and } p^2 + q^2 = p.$$

The proof of this statement is requested as Question 14 in Exercise 8.6.

Example 5   For each matrix M, (i) check whether it is the matrix of a projection, and if so, (ii) specify the line of the projection.

(a) $M = \begin{bmatrix} 1 & 0 \\ 0 & 0 \end{bmatrix}$ (b) $M = \begin{bmatrix} \frac{1}{2} & \frac{\sqrt{2}}{2} \\ \frac{\sqrt{2}}{2} & \frac{1}{2} \end{bmatrix}$

Solution   (a) (i)   Naming the entries as $\begin{bmatrix} p & q \\ r & s \end{bmatrix}$, we note that

$$q = r = 0 \text{ and that } p + s = 1 + 0 = 1$$

Also, $p^2 + q^2 = 1^2 + 0^2 = 1 = p$

So, this is the matrix of a projection.

(ii) To determine the line of the projection, we use the fact that the matrix of a projection is of the form

$$T = \begin{bmatrix} b^2 & -ab \\ -ab & a^2 \end{bmatrix}$$

to say that $b^2 = 1$. This indicates that $b = \pm 1$.

Also, $a^2 = 0$, so $a = 0$.

Thus, the line onto which the image of a point is projected is given by $0x + \pm y = 0$; that is, $y = 0$, the x-axis.

(b) Naming the entries as $\begin{bmatrix} p & q \\ r & s \end{bmatrix}$, we note that

$$q = r = \tfrac{\sqrt{2}}{2} \text{ and } p + s = \tfrac{1}{2} + \tfrac{1}{2} = 1$$

However, $p^2 + q^2 = \left(\tfrac{1}{2}\right)^2 + \left(\tfrac{\sqrt{2}}{2}\right)^2 = \tfrac{1}{4} + \tfrac{2}{4} \neq p$

so, this is not the matrix of a projection.

EXERCISE 8.6

A 1. For each matrix, determine whether or not it is the matrix of a reflection.

(a) $\begin{bmatrix} 1 & 0 \\ 0 & -1 \end{bmatrix}$

(b) $\begin{bmatrix} 0 & -1 \\ 1 & 0 \end{bmatrix}$

(c) $\begin{bmatrix} -\tfrac{7}{25} & -\tfrac{24}{25} \\ -\tfrac{24}{25} & \tfrac{7}{25} \end{bmatrix}$

(d) $\begin{bmatrix} 1 & 0 \\ 0 & 1 \end{bmatrix}$

2. For each matrix, determine whether or not it is the matrix of a projection.

(a) $\begin{bmatrix} 0 & 0 \\ 0 & 1 \end{bmatrix}$

(b) $\begin{bmatrix} 1 & 0 \\ 0 & -1 \end{bmatrix}$

(c) $\begin{bmatrix} \tfrac{4}{5} & \tfrac{2}{5} \\ \tfrac{2}{5} & \tfrac{1}{5} \end{bmatrix}$

(d) $\begin{bmatrix} \tfrac{1}{2} & -\tfrac{1}{2} \\ -\tfrac{1}{2} & \tfrac{1}{2} \end{bmatrix}$

B 3. Find the matrix of the reflection in each line.

(a) $x + 2y = 0$

(b) $4x - 3y = 0$

4. Find the matrix of the projection onto each line.

(a) $x - y = 0$

(b) $2x + y = 0$

(c) $3x - 4y = 0$

5. For each matrix in Question 1 which is the matrix of a reflection, determine the line of reflection.

6. For each matrix in Question 2 which is the matrix of a projection, determine the line of projection.

7. Find the image of the point $P(1, -2)$ under reflection in each of the lines indicated. For each case, draw a graph showing both P and its image.
   (a) the line $x + \sqrt{3}y = 0$ (b) the line $3x - y = 0$

8. Find the images, P' and Q', of the points $P(5, 0)$ and $Q(2, 3)$ under reflection in each of the lines specified.
   (a) the line $2x + y = 0$ (b) the line $4x - 3y = 0$

9. Find the image of the point $P(-2, 1)$ under projection onto the line l. In each case, draw a graph showing both P and its image.
   (a) $l: x + y = 0$ (b) $l: x - 2y = 0$

   (c) $l: 3y = x$ (d) $l: x + \dfrac{y}{2} = 0$

10. Consider the projection onto the line l through the origin given by $ax + by = 0$ where $a^2 + b^2 = 1$. Let P' denote the image of point $P(x_P, y_P)$.
    (a) Find an equation of the line l' through P and P'. (To solve for the constant, substitute the coordinates of P into the equation.)
    (b) To obtain one equation in $x_{P'}$ and $y_{P'}$ substitute into the equation from (a) the coordinates of P'. Why is this equation true?
    (c) To obtain a second equation in $x_{P'}$ and $y_{P'}$ substitute the coordinates of P' into the equation for l. Why is this equation true?
    (d) Solve the equations from (b) and (c) for $x_{P'}$ and $y_{P'}$. (Recall that $a^2 + b^2 = 1$.)
    (e) By comparing the formulas obtained in (d) to the general system of equations giving the image under a transformation defined by a matrix, determine the matrix of the projection onto the line $ax + by = 0$ where $a^2 + b^2 = 1$.

11. Using the matrix representation of a reflection, prove that a reflection is a rigid motion; that is,
    Given: Points P and Q and their images P' and Q' under a reflection in a line through the origin.
    Prove: the length of PQ = the length of $P'Q'$.

C 12. (a) Find the image P' of the point P given by $X_P = \begin{bmatrix} x_P \\ y_P \end{bmatrix}$ under the reflection in the line $l: ax + by = 0$ where $a^2 + b^2 = 1$.
    (b) Find the image P'' of P' under the reflection in $l: ax + by = 0$, $a^2 + b^2 = 1$.
    (c) Form a conclusion about the effect of the reflection in a line followed by a reflection in the same line.

13. Given: 2×2 matrix $M = \begin{bmatrix} p & q \\ r & s \end{bmatrix}$ where $p + s = 0$,
$q = r, p^2 + q^2 = 1$.
Prove: M is the matrix of a reflection in a line through the origin.

14. Given: 2×2 matrix $M = \begin{bmatrix} p & q \\ r & s \end{bmatrix}$ where $q = r, p + s = 1$, and
$p^2 + q^2 = p$.
Prove: M is the matrix of a projection onto a line through the origin.

15. Following the technique of this section, show that the matrix equation for $X_{P'}$ where P' is the image of a point P under the reflection in the line $ax + by = c$ with $a^2 + b^2 = 1$ is

$$X_{P'} = TX_P + B$$

where $T = \begin{bmatrix} b^2 - a^2 & -2ab \\ -2ab & a^2 - b^2 \end{bmatrix}$ and $B = 2c \begin{bmatrix} a \\ b \end{bmatrix}$

16. Using the matrix equation from Question 15,
    (a) find the image P' of the general point P given by $X_P = \begin{bmatrix} x_P \\ y_P \end{bmatrix}$
    under the reflection in the line $ax + by = c_1$ where $a^2 + b^2 = 1$,
    (b) find the image of P' under the reflection in the parallel line $ax + by = c_2$ where $a^2 + b^2 = 1$, and
    (c) thus, show that the result of a reflection in one line followed by a reflection in a parallel line is a translation.

17. Using the matrix representations of the transformations, prove that, for lines l and l' which intersect at the origin, the reflection in l followed by the reflection in l' has the same effect as the rotation through the angle 2θ where θ is the smaller angle between l and l'.

18. For a 2×2 matrix M, we define $M^2 = MM$.
    (a) By calculating P^2 for the matrix P of a projection onto a line through the origin, form a conclusion about the effect of one projection in a line followed by another projection in the same line.
    (b) By calculating R^2 for R the matrix of a reflection in a line through the origin, form a conclusion about the effect of one reflection in a line through the origin followed by another reflection in the same line.
    (c) By calculating $\left(\dfrac{I + R}{2}\right)^2$ for I the identity matrix and R the matrix of a reflection in a line through the origin, form a conclusion about the matrix $\dfrac{I + R}{2}$.

adding matrices
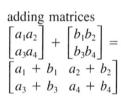
$$\begin{bmatrix} a_1 a_2 \\ a_3 a_4 \end{bmatrix} + \begin{bmatrix} b_1 b_2 \\ b_3 b_4 \end{bmatrix} =$$
$$\begin{bmatrix} a_1 + b_1 & a_2 + b_2 \\ a_3 + b_3 & a_4 + b_4 \end{bmatrix}$$

19. Develop the transformation of a projection onto a line through the origin using the idea that the image of a point under a projection onto a line l is the midpoint of the line between a point and its image under a reflection in l.

8.7 REVIEW EXERCISE

1. Write the matrix of the transformation given by each system of equations.

   (a) $\begin{cases} x_{P'} = 3x_P - 2y_P \\ y_{P'} = x_P + y_P \end{cases}$

   (b) $\begin{cases} x_{P'} = -y_P \\ y_{P'} = 2x_P \end{cases}$

2. Multiply the matrices.

   (a) $\begin{bmatrix} 1 & 3 \\ 0 & 2 \end{bmatrix} \begin{bmatrix} -1 \\ 1 \end{bmatrix}$

   (b) $\begin{bmatrix} 2 & 4 \\ 1 & 0 \end{bmatrix} \begin{bmatrix} 3 \\ -2 \end{bmatrix}$

   (c) $\begin{bmatrix} 0 & -1 \\ 1 & 0 \end{bmatrix} \begin{bmatrix} 3 \\ 6 \end{bmatrix}$

   (d) $\begin{bmatrix} 4 & 1 \\ 1 & -4 \end{bmatrix} \begin{bmatrix} -3 \\ 5 \end{bmatrix}$

   (e) $\begin{bmatrix} 2 & 0 \\ -1 & 1 \end{bmatrix} \begin{bmatrix} 3 & 1 \\ 5 & 3 \end{bmatrix}$

   (f) $\begin{bmatrix} 7 & 2 \\ -3 & 2 \end{bmatrix} \begin{bmatrix} -1 & 3 \\ 2 & 1 \end{bmatrix}$

   (g) $\begin{bmatrix} 3 & 2 \\ 2 & -1 \end{bmatrix} \begin{bmatrix} 1 & 0 \\ 0 & 1 \end{bmatrix}$

   (h) $\begin{bmatrix} 1 & 4 \\ 4 & 1 \end{bmatrix} \begin{bmatrix} 2 & -1 \\ 3 & 5 \end{bmatrix}$

3. Find the image of the point P under the transformation given by the matrix M.

   (a) $P(2, 3); M = \begin{bmatrix} 1 & -4 \\ 5 & 0 \end{bmatrix}$

   (b) $P(0, 3); M = \begin{bmatrix} 2 & 3 \\ -3 & 2 \end{bmatrix}$

4. Find the image of the point $P(3, 5)$ under the transformation given by each matrix.

   (a) $\begin{bmatrix} 1 & 0 \\ 0 & 0 \end{bmatrix}$

   (b) $\begin{bmatrix} 3 & 0 \\ 0 & 3 \end{bmatrix}$

   (c) $\begin{bmatrix} 1 & 0 \\ 0 & 1 \end{bmatrix}$

   (d) $\begin{bmatrix} 1 & 0 \\ 0 & -1 \end{bmatrix}$

   (e) $\begin{bmatrix} 0 & -1 \\ 1 & 0 \end{bmatrix}$

   (f) $\begin{bmatrix} 1 & 0 \\ 0 & 4 \end{bmatrix}$

   (g) $\begin{bmatrix} 1 & 0 \\ k & 1 \end{bmatrix}$

   (h) $\begin{bmatrix} 0 & -1 \\ -1 & 0 \end{bmatrix}$

5. Identify the type of transformation given by each matrix in Question 4.

6. Find the image of $P(4, 0)$ under each of the following transformations. Where possible use the definition of the transformation but in each case verify your answer by multiplying by the column vector $\begin{bmatrix} 4 \\ 0 \end{bmatrix}$ by the appropriate transformation matrix.

   (b) rotation through $\dfrac{\pi}{2}$ about the origin

   (c) dilatation by a factor of 3

   (d) reflection in the line $y = x$

   (e) horizontal shear by a factor of 5

   (f) vertical stretch by a factor of 2

   (g) reflection in the x-axis followed by reflection in the y-axis.

7. Repeat Question 6 for the point $P(4, -1)$. In each case draw a graph showing the original point P and the image point P'.

8. Explain why the matrix of reflection in the y-axis is $\begin{bmatrix} -1 & 0 \\ 0 & 1 \end{bmatrix}$.

9. (a) Using the definition of a reflection graph the image of the figure shown under reflection in the line $x + y = 0$.
   (b) Check your graph by finding the image of each of the vertices of the figure.

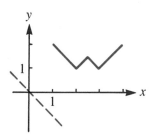

10. (a) Using the definition of a rotation find the image of the figure shown under rotation through $135°$ about the origin.
    (b) Check your graph by finding the image of each of the vertices of the figure.

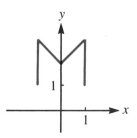

11. Find the image of the point $P(2, -3)$ under each of the following compound transformations.
    (a) projection onto the y-axis followed by a dilatation of factor 4
    (b) reflection in the x-axis followed by a horizontal stretch by a factor of 2
    (c) rotation through π about the origin followed by projection onto the y-axis
    (d) AB where $A = \begin{bmatrix} 2 & 1 \\ 3 & -1 \end{bmatrix}$ and $B = \begin{bmatrix} 0 & 1 \\ 2 & 1 \end{bmatrix}$

12. Using two specific matrices, illustrate the non-commutativity of multiplication for 2×2 matrices.

13. (a) Illustrate the fact that *reflections preserve lengths*; that is, that the length of the line segment PQ is the same as that of the line joining the image points P' and Q'.
    (b) Illustrate the fact that *projections do not preserve length*.

14. Explain why the order of performing rotations does not matter.
15. Without performing any matrix multiplication, give the matrix of the following compound transformation:
    (a) a rotation through 45° followed by a rotation through 90° followed by a rotation through $-135°$.
    (b) projection onto the y-axis followed by projection onto the x-axis,
    (c) a horizontal stretch by a factor of 5 followed by a vertical stretch by a factor of 5.
16. Find an angle of rotation for the rotation defined by the matrix
    $$\begin{bmatrix} 0.6 & -0.8 \\ 0.8 & 0.6 \end{bmatrix}$$
17. Check whether each matrix is that of a reflection, a rotation, a projection, or none of these.

    (a) $\begin{bmatrix} 0.5 & -0.5 \\ -0.5 & 0.5 \end{bmatrix}$
    (b) $\begin{bmatrix} \frac{1}{\sqrt{5}} & -\frac{2}{\sqrt{5}} \\ \frac{2}{\sqrt{5}} & \frac{1}{\sqrt{5}} \end{bmatrix}$

    (c) $\begin{bmatrix} -1 & 0 \\ 0 & -1 \end{bmatrix}$
    (d) $\begin{bmatrix} -\frac{\sqrt{2}}{2} & -\frac{\sqrt{2}}{2} \\ \frac{\sqrt{2}}{2} & -\frac{\sqrt{2}}{2} \end{bmatrix}$

    (e) $\begin{bmatrix} \frac{3+\sqrt{5}}{6} & \frac{1}{3} \\ \frac{1}{3} & \frac{3-\sqrt{5}}{6} \end{bmatrix}$
    (f) $\begin{bmatrix} 1 & 0 \\ 0 & -1 \end{bmatrix}$

18. (a) For each matrix in Question 17 that is the matrix of a reflection, find the line of the reflection.
    (b) For each matrix in Question 17 that is the matrix of a rotation, find a possible angle of the rotation.
    (c) For each matrix in Question 17 that is the matrix of a projection, find the line of the projection.

PROBLEMS PLUS

Scalar Matrices

A matrix of the form $\begin{bmatrix} a & 0 \\ 0 & a \end{bmatrix}$ is called a *scalar matrix*. Why is this a suitable name?

8.8 CHAPTER 8 TEST

1. Multiply each pair of matrices.

   (a) $\begin{bmatrix} 5 & 2 \\ 7 & 1 \end{bmatrix} \begin{bmatrix} -3 \\ 2 \end{bmatrix}$

   (b) $\begin{bmatrix} 2 & 0 \\ 4 & -1 \end{bmatrix} \begin{bmatrix} 3 & 5 \\ 1 & 3 \end{bmatrix}$

2. Find the image of the point $P(2, -3)$ under each transformation.

   (a) the transformation defined by the matrix $\begin{bmatrix} 1 & 4 \\ 6 & 0 \end{bmatrix}$

   (b) a vertical shear by a factor of 2.5

3. From the definition of a rotation through an angle about the origin, develop the matrix of such a transformation.

4. Find the matrix of the compound transformation defined by applying transformation S followed by transformation T where

$$S = \begin{bmatrix} 3 & -1 \\ 4 & 6 \end{bmatrix} \text{ and } T = \begin{bmatrix} 2 & -8 \\ 4 & 1 \end{bmatrix}$$

5. Using matrix multiplication, show that

   (a) projection onto the x-axis followed by projection onto the y-axis has the same effect as the zero transformation,

   (b) reflection in the line $y = x$ followed by another reflection in the line $y = x$ has the same effect as the identity transformation.

6. Graph the image of the figure shown under a dilatation by a factor of $\frac{1}{3}$. Label 5 key points on the image figure.

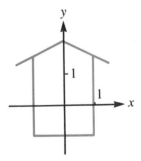

7. The graph shown in red is the image of the graph shown in black. Using the general form of matrix of a rotation determine a possible angle of rotation.

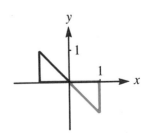

PROBLEMS PLUS

Inverse of a Matrix II (coding/decoding)

(a) Matrix multiplication can be used *to code a message* using the following procedure:

   (i) Match the letters of the alphabet with 26 numbers, say the first 26 even numbers (that is, $A = 2$, $B = 4$, $C = 6$, and so on).

  (ii) Group the letters of the message in groups of four, corresponding to the four entries of a 2×2 matrix. For example, THIS IS A SECRET MESSAGE becomes THIS/ISAS/ECRE/TMES/SAGE.

  (iii) Enter the numbers corresponding to the letters in 2×2 matrices.

  (iv) Multiply each matrix, on the left, by a 2×2 coding matrix.

   Build the matrix form of the message THIS IS A SECRET MESSAGE. Code this message using the coding matrix $\begin{bmatrix} 3 & -2 \\ 1 & 0 \end{bmatrix}$.

(b) To *decode such a message* we multiply the coded matrices by a decoder matrix, that is, the inverse of the coding matrix.

  Use the decoding matrix $\begin{bmatrix} 0 & 1 \\ -\frac{1}{2} & \frac{3}{2} \end{bmatrix}$ to decode the message you encoded in part (a).

  Decode the following message using this same decoder:

$$\begin{bmatrix} 78 & -46 \\ 30 & 2 \end{bmatrix} \begin{bmatrix} -26 & 84 \\ 2 & 40 \end{bmatrix} \begin{bmatrix} 82 & 14 \\ 38 & 6 \end{bmatrix} \begin{bmatrix} 52 & 16 \\ 24 & 24 \end{bmatrix} \begin{bmatrix} -14 & 26 \\ 14 & 18 \end{bmatrix}$$

TWENTIETH CENTURY MATHEMATICIANS

Professor Olga Taussky-Todd is a Professor Emeritus at Caltech in Pasadena, California. In her youth, it was very uncommon for a girl to want to be a mathematician. She says: "When I entered the university in the fall of 1925, I had no idea what it meant to study mathematics. I did, of course, plan to work hard. Although I did not expect to fail, I had no idea how I would compare to my colleagues. But that was my least worry. I had come to study and not to engage in a competition."

She studied the theory of numbers which concerns itself with divisibility and primality. Although number theory is reputed to be the least applicable of mathematical subjects, it is currently being used in significant ways in the computer industry.

Since its invention last century, matrix theory, which is partially explored in Chapters 8 and 9, has come to occupy a central position in many parts of mathematics. Dr. Taussky-Todd was one of the leaders in developing the applications of matrix theory. For example, her knowledge of matrix theory enabled her to solve some problems in aerodynamics that were formerly tackled using differential equations.

In her retirement, she continues to explore number theory: "Some facts in modern number theory have been better understood by considering numbers as one-dimensional matrices, and then generalizing to matrices of higher dimensions. Some of these ideas go back to Poincaré who had great ideas in more subjects than people realize. I have gone my own way in this kind of work."

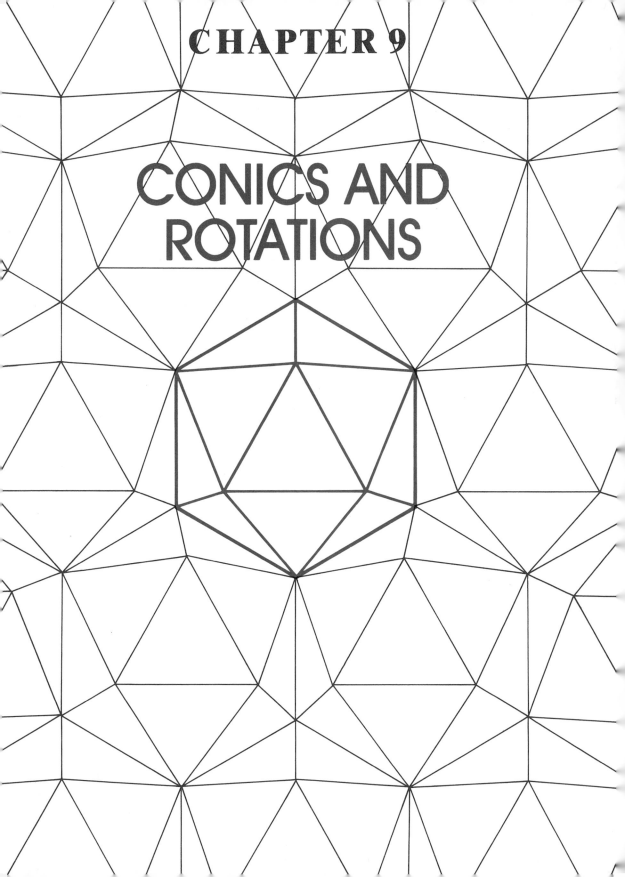

CHAPTER 9

CONICS AND ROTATIONS

REVIEW AND PREVIEW TO
CHAPTER 9

Double Angle Formulas

From the addition formulas for sine and cosine we can establish the following formulas:

$$\sin 2\theta = 2 \sin \theta \cos \theta$$
$$\cos 2\theta = \cos^2 \theta - \sin^2 \theta$$
$$= 2 \cos^2 \theta - 1$$
$$= 1 - 2 \sin^2 \theta$$

Example 1 Given $\sin \theta = \frac{3}{5}$, and $\frac{\pi}{2} < \theta < \pi$, find $\sin 2\theta$ and $\cos 2\theta$.

Solution Because $\cos^2 \theta + \sin^2 \theta = 1$,

$$\cos^2 \theta = 1 - \sin^2 \theta$$
$$= 1 - \left(\tfrac{3}{5}\right)^2$$
$$= \tfrac{16}{25}$$

Since $\frac{\pi}{2} < \theta < \pi$, $\cos \theta$ is negative, so

$$\cos \theta = -\tfrac{4}{5}$$

Hence, by the double angle formulas,

$$\sin 2\theta = 2 \sin \theta \cos \theta \quad \text{and} \quad \cos 2\theta = \cos^2 \theta - \sin^2 \theta$$
$$= 2 \left(\tfrac{3}{5}\right)\left(-\tfrac{4}{5}\right) \qquad\qquad\qquad = \left(-\tfrac{4}{5}\right)^2 - \left(\tfrac{3}{5}\right)^2$$
$$= -\tfrac{24}{25} \qquad\qquad\qquad\qquad = \tfrac{7}{25}$$

The double angle formulas may also be used in reverse: given $\cos 2\theta$ we can find $\cos \theta$ and $\sin \theta$.

$$\cos^2 \theta = \tfrac{1}{2}(1 + \cos 2\theta)$$
$$\sin^2 \theta = \tfrac{1}{2}(1 - \cos 2\theta)$$

Example 2 Given $\cos 2\theta = \frac{1}{2}$ and $\frac{\pi}{2} < \theta < \pi$, find $\cos \theta$ and $\sin \theta$.

Solution   We use the formulas just stated to deduce

$$\cos^2 \theta = \tfrac{1}{2}\left(1 + \tfrac{1}{2}\right) \quad \text{and} \quad \sin^2 \theta = \tfrac{1}{2}\left(1 - \tfrac{1}{2}\right)$$

$$= \tfrac{3}{4} \qquad\qquad\qquad = \tfrac{1}{4}$$

Since θ is between $\dfrac{\pi}{2}$ and π, $\cos \theta < 0$ and $\sin \theta > 0$, so

$$\cos \theta = -\frac{\sqrt{3}}{2} \text{ and } \sin \theta = \frac{1}{2}.$$

EXERCISE 1

1. From the information given find $\cos 2\theta$ and $\sin 2\theta$.

    (a) $\sin \theta = -\tfrac{4}{5}$, $\pi < \theta < \dfrac{3\pi}{2}$ (b) $\cos \theta = \tfrac{5}{13}$, $0 < \theta < \dfrac{\pi}{2}$

    (c) $\cos \theta = \tfrac{1}{2}$, $0 < \theta < \dfrac{\pi}{2}$ (d) $\sin \theta = -\tfrac{5}{13}$, $\pi < \theta < \dfrac{3\pi}{2}$

    (e) $\sin \theta = 0.6$, $0 < \theta < \dfrac{\pi}{2}$ (f) $\cos \theta = -0.8$, $\dfrac{\pi}{2} < \theta < \pi$

    (g) $\sin \theta = 0.8$, $\dfrac{\pi}{2} < \theta < \pi$ (h) $\cos \theta = -\tfrac{1}{3}$, $\pi < \theta < \dfrac{3\pi}{2}$

2. Find $\cos \theta$ and $\sin \theta$ given that

    (a) $\cos 2\theta = -\tfrac{1}{2}$, $0 < \theta < \dfrac{\pi}{2}$ (b) $\cos 2\theta = \tfrac{1}{3}$, $\pi < \theta < \dfrac{3\pi}{2}$

    (c) $\cos 2\theta = 0.6$, $\dfrac{\pi}{2} < \theta < \pi$ (d) $\cos 2\theta = -1$, $\pi < \theta < 2\pi$

    (e) $\cos 2\theta = \dfrac{1}{\sqrt{2}}$, $0 < \theta < \dfrac{\pi}{2}$ (f) $\cos 2\theta = -\dfrac{\sqrt{3}}{2}$, $\dfrac{\pi}{2} < \theta < \pi$

    (g) $\cos 2\theta = 0.9$, $\dfrac{3\pi}{2} < \theta < 2\pi$

    (h) $\cos 2\theta = -0.1$, $\pi < \theta < \dfrac{3\pi}{2}$

3. Using
    $$\cos(\theta_1 + \theta_2) = \cos \theta_1 \cos \theta_2 - \sin \theta_1 \sin \theta_2$$
    and
    $$\sin(\theta_1 + \theta_2) = \sin \theta_1 \cos \theta_2 + \cos \theta_1 \sin \theta_2$$
    prove the double angle formulas.

4. Using $\cos^2 \theta + \sin^2 \theta = 1$ and the double angle formulas show that
    $$\cos^2 \theta = \tfrac{1}{2}(1 + \cos 2\theta) \quad \text{and} \quad \sin^2 \theta = \tfrac{1}{2}(1 - \cos 2\theta)$$

The Cotangent Function

The cotangent function, denoted by cot θ, is defined to be

$$\cot \theta = \frac{\cos \theta}{\sin \theta}, \ \theta \ne n\pi$$

The graph of $y = \cot \theta$ is given:

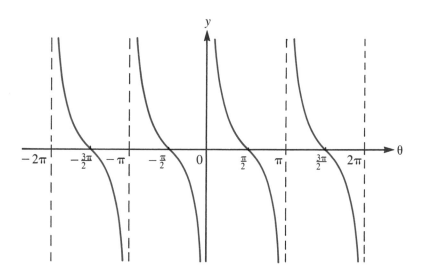

We see that for $0 < \theta < \pi$, cot θ takes on every real value once, and only once. Hence given a number c there is a unique θ satisfying $0 < \theta < \pi$ and cot $\theta = c$.

Example 3 (a) Given cot $\theta = \frac{3}{4}$ find θ between 0 and π.

(b) Given cot $\theta = -\frac{3}{4}$ find θ between 0 and π.

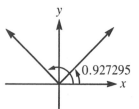

Solution (a) From the graph of the cotangent function we see that if

cot $\theta = \frac{3}{4}$ then $0 < \theta < \dfrac{\pi}{2}$. So cos θ and sin θ are both positive.

From the triangle at the left we see that cos $\theta = \frac{3}{5}$ and

sin $\theta = \frac{4}{5}$. Using either of these values and a calculator we find

that $\theta \doteq 0.927\ 295$.

(b) From the graph of the cotangent function, if cot $\theta = -\frac{3}{4}$ then

$\dfrac{\pi}{2} < \theta < \pi$. Thus sin $\theta > 0$ and cos $\theta < 0$. So sin $\theta = \frac{4}{5}$,

$\doteq$ cos $\theta = -\frac{3}{5}$, and $\theta = \pi - 0.927\ 295 \doteq 2.214\ 298$.

The following identities can be used to obtain values of $\cos^2 \theta$ and $\sin^2 \theta$ directly from $\cot \theta$.

$$\cos^2 \theta = \frac{\cot^2 \theta}{1 + \cot^2 \theta} \quad \text{and} \quad \sin^2 \theta = \frac{1}{1 + \cot^2 \theta}$$

Therefore, if $0 < \theta < \pi$,

$$\cos \theta = \frac{\cot \theta}{\sqrt{1 + \cot^2 \theta}} \quad \text{and} \quad \sin \theta = \frac{1}{\sqrt{1 + \cot^2 \theta}}$$

since $\cos \theta$ and $\cot \theta$ have the same sign, and $\sin \theta$ is positive, for $0 < \theta < \pi$.

EXERCISE 2

1. Solve for θ between 0 and π.
    (a) $\cot \theta = 1$ (b) $\cot \theta = -1$
    (c) $\cot \theta = \sqrt{3}$ (d) $\cot \theta = -\sqrt{3}$
    (e) $\cot \theta = \dfrac{1}{\sqrt{3}}$ (f) $\cot \theta = -\dfrac{1}{\sqrt{3}}$
    (g) $\cot \theta = 1.56$ (h) $\cot \theta = -10$

2. Show that the formulas $\cos^2 \theta = \dfrac{\cot^2 \theta}{1 + \cot^2 \theta}$ and

    $\sin^2 \theta = \dfrac{1}{1 + \cot^2 \theta}$ are correct.

3. Suppose $0 < \theta < \dfrac{\pi}{2}$ and $\cot 2\theta$ is given, find $\cos \theta$ and $\sin \theta$.

    (a) $\cot 2\theta = 1$ (b) $\cot 2\theta = \frac{7}{9}$

    (c) $\cot 2\theta = -3$ (d) $\cot 2\theta = -\frac{7}{24}$

    (e) $\cot 2\theta = \dfrac{1}{\sqrt{3}}$ (f) $\cot 2\theta = -\sqrt{3}$

INTRODUCTION

In Chapter 7 we showed that, by means of a suitable translation, the curve

$$ax^2 + 2hxy + by^2 + 2gx + 2fy + c = 0$$

has an image whose equation is

$$ax^2 + 2hxy + by^2 + c' = 0$$

as long as $ab - h^2 \neq 0$. In this chapter we show that, under a suitable rotation the curve whose equation is

$$ax^2 + 2hxy + by^2 + c' = 0$$

has an image whose equation is

$$a'x^2 + b'y^2 + c'' = 0.$$

As a result we can identify all curves whose equations are of second degree. Our approach is to restate equations in matrix form, and use the results on rotations proved in Chapter 8.

9.1 MATRIX OPERATIONS

We need to know how to multiply matrices, and how to take their transposes, in order to write second degree equations in matrix form.

Matrix Multiplication

m, *n*, and *p* will be 1 or 2 in our uses

We multiply an $m \times n$ matrix by an $n \times p$ matrix to obtain an $m \times p$ matrix by the "row into column" multiplication introduced in Chapter 8.

Example 1 Find the following:

(a) $[1 \quad 2]\begin{bmatrix} 3 \\ 4 \end{bmatrix}$

(b) $[1 \quad 2]\begin{bmatrix} 3 & 5 \\ 4 & 6 \end{bmatrix}$

(c) $[x \quad y]\begin{bmatrix} 2 & 0 \\ 0 & 3 \end{bmatrix}\begin{bmatrix} x \\ y \end{bmatrix}$

(d) $[x \quad y]\begin{bmatrix} 3 & 2 \\ 2 & 5 \end{bmatrix}\begin{bmatrix} x \\ y \end{bmatrix}$

Solution

(a) $[1 \quad 2]\begin{bmatrix} 3 \\ 4 \end{bmatrix} = 1(3) + 2(4) = 11$

When the product matrix is [*x*], we write it as a number.

(b) $[1 \quad 2]\begin{bmatrix} 3 & 5 \\ 4 & 6 \end{bmatrix} = [1(3) + 2(4) \quad 1(5) + 2(6)] = [11 \quad 17]$

(c) $\begin{bmatrix} x & y \end{bmatrix} \begin{bmatrix} 2 & 0 \\ 0 & 3 \end{bmatrix} \begin{bmatrix} x \\ y \end{bmatrix} = \begin{bmatrix} x & y \end{bmatrix} \begin{bmatrix} 2(x) + 0(y) \\ 0(x) + 3(y) \end{bmatrix}$

$$= \begin{bmatrix} x & y \end{bmatrix} \begin{bmatrix} 2x \\ 3y \end{bmatrix}$$

$$= 2x^2 + 3y^2$$

(d) $\begin{bmatrix} x & y \end{bmatrix} \begin{bmatrix} 3 & 2 \\ 2 & 5 \end{bmatrix} \begin{bmatrix} x \\ y \end{bmatrix} = \begin{bmatrix} x & y \end{bmatrix} \begin{bmatrix} 3x + 2y \\ 2x + 5y \end{bmatrix}$

$$= 3x^2 + 2xy + 2yx + 5y^2$$

$$= 3x^2 + 4xy + 5y^2$$

Example 2   Find the following products.

(a) $\begin{bmatrix} 1 & 4 \\ 2 & 3 \end{bmatrix} \begin{bmatrix} 5 & 7 \\ 1 & 6 \end{bmatrix}$ (b) $\begin{bmatrix} 2 & -3 \\ -1 & 8 \end{bmatrix} \begin{bmatrix} 3 & -4 \\ 5 & -6 \end{bmatrix}$

Solution   (a) $\begin{bmatrix} 1 & 4 \\ 2 & 3 \end{bmatrix} \begin{bmatrix} 5 & 7 \\ 1 & 6 \end{bmatrix} = \begin{bmatrix} 1(5) + 4(1) & 1(7) + 4(6) \\ 2(5) + 3(1) & 2(7) + 3(6) \end{bmatrix}$

$$= \begin{bmatrix} 9 & 31 \\ 13 & 32 \end{bmatrix}$$

(b) $\begin{bmatrix} 2 & -3 \\ -1 & 8 \end{bmatrix} \begin{bmatrix} 3 & -4 \\ 5 & -6 \end{bmatrix} = \begin{bmatrix} 6 - 15 & -8 + 18 \\ -3 + 40 & 4 - 48 \end{bmatrix}$

$$= \begin{bmatrix} -9 & 10 \\ 37 & -44 \end{bmatrix}$$

Matrix Transposition

We **transpose** a matrix M by interchanging its rows and columns; the matrix M^t we obtain is called the **transpose** of the original. Here are some examples:

M	M^t
$\begin{bmatrix} 2 \\ 3 \end{bmatrix}$	$\begin{bmatrix} 2 & 3 \end{bmatrix}$
$\begin{bmatrix} -1 & 6 \end{bmatrix}$	$\begin{bmatrix} -1 \\ 6 \end{bmatrix}$
$\begin{bmatrix} 2 & 3 \\ 4 & 5 \end{bmatrix}$	$\begin{bmatrix} 2 & 4 \\ 3 & 5 \end{bmatrix}$
$\begin{bmatrix} 1 & 2 \\ 2 & -1 \end{bmatrix}$	$\begin{bmatrix} 1 & 2 \\ 2 & -1 \end{bmatrix}$

In each case the first row of the transpose is the first column of the original, and similarly for the other rows. If we transpose a matrix M

to obtain M^t and then transpose M^t to obtain $(M^t)^t$, the result is the original matrix M.

$$(M^t)^t = M^{tt} = M$$

The proof of this result is requested in Exercise 9.1.

The following result will be used often in the rest of the chapter. Let M and N be matrices. Then

$$(MN)^t = N^t M^t$$

In words: the transpose of a product is the product of the transposes *in reverse order*. We verify this in the next example.

Example 3 Let $M = \begin{bmatrix} 2 & -1 \\ 3 & -2 \end{bmatrix}$ and $N = \begin{bmatrix} 4 & 3 \\ 9 & 7 \end{bmatrix}$

Show that

(a) $(MN)^t = N^t M^t$

(b) $(MN)^t \neq M^t N^t$

Solution (a)

$$MN = \begin{bmatrix} 2 & -1 \\ 3 & -2 \end{bmatrix} \begin{bmatrix} 4 & 3 \\ 9 & 7 \end{bmatrix}$$

$$= \begin{bmatrix} 2(4) - 1(9) & 2(3) - 1(7) \\ 3(4) - 2(9) & 3(3) - 2(7) \end{bmatrix}$$

$$= \begin{bmatrix} -1 & -1 \\ -6 & -5 \end{bmatrix}$$

So $(MN)^t = \begin{bmatrix} -1 & -6 \\ -1 & -5 \end{bmatrix}$

On the other hand

$$N^t M^t = \begin{bmatrix} 4 & 9 \\ 3 & 7 \end{bmatrix} \begin{bmatrix} 2 & 3 \\ -1 & -2 \end{bmatrix}$$

$$= \begin{bmatrix} 4(2) + 9(-1) & 4(3) + 9(-2) \\ 3(2) + 7(-1) & 3(3) + 7(-2) \end{bmatrix}$$

$$= \begin{bmatrix} -1 & -6 \\ -1 & -5 \end{bmatrix}$$

Therefore $(MN)^t = N^t M^t$.

(b) $M^t N^t = \begin{bmatrix} 2 & 3 \\ -1 & -2 \end{bmatrix} \begin{bmatrix} 4 & 9 \\ 3 & 7 \end{bmatrix}$

$$= \begin{bmatrix} 2(4) + 3(3) & 2(9) + 3(7) \\ -1(4) - 2(3) & -1(9) - 2(7) \end{bmatrix}$$

$$= \begin{bmatrix} 17 & 39 \\ -10 & -23 \end{bmatrix}$$

$$\neq (MN)^t$$

Symmetric Matrices

The square matrix M is **symmetric** if, and only if, it equals its transpose:

$$M = M^t$$

Example 4 (a) $M = \begin{bmatrix} 1 & 2 \\ 2 & -1 \end{bmatrix}$ is symmetric, since $M^t = \begin{bmatrix} 1 & 2 \\ 2 & -1 \end{bmatrix} = M$.

(b) $N = \begin{bmatrix} 1 & 2 \\ -1 & 2 \end{bmatrix}$ is not symmetric, since $N^t = \begin{bmatrix} 1 & -1 \\ 2 & 2 \end{bmatrix} \neq N$.

EXERCISE 9.1

A **1.** Identify the symmetric matrices.

(a) $\begin{bmatrix} 2 & 1 \\ 1 & 3 \end{bmatrix}$

(b) $\begin{bmatrix} 3 & 4 \\ 4 & 6 \end{bmatrix}$

(c) $\begin{bmatrix} e & c \\ d & e \end{bmatrix}$

(d) $\begin{bmatrix} a & h \\ h & b \end{bmatrix}$

B **2.** Find the following matrix products.

(a) $[-1 \quad 3]\begin{bmatrix} 4 \\ -7 \end{bmatrix}$

(b) $[0 \quad 6]\begin{bmatrix} 5 \\ 0 \end{bmatrix}$

(c) $[8 \quad 1]\begin{bmatrix} -2 \\ 9 \end{bmatrix}$

(d) $[4 \quad 7]\begin{bmatrix} 2 \\ -11 \end{bmatrix}$

3. For each matrix M below compute $[x \quad y] M \begin{bmatrix} x \\ y \end{bmatrix}$.

(a) $\begin{bmatrix} -1 & 0 \\ 0 & 2 \end{bmatrix}$

(b) $\begin{bmatrix} 2 & -3 \\ -3 & 7 \end{bmatrix}$

(c) $\begin{bmatrix} 0 & -1 \\ -1 & 2 \end{bmatrix}$

(d) $\begin{bmatrix} 4 & -2 \\ -2 & 4 \end{bmatrix}$

(e) $\begin{bmatrix} 3 & 1 \\ 1 & 1 \end{bmatrix}$

(f) $\begin{bmatrix} 6 & \frac{1}{2} \\ \frac{1}{2} & 0 \end{bmatrix}$

4. For each matrix M below compute $M^t M$ and $M M^t$.

(a) $[-1 \quad 3]$

(b) $[4 \quad -7]$

(c) $[0 \quad 6]$

(d) $[5 \quad 0]$

(e) $\begin{bmatrix} 8 \\ 1 \end{bmatrix}$

(f) $\begin{bmatrix} -2 \\ 9 \end{bmatrix}$

(g) $\begin{bmatrix} 4 \\ -7 \end{bmatrix}$

(h) $\begin{bmatrix} 2 \\ -11 \end{bmatrix}$

5. For each pair of matrices M and N compute MN, $(MN)^t$, and $N^t M^t$.

   (a) $M = \begin{bmatrix} 1 & 2 \end{bmatrix}$ $N = \begin{bmatrix} 3 & 5 \\ -1 & -2 \end{bmatrix}$

   (b) $M = \begin{bmatrix} 3 & 5 \\ -1 & -2 \end{bmatrix}$ $N = \begin{bmatrix} 0 \\ -1 \end{bmatrix}$

   (c) $M = \begin{bmatrix} 1 & 2 \\ 3 & 0 \end{bmatrix}$ $N = \begin{bmatrix} 0 & -2 \\ 3 & 5 \end{bmatrix}$

6. Let $M = \begin{bmatrix} 2 & 3 \\ 4 & 5 \end{bmatrix}$ and $A = \begin{bmatrix} 2 & 1 \\ 1 & 1 \end{bmatrix}$. Evaluate MAM^t and verify that it is symmetric.

7. For each matrix M, show that $M^{tt} = M$ by first finding M^t and transposing it.

   (a) $M = \begin{bmatrix} s & t \end{bmatrix}$ (b) $M = \begin{bmatrix} s & t \\ u & v \end{bmatrix}$

   (c) $\begin{bmatrix} x \\ y \end{bmatrix}$

8. For each pair of matrices, prove that $(MN)^t = N^t M^t$.

   (a) $M = \begin{bmatrix} s & t \end{bmatrix}$ $N = \begin{bmatrix} w \\ y \end{bmatrix}$

   (b) $M = \begin{bmatrix} s & t \end{bmatrix}$ $N = \begin{bmatrix} w & x \\ y & z \end{bmatrix}$

   (c) $M = \begin{bmatrix} s & t \\ u & v \end{bmatrix}$ $N = \begin{bmatrix} w \\ y \end{bmatrix}$

   (d) $M = \begin{bmatrix} s & t \\ u & v \end{bmatrix}$ $N = \begin{bmatrix} w & x \\ y & z \end{bmatrix}$

C 9. Suppose that A is a symmetric matrix and M is a matrix. Prove that MAM^t is symmetric. [Hint: Find $(MAM^t)^t$ using the rule for the transpose of a product.]

10. Show that if M is the matrix of a reflection then $M^t M = I$.

PROBLEMS PLUS

A square of side two, lying always in the first quadrant of the xy-plane, moves so that two consecutive vertices are always on the x- and y-axes respectively. Prove that a point within the square will, in general, describe a portion of an ellipse.

9.2   WRITING $ax^2 + 2hxy + by^2 = k$ IN MATRIX FORM

> The **coefficient matrix** A of the expression $ax^2 + 2hxy + by^2$ is the matrix
> $$A = \begin{bmatrix} a & h \\ h & b \end{bmatrix}$$
> *Note*: A is symmetric.

Example 1   Find the coefficient matrix A of each of the following.

(a) $x^2 + y^2$ (b) $x^2 + xy - y^2$ (c) xy

Solution   Our strategy is to write each of the above expressions as $ax^2 + 2hxy + by^2$ for appropriate a, h, b and from this write down the coefficient matrix.

(a) $x^2 + y^2 = 1x^2 + 2(0)xy + 1y^2$

so $A = \begin{bmatrix} 1 & 0 \\ 0 & 1 \end{bmatrix}$

(b) $x^2 + xy - y^2 = 1x^2 + 2(\tfrac{1}{2})xy + (-1)y^2$

so $A = \begin{bmatrix} 1 & \tfrac{1}{2} \\ \tfrac{1}{2} & -1 \end{bmatrix}$

(c) $xy = 0x^2 + 2(\tfrac{1}{2})xy + 0y^2$

so $A = \begin{bmatrix} 0 & \tfrac{1}{2} \\ \tfrac{1}{2} & 0 \end{bmatrix}$

Example 2   (a) Find the coefficient matrix A of $2x^2 - 4xy + 3y^2$.

(b) Evaluate $X'AX$ where $X = \begin{bmatrix} x \\ y \end{bmatrix}$.

Solution   (a) Since

$$2x^2 - 4xy + 3y^2 = 2x^2 + 2(-2)xy + 3y^2$$

the coefficient matrix A is

$$\begin{bmatrix} 2 & -2 \\ -2 & 3 \end{bmatrix}$$

(b) $X'AX = \begin{bmatrix} x & y \end{bmatrix} \begin{bmatrix} 2 & -2 \\ -2 & 3 \end{bmatrix} \begin{bmatrix} x \\ y \end{bmatrix}$

$= \begin{bmatrix} x & y \end{bmatrix} \begin{bmatrix} 2x - 2y \\ -2x + 3y \end{bmatrix}$

$= 2x^2 - 2xy - 2yx + 3y^2$

$= 2x^2 - 4xy + 3y^2$

This example gives us the pattern for writing equations in matrix form.

Matrix Form of Equations

The equation $ax^2 + 2hxy + by^2 = k$ may be written as

$$X'AX = k$$

where $A = \begin{bmatrix} a & h \\ h & b \end{bmatrix}$ is the coefficient matrix of $ax^2 + 2hxy + by^2$

and $X = \begin{bmatrix} x \\ y \end{bmatrix}$.

Example 3   Verify that $X'AX = k$ is the matrix form of $x^2 - xy + y^2 = k$, where $A = \begin{bmatrix} 1 & -\frac{1}{2} \\ -\frac{1}{2} & 1 \end{bmatrix}$.

Solution
$$X'AX = k$$

$$[x \ \ y] \begin{bmatrix} 1 & -\frac{1}{2} \\ -\frac{1}{2} & 1 \end{bmatrix} \begin{bmatrix} x \\ y \end{bmatrix} = k$$

$$[x \ \ y] \begin{bmatrix} x - \frac{1}{2}y \\ -\frac{1}{2}x + y \end{bmatrix} = k$$

$$x^2 - \tfrac{1}{2}xy - \tfrac{1}{2}yx + y^2 = k$$

$$x^2 - xy + y^2 = k$$

We stress that in writing $ax^2 + 2hxy + by^2 = k$ in matrix form, the matrix A is symmetric. It is symmetric because it is the coefficient matrix of the expression $ax^2 + 2hxy + by^2$. The next example demonstrates that this matrix is unique.

Example 4   (a) Find all matrices $M = \begin{bmatrix} a & b \\ c & d \end{bmatrix}$ such that $X'MX = x^2 - 2xy + 3y^2$.

(b) Show that $A = \begin{bmatrix} 1 & -1 \\ -1 & 3 \end{bmatrix}$ is the only symmetric matrix such that $X'AX = x^2 - 2xy + 3y^2$.

Solution   (a)
$$[x \ \ y] \begin{bmatrix} a & b \\ c & d \end{bmatrix} \begin{bmatrix} x \\ y \end{bmatrix} = [x \ \ y] \begin{bmatrix} ax + by \\ cx + dy \end{bmatrix}$$

$$= ax^2 + bxy + cxy + dy^2$$

$$= ax^2 + (b + c)xy + dy^2$$

We require that $X'AX = x^2 - 2xy + 3y^2$ so, equating coefficients, we have $a = 1$, $b + c = -2$, and $d = 3$. Hence, for each choice of b,

$$M = \begin{bmatrix} 1 & b \\ -2 - b & 3 \end{bmatrix}$$

satisfies $X'MX = x^2 - 2xy + 3y^2$.

(b) If M is symmetric then

$$b = -2 - b$$
hence $b = -1$

Thus the only symmetric matrix A satisfying $X'AX = x^2 - 2xy + 3y^2$ is

$$A = \begin{bmatrix} 1 & -1 \\ -1 & 3 \end{bmatrix}$$

This is the coefficient matrix of $x^2 - 2xy + 3y^2$.

EXERCISE 9.2

B **1.** Find the coefficient matrix A of each expression and evaluate $X'AX$.

(a) $x^2 - y^2$ (b) $2xy + 5y^2$

(c) $5x^2 - 6xy - 7y^2$ (d) $3x^2 - xy + 5y^2$

(e) $\dfrac{x^2}{a^2} + \dfrac{y^2}{b^2}$ (f) $\dfrac{x^2}{a^2} - \dfrac{y^2}{b^2}$

2. Find the unique symmetric matrix A such that $X'AX = 1$ is the matrix form of the equation.

(a) $x^2 + xy = 1$ (b) $4xy = 1$

(c) $3x^2 - 2xy + 7y^2 = 1$ (d) $11xy - y^2 = 1$

(e) $-x^2 + 2y^2 = 1$ (f) $ax^2 + 2hxy + by^2 = 1$

3. (a) Find $M = \begin{bmatrix} a & b \\ 0 & c \end{bmatrix}$ such that $X'MX = 2xy + 5y^2$.

(b) Is M the coefficient matrix of $2xy + 5y^2$?

4. Find all matrices M such that $X'MX = 0$.

5. Show that for every number c the equation $x^2 + xy + y^2 = 3$ may be written $X'MX = 3$ where $M = \begin{bmatrix} 1 & \frac{1}{2} + c \\ \frac{1}{2} - c & 1 \end{bmatrix}$.

C **6.** Show that:

(a) for any number c, $X'\begin{bmatrix} a & h + c \\ h - c & b \end{bmatrix} X = X'\begin{bmatrix} a & h \\ h & b \end{bmatrix} X$,

(b) if $X'\begin{bmatrix} d & e \\ f & g \end{bmatrix} X = X'\begin{bmatrix} a & h \\ h & b \end{bmatrix} X$ then there is a number c such that $e = h + c$, $f = h - c$, $d = a$, and $g = b$.

(c) Relate this to Questions 4 and 5.

9.3 ROTATING ELLIPSES AND HYPERBOLAS

In this section we find the equation of the image of a curve under a rotation given by $X_{P'} = RX_P$. We approach these problems in the same way that we approached the analogous problems for translations. We take any point P' on the image curve and the corresponding point P on the original curve. The equation $X_P^t A X_P = k$ will give us an equation for $X_{P'}$ if we can solve $X_{P'} = RX_P$ for X_P and substitute.

> **Theorem**
>
> Let R be a 2×2 matrix of a rotation. Then
>
> $$R^t R = R R^t = I = \begin{bmatrix} 1 & 0 \\ 0 & 1 \end{bmatrix}$$

Proof As we saw in Chapter 8 the matrix R of a rotation (about the origin) through an angle of θ radians is

$$R = \begin{bmatrix} \cos \theta & -\sin \theta \\ \sin \theta & \cos \theta \end{bmatrix}$$

$\cos(-\theta) = \cos \theta$
$\sin(-\theta) = -\sin \theta$

Now
$$R^t = \begin{bmatrix} \cos \theta & \sin \theta \\ -\sin \theta & \cos \theta \end{bmatrix}$$

$$= \begin{bmatrix} \cos(-\theta) & -\sin(-\theta) \\ \sin(-\theta) & \cos(-\theta) \end{bmatrix}$$

So R^t is the matrix of a rotation through an angle of $-\theta$ radians. Thus $R^t R$ applied to a column vector first rotates it through θ, then rotates the image through $-\theta$, clearly coming back to the original point. So $R^t R$ has no net effect whatsoever: that is

$$R^t R = \begin{bmatrix} 1 & 0 \\ 0 & 1 \end{bmatrix}$$

the identity matrix I.

(An alternative, strictly computational, proof is asked for in Exercise 9.3)

We can now use this result to isolate X_P in the equation $X_{P'} = RX_P$.

Corollary If $X_{P'} = RX_P$ then $X_P = R^t X_{P'}$.

Proof Since $X_{P'} = RX_P$, multiplying by R^t on both sides we obtain

$$R^t X_{P'} = R^t R X_P$$

$$R^t X_{P'} = I X_P$$

$$R^t X_{P'} = X_P$$

Let us see how this corollary works in practice.

Example 1   Find an equation for the image $\mathscr{C}'$ of the hyperbola $\mathscr{C}: x^2 - y^2 = 1$ under the rotation $X_{P'} = RX_P$ where

$$R = \begin{bmatrix} \dfrac{1}{\sqrt{2}} & -\dfrac{1}{\sqrt{2}} \\ \dfrac{1}{\sqrt{2}} & \dfrac{1}{\sqrt{2}} \end{bmatrix}$$

Solution   We first write the equation for $\mathscr{C}$ in matrix form $X^t A X = 1$ where $A = \begin{bmatrix} 1 & 0 \\ 0 & -1 \end{bmatrix}$ is the coefficient matrix of $x^2 - y^2$. Now let P' be any point on $\mathscr{C}'$ and P be the corresponding point on $\mathscr{C}$. Then $X_{P'} = RX_P$ and by the corollary,

$$X_P = R^t X_{P'}$$

Since P is on the curve, $X_P^t A X_P = 1$. Substituting for X_P, we obtain

$$(R^t X_{P'})^t A (R^t X_{P'}) = 1$$

$$X_{P'}^t R^{tt} A R^t X_{P'} = 1 \qquad \text{since } (MN)^t = N^t M^t$$

$$X_{P'}^t (RAR^t) X_{P'} = 1 \qquad \text{since } R^{tt} = R$$

So the matrix equation for $\mathscr{C}'$ is

$$X^t (RAR^t) X = 1$$

Finally we compute the coefficient matrix RAR^t: it is only at this point that we need to know R and A explicitly.

$$RAR^t = \begin{bmatrix} \dfrac{1}{\sqrt{2}} & -\dfrac{1}{\sqrt{2}} \\ \dfrac{1}{\sqrt{2}} & \dfrac{1}{\sqrt{2}} \end{bmatrix} \begin{bmatrix} 1 & 0 \\ 0 & -1 \end{bmatrix} \begin{bmatrix} \dfrac{1}{\sqrt{2}} & \dfrac{1}{\sqrt{2}} \\ -\dfrac{1}{\sqrt{2}} & \dfrac{1}{\sqrt{2}} \end{bmatrix}$$

$$= \begin{bmatrix} \dfrac{1}{\sqrt{2}} & -\dfrac{1}{\sqrt{2}} \\ \dfrac{1}{\sqrt{2}} & \dfrac{1}{\sqrt{2}} \end{bmatrix} \begin{bmatrix} \dfrac{1}{\sqrt{2}} & \dfrac{1}{\sqrt{2}} \\ \dfrac{1}{\sqrt{2}} & -\dfrac{1}{\sqrt{2}} \end{bmatrix}$$

$$= \begin{bmatrix} \dfrac{1}{2} - \dfrac{1}{2} & \dfrac{1}{2} + \dfrac{1}{2} \\ \dfrac{1}{2} + \dfrac{1}{2} & \dfrac{1}{2} - \dfrac{1}{2} \end{bmatrix}$$

$$= \begin{bmatrix} 0 & 1 \\ 1 & 0 \end{bmatrix}$$

Notice that RAR' is symmetric and that it is the coefficient matrix of $2xy$, So the equation for $\mathscr{C}'$ is

$$2xy = 1$$

Here are sketches of $\mathscr{C}$ and $\mathscr{C}'$ in Example 1.

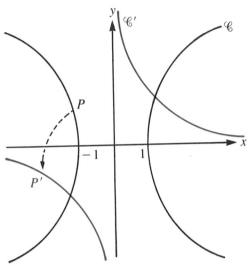

In the course of doing the example, we demonstrated the following result.

Equation for Image Curve (Matrix Form)

If $\mathscr{C}$ has the matrix equation $X'AX = k$ and $\mathscr{C}'$ is the image of $\mathscr{C}$ under the rotation $X_{P'} = RX_P$, then a matrix equation for $\mathscr{C}'$ is

$$X'(RAR')X = k$$

Example 2 Let $\mathscr{C}$ be the ellipse, in standard position, whose equation is
$$\frac{x^2}{25} + \frac{y^2}{9} = 1.$$

Let $\mathscr{C}'$ be the image of $\mathscr{C}$ under a rotation of $\frac{\pi}{2}$. Find an equation for $\mathscr{C}'$. Sketch $\mathscr{C}$ and $\mathscr{C}'$.

Solution The matrix form of the equation for $\mathscr{C}$ is $X'AX = 1$, where

$$A = \begin{bmatrix} \frac{1}{25} & 0 \\ 0 & \frac{1}{9} \end{bmatrix}$$

Hence the matrix equation for $\mathscr{C}'$ is:

$$X'(RAR')\, X = 1$$

Next we identify the matrix R of the rotation:

$$R = \begin{bmatrix} \cos\dfrac{\pi}{2} & -\sin\dfrac{\pi}{2} \\ \sin\dfrac{\pi}{2} & \cos\dfrac{\pi}{2} \end{bmatrix} = \begin{bmatrix} 0 & -1 \\ 1 & 0 \end{bmatrix}$$

To put this in the usual form we compute

$$RAR^t = \begin{bmatrix} 0 & -1 \\ 1 & 0 \end{bmatrix} \begin{bmatrix} \frac{1}{25} & 0 \\ 0 & \frac{1}{9} \end{bmatrix} \begin{bmatrix} 0 & 1 \\ -1 & 0 \end{bmatrix}$$

$$= \begin{bmatrix} 0 & -1 \\ 1 & 0 \end{bmatrix} \begin{bmatrix} 0 & \frac{1}{25} \\ -\frac{1}{9} & 0 \end{bmatrix}$$

$$= \begin{bmatrix} \frac{1}{9} & 0 \\ 0 & \frac{1}{25} \end{bmatrix}$$

So an equation for $\mathscr{C}'$ is $\dfrac{x^2}{9} + \dfrac{y^2}{25} = 1$.

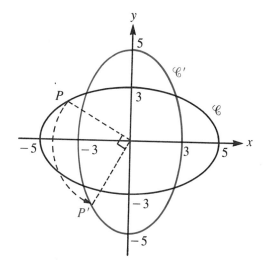

Example 3 Let $\mathscr{C}$ be given by $\dfrac{x^2}{9} + \dfrac{y^2}{4} = 1$. Rotate $\mathscr{C}$ through 60° to obtain the ellipse $\mathscr{C}'$. Find an equation for $\mathscr{C}'$. Sketch both $\mathscr{C}$ and $\mathscr{C}'$.

Solution First we put the equation for $\mathscr{C}$ in matrix form: $X^t A X = 1$, where

$$A = \begin{bmatrix} \frac{1}{9} & 0 \\ 0 & \frac{1}{4} \end{bmatrix}$$

So the matrix equation for $\mathscr{C}'$, the image curve, is

$$X^t\, RAR^t\, X = 1$$

Next we identify the matrix R of the rotation

$$R = \begin{bmatrix} \cos 60° & -\sin 60° \\ \sin 60° & \cos 60° \end{bmatrix} = \begin{bmatrix} \dfrac{1}{2} & -\dfrac{\sqrt{3}}{2} \\ \dfrac{\sqrt{3}}{2} & \dfrac{1}{2} \end{bmatrix}$$

Finally we evaluate

$$RAR' = \begin{bmatrix} \dfrac{1}{2} & -\dfrac{\sqrt{3}}{2} \\ \dfrac{\sqrt{3}}{2} & \dfrac{1}{2} \end{bmatrix} \begin{bmatrix} \dfrac{1}{9} & 0 \\ 0 & \dfrac{1}{4} \end{bmatrix} \begin{bmatrix} \dfrac{1}{2} & \dfrac{\sqrt{3}}{2} \\ -\dfrac{\sqrt{3}}{2} & \dfrac{1}{2} \end{bmatrix}$$

$$= \begin{bmatrix} \dfrac{1}{2} & -\dfrac{\sqrt{3}}{2} \\ \dfrac{\sqrt{3}}{2} & \dfrac{1}{2} \end{bmatrix} \begin{bmatrix} \dfrac{1}{18} & \dfrac{\sqrt{3}}{18} \\ -\dfrac{\sqrt{3}}{8} & \dfrac{1}{8} \end{bmatrix}$$

$$= \begin{bmatrix} \dfrac{1}{36} + \dfrac{3}{16} & \dfrac{\sqrt{3}}{36} - \dfrac{\sqrt{3}}{16} \\ \dfrac{\sqrt{3}}{36} - \dfrac{\sqrt{3}}{16} & \dfrac{3}{36} + \dfrac{1}{16} \end{bmatrix}$$

$$= \begin{bmatrix} \dfrac{4 + 27}{144} & \dfrac{\sqrt{3}}{144}(4 - 9) \\ \dfrac{\sqrt{3}}{144}(4 - 9) & \dfrac{12 + 9}{144} \end{bmatrix}$$

$$= \begin{bmatrix} \dfrac{31}{144} & -\dfrac{5\sqrt{3}}{144} \\ -\dfrac{5\sqrt{3}}{144} & \dfrac{21}{144} \end{bmatrix}$$

So an equation for $\mathscr{C}'$ is

$$\frac{31}{144}x^2 - \frac{10\sqrt{3}}{144}xy + \frac{21}{144}y^2 = 1$$

or $31x^2 - 10\sqrt{3}xy + 21y^2 = 144$

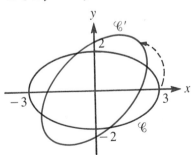

We see that the equation for $\mathscr{C}'$ in Example 3 has a non-zero xy-term.

$$\mathscr{C}: 16x^2 + 36y^2 = 144 \qquad\qquad A = \begin{bmatrix} 16 & 0 \\ 0 & 36 \end{bmatrix}$$

$$\mathscr{C}': 31x^2 - 10\sqrt{3}xy + 21y^2 = 144 \quad A = \begin{bmatrix} 33 & -5\sqrt{3} \\ -5\sqrt{3} & 21 \end{bmatrix}$$

These two equations are quite different but there are some connections between them. Let us compute $ab - h^2$ for $\mathscr{C}$, and for $\mathscr{C}'$.

For $\mathscr{C}$, $ab - h^2 = (16)(36) - 0^2 = 576$
For $\mathscr{C}'$, $ab - h^2 = (31)(21) - (-5\sqrt{3})^2 = 651 - 75 = 576$

The value of $ab - h^2$ has remained the same.

EXERCISE 9.3

B **1.** For each rotation matrix R compute $R'R$.

(a) $\begin{bmatrix} 0 & -1 \\ 1 & 0 \end{bmatrix}$

(b) $\begin{bmatrix} \dfrac{1}{\sqrt{2}} & \dfrac{1}{\sqrt{2}} \\ -\dfrac{1}{\sqrt{2}} & \dfrac{1}{\sqrt{2}} \end{bmatrix}$

(c) $\begin{bmatrix} \dfrac{1}{2} & -\dfrac{\sqrt{3}}{2} \\ \dfrac{\sqrt{3}}{2} & \dfrac{1}{2} \end{bmatrix}$

(d) $\begin{bmatrix} \dfrac{2}{\sqrt{5}} & -\dfrac{1}{\sqrt{5}} \\ \dfrac{1}{\sqrt{5}} & \dfrac{2}{\sqrt{5}} \end{bmatrix}$

(e) $\begin{bmatrix} \dfrac{3}{5} & \dfrac{4}{5} \\ -\dfrac{4}{5} & \dfrac{3}{5} \end{bmatrix}$

(f) $\begin{bmatrix} \dfrac{12}{13} & -\dfrac{5}{13} \\ \dfrac{5}{13} & \dfrac{12}{13} \end{bmatrix}$

2. Find an equation of the form $ax^2 + 2hxy + by^2 = 1$ for the image $\mathscr{C}'$ of the hyperbola $\mathscr{C}: x^2 - y^2 = 1$ under the rotation $X_{P'} = RX_P$, where R is given by:

(a) $\begin{bmatrix} 0 & -1 \\ 1 & 0 \end{bmatrix}$

(b) $\begin{bmatrix} \dfrac{1}{2} & -\dfrac{\sqrt{3}}{2} \\ \dfrac{\sqrt{3}}{2} & \dfrac{1}{2} \end{bmatrix}$

(c) $\begin{bmatrix} \dfrac{2}{\sqrt{5}} & -\dfrac{1}{\sqrt{5}} \\ \dfrac{1}{\sqrt{5}} & \dfrac{2}{\sqrt{5}} \end{bmatrix}$
(d) $\begin{bmatrix} \dfrac{3}{5} & \dfrac{4}{5} \\ -\dfrac{4}{5} & \dfrac{3}{5} \end{bmatrix}$

3. Find an equation of the form $ax^2 + 2hxy + by^2 = 1$ for the image $\mathscr{C}'$ of the ellipse $\mathscr{C}: \dfrac{x^2}{25} + \dfrac{y^2}{9} = 1$ under the rotation $X_{P'} = RX_P$, where R is given below. In each case compute $ab - h^2$ for $\mathscr{C}$ and $\mathscr{C}'$.

(a) $\begin{bmatrix} \dfrac{1}{\sqrt{2}} & -\dfrac{1}{\sqrt{2}} \\ \dfrac{1}{\sqrt{2}} & \dfrac{1}{\sqrt{2}} \end{bmatrix}$
(b) $\begin{bmatrix} \dfrac{1}{2} & \dfrac{\sqrt{3}}{2} \\ -\dfrac{\sqrt{3}}{2} & \dfrac{1}{2} \end{bmatrix}$

(c) $\begin{bmatrix} \dfrac{2}{\sqrt{5}} & -\dfrac{1}{\sqrt{5}} \\ \dfrac{1}{\sqrt{5}} & \dfrac{2}{\sqrt{5}} \end{bmatrix}$
(d) $\begin{bmatrix} \dfrac{4}{5} & -\dfrac{3}{5} \\ \dfrac{3}{5} & \dfrac{4}{5} \end{bmatrix}$

4. Rotate each of the curves through $45°$. Find the equation of the image and identify the given curve.
   (a) $x^2 + xy + y^2 = 1$
   (b) $x^2 + 4xy + y^2 = 1$
   (c) $2x^2 + 3xy + 2y^2 = 1$
   (d) $2x^2 + 5xy + 2y^2 = 1$

5. Rotate each of the curves through $-\dfrac{\pi}{3}$. Find the equation of the image and identify the curve.
   (a) $7x^2 - 2\sqrt{3}xy + 5y^2 = 1$
   (b) $-2x^2 + 4\sqrt{3}xy + 2y^2 = 1$
   (c) $5x^2 - 2\sqrt{3}xy + 3y^2 = 1$
   (d) $-x^2 + \sqrt{3}xy = 1$

6. Let $R = \begin{bmatrix} \cos\theta & -\sin\theta \\ \sin\theta & \cos\theta \end{bmatrix}$. Show that $R^t R = I$.

C 7. Rotate the curve $\mathscr{C}: ax^2 + 2hxy + ay^2 = 1$ through $\dfrac{\pi}{4}$. Assume $2a$ is greater than zero. Show that if $a^2 - h^2 > 0$, $\mathscr{C}$ is an ellipse; and if $a^2 - h^2 < 0$, it is an hyperbola. What curve is $\mathscr{C}$ if $a^2 - h^2 = 0$?

8. Rotate the curve $\mathscr{C}: (a + 3b)x^2 + 2\sqrt{3}(a - b)xy + (3a + b)y^2 = 4$ through $-60°$. Assume $4(a + b)$ is greater than zero. Show that $\mathscr{C}$ is an ellipse if $(a + 3b)(3a + b) - (\sqrt{3}(a - b))^2$ is positive, and an hyperbola if it is negative.

9. Suppose $\mathscr{C}$ has the matrix equation $X^tAX = k$. Suppose $X_{P'} = MX_P$ is a reflection, so $M = M^t$ and $M^2 = I$, and $\mathscr{C}'$ is the image of $\mathscr{C}$ under this reflection. Find the matrix equation of $\mathscr{C}'$.

9.4   ROTATIONS THAT ELIMINATE THE *xy*-TERM

What does the curve $\mathscr{C}$: $73x^2 + 72xy + 52y^2 = 25$ look like? Since $a = 73$, $b = 52$, and $h = 36$, we see that
$$ab - h^2 = (73)(52) - 36^2 = 2500$$
which is positive, so we might suspect from our investigations so far that this is an ellipse. Before jumping in and plotting points it is worthwhile to see if we can find a rotation such that the image of this curve is easier to graph. An equation without an *xy*-term is easier to graph; so we look for a rotation that eliminates the *xy*-term.

In matrix terms an equation for $\mathscr{C}$ is $X'AX = 25$, $A = \begin{bmatrix} 73 & 36 \\ 36 & 52 \end{bmatrix}$ and its image $\mathscr{C}'$ has the equation $X^t\,RAR^t\,X = 25$ under the rotation $X_{P'} = RX_P$. What we want to find is R such that
$$R \begin{bmatrix} 73 & 36 \\ 36 & 52 \end{bmatrix} R^t = \begin{bmatrix} a' & 0 \\ 0 & b' \end{bmatrix}$$

The important point is that zeros be present in the off-diagonal entries.

Example 1   (a)   Find all rotation matrices $R = \begin{bmatrix} \cos\theta & -\sin\theta \\ \sin\theta & \cos\theta \end{bmatrix}$ with θ between 0 and $\dfrac{\pi}{2}$ such that $R \begin{bmatrix} 73 & 36 \\ 36 & 52 \end{bmatrix} R^t = \begin{bmatrix} a' & 0 \\ 0 & b' \end{bmatrix}$

   (b)   Identify the numbers a' and b'
   (c)   Identify the curve $\mathscr{C}$: $73x^2 + 72xy + 52y^2 = 25$

Solution   (a)   For brevity we write $c = \cos\theta$ and $s = \sin\theta$. Then

$$\begin{bmatrix} a' & 0 \\ 0 & b' \end{bmatrix} = R \begin{bmatrix} 73 & 36 \\ 36 & 52 \end{bmatrix} R^t$$

$$= \begin{bmatrix} c & -s \\ s & c \end{bmatrix} \begin{bmatrix} 73 & 36 \\ 36 & 52 \end{bmatrix} \begin{bmatrix} c & s \\ -s & c \end{bmatrix}$$

$$= \begin{bmatrix} c & -s \\ s & c \end{bmatrix} \begin{bmatrix} 73c - 36s & 73s + 36c \\ 36c - 52s & 36s + 52c \end{bmatrix}$$

$$= \begin{bmatrix} 73c^2 - 36cs - 36sc + 52s^2 & 73cs + 36c^2 - 36s^2 - 52sc \\ 73sc - 36s^2 + 36c^2 - 52cs & 73s^2 + 36sc + 36cs + 52c^2 \end{bmatrix}$$

$$= \begin{bmatrix} 73c^2 - 72cs + 52s^2 & 36c^2 + 21cs - 36s^2 \\ 36c^2 + 21cs - 36s^2 & 52c^2 + 72cs + 73s^2 \end{bmatrix}$$

So
$$a' = 73c^2 - 72cs + 52s^2 \quad ①$$
$$b' = 52c^2 + 72cs + 73s^2 \quad ②$$
$$0 = 36c^2 + 21cs - 36s^2 \quad ③$$

We return to the use of $\cos\theta$ for c and $\sin\theta$ for s, in order to make use of Equation 3.

$$36\cos^2\theta + 21\cos\theta\sin\theta - 36\sin^2\theta = 0$$
$$36(\cos^2\theta - \sin^2\theta) = -21\cos\theta\sin\theta$$
$$36\cos 2\theta = -\tfrac{21}{2}\sin 2\theta$$
$$\cot 2\theta = -\tfrac{21}{72}$$
$$= -\tfrac{7}{24}$$

25   24
2θ
7

Since $0 < 2\theta < \pi$ and $\cot 2\theta < 0$, we have $\dfrac{\pi}{2} < 2\theta < \pi$ and $\cos 2\theta < 0$. Thus $\cos 2\theta = -\tfrac{7}{25}$

Now $\cos^2\theta = \tfrac{1}{2}(1 + \cos 2\theta)$ and $\sin^2\theta = \tfrac{1}{2}(1 - \cos 2\theta)$

$$= \tfrac{1}{2}\left(1 - \tfrac{7}{25}\right) \qquad\qquad = \tfrac{1}{2}\left(1 + \tfrac{7}{25}\right)$$
$$= \tfrac{9}{25} \qquad\qquad\qquad\quad = \tfrac{16}{25}$$

Since $\dfrac{\pi}{2} < 2\theta < \pi$, then $\dfrac{\pi}{4} < \theta < \dfrac{\pi}{2}$ so that $\cos\theta > 0$ and $\sin\theta > 0$. Hence

$$\cos\theta = \tfrac{3}{5} \quad\text{and}\quad \sin\theta = \tfrac{4}{5}$$

So $R = \begin{bmatrix} \tfrac{3}{5} & -\tfrac{4}{5} \\ \tfrac{4}{5} & \tfrac{3}{5} \end{bmatrix}$

(b) From Equations 1 and 2

$$a' = 73\cos^2\theta - 72\cos\theta\sin\theta + 52\sin^2\theta$$
$$= 73\left(\tfrac{9}{25}\right) - 72\left(\tfrac{3}{5}\right)\left(\tfrac{4}{5}\right) + 52\left(\tfrac{16}{25}\right)$$
$$= \frac{73(9) - 72(12) + 52(16)}{25}$$
$$= \tfrac{625}{25}$$
$$= 25$$

and $b' = 52\cos^2\theta + 72\cos\theta\sin\theta + 73\sin^2\theta$
$$= 52\left(\tfrac{9}{25}\right) + 72\left(\tfrac{3}{5}\right)\left(\tfrac{4}{5}\right) + 73\left(\tfrac{16}{25}\right)$$
$$= \tfrac{2500}{25}$$
$$= 100$$

So $a' = 25$ and $b' = 100$.

(c) The image curve $\mathscr{C}'$ has the matrix equation $X^t \begin{bmatrix} 25 & 0 \\ 0 & 100 \end{bmatrix} X = 25$.

So
$$25x^2 + 100y^2 = 25$$
$$x^2 + 4y^2 = 1$$

Hence both $\mathscr{C}'$ and $\mathscr{C}$ are ellipses.

We remark that $\mathscr{C}$ has an equation $ax^2 + 2hxy + by^2 = 25$ with
$$a + b = 73 + 52 = 125$$
and
$$ab - h^2 = 73(52) - 36^2 = 2500,$$

The equations for $\mathscr{C}$ and $\mathscr{C}'$ have the same constant term.

and $\mathscr{C}'$ has an equation $a'x^2 + 2h'xy + b'y^2 = 25$ with
$$a' + b' = 25 + 100 = 125$$
and
$$a'b' - (h')^2 = 25(100) - 0^2 = 2500.$$

This is useful now for checking calculations and even more useful later on.

What has been done in the example can also be done in general, and with hardly any more effort.

Theorem

Let $\mathscr{C}$ be a curve with equation $ax^2 + 2hxy + by^2 = k$ where $h \neq 0$. There is a rotation $X_{P'} = RX_P$ such that the image curve $\mathscr{C}'$ has the equation $a'x^2 + b'y^2 = k$. The matrix R is given by

$$R = \begin{bmatrix} \cos\theta & -\sin\theta \\ \sin\theta & \cos\theta \end{bmatrix}$$

where $0 < \theta < \dfrac{\pi}{2}$ and $\cot 2\theta = \dfrac{b - a}{2h}$.

Proof   As usual write $c = \cos\theta$ and $s = \sin\theta$. Then

$$RAR^t = \begin{bmatrix} c & -s \\ s & c \end{bmatrix} \begin{bmatrix} a & h \\ h & b \end{bmatrix} \begin{bmatrix} c & s \\ -s & c \end{bmatrix}$$

$$= \begin{bmatrix} c & -s \\ s & c \end{bmatrix} \begin{bmatrix} ac - hs & as + hc \\ hc - bs & hs + bc \end{bmatrix}$$

$$= \begin{bmatrix} ac^2 - hcs - hsc + bs^2 & acs + hc^2 - hs^2 - bsc \\ asc - hs^2 + hc^2 - bcs & as^2 + hsc + hcs + bc^2 \end{bmatrix}$$

We require $RAR^t = \begin{bmatrix} a' & 0 \\ 0 & b' \end{bmatrix}$, so returning to $\cos\theta = c$ and $\sin\theta = s$,

$$a\cos^2\theta - 2h\cos\theta\sin\theta + b\sin^2\theta = a' \quad \text{①}$$
$$b\cos^2\theta + 2h\cos\theta\sin\theta + a\sin^2\theta = b' \quad \text{②}$$
$$h\cos^2\theta + (a - b)\cos\theta\sin\theta - h\sin^2\theta = 0 \quad \text{③}$$

As we saw in the example, it is Equation 3 that fixes our choice of θ and so our choice of R.

$$h \cos^2 \theta + (a - b)\cos \theta \sin \theta - h \sin^2 \theta = 0$$
$$h(\cos^2 \theta - \sin^2 \theta) = (b - a)\sin \theta \cos \theta$$
$$h \cos 2\theta = (b - a)\tfrac{1}{2} \sin 2\theta$$
$$\cot 2\theta = \frac{b - a}{2h}$$

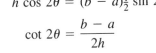

Let us do an example using the result of the theorem.

Example 2   Find a rotation matrix $R = \begin{bmatrix} \cos \theta & -\sin \theta \\ \sin \theta & \cos \theta \end{bmatrix}$ such that the image $\mathscr{C}'$ of $\mathscr{C}$: $x^2 + xy + 2y^2 = 1$ under the rotation, $X_{P'} = RX_P$, has no xy-term in its equation.

Solution   Here $a = 1$, $h = \tfrac{1}{2}$, and $b = 2$. By the theorem we choose θ between 0 and $\dfrac{\pi}{2}$ such that

$$\cot 2\theta = \frac{b - a}{2h} = \frac{2 - 1}{1} = 1$$

Therefore

$$\cos 2\theta = \frac{1}{\sqrt{2}}$$

So

$$\cos^2 \theta = \tfrac{1}{2}\left(1 + \frac{1}{\sqrt{2}}\right) \quad \text{and} \quad \sin^2 \theta = \tfrac{1}{2}\left(1 - \frac{1}{\sqrt{2}}\right)$$

Hence

$$R = \begin{bmatrix} \sqrt{\tfrac{1}{2}\left(1 + \frac{1}{\sqrt{2}}\right)} & -\sqrt{\tfrac{1}{2}\left(1 - \frac{1}{\sqrt{2}}\right)} \\ \sqrt{\tfrac{1}{2}\left(1 - \frac{1}{\sqrt{2}}\right)} & \sqrt{\tfrac{1}{2}\left(1 + \frac{1}{\sqrt{2}}\right)} \end{bmatrix}$$

PROBLEMS PLUS

The points $(1, 4)$, $(2, 8)$, $(5, 7)$ and $(4, 2)$, $(8, 5)$, $(7, 1)$ lie on an ellipse $ax^2 + 2hxy + by^2 + 2gx + 2fy + c = 0$.

Find a, b, c, f, g and h. (Note $\tfrac{1}{7} = 0.142857 \ldots$)

EXERCISE 9.4

B **1.** Determine, using the theorem proved in this section, a rotation

matrix $R = \begin{bmatrix} \cos\theta & -\sin\theta \\ \sin\theta & \cos\theta \end{bmatrix}$, with $0 < \theta < \dfrac{\pi}{2}$, such that RAR'

equals $\begin{bmatrix} a' & 0 \\ 0 & b' \end{bmatrix}$

(a) $\begin{bmatrix} 2 & 1 \\ 1 & 5 \end{bmatrix}$

(b) $\begin{bmatrix} 3 & -1 \\ -1 & -3 \end{bmatrix}$

(c) $\begin{bmatrix} -1 & 2 \\ 2 & 0 \end{bmatrix}$

(d) $\begin{bmatrix} 4 & 3 \\ 3 & 2 \end{bmatrix}$

(e) $\begin{bmatrix} 5 & 2 \\ 2 & 1 \end{bmatrix}$

(f) $\begin{bmatrix} 4 & 1 \\ 1 & 4 \end{bmatrix}$

2. Find a rotation that eliminates the xy-term from the given equation, and find the equation of the image curve.

(a) $2x^2 + 2xy + 5y^2 = 3$

(b) $3x^2 - 2xy - 3y^2 = 4$

(c) $-x^2 + 4xy = -1$

(d) $4x^2 + 6xy + 2y^2 = 9$

(e) $5x^2 + 4xy + y^2 = 5$

(f) $4x^2 + 2xy + 4y^2 = 1$

3. Under a rotation through the angle θ, $0 < \theta < \dfrac{\pi}{2}$, the given

curve $ax^2 + 2hxy + by^2 = k$ has an image whose equation is $a'x^2 + b'y^2 = k$. Find a' and b'. Verify that $a' + b' = a + b$ and $a'b' = ab - h^2$.

(a) $x^2 + 2\sqrt{3}xy - y^2 = k$

(b) $3x^2 - 4\sqrt{3}xy - y^2 = k$

(c) $6x^2 + 4xy + 9y^2 = k$

(d) $-x^2 + 16xy + 11y^2 = k$

4. Suppose $\cot 2\theta = \dfrac{b - a}{2h}$ where $h \neq 0$. Using

$\cos 2\theta = \dfrac{\cot 2\theta}{\sqrt{1 + \cot^2 2\theta}}$ find formulas for $\cos\theta$ and $\sin\theta$.

Give your answers when $h > 0$, and when $h < 0$, using the notation $\Delta = \sqrt{(b - a)^2 + 4h^2}$.

C **5.** Find a rotation through an angle θ, with $0 \le \theta \le \dfrac{\pi}{2}$, such that the

image $\mathscr{C}'$ of $\mathscr{C}$: $ax^2 + 2hxy + by^2 = k$ has the equation $\mathscr{C}'$: $bx^2 - 2hxy + ay^2 = k$. Which of these curves have the property that $\mathscr{C} = \mathscr{C}'$?

6. Show that there is a reflection matrix $M = \begin{bmatrix} \cos\theta & \sin\theta \\ \sin\theta & -\cos\theta \end{bmatrix}$ such

that $MAM = \begin{bmatrix} a' & 0 \\ 0 & b' \end{bmatrix}$, where $A = \begin{bmatrix} a & h \\ h & b \end{bmatrix}$ as usual.

**9.5 CLASSIFYING CENTRAL CONICS

In this section we develop a streamlined method for finding the equation of an image in standard position. In the preceding section we showed that for a given coefficient matrix

$$A = \begin{bmatrix} a & h \\ h & b \end{bmatrix}$$

we could find a rotation matrix

$$R = \begin{bmatrix} \cos\theta & -\sin\theta \\ \sin\theta & \cos\theta \end{bmatrix}$$

where $0 \le \theta \le \dfrac{\pi}{2}$, such that

$$RAR' = \begin{bmatrix} a' & 0 \\ 0 & b' \end{bmatrix}$$

In this section we alter our focus a little and concentrate on determining a' and b' above, without explicitly finding R: knowing that R exists will be sufficient.

In all the examples we did, we saw that both $a + b$ and $ab - h^2$ were unchanged by a rotation. This is true generally:

If the curve $\mathscr{C}$ has the equation $ax^2 + 2hxy + by^2 = k$ and under a rotation the image $\mathscr{C}'$ has the equation $a'x^2 + 2h'xy + b'y^2 = k$ then

$$a + b = a' + b' \quad \text{and} \quad ab - h^2 = a'b' - (h')^2$$

Example 1   Show that there is no rotation that maps the curve
$\mathscr{C}: x^2 + 2xy + 3y^2 = k$ to the curve $\mathscr{D}: 2x^2 + xy + 2y^2 = k$.

Solution   If $\mathscr{D}$ is a rotated image of $\mathscr{C}$ then

$$\begin{aligned} a + b &= a' + b' \\ 1 + 3 &= 2 + 2 \\ 4 &= 4 \end{aligned} \qquad \text{and} \qquad \begin{aligned} ab - h^2 &= a'b' - (h')^2 \\ 1(3) - 1^2 &= 2(2) - \left(\tfrac{1}{2}\right)^2 \\ 2 &= \tfrac{15}{4} \end{aligned}$$

Since $2 \ne \tfrac{15}{4}$ it cannot be that $\mathscr{D}$ is a rotated image of $\mathscr{C}$.

We showed in Section 9.4 that any curve whose equation is of the form $ax^2 + 2hxy + by^2 = k$ can be rotated to have an image whose equation is $a'x^2 + b'y^2 = k$.

Now we can say more:

$\mathscr{C}'$: $a'x^2 + b'y^2 = k$ is the image of $\mathscr{C}$: $ax^2 + 2hxy + by^2 = k$ if, and only if,

$$a' + b' = a + b \quad \text{and} \quad a'b' = ab - h^2$$

Example 2   Find a' and b' such that $\mathscr{C}'$: $a'x^2 + b'y^2 = 1$ is the image of $\mathscr{C}$: $x^2 + xy + y^2 = 1$ under some rotation.

Solution   Here $a = 1$, $h = \frac{1}{2}$, and $b = 1$, so a' and b' must satisfy

$$\begin{aligned} a' + b' &= 1 + 1 \\ a' + b' &= 2 \\ b' &= 2 - a' \end{aligned} \qquad \text{and} \qquad \begin{aligned} a'b' &= 1(1) - \left(\tfrac{1}{2}\right)^2 \\ a'b' &= \tfrac{3}{4} \end{aligned}$$

Substituting we obtain

$$a'(2 - a') = \tfrac{3}{4}$$
$$(a')^2 - 2a' + \tfrac{3}{4} = 0$$
$$\left(a' - \tfrac{1}{2}\right)\left(a' - \tfrac{3}{2}\right) = 0$$
$$a' = \tfrac{1}{2} \quad \text{or} \quad a' = \tfrac{3}{2}$$

Hence

$$a' = \tfrac{1}{2} \text{ and } b' = \tfrac{3}{2} \quad \text{or} \quad a' = \tfrac{3}{2} \text{ and } b' = \tfrac{1}{2}$$

There are two possibilities for $\mathscr{C}'$:

$$\tfrac{1}{2}x^2 + \tfrac{3}{2}y^2 = 1 \quad \text{or} \quad \tfrac{3}{2}x^2 + \tfrac{1}{2}y^2 = 1$$

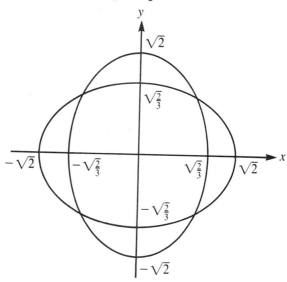

We end this section with a classification theorem.

Let the curve $\mathscr{C}$ have the equation $ax^2 + 2hxy + by^2 = k$.
(i) If $ab - h^2 > 0$ then $\mathscr{C}$ is an ellipse, a circle, a point, or empty.
(ii) If $ab - h^2 < 0$ then $\mathscr{C}$ is a hyperbola or a pair of straight lines through the origin.

Proof We showed in the previous section that $\mathscr{C}: ax^2 + 2hxy + by^2 = k$ has an image $\mathscr{C}: a'x^2 + b'y^2 = k$ under a suitably chosen rotation $X_{P'} = RX_P$.

We also know that $a'b' = ab - h^2$. So if $ab - h^2 > 0$ then $a'b' > 0$. So either both a' and b' are positive or both are negative. Depending on the value of k, $a'x^2 + b'y^2 = k$ gives an ellipse, circle, point, or empty set.

If $ab - h^2 < 0$ then $a'b' < 0$. So a' and b' have opposite signs. If $k \neq 0$, the equation $a'x^2 + b'y^2 = k$ gives a hyperbola, and if $k = 0$ it gives a pair of lines through the origin. ⬡

Remark

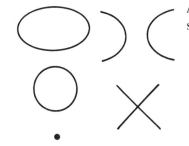

All these possibilities do, in fact, occur as the following six curves show.

$x^2 + 2y^2 = 1$	ellipse	$ab - h^2 = 2 > 0$
$x^2 + y^2 = 1$	circle	$ab - h^2 = 1 > 0$
$x^2 + 2y^2 = 0$	point	$ab - h^2 = 2 > 0$
$x^2 + 2y^2 = -1$	empty	$ab - h^2 = 2 > 0$
$x^2 - y^2 = 1$	hyperbola	$ab - h^2 = -1 < 0$
$x^2 - y^2 = 0$	pair of lines	$ab - h^2 = -1 < 0$

Example 3 Identify the following curves.
(a) $x^2 + 2xy + 3y^2 = 4$ (b) $xy = 0$
(c) $x^2 - 4xy - y^2 = 2$ (d) $3x^2 - xy + y^2 = -3$

Solution (a) Here $ab - h^2 = (1)(3) - 1^2 = 2 > 0$. So the curve belongs to the ellipse, circle, point, or empty set collection of curves. Since the two distinct points $(2, 0)$ and $(-2, 0)$ lie on the curve (by inspection) it must be an ellipse or a circle. Since $a \neq b$, the curve is not a circle. So the curve is an ellipse.

(b) Because $ab - h^2 = -\frac{1}{4} < 0$ this is a pair of lines.

(c) Here $ab - h^2 = (1)(-1) - 2^2 = -5 < 0$. So it is a hyperbola or a pair of lines. Since $k = 2 \neq 0$ it is a hyperbola.

(d) Since $ab - h^2 = (3)(1) - \left(\frac{1}{2}\right)^2 > 0$, it is in the ellipse family. It has an image with the equation $a'x^2 + b'y^2 = -3$. But $a' + b' = 3 + 1 = 4$, and $a'b' > 0$, so both a' and b'

are positive. Hence $a'x^2 + b'y^2 \geq 0$. So $a'x^2 + b'y^2 = -3$ has no points: it is the empty curve. So the original curve $3x^2 - xy + y^2 = -3$ has no points; it is empty.

EXERCISE 9.5

B **1.** State why there is no rotation that maps the first curve to the second.
(a) $x^2 + 2xy + 3y^2 = 1$ $2x^2 - 4xy + 5y^2 = 1$
(b) $2x^2 - 3xy - y^2 = 4$ $2x^2 - 3xy + y^2 = 4$
(c) $x^2 + 2xy + 3y^2 = 1$ $x^2 + 4xy + 3y^2 = 1$
(d) $4x^2 - y^2 = 2$ $3x^2 + xy = 2$

2. Find both curves $a'x^2 + b'y^2 = k$ that are rotated images of the following.
(a) $x^2 + xy - y^2 = 1$ (b) $3x^2 + xy = 2$
(c) $3x^2 + 2xy + 2y^2 = 3$ (d) $\dfrac{x^2}{9} + \dfrac{xy}{6} + \dfrac{y^2}{4} = 1$

3. Identify the curves.
(a) $x^2 + xy - y^2 = 1$ (b) $3x^2 + xy = 2$
(c) $3x^2 + 2xy + 2y^2 = 3$ (d) $\dfrac{x^2}{9} + \dfrac{xy}{6} + \dfrac{y^2}{4} = 1$
(e) $x^2 + y^2 = 4$ (f) $2xy = 5$

4. Identify the curves.
(a) $x^2 + xy - y^2 = -2$ (b) $3x^2 + xy = 0$
(c) $3x^2 + 2xy + 2y^2 = -2$ (d) $\dfrac{x^2}{9} + \dfrac{xy}{6} + \dfrac{y^2}{4} = 0$

5. Identify the curves.
(a) $\cos \theta \, x^2 - 2 \sin \theta \, xy + \cos \theta \, y^2 = 1, 0 < \theta < \dfrac{\pi}{4}$
(b) $ax^2 + \left(h + \dfrac{1}{h} \right) xy + \dfrac{1}{a} y^2 = -1, a > 0$ and $h > 1$
(c) $(1 + c^2)x^2 + 4cxy + (1 + c^2)y^2 = -2, c > 1$
(d) $ax^2 - 2\sqrt{ab}xy + 2by^2 = 0, ab > 0$

6. Let $R = \begin{bmatrix} \cos \theta & -\sin \theta \\ \sin \theta & \cos \theta \end{bmatrix}$ and $A = \begin{bmatrix} a & h \\ h & b \end{bmatrix}$. Set $RAR^t = \begin{bmatrix} a' & h' \\ h' & b' \end{bmatrix}$.
Prove that
(a) $a' + b' = a + b$
(b) $a'b' - (h')^2 = ab - h^2$

C

For any matrix $M = \begin{bmatrix} a & b \\ c & d \end{bmatrix}$ *we define*

$\text{tr } M = a + d$ *(the **trace** of M)*
and $\det M = ad - bc$ *(the **determinant** of M)*

7. Let $M = \begin{bmatrix} a & b \\ c & d \end{bmatrix}$ and $N = \begin{bmatrix} e & f \\ g & h \end{bmatrix}$. Prove that
   (a) $\text{tr}(MN) = \text{tr}(NM)$
   (b) $\det(MN) = \det(NM)$

8. Use Question 7 to prove the results in Question 6 by noting that $R^tR = I$. [Hint: $\text{tr}(RAR^t) = \text{tr}((RA)R^t) = \ldots$]

9. Suppose $a'x^2 + b'y^2 = k$ is a rotated image of $ax^2 + 2hxy + by^2 = k$.
   (a) Prove that a' and b' are the roots of the quadratic equation
   $$t^2 - (a + b)t + ab - h^2 = 0$$
   (b) Prove that either
   $$a' = \frac{a + b + \sqrt{(a - b)^2 + 4h^2}}{2}$$
   or
   $$a' = \frac{a + b - \sqrt{(a - b)^2 + 4h^2}}{2}$$

9.6 REVIEW EXERICSE

1. Identify the symmetric matrices.
   (a) $\begin{bmatrix} 4 & 1 \\ 0 & 4 \end{bmatrix}$
   (b) $\begin{bmatrix} 3 & 5 \\ 3 & 5 \end{bmatrix}$
   (c) $\begin{bmatrix} 1 & -1 \\ -1 & 0 \end{bmatrix}$
   (d) $\begin{bmatrix} a & h + 1 \\ h - 1 & b \end{bmatrix}$

2. Find the product matrices.
   (a) $[4 \quad 1] \begin{bmatrix} 0 \\ 4 \end{bmatrix}$
   (b) $[4 \quad 1] \begin{bmatrix} 1 & 0 \\ 0 & 1 \end{bmatrix} \begin{bmatrix} 2 \\ -1 \end{bmatrix}$
   (c) $\begin{bmatrix} 2 & 3 \\ 5 & 8 \end{bmatrix} \begin{bmatrix} 8 & -3 \\ -5 & 2 \end{bmatrix}$
   (d) $\begin{bmatrix} a & b \\ c & d \end{bmatrix} \begin{bmatrix} d & -b \\ -c & a \end{bmatrix}$
   (e) $\begin{bmatrix} 1 & a \\ 0 & 1 \end{bmatrix} \begin{bmatrix} 1 & b \\ 0 & 1 \end{bmatrix}$
   (f) $\begin{bmatrix} 2 \\ 3 \end{bmatrix} [-1 \quad 3]$

3. For the given matrix M find M^t.
   (a) $\begin{bmatrix} 1 & 2 \\ 3 & 4 \end{bmatrix}$
   (b) $\begin{bmatrix} -1 & 1 \\ -2 & 2 \end{bmatrix}$
   (c) $\begin{bmatrix} a & b \\ c & d \end{bmatrix}$
   (d) $\begin{bmatrix} 3 & 1 \\ 1 & -2 \end{bmatrix}$

4. For each matrix M compute MM^t.
   (a) $\begin{bmatrix} 1 & 2 \\ 3 & 4 \end{bmatrix}$
   (b) $\begin{bmatrix} -1 & 1 \\ -2 & 2 \end{bmatrix}$
   (c) $\begin{bmatrix} 3 & 1 \\ 1 & -2 \end{bmatrix}$
   (d) $\begin{bmatrix} a & b \\ c & d \end{bmatrix}$

5. Let $A = \begin{bmatrix} a & h \\ h & b \end{bmatrix}$. Evaluate RAR' for the given R.

(a) $\begin{bmatrix} \dfrac{1}{\sqrt{2}} & -\dfrac{1}{\sqrt{2}} \\ \dfrac{1}{\sqrt{2}} & \dfrac{1}{\sqrt{2}} \end{bmatrix}$

(b) $\begin{bmatrix} -\dfrac{1}{\sqrt{5}} & \dfrac{2}{\sqrt{5}} \\ -\dfrac{2}{\sqrt{5}} & -\dfrac{1}{\sqrt{5}} \end{bmatrix}$

(c) $\begin{bmatrix} \dfrac{\sqrt{3}}{2} & \dfrac{1}{2} \\ -\dfrac{1}{2} & \dfrac{\sqrt{3}}{2} \end{bmatrix}$

(d) $\begin{bmatrix} \dfrac{4}{5} & -\dfrac{3}{5} \\ \dfrac{3}{5} & \dfrac{4}{5} \end{bmatrix}$

6. Let $A = \begin{bmatrix} 1 & 0 \\ 0 & 1 \end{bmatrix}$. Evaluate $X'AX$ for the given 2×1 matrix X.

(a) $\begin{bmatrix} 1 \\ 0 \end{bmatrix}$

(b) $\begin{bmatrix} 0 \\ 1 \end{bmatrix}$

(c) $\begin{bmatrix} 1 \\ 1 \end{bmatrix}$

(d) $\begin{bmatrix} 1 \\ -1 \end{bmatrix}$

7. Find the coefficient matrix A of each of the expressions.

(a) $x^2 + y^2$

(b) $x^2 - y^2$

(c) xy

(d) $\dfrac{x^2}{4} + y^2$

(e) $\dfrac{x^2}{9} - \dfrac{y^2}{4}$

(f) $x^2 + xy + 2y^2$

(g) $2x^2 - 3xy + 4y^2$

(h) $x^2 + 2xy - y^2$

(i) $\dfrac{x^2}{4} - \dfrac{xy}{2} + \dfrac{y^2}{9}$

(j) $2xy - 3y^2$

8. Find the unique symmetric matrix A such that $X'AX = k$ is the matrix form of the equation.

(a) $x^2 + y^2 = k$

(b) $\dfrac{x^2}{4} + y^2 = k$

(c) $-2xy - 5y^2 = k$

(d) $\dfrac{x^2}{9} + \dfrac{y^2}{16} = k$

(e) $xy = k$

(f) $x^2 + xy + y^2 = k$

9. For the given matrix R compute RR'.

(a) $\begin{bmatrix} \dfrac{1}{\sqrt{2}} & -\dfrac{1}{\sqrt{2}} \\ \dfrac{1}{\sqrt{2}} & \dfrac{1}{\sqrt{2}} \end{bmatrix}$

(b) $\begin{bmatrix} \dfrac{\sqrt{3}}{2} & -\dfrac{1}{2} \\ \dfrac{1}{2} & \dfrac{\sqrt{3}}{2} \end{bmatrix}$

(c) $\begin{bmatrix} -\dfrac{3}{5} & \dfrac{4}{5} \\ -\dfrac{4}{5} & -\dfrac{3}{5} \end{bmatrix}$

(d) $\begin{bmatrix} \dfrac{2}{\sqrt{5}} & \dfrac{1}{\sqrt{5}} \\ -\dfrac{1}{\sqrt{5}} & \dfrac{2}{\sqrt{5}} \end{bmatrix}$

10. Find an equation of the form $a'x^2 + 2h'xy + b'y^2 = 1$ for the image $\mathscr{C}'$ of the ellipse $\mathscr{C}: \dfrac{x^2}{9} + \dfrac{y^2}{4} = 1$ under the rotation $X_{P'} = RX_P$, where R is given.

(a) $\begin{bmatrix} \dfrac{\sqrt{3}}{2} & -\dfrac{1}{2} \\[2mm] \dfrac{1}{2} & \dfrac{\sqrt{3}}{2} \end{bmatrix}$

(b) $\begin{bmatrix} \dfrac{2}{\sqrt{5}} & \dfrac{1}{\sqrt{5}} \\[2mm] -\dfrac{1}{\sqrt{5}} & \dfrac{2}{\sqrt{5}} \end{bmatrix}$

(c) $\begin{bmatrix} \dfrac{1}{\sqrt{2}} & -\dfrac{1}{\sqrt{2}} \\[2mm] \dfrac{1}{\sqrt{2}} & \dfrac{1}{\sqrt{2}} \end{bmatrix}$

(d) $\begin{bmatrix} \dfrac{5}{13} & \dfrac{12}{13} \\[2mm] -\dfrac{12}{13} & \dfrac{5}{13} \end{bmatrix}$

11. Rotate $\mathscr{C}: x^2 + xy + 2y^2 = 1$ through the given angle θ and find the equation of the image.

(a) $\dfrac{\pi}{4}$

(b) $-\dfrac{\pi}{6}$

(c) $\dfrac{\pi}{3}$

(d) $\dfrac{\pi}{2}$

(e) $\dfrac{4\pi}{3}$

(f) $\dfrac{7\pi}{6}$

12. Rotate each of the following curves through $120°$. Find the equation of the image.

(a) $x^2 + \sqrt{3}xy + y^2 = 1$ (b) $2x^2 - 3y^2 = 1$
(c) $xy = 1$ (d) $2xy + 5y^2 = 1$

13. Find $R = \begin{bmatrix} \cos\theta & -\sin\theta \\ \sin\theta & \cos\theta \end{bmatrix}$, $0 < \theta < \dfrac{\pi}{2}$, such that the rotation $X_{P'} = RX_P$ eliminates the xy-term from the equation of the curve.

(a) $2x^2 + 2xy - 5y^2 = 1$ (b) $2x^2 + xy + 2y^2 = 5$
(c) $3x^2 + 4xy + 6y^2 = 1$ (d) $xy - y^2 = 2$
(e) $4x^2 - 2xy + (4 - 2\sqrt{3})y^2 = 1$ (f) $x^2 - 4xy - 7y^2 = 11$

14. Find a' and b' with $a' < b'$ such that $a'x^2 + b'y^2 = k$ is the image of $\mathscr{C}$ under a rotation; the equation of $\mathscr{C}$ is given.

(a) $xy - y^2 = k$ (b) $4x^2 - 2xy + (4 - 2\sqrt{3})y^2 = k$
(c) $x^2 - 4xy - 7y^2 = k$ (d) $2x^2 + 2xy + 5y^2 = k$

15. For which values of k is each curve a hyperbola?

(a) $2x^2 - 4xy + 5y^2 = k$ (b) $x^2 + 2xy + 3y^2 = k$
(c) $3x^2 + xy = k$ (d) $x^2 + 26xy - 6y^2 = k$

16. For which value of k is each curve an ellipse?

(a) $x^2 + 2xy + 5y^2 = k$ (b) $3x^2 - 7xy = k$
(c) $2x^2 - 6xy + 5y^2 = k$ (d) $2x^2 + 8xy + 5y^2 = k$

9.7 CHAPTER 9 TEST

1. Let $M = \begin{bmatrix} 2 & 3 \\ -1 & -4 \end{bmatrix}$. Evaluate

   (a) M^t

   (b) MM^t

   (c) M^tM

   (d) M^2

2. Find the coefficient matrix of the expression $X^t \begin{bmatrix} 2 & 3 \\ -1 & -4 \end{bmatrix} X$.

3. Suppose a curve $\mathscr{C}$ has the matrix equation $X^t AX = k$ where A is a given symmetric matrix. Let $\mathscr{C}'$ denote the image of $\mathscr{C}$ under the rotation $X_{P'} = RX_P$. What is the matrix equation for $\mathscr{C}'$?

4. Find an equation of the form $ax^2 + 2hxy + by^2 = 1$ for the image $\mathscr{C}'$ of the ellipse $\mathscr{C}: \dfrac{x^2}{4} + y^2 = 1$ under a rotation of 60°.

5. Find a rotation $R = \begin{bmatrix} \cos\theta & -\sin\theta \\ \sin\theta & \cos\theta \end{bmatrix}$ with $0 < \theta < \dfrac{\pi}{2}$ that eliminates the xy-term from $\mathscr{C}: 5x^2 + 4xy + 2y^2 = 25$. Sketch $\mathscr{C}'$.

CUMULATIVE REVIEW FOR CHAPTERS 7 TO 9

1. Find the translation of the form
   $$x_{P'} = x_P + r$$
   $$y_{P'} = y_P$$
   that maps the line $l: 3x - 2y + 5 = 0$ to the line $l': 3x - 2y - 13 = 0$.

2. Find s such that the image l' of the line $l: x + 3y + 8 = 0$ under the translation
   $$x_{P'} = x_P$$
   $$y_{P'} = y_P + s$$
   passes through the point $P(4, -1)$.

3. Under what conditions is $l': 2x + 3y = 0$ the image of $l: 2x + 3y + 1 = 0$ under the translation
   $$x_{P'} = x_P + r$$
   $$y_{P'} = y_P + s$$

4. For the circle $\mathscr{C}: x^2 + y^2 + 4x - 6y + 12 = 0$ find a translation that maps the centre to the origin and find the equation of the image circle.

5. Find an equation for the image $\mathcal{C}'$ of the curve
$$\mathcal{C}: 3x^2 - y^2 + 6x + 4y - 1 = 0$$
under the translation
$$x_{P'} = x_P + 2$$
$$y_{P'} = y_P - 1$$

6. Find r and s such that the translation
$$x_{P'} = x_P + r$$
$$y_{P'} = y_P + s$$
eliminates the first degree terms from
$$2x^2 + 3y^2 + 12x - 12y + 24 = 0.$$
Identify the image curve as an ellipse or hyperbola.

7. For the parabola $\mathcal{C}: y^2 + 8x + 8y = 0$ find a translation that reduces the equation of the image to standard form.

8. Write the matrix of the transformation
$$x_{P'} = x_P + y_P$$
$$y_{P'} = -3x_P + 5y_P$$

9. Multiply $\begin{bmatrix} 2 & -1 \\ 3 & 5 \end{bmatrix} \begin{bmatrix} 1 & 4 \\ 4 & 1 \end{bmatrix}$.

10. Find the image of the point $P(-3, 1)$ under the transformation whose matrix is
$$\begin{bmatrix} 3 & 1 \\ -4 & -2 \end{bmatrix}$$

11. What type of transformation has the matrix $\begin{bmatrix} 1 & 4 \\ 0 & 1 \end{bmatrix}$?

12. Find the image of the point $P(-3, 2)$ under the compound transformation: reflection in the line $x - y = 0$ followed by a dilatation of factor 3.

13. Without performing any matrix multiplication, give the matrix of the compound transformation: a rotation through $\dfrac{\pi}{3}$ followed by a rotation through $\dfrac{\pi}{6}$.

14. Find the angle of rotation for the rotation defined by the matrix.
$$\begin{bmatrix} -\dfrac{\sqrt{3}}{2} & -\dfrac{1}{2} \\ \dfrac{1}{2} & -\dfrac{\sqrt{3}}{2} \end{bmatrix}$$

15. Let $M = \begin{bmatrix} 3 & -1 \\ -2 & 5 \end{bmatrix}$. Find MM^t and M^tM.

16. Let $R = \begin{bmatrix} -0.6 & -0.8 \\ 0.8 & -0.6 \end{bmatrix}$, $A = \begin{bmatrix} 1 & 2 \\ 2 & 5 \end{bmatrix}$. Evaluate RAR^t.

17. Find the coefficient matrix A for the expression $x^2 + 2xy - 3y^2$.

18. Find the unique symmetric matrix A such that $X'AX = 5$ is the matrix form of the equation $-2xy + y^2 = 5$.

19. Let $R = \begin{bmatrix} -0.8 & 0.6 \\ -0.6 & -0.8 \end{bmatrix}$. Compute RR'.

20. Find an equation of the form $a'x^2 + 2h'xy + b'y^2 = 1$ for the image $\mathscr{C}'$ of the ellipse $\dfrac{x^2}{4} + y^2 = 1$ under the rotation $X_{P'} = RX_P$, where

$$R = \begin{bmatrix} \frac{12}{13} & -\frac{5}{13} \\ \frac{5}{13} & \frac{12}{13} \end{bmatrix}$$

21. Rotate $\mathscr{C}: x^2 + 2xy - 2y^2 = 1$ through $\dfrac{\pi}{6}$ and find the equation of the image.

22. Rotate $\mathscr{C}: x^2 + \sqrt{3}xy + y^2 = 1$ through $240°$ and find the equation of the image.

23. Find $R = \begin{bmatrix} \cos\theta & -\sin\theta \\ \sin\theta & \cos\theta \end{bmatrix}$, $0 < \theta < \dfrac{\pi}{2}$, such that the rotation $X_{P'} = RX_P$ eliminates the xy-term from the equation $6x^2 - 4xy + 3y^2 = 1$.

24. Find a' and b' with $a' < b'$ such that $\mathscr{C}': a'x^2 + b'y^2 = 1$ is the image of $\mathscr{C}: -x^2 + 6xy + 7y^2 = 1$ under a rotation. Is $\mathscr{C}$ an ellipse or a hyperbola?

25. Find a' and b' with $a' < b'$ such that $\mathscr{C}': a'x^2 + b'y^2 = 1$ is the image of $\mathscr{C}: 3x^2 - 4xy + 3y^2 = 1$ under a rotation.

26. Let $\mathscr{C}$ have the equation $3x^2 + 2hxy + 12y^2 = 1$.
 (a) For which values of the parameter h is $\mathscr{C}$ an ellipse?
 (b) If $\mathscr{C}$ is neither an ellipse nor an hyperbola, what is the value of h? What is $\mathscr{C}$ in this case?

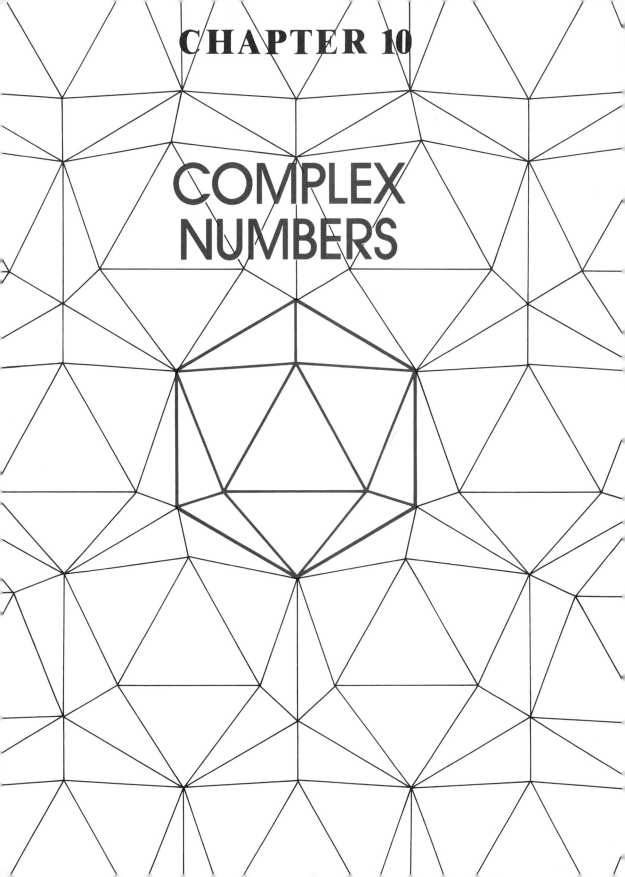

CHAPTER 10

COMPLEX NUMBERS

REVIEW AND PREVIEW TO CHAPTER 10

Trigonometry

A point on a *unit circle* has coordinates $(\cos\theta, \sin\theta)$ where θ is the rotation angle from the positive x-axis.

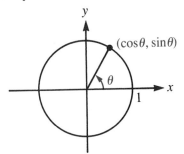

Three common rotation angles are $\dfrac{\pi}{6}$, $\dfrac{\pi}{4}$, and $\dfrac{\pi}{3}$.

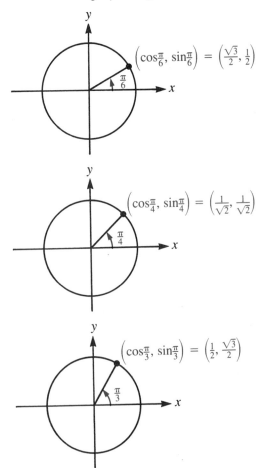

$\left(\cos\dfrac{\pi}{6}, \sin\dfrac{\pi}{6}\right) = \left(\dfrac{\sqrt{3}}{2}, \dfrac{1}{2}\right)$

$\left(\cos\dfrac{\pi}{4}, \sin\dfrac{\pi}{4}\right) = \left(\dfrac{1}{\sqrt{2}}, \dfrac{1}{\sqrt{2}}\right)$

$\left(\cos\dfrac{\pi}{3}, \sin\dfrac{\pi}{3}\right) = \left(\dfrac{1}{2}, \dfrac{\sqrt{3}}{2}\right)$

EXERCISE 1

1. Using the symmetry of the unit circle, determine the ordered pairs for each indicated point on the unit circle and also its rotation angle θ, $0 \leqslant \theta \leqslant 2\pi$.

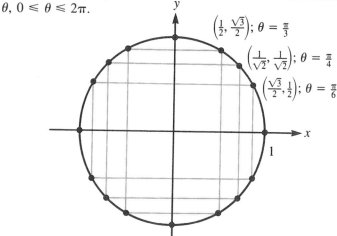

$\left(\frac{1}{2}, \frac{\sqrt{3}}{2}\right); \theta = \frac{\pi}{3}$

$\left(\frac{1}{\sqrt{2}}, \frac{1}{\sqrt{2}}\right); \theta = \frac{\pi}{4}$

$\left(\frac{\sqrt{3}}{2}, \frac{1}{2}\right); \theta = \frac{\pi}{6}$

2. Using the completed diagram from Question 1, determine the following trigonometric values.

   (a) $\sin \dfrac{\pi}{3}$ (b) $\cos \dfrac{\pi}{4}$ (c) $\sin \pi$

   (d) $\cos \dfrac{\pi}{6}$ (e) $\sin \dfrac{2\pi}{3}$ (f) $\cos \dfrac{\pi}{3}$

   (g) $\sin \dfrac{3\pi}{4}$ (h) $\cos \dfrac{5\pi}{6}$ (i) $\sin 2\pi$

   (j) $\cos \dfrac{3\pi}{2}$ (k) $\sin \dfrac{5\pi}{3}$ (l) $\cos \dfrac{4\pi}{3}$

   (m) $\sin \dfrac{7\pi}{4}$ (n) $\cos \dfrac{7\pi}{6}$ (o) $\cos \dfrac{\pi}{2}$

3. The tangent function is related to the sine and cosine function.

   $$\tan \theta = \frac{\sin \theta}{\cos \theta}$$

   Use the diagram from Question 1 and the relationship above to determine the following values.

   (a) $\tan \dfrac{\pi}{4}$ (b) $\tan \dfrac{\pi}{6}$ (c) $\tan \dfrac{\pi}{3}$

   (d) $\tan \dfrac{\pi}{2}$ (e) $\tan \pi$ (f) $\tan \dfrac{2\pi}{3}$

   (g) $\tan \dfrac{7\pi}{6}$ (h) $\tan \dfrac{4\pi}{3}$ (i) $\tan \dfrac{7\pi}{4}$

   (j) $\tan \dfrac{3\pi}{2}$ (k) $\tan \dfrac{5\pi}{6}$ (l) $\tan 2\pi$

4. Use the diagram from Question 1 to determine the *two* possible values for θ, $0 \leqslant \theta \leqslant 2\pi$, given the following.

(a) $\sin \theta = \dfrac{1}{\sqrt{2}}$ (b) $\cos \theta = \dfrac{\sqrt{3}}{2}$ (c) $\sin \theta = -\dfrac{1}{2}$

(d) $\cos \theta = -\dfrac{1}{2}$ (e) $\sin \theta = -\dfrac{1}{\sqrt{2}}$ (f) $\cos \theta = -\dfrac{1}{\sqrt{2}}$

(g) $\tan \theta = 1$ (h) $\tan \theta = -\sqrt{3}$ (i) $\tan \theta = \sqrt{3}$

(j) $\tan \theta = \dfrac{1}{\sqrt{3}}$ (k) $\tan \theta = -1$ (l) $\tan \theta = \dfrac{-1}{\sqrt{3}}$

5. Use a calculator to determine the *two* possible values for θ, $0 \leqslant \theta \leqslant 2\pi$, given the following. Express your answer in radians.

(a) $\tan \theta = 1.5$ (b) $\tan \theta = -2$ (c) $\tan \theta = 0.32$

(d) $\sin \theta = 0.23$ (e) $\tan \theta = -\sqrt{2}$ (f) $\cos \theta = -0.75$

Trigonometric Formulas

Addition formulas:

$$\cos(\theta_1 + \theta_2) = \cos \theta_1 \cos \theta_2 - \sin \theta_1 \sin \theta_2$$
$$\sin(\theta_1 + \theta_2) = \sin \theta_1 \cos \theta_2 + \cos \theta_1 \sin \theta_2$$

Double angle formulas:

$$\cos 2\theta = \cos^2 \theta - \sin^2 \theta$$
$$\sin 2\theta = 2 \sin \theta \cos \theta$$

EXERCISE 2

1. Show how the double angle formulas are derived from the compound angle formulas.

2. (a) Develop a formula for $\cos 3\theta$ in terms of $\cos \theta$.
   (b) Develop a formula for $\sin 3\theta$ in terms of $\sin \theta$.
   (c) Using parts (a) and (b), show that

   $$\tan 3\theta = \tan \theta \left(\frac{3 - 4 \sin^2 \theta}{4 \cos^2 \theta - 3} \right)$$

INTRODUCTION

The form of an equation dictates the number system in which the equation has a solution. For example,

$$x - 2 = 0 \quad \text{has the solution } x = 2, \text{ an integer;}$$

$$2x - 1 = 0 \quad \text{has the solution } x = \tfrac{1}{2}, \text{ a rational number,}$$
but is not an integer;

$$x^2 - 3 = 0 \quad \text{has the solutions } x = \sqrt{3} \text{ or } x = -\sqrt{3},$$
real numbers, but not rationals.

The equation $x^2 + 1 = 0$ has no solution in the real number system. In order for us to write solutions to equations such as this we must extend the real number system. We introduce a new number which we denote by i. This new number has the property $i^2 = -1$. Our solution to the equation $x^2 + 1 = 0$ is now $x = i$ or $x = -i$. These solutions are members of the complex number system which we will study in this chapter.

This notation was first introduced by Leonard Euler in 1748.

10.1   THE NUMBER i

$$\boxed{i^2 = -1}$$

Example 1   Solve for z: $z^2 = -25$

Solution   We see that the square of z must be negative so it will be necessary to use the new number i.

$$z^2 = -25$$
$$= (25)(-1)$$
$$= 25i^2$$

So, $z = 5i$ or $z = -5i$

Example 2   Solve for z: $(z - 1)^2 = -16$

Solution   Let us solve for $(z - 1)$ first. Using the same reasoning as in Example 1 we conclude

$$(z - 1) = 4i \quad \text{or} \quad (z - 1) = -4i$$

which we can simplify to

$$z = 1 + 4i \quad \text{or} \quad z = 1 - 4i$$

The roots of the equation are $1 + 4i$ and $1 - 4i$.

The roots of the equations in the above two examples are members of the number system called **the complex numbers**. In general, every complex number can be written in the form $a + bi$. The real number a is called the **real part**, and the real number b is called the **imaginary part**. Since every complex number is made up of two parts we can represent the complex number as an ordered pair (a, b), which in turn can be represented on rectangular coordinate axes. The horizontal axis is the **real axis** and the vertical axis is the **imaginary axis**. In order to locate the complex number $a + bi$ on the complex plane we go horizontally a units and vertically b units from the origin.

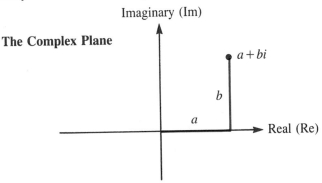

Two complex numbers are said to be **equal** if their real parts are equal and their imaginary parts are equal.

Example 3   Identify the real parts and the imaginary parts of the following complex numbers and represent them on the complex plane.
(a) $3 - 2i$ (b) $2i$ (c) -4

Solution   (a) The real part of $3 - 2i$ is 3 and the imaginary part is -2. The number on the complex plane is 3 units right and 2 units down from the origin.

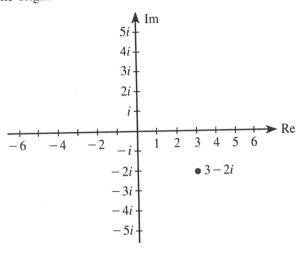

(b) The complex number $2i$ is equivalent to $0 + 2i$ with real part 0 and imaginary part 2. The number on the complex plane is 2 units up from the origin on the imaginary axis.

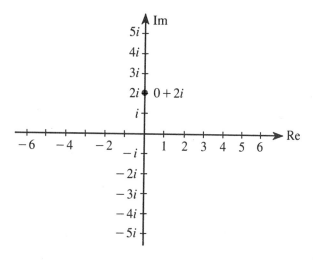

(c) The complex number -4 is equivalent to $-4 + 0i$ with real part -4 and imaginary part 0. The number is 4 units left of the origin on the real axis.

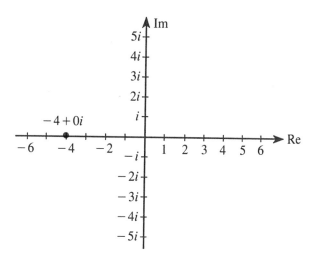

The magnitude of a *real* number (or its distance from the number zero) is its *absolute value*. For example, $|-3| = 3$ which indicates that the number -3 is 3 units from zero. Similarly, the magnitude of a complex number is its distance from the origin (zero) of the complex plane.

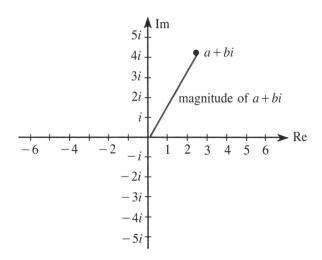

This distance is called the **modulus** of the complex number and is denoted by $|a + bi|$. It is easily shown to be equal to $\sqrt{a^2 + b^2}$.

> The modulus of a complex number, z, is
> $$|z| = |a + bi| = \sqrt{a^2 + b^2}$$

Example 4 (a) Determine the modulus of $7 - 2i$.

(b) Describe the set of complex numbers that satisfy $|z| = 1$.

(c) Describe the set of complex numbers that satisfy $|z| < 4$.

Solution (a) $|7 - 2i| = \sqrt{7^2 + (-2)^2}$
$= \sqrt{53}$

(b) The complex numbers satisfying $|z| = 1$ are those that are one unit from the origin of the complex plane. Hence the set of complex numbers is a circle of radius one, centre the origin.

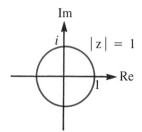

(c) The complex numbers satisfying $|z| < 4$ are those that are less than four units from the origin. The set consists of all of the points within a circle of radius 4.

Im

4i

$|z| < 4$

Re

4

Example 5   Solve the following equation by completing the square. Represent the roots of the equation on the complex plane with their moduli labelled on the diagram.

$$z^2 + 6z + 13 = 0$$

Solution

$$z^2 + 6z + 13 = 0$$
$$z^2 + 6z = -13$$
$$z^2 + 6z + 3^2 = -13 + 3^2$$
$$(z + 3)^2 = -4$$

We might be tempted to use the quadratic formula here but the $\sqrt{}$ notation is only defined for positive real numbers. Its misuse can lead to fallacies!

$$6 = \sqrt{36}$$
$$= \sqrt{(-4)(-9)}$$
$$= \sqrt{-4}\,\sqrt{-9}$$
$$= 2i\,3i$$
$$= 6i^2$$
$$= -6$$

We have just 'shown' that $6 = -6$!

so, $z + 3 = 2i$ or $z + 3 = -2i$
$$z = -3 + 2i \qquad\qquad z = -3 - 2i$$

and $|z| = \sqrt{(-3)^2 + 2^2}$ or $|z| = \sqrt{(-3)^2 + (-2)^2}$
$$= \sqrt{13} \qquad\qquad\qquad\qquad = \sqrt{13}$$

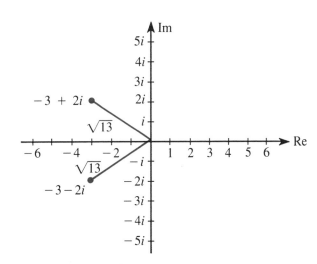

EXERCISE 10.1

A **1.** Identify the real parts and the imaginary parts of the following complex numbers.

(a) $3 + 6i$

(b) $-1 - i\sqrt{2}$

(c) $(2 + \sqrt{2}) + i(3 - \sqrt{2})$

(d) $2i$

(e) $\pi - \pi i$

(f) 13

(g) $\frac{2}{5} - \frac{3}{5}i$

(h) $3i - 7$

(i) $\cos 1 + i\sin 1$

(j) 0

(k) $(1, \sqrt{2})$

(l) $(-\sqrt{3}, 2)$

B **2.** Plot the following complex numbers in the complex plane.

(a) $3i$

(b) 11

(c) $1 + i$

(d) $-4 + 2i$

(e) $-2 - 3i$

(f) $-5i$

(g) $3 - 2i$

(h) i

3. Solve the following equations in the domain of the complex numbers and write your answers in the form $a + bi$.

(a) $z^2 + 2 = 0$

(b) $z^2 + 2z + 3 = 0$

(c) $z^2 - 2z + 2 = 0$

(d) $3z^2 + 3z + 1 = 0$

(e) $4z^2 + 8z + 12 = 0$

(f) $2z^2 - 4z + 3 = 0$

(g) $z^2 - 3z + 4 = 0$

(h) $(z - 5)^2 + 3 = 0$

4. Determine the moduli of the following complex numbers.

(a) $2 + i$

(b) $-1 - i$

(c) $5 + 4i$

(d) $-3 + 2i$

(e) $\sqrt{2} + \sqrt{2}i$

(f) $5 - 3i$

(g) $(2, 3)$

(h) $(-1, 2)$

5. Sketch the sets of complex numbers that would satisfy the following equations:

(a) $z = 2$

(b) $|z| = 2$

(c) $z = 0 + bi, b \in R$

(d) $z = k + ki, k \in R$

(e) $|z| = k, k \in N$

(f) $|z| > 3$

10.2 COMPLEX NUMBER ARITHMETIC: ADDITION, SUBTRACTION, MULTIPLICATION

The rules for addition, subtraction, and multiplication of complex numbers will be developed in this section.

Addition: We add the real parts and we add the imaginary parts. For example,

$$(3 + 4i) + (-7 + 2i) = [3 + (-7)] + (4 + 2)i$$
$$= -4 + 6i$$

$$\boxed{(a + bi) + (c + di) = (a + c) + (b + d)i}$$

Complex numbers can be represented as *vectors* joining the origin of the complex plane to the number. This representation allows us to visualize some of the operations we perform on the numbers. The geometric effect of adding two complex numbers is to add their vectors.

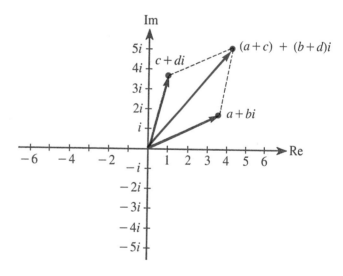

Subtraction:

$$\boxed{(a + bi) - (c + di) = (a - c) + (b - d)i}$$

For example,

$$(5 - 2i) - (3 + 7i) = (5 - 3) + (-2 - 7)i$$
$$= 2 - 9i$$

Subtraction can be visualized vectorially as well.

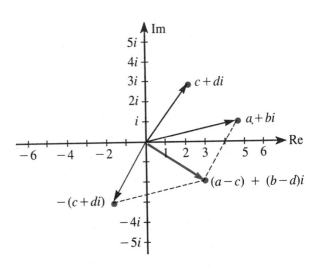

Example 1   Given the complex numbers $z_1 = 1 + 2i$ and $z_2 = -2 + i$ locate the following complex numbers on the plane.

(a) $z_1 + 1$

(b) $z_2 - 3i$

(c) $z_1 + z_2$

Solution   (a) The number $z_1 + 1$ is the number on the plane one unit to the right of z_1. We verify this result algebraically.

$$z_1 + 1 = (1 + 2i) + (1 + 0i)$$
$$= 2 + 2i$$

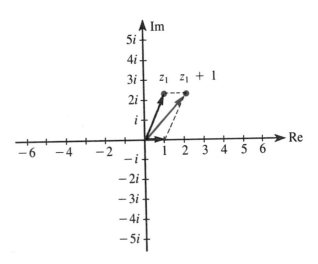

(b) The complex number $z_2 - 3i$ is three units down from z_2.

$$z_2 - 3i = (-2 + i) - (0 + 3i)$$
$$= -2 - 2i$$

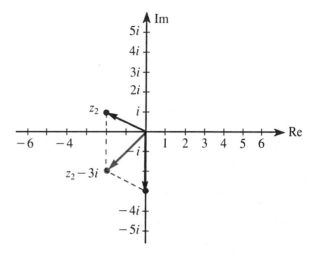

(c) z_2 equals $-2 + i$, so $z_1 + z_2$ is 2 units to the left and one unit up from z_1.

$$z_1 + z_2 = (1 + 2i) + (-2 + i)$$
$$= -1 + 3i$$

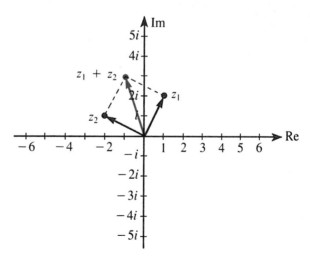

Multiplication: Multiplication of complex numbers is an extension of multiplication of real numbers. We will look at multiplication in stages before we draw a general conclusion. What happens if we multiply a complex number by a real number? If $z = 3 + i$ then $3z = 9 + 3i$.

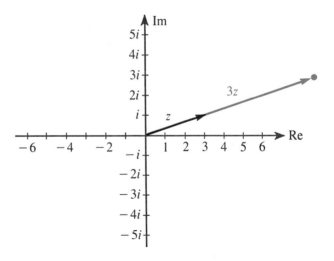

Multiplication of a complex number by a real number stretches its vector in the complex plane.

What happens if we multiply a complex number by i? For example, if $z = 3 + i$ then $iz = i(3 + i) = 3i + i^2 = -1 + 3i$.

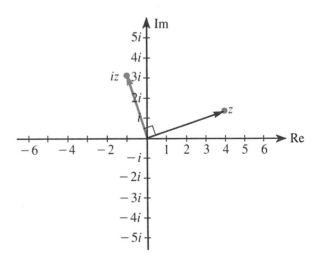

Multiplication by i *has the effect of rotating the complex number 90°.* The explanation of why this effect occurs will be developed in Section 10.5.

We can combine these two multiplicative results and consider how a complex number like $(2 + i)z$ compares to z. The number $(2 + i)z$ is equivalent to $2z + iz$, so the resultant vector would be the vector sum of a stretched vector plus a vector rotated 90°.

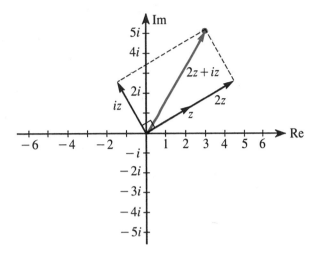

Let us now consider the algebra of complex number multiplication. The distributive property that we know from real number algebra also holds for the complex numbers.

$$(a + bi)(c + di) = a(c + di) + bi(c + di)$$
$$= ac + adi + bci + bdi^2$$
$$= ac + (ad + bc)i + bd(-1)$$
$$= (ac - bd) + (ad + bc)i$$

$$\boxed{(a + bi)(c + di) = (ac - bd) + (ad + bc)i}$$

Example 2   Find the following products.
(a) $(3 + 2i)(5 + 7i)$
(b) $(1 - i)^2$

Solution   (a) $(3 + 2i)(5 + 7i) = 3(5 + 7i) + 2i(5 + 7i)$
$$= 15 + 21i + 10i + 14i^2$$
$$= 15 + 31i + 14(-1)$$
$$= 1 + 31i$$
(b) $(1 + i)^2 = (1 - i)(1 - i)$
$$= 1 - 2i + i^2$$
$$= 1 - 2i + (-1)$$
$$= -2i$$

PROBLEMS PLUS

For how many integers n is $(n + i)^4$ an integer?

EXERCISE 10.2

B 1. Perform the following complex number arithmetic.

(a) $(3 + 2i) + (7 - 3i)$ (b) $2i(2 - i)$

(c) $(7 - 3i) - (3 - 6i)$ (d) $(w + vi) + (c + di)$

(e) $(1 + i)(1 - i)$ (f) $(4 - 3i)(4 + 3i)$

(g) $(3i)(3i)$ (h) $(i^2)(i^2)$

(i) $(9 - i)(9 + i)$ (j) $(4 - i) + 4$

(k) $(0 + 0i)(1 + 1i)$ (l) $-2i(4 - 2i)$

(m) $(7 - 10i)(7 + 10i)$ (n) $(a + ib)(a - ib)$

(o) $(3 - i)(3 + i)$ (p) $(u + vi) - (u + vi)$

(q) $(a + ia)(a - ia)$ (r) $-i(1 - i)$

2. If $z = 2 + i$ and $w = -1 - 3i$, determine the following related complex numbers and use vector diagrams to illustrate their relationship with the original complex number.

(a) $2z$ (b) $w + 3$ (c) $z - 2i$

(d) $-3w$ (e) $w - 5$ (f) z^2

(g) $0.5z$ (h) $z + w$ (i) $z - w$

(j) $2z + 3w$ (k) iz (l) iw

(m) $iz + iw$ (n) $3iz$ (o) $-4iw$

3. Solve for z in the following equations and leave your answer in the form $a + bi$, where a and b are real.

(a) $(2 - i) + z = 3 - 2i$

(b) $(5 + i) + z = 2z - (2 + 2i)$

(c) $z - (1 + i) = (2 - i)(3 + 2i)$

(d) $(1 + i)^2 = (2 - i)^2 + z$

4. (a) Evaluate i^k for $k = 1, 2, 3, 4, 5, 6, 7, 8$. Sketch each power on the complex plane.

(b) Make a general statement about i^k for $k \in N$.

(c) Evaluate: (i) i^{17} (ii) i^{40}

                 (iii) i^{27} (iv) i^{99}

                 (v) $(-i)^{39}$ (vi) i^{1001}

C 5. Sketch the sets of complex numbers in the complex plane that satisfy the following:

(a) $|z - 1| = 2$ (b) $|z - 5| = 3$

(c) $|z - 3i| = 1$ (d) $|z - 5 + 2i| = 2$

10.3   COMPLEX NUMBER ARITHMETIC: DIVISION

Before we can consider division of complex numbers we must introduce a related complex number called *the conjugate complex number*.

> If $z = a + bi$ then the **conjugate** of z, denoted $\bar{z}$, is defined to be $\bar{z} = a - bi$.

For example, if $z = -2 + i$ then the conjugate is $z = -2 - i$; if $z = 5i$ then $\bar{z} = -5i$; and if $z = 7$ then $\bar{z} = 7$.

Geometrically, the conjugate complex number is *a reflection* of the complex number *in the real axis*.

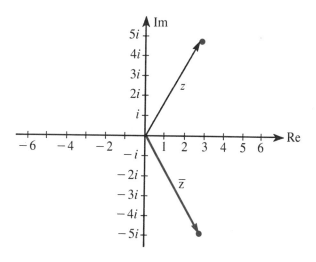

Example 1   If z and w are two complex numbers, show that $\overline{z + w} = \bar{z} + \bar{w}$.

Solution   Let $z = a + bi$ and $w = c + di$. We expand each side of the identity to show that they are equal.

The left side is
$$\overline{z + w} = \overline{(a + bi) + (c + di)}$$
$$= \overline{(a + c) + (b + d)i}$$
$$= (a + c) - (b + d)i$$

The right side is
$$\bar{z} + \bar{w} = \overline{(a + bi)} + \overline{(c + di)}$$
$$= (a - bi) + (c - di)$$
$$= (a + c) - (b + d)i$$

The two sides are equal so the identity is true.

A very useful property relating a complex number and its conjugate is:

> $$z\bar{z} = |z|^2$$

Proof

Let $z = a + bi$, then $\bar{z} = a - bi$.

$$z\bar{z} = (a + bi)(a - bi)$$
$$= a^2 + abi - abi - b^2i^2$$
$$= a^2 - b^2(-1)$$
$$= a^2 + b^2$$

and $\quad |z|^2 = (\sqrt{a^2 + b^2})^2 \qquad$ (definition of modulus)
$$= a^2 + b^2$$

Hence the property is true.

This result can be rearranged to the equivalent form:

$$\boxed{\frac{1}{z} = \frac{\bar{z}}{|z|^2}}$$

We can now interpret the *reciprocal* of a complex number. Geometrically, to locate the reciprocal we reflect the vector of the complex number in the real axis as well as shrink the vector by a factor equal to the square of the modulus of the complex number. For example, if $z = 2 + i$ then the reciprocal, $\frac{1}{z}$, would be:

$$\frac{1}{2 + i} = \frac{2 - i}{2^2 + 1^2}$$
$$= \tfrac{2}{5} - \tfrac{1}{5}i$$

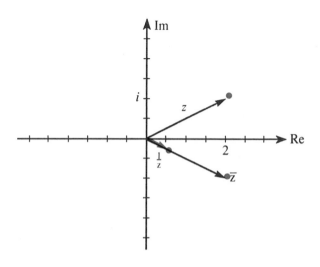

We are now ready to look at the division of complex numbers.

Division: We treat division of two complex numbers as multiplication of one complex number by the reciprocal of another, that is, given the complex numbers z and w, $\dfrac{z}{w} = z\dfrac{1}{w}$. We can express this in a form that will be easy to remember and manipulate.

$$\frac{z}{w} = z\,\frac{1}{w}$$

$$= z\,\frac{\bar{w}}{|w|^2}$$

$$= \frac{z\bar{w}}{w\bar{w}}$$

So, to divide two complex numbers we multiply the numerator and the denominator by the conjugate of the denominator.

$$\boxed{\dfrac{z}{w} = \dfrac{z\bar{w}}{w\bar{w}}}$$

Example 2 Determine the indicated quotients.

    (a) $\dfrac{3 + 2i}{5 + i}$ (b) $\dfrac{i}{1 + i}$ (c) $\dfrac{3}{2 - i}$

Solution   (a) $\dfrac{3 + 2i}{5 + i} = \dfrac{(3 + 2i)(5 - i)}{(5 + i)(5 - i)}$

$$= \frac{15 + 7i - 2i^2}{5^2 + 1^2}$$

$$= \frac{17 + 7i}{26}$$

$$= \tfrac{17}{26} + \tfrac{7}{26}i$$

(b) $\dfrac{i}{1 + i} = \dfrac{i(1 - i)}{(1 + i)(1 - i)}$

$$= \frac{i - i^2}{1^2 + 1^2}$$

$$= \tfrac{1}{2} + \tfrac{1}{2}i$$

(c) $\dfrac{3}{2 - i} = \dfrac{3(2 + i)}{4 + 1}$

$$= \tfrac{6}{5} + \tfrac{3}{5}i$$

Example 3   Solve for the complex variable z and express z in the form $a + bi$:

$$(3 + 2i)z = (5 - i) + 2z$$

Solution

$$\begin{aligned}
(3 + 2i)z &= (5 - i) + 2z \\
(3 + 2i)z - 2z &= 5 - i \\
z(3 + 2i - 2) &= 5 - i \\
z(1 + 2i) &= 5 - i \\
z &= \frac{5 - i}{1 + 2i} \\
&= \frac{(5 - i)(1 - 2i)}{1 + 4} \qquad \text{(complex number division)} \\
&= \frac{5 - 11i + 2i^2}{5} \\
&= \tfrac{3}{5} - \tfrac{11}{5}i
\end{aligned}$$

EXERCISE 10.3

A 1. State the complex conjugates of the following complex numbers.

(a) $3 - 5i$ (b) $9 + 2i$

(c) $-3 - 3i$ (d) $2i$

(e) $-3i$ (f) 22

(g) $17 - 4i$ (h) $5i + 3$

(i) i^2 (j) i

(k) 0 (l) $a + bi$

B 2. If $z = 1 + i$ and $w = -3 + 4i$, determine the following related complex numbers and use vector diagrams to illustrate their relationship with the original complex number.

(a) $\dfrac{1}{z}$ (b) $\dfrac{1}{w}$ (c) $\overline{z}$

(d) $\overline{w}$ (e) $\dfrac{1}{\overline{z}}$ (f) $\dfrac{1}{\overline{w}}$

(g) $3\overline{z}$ (h) $\dfrac{\overline{z}}{|z|^2}$ (i) $\dfrac{\overline{w}}{|w|^2}$

3. Perform the following complex number arithmetic. Express all answers in the form $a + bi$, where a and b are real.

(a) $(2 - 5i)(3 + i)$ (b) $\dfrac{7 + i}{1 + i}$

(c) $\dfrac{1}{i}$ (d) $(2 + 2i)^2$

(e) $(1 - i)^3$ (f) $\dfrac{3}{2 - i}$

(g) $\dfrac{-1}{i} + 2i$ (h) $\dfrac{2 - 3i}{3i}$

(i) $\dfrac{-2i}{1 + 2i}$ (j) $\dfrac{1 - i}{1 + i}$

(k) $3 + 2i - \dfrac{3}{5i}$ (l) $\dfrac{(2 - i)^2}{(1 - 2i)^2}$

(m) $\dfrac{3i}{5 - i}$ (n) $\dfrac{5i}{(3 - 4i)^2}$

(o) $\dfrac{3}{2i} + \dfrac{5}{1 + i} - i$ (p) $\dfrac{1 - i}{i^3}$

(q) $\dfrac{2 + 3i}{3i}$ (r) $\left(\dfrac{4 - i}{2 + 2i}\right)^2$

4. Solve for z in the following equations and leave your answers in the form $a + bi$, where a and b are real.
   (a) $(3 + i)z = 1 - i$ (b) $5 + 7i = -2iz$
   (c) $(5 - i)z + (1 - 3i)z = i$ (d) $iz = 2z - 2i$
   (e) $(3 - 2i)(4 + i) = (2 - i)z$ (f) $(3 + i)z = (1 - i)^2$

5. Prove the following identities.
   (a) $\overline{z_1 + z_2 + z_3} = \overline{z_1} + \overline{z_2} + \overline{z_3}$ (b) $\overline{z_1 z_2} = \overline{z_1}\,\overline{z_2}$

6. (a) Show that the imaginary part of $\dfrac{6}{i}$ equals -6.

   (b) Show that, in general, the imaginary part of $\dfrac{k}{i}$, $k \in R$, is $-k$.

   (c) Show that, in general, the imaginary part of $\dfrac{z}{i}$, where $z = a + bi$, equals $-a$.

C 7. Solve for the complex variables z and w and express your answers in the form $a + bi$.
   (a) $2z - iw = i$ (b) $(1 + i)z - w = 2 + i$
       $iz + 3w = 2$ $3iz + (2 - i)w = 1$

10.4 POLAR FORM: THE FUNCTION CIS

Evaluating powers of numbers in the real number system is not difficult with the use of a calculator. For example, $3.127^{11} \doteq 279\ 516.01$. However, to evaluate the power of a complex number such as $(1 - i)^{11}$ directly, we would be required to expand and simplify the product:

$$(1 - i)(1 - i)(1 - i)(1 - i)(1 - i)(1 - i)(1 - i)(1 - i)(1 - i)(1 - i)(1 - i)$$

which is not an easy task. This section and the following two sections will develop the theory to allow us to compute such powers of complex numbers with relative ease.

When we plot a complex number in the complex plane we can describe its location by its distance, r, from zero (its modulus) and its angle of rotation, θ, from the positive real axis. The angle θ is referred to as the **argument** of z.

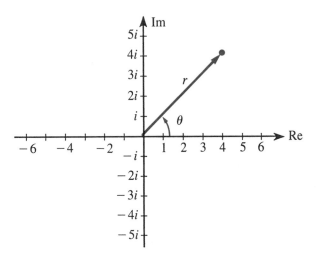

Recall that the points on the unit circle in the Cartesian plane are given by ($\cos\theta, \sin\theta$). Similarly in the complex plane, a point on a unit circle has the ordered pair ($\cos\theta, \sin\theta$) or, written in the form $a + bi$, $\cos\theta + i\sin\theta$. All points in the complex plane can be regarded as r times a point on the unit circle where r is the modulus of the complex number (remember that rz is a stretch of the vector z by a factor of r).

$$z = r(\cos\theta + i\sin\theta) = |z|(\cos\theta + i\sin\theta)$$

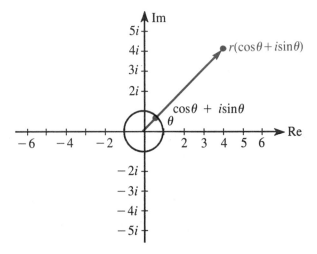

We now have two ways of representing complex numbers: $a + bi$, the **rectangular form**, or $r(\cos\theta + i\sin\theta)$. The form $r(\cos\theta + i\sin\theta)$ is often abbreviated to r **cis** θ. When a complex number is written in the form r **cis** θ we refer to this as the **polar form** of the complex number.

Example 1 Plot the following complex numbers in the complex plane:

(a) $2\ \text{cis}\ \dfrac{\pi}{4}$

(b) $5\left(\cos\dfrac{\pi}{2} + i\sin\dfrac{\pi}{2}\right)$

(c) $3\ \text{cis}\ 0$

(d) $4\ \text{cis}\left(-\dfrac{3\pi}{4}\right)$

(e) $2\cos\pi + 2\,i\sin\pi$

Solution (a) $2\ \text{cis}\ \dfrac{\pi}{4}$ is 2 units from the origin at an angle of $\dfrac{\pi}{4}$ from the positive

real axis, that is, its argument is $\dfrac{\pi}{4}$.

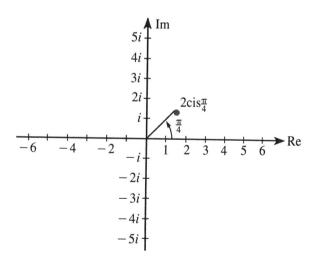

(b) $5\left(\cos\dfrac{\pi}{2} + i\sin\dfrac{\pi}{2}\right)$ is 5 units above the origin on the imaginary axis.

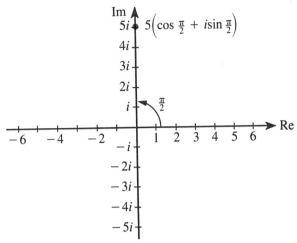

(c) 3 cis 0 is 3 units along the positive real axis.

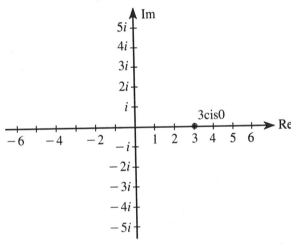

(d) $4 \operatorname{cis}\left(-\dfrac{3\pi}{4}\right)$ is 4 units from the origin at an angle of $-\dfrac{3\pi}{4}$.

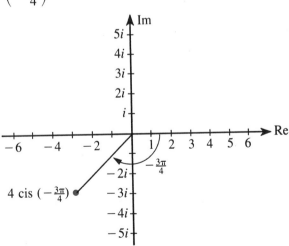

(e) $2 \cos \pi + 2 i \sin \pi = 2 \text{ cis } \pi$ which is 2 units from the origin
on the negative real axis.

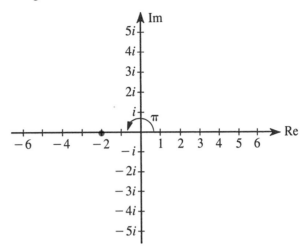

It is often necessary to convert from one form of representation of
the complex numbers to another.

Rectangular form to polar form:
If a complex number z is in the form $a + bi$, then to convert z into
its polar form we need to determine its modulus, r, and its argument,
θ.
We use the relationships:

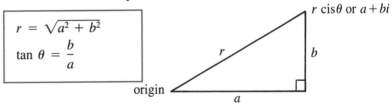

$$r = \sqrt{a^2 + b^2}$$
$$\tan \theta = \frac{b}{a}$$

Example 2   Write the following complex numbers in polar form.
(a) $-\sqrt{3} - i$ (b) $-1 + 2i$

Solution   (a) We plot the number in the complex plane. We have $a = -\sqrt{3}$
and $b = -1$, so

$$r = \sqrt{(-\sqrt{3})^2 + (-1)^2}$$
$$= 2$$

and $\tan \theta = \dfrac{1}{\sqrt{3}}$, so $\theta = \dfrac{\pi}{6}$ or $\dfrac{7\pi}{6}$.

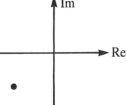

We see from the diagram that the argument is $\dfrac{7\pi}{6}$. The polar form

of $-\sqrt{3} - i$ is $2 \text{ cis } \dfrac{7\pi}{6}$.

(b) We plot the number in the complex plane.
We have $a = -1$ and $b = 2$, so
$$r = \sqrt{(-1)^2 + 2^2}$$
$$= \sqrt{5}$$
and $\tan \theta = -2$, so $\theta \doteq -1.107$ or $\pi - 1.107$

We see from the diagram that the argument is $\pi - 1.107$ or approximately 2.034 (radians). The polar form of $-1 + 2i$ is $\sqrt{5} \text{ cis}(2.034)$.

Note that the argument θ of a complex number is not unique. In Example 2, part (a), we could have described $-\sqrt{3} - i$ not only as $2 \text{ cis } \dfrac{7\pi}{6}$ but as $2 \text{ cis}\left(\dfrac{7\pi}{6} + 2\pi\right)$, or $2 \text{ cis}\left(\dfrac{7\pi}{6} + 4\pi\right)$, or generally as $2 \text{ cis}\left(\dfrac{7\pi}{6} + 2k\pi\right)$, $k \in I$.

Rectangular to Polar

$$z = a + bi = r \text{ cis}(\theta + 2k\pi)$$

where $r = \sqrt{a^2 + b^2}$ and $\tan \theta = \dfrac{b}{a}$

and θ is determined by referring to a diagram.

Polar form to rectangular form:
A complex number expressed in polar form can be converted into rectangular form by evaluating the trigonometric terms.

Example 3 Write the complex number $3 \text{ cis } \dfrac{3\pi}{4}$ in rectangular form.

Solution

$$3 \text{ cis } \frac{3\pi}{4} = 3\left(\cos \frac{3\pi}{4} + i \sin \frac{3\pi}{4}\right)$$

$$= 3\left(\frac{-1}{\sqrt{2}} + i\frac{1}{\sqrt{2}}\right)$$

$$= \frac{-3}{\sqrt{2}} + \frac{3}{\sqrt{2}} i$$

EXERCISE 10.4

A **1.** For the following complex numbers, state (i) the modulus, r, (ii) the tangent of the argument, $\tan \theta$, and (iii) the quadrant or axis where the complex number is found.

(a) $1 + i$
(b) $3i$
(c) $-2 - 3i$
(d) $4 - i$
(e) -5
(f) $3 - 4i$
(g) $\pi - 2i$
(h) $-k - ki$
(i) $1 - i\sqrt{2}$
(j) $i\sqrt{3}$
(k) $-\sqrt{5}$
(l) $2 + 2i$

2. State the polar form equivalent of the following complex numbers.

(a) 2
(b) 5
(c) -2
(d) -1
(e) $2i$
(f) $7i$
(g) $-i$
(h) $-3i$
(i) 0
(j) π
(k) $-\sqrt{2}$
(l) $\sqrt{3}i$

B **3.** Write the following complex numbers in rectangular form.

(a) $3 \text{ cis } \pi$
(b) $2 \text{ cis } \dfrac{\pi}{2}$
(c) $\text{cis } \dfrac{3\pi}{2}$

(d) $2 \text{ cis } 0$
(e) $5 \text{ cis } \pi$
(f) $\sqrt{2} \text{ cis } \dfrac{\pi}{4}$

(g) $2 \text{ cis } \dfrac{5\pi}{3}$
(h) $\sqrt{2} \text{ cis}\left(-\dfrac{\pi}{4}\right)$
(i) $\text{cis } 0$

(j) $3 \text{ cis } \dfrac{7\pi}{4}$
(k) $2 \text{ cis } 1$
(l) $5 \text{ cis } 1.1$

(m) $3 \text{ cis } 3$
(n) $\text{cis } 6$
(o) $2 \text{ cis } 3.1415$

4. Write the following complex numbers in polar form.

(a) 1
(b) i
(c) $1 + i$
(d) $-1 - i$
(e) $1 - i$
(f) $-1 + i$
(g) $3 - 5i$
(h) $-3 + 5i$
(i) $\dfrac{1}{2} + \dfrac{\sqrt{3}}{2}i$
(j) $-\dfrac{1}{2} - \dfrac{\sqrt{3}}{2}i$
(k) $3\sqrt{3} - 6i$
(l) $-3\sqrt{3} + 6i$
(m) $-\sqrt{3}$
(n) $\sqrt{3}$
(o) $i\sqrt{3}$
(p) $-i\sqrt{3}$
(q) $7 - 2i$
(r) $-3 + 2i$
(s) $11 + 12i$
(t) $-7 - 9i$
(u) $0.5 - 0.5i$

PROBLEMS PLUS

Suppose $z = a + bi$ is a solution of the equation
$$z^4 + iz^3 + z^2 + iz + 1 = 0.$$
Show that $-a + bi$ must also be a solution

10.5 COMPLEX NUMBER ARITHMETIC IN POLAR FORM

We now look at complex number arithmetic in polar form.

Addition:

$$z_1 + z_2 = r_1 \text{ cis } \theta_1 + r_2 \text{ cis } \theta_2$$
$$= r_1(\cos \theta_1 + i \sin \theta_1) + r_2(\cos \theta_2 + i \sin \theta_2)$$
$$= (r_1 \cos \theta_1 + r_2 \cos \theta_2) + i(r_1 \sin \theta_1 + r_2 \sin \theta_2)$$

The polar form does not offer any advantage over the rectangular form when adding complex numbers.

Subtraction:

$$z_1 - z_2 = r_1 \text{ cis } \theta_1 - r_2 \text{ cis } \theta_2$$
$$= r_1(\cos \theta_1 + i \sin \theta_1) - r_2(\cos \theta_2 + i \sin \theta_2)$$
$$= (r_1 \cos \theta_1 - r_2 \cos \theta_2) + i(r_1 \sin \theta_1 - r_2 \sin \theta_2)$$

Similarly, we conclude that the polar form does not offer any advantage over the rectangular form when subtracting complex numbers.

Multiplication:

$$
\begin{aligned}
z_1 z_2 &= (r_1 \text{ cis } \theta_1)(r_2 \text{ cis } \theta_2) \\
&= r_1(\cos \theta_1 + i \sin \theta_1) \, r_2(\cos \theta_2 + i \sin \theta_2) \\
&= r_1 r_2(\cos \theta_1 + i \sin \theta_1)(\cos \theta_2 + i \sin \theta_2) \\
&= r_1 r_2[(\cos \theta_1 \cos \theta_2 - \sin \theta_1 \sin \theta_2) + i(\cos \theta_1 \sin \theta_2 + \sin \theta_1 \cos \theta_2)] \\
&= r_1 r_2[\cos(\theta_1 + \theta_2) + i \sin(\theta_1 + \theta_2)] \qquad \text{(compound angle formulas)} \\
&= r_1 r_2 \text{ cis}(\theta_1 + \theta_2)
\end{aligned}
$$

Multiplication in polar form is immediate. We merely multiply the moduli and add the arguments.

Multiplication in Polar Form:

$$z_1 z_2 = (r_1 \text{ cis } \theta_1)(r_2 \text{ cis } \theta_2) = r_1 r_2 \text{ cis}(\theta_1 + \theta_2)$$

Geometrically, the sum of the arguments suggests a rotation. The product of two complex numbers is the complex number that has been rotated through an angle of $\theta_1 + \theta_2$ from the positive real axis and whose modulus is the product of the moduli of the two complex numbers.

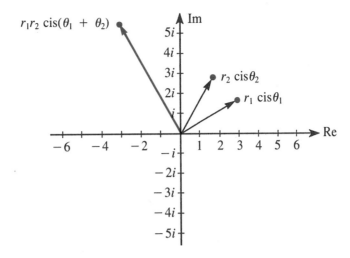

Example 1   Determine the following product and illustrate the result in the complex plane.

$$\left(3 \text{ cis } \frac{\pi}{4}\right)\left(2 \text{ cis } \frac{\pi}{2}\right)$$

Solution $$\left(3 \text{ cis } \frac{\pi}{4}\right)\left(2 \text{ cis } \frac{\pi}{2}\right) = (3)(2) \text{ cis}\left(\frac{\pi}{4} + \frac{\pi}{2}\right)$$

$$= 6 \text{ cis } \frac{3\pi}{4}$$

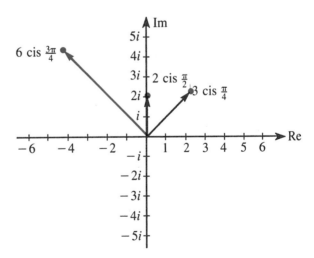

The conjugate complex number is the reflection of the complex number in the real axis. Hence its polar form is $r \text{ cis}(-\theta)$.

> The conjugate of $r \text{ cis } \theta$ is $r \text{ cis}(-\theta)$.

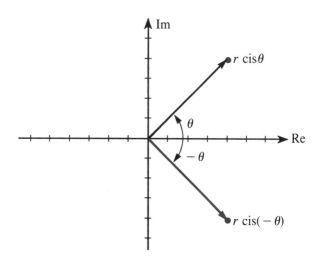

Division:

We now divide complex numbers in polar form.

$$\frac{z_1}{z_2} = \frac{z_1\,\overline{z_2}}{z_2\,\overline{z_2}} \qquad \text{(complex number division)}$$

$$= \frac{z_1\,\overline{z_2}}{|z_2|^2} \qquad \text{(using } z\overline{z} = |z|^2 \text{)}$$

$$= \frac{r_1\,\text{cis}\,\theta_1\,r_2\,\text{cis}(-\theta_2)}{r_2^{\,2}}$$

$$= \frac{r_1}{r_2}\,\text{cis}(\theta_1 - \theta_2)$$

Division in polar form is immediate as well. We divide the moduli and subtract the arguments.

Division in Polar Form

$$\frac{z_1}{z_2} = \frac{r_1\,\text{cis}\,\theta_1}{r_2\,\text{cis}\,\theta_2} = \frac{r_1}{r_2}\,\text{cis}(\theta_1 - \theta_2)$$

Example 2   Determine the following quotient: $\dfrac{3\,\text{cis}\,\dfrac{\pi}{2}}{6\,\text{cis}\,\dfrac{\pi}{4}}$

Solution

$$\frac{3\,\text{cis}\,\dfrac{\pi}{2}}{6\,\text{cis}\,\dfrac{\pi}{4}} = \frac{3}{6}\,\text{cis}\!\left(\frac{\pi}{2} - \frac{\pi}{4}\right)$$

$$= \frac{1}{2}\,\text{cis}\,\frac{\pi}{4}$$

Example 3   Use polar form arithmetic to evaluate the following. Write the final answer in the form $a + bi$.

$$\frac{(1 + i)(1 - \sqrt{3}\, i)}{-\sqrt{3} + i}$$

Solution   We convert each complex number in the expression to its polar form.

$1 + i$: We have $a = 1$ and $b = 1$, so $r = \sqrt{1 + 1} = \sqrt{2}$, and $\tan \theta = 1$ so $\theta = \dfrac{\pi}{4}$ or $\dfrac{5\pi}{4}$. From a plot of the point we see

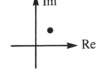

that the argument is $\theta = \dfrac{\pi}{4}$. So the polar form of $1 + i$ is $\sqrt{2} \operatorname{cis} \dfrac{\pi}{4}$.

$1 - \sqrt{3}i$: We have $a = 1$ and $b = -\sqrt{3}$ so $r = 2$, and $\tan \theta = -\sqrt{3}$ so $\theta = -\dfrac{\pi}{3}$ or $\dfrac{2\pi}{3}$. From a diagram we see the argument is $-\dfrac{\pi}{3}$. So the polar form of $1 - \sqrt{3}\, i$ is $2 \operatorname{cis}\left(-\dfrac{\pi}{3}\right)$.

$-\sqrt{3} + i$: We have $a = -\sqrt{3}$ and $b = 1$, so $r = 2$ and $\tan \theta = -\dfrac{1}{\sqrt{3}}$, so $\theta = -\dfrac{\pi}{6}$ or $\dfrac{5\pi}{6}$. From a diagram,

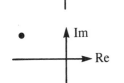

$\theta = \dfrac{5\pi}{6}$. So the polar form of $\sqrt{3} - i$ is $2 \operatorname{cis} \dfrac{5\pi}{6}$.

Now we write the expression in polar form and evaluate.

$$\frac{(1 + i)(1 - \sqrt{3}\, i)}{-\sqrt{3} + i} = \frac{\left(\sqrt{2} \operatorname{cis} \dfrac{\pi}{4}\right)\left(2 \operatorname{cis}\left(-\dfrac{\pi}{3}\right)\right)}{2 \operatorname{cis} \dfrac{5\pi}{6}}$$

$$= \frac{2\sqrt{2} \operatorname{cis}\left(\dfrac{\pi}{4} + \left(-\dfrac{\pi}{3}\right)\right)}{2 \operatorname{cis} \dfrac{5\pi}{6}}$$

$$= \frac{\sqrt{2} \operatorname{cis}\left(-\dfrac{\pi}{12}\right)}{\operatorname{cis} \dfrac{5\pi}{6}}$$

$$= \sqrt{2} \operatorname{cis}\left(-\dfrac{\pi}{12} - \dfrac{5\pi}{6}\right)$$

$$= \sqrt{2} \operatorname{cis}\left(-\dfrac{11\pi}{12}\right)$$

Returning to rectangular form, we have

$$\sqrt{2}\operatorname{cis}\left(-\frac{11\pi}{12}\right) = \sqrt{2}\left[\cos\left(-\frac{11\pi}{12}\right) + i\sin\left(-\frac{11\pi}{12}\right)\right]$$
$$\doteq \sqrt{2}(-0.9659 - 0.2588\,i)$$
$$\doteq -1.3660 - 0.3660\,i$$

EXERCISE 10.5

A **1.** Perform the indicated operations on the complex numbers and give your answers in polar form.

(a) $(3\operatorname{cis}\pi)\left(2\operatorname{cis}\dfrac{\pi}{2}\right)$

(b) $(\operatorname{cis}1)(\operatorname{cis}2)$

(c) $\dfrac{4\operatorname{cis}\dfrac{3\pi}{4}}{2\operatorname{cis}\dfrac{\pi}{4}}$

(d) $\dfrac{24\operatorname{cis}\pi}{6\operatorname{cis}\dfrac{\pi}{2}}$

(e) $\left(5\operatorname{cis}\dfrac{\pi}{4}\right)\left(2\operatorname{cis}\dfrac{\pi}{2}\right)\left(3\operatorname{cis}\dfrac{\pi}{4}\right)$

(f) $\dfrac{(3\operatorname{cis}\pi)\left(2\operatorname{cis}\dfrac{\pi}{2}\right)}{6\operatorname{cis}\pi}$

(g) $\dfrac{20\operatorname{cis}\dfrac{\pi}{3}}{5\operatorname{cis}\dfrac{\pi}{3}}\left(2\operatorname{cis}\dfrac{\pi}{2}\right)$

(h) $\left(3\operatorname{cis}\dfrac{\pi}{2}\right)^{2}$

(i) $(r\operatorname{cis}\theta)^{2}$

(j) $(r\operatorname{cis}\theta)^{3}$

B **2.** Solve the following equations for z. Leave the final answer in polar form.

(a) $(3\operatorname{cis}\pi)z = 2\operatorname{cis}\dfrac{\pi}{2}$

(b) $\left(2\operatorname{cis}\dfrac{\pi}{4}\right)z = (3\operatorname{cis}\pi)\left(6\operatorname{cis}\dfrac{\pi}{2}\right)$

(c) $(5\operatorname{cis}\pi)\left(2\operatorname{cis}\dfrac{\pi}{3}\right)z = \left(2\operatorname{cis}\dfrac{\pi}{2}\right)\left(15\operatorname{cis}\dfrac{\pi}{3}\right)$

(d) $\dfrac{6\operatorname{cis}\dfrac{3\pi}{4}}{2\operatorname{cis}\dfrac{\pi}{4}}z = 4\operatorname{cis}\dfrac{\pi}{2}$

3. Evaluate the following by converting each complex number into its polar form and using the multiplication and division rules for complex numbers in polar form. Write your final answer in the rectangular form $a + bi$.

   (a) $\dfrac{(1 + i)(1 - i)(-1 - i)}{(1 + i\sqrt{3})(-1 - i\sqrt{3})}$

   (b) $\dfrac{(1 + i)(\sqrt{3} + i)(6i)}{(3\sqrt{2} - 3i\sqrt{2})(-2\sqrt{3} + 2i)}$

   (c) $\dfrac{(-1 + i)^2(1 + i\sqrt{3})^2}{(-\sqrt{3} + i)^2(-1 - i\sqrt{3})^2}$

   (d) $\dfrac{(3 + 2i)(-1 + 4i)(3 - i)}{(4 + 2i)(-2 - 5i)(2 - i)}$

   (e) $\dfrac{(7 - 9i)(3 + 11i)^2}{(5 + 7i)^2(3 - 2i)}$

4. (a) Use multiplication in polar form to show that $z\bar{z} = |z|^2$.
   (b) Use the vector interpretation of multiplication to illustrate the result $z\bar{z} = |z|^2$.

5. In section 10.2 it was stated that "*Multiplication by* i *has the effect of rotating the complex number by 90°.*" Use polar form multiplication to verify this statement.

PROBLEMS PLUS

The origin and the complex number $2 + 2i$ are opposite vertices of a regular hexagon. Determine the complex numbers corresponding to the other vertices of the hexagon. (Express them in the polar form.)

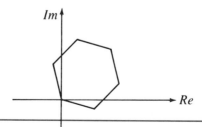

10.6 DE MOIVRE'S THEOREM

We now consider powers of complex numbers. Using the multiplication rule for the polar form of complex numbers we see that:

$$(r \text{ cis } \theta)^1 = r \text{ cis } \theta$$
$$(r \text{ cis } \theta)^2 = (r \text{ cis } \theta)(r \text{ cis } \theta) = r^2 \text{ cis } 2\theta$$
$$(r \text{ cis } \theta)^3 = (r \text{ cis } \theta)(r \text{ cis } \theta)(r \text{ cis } \theta)$$
$$= r^2 \text{ cis } 2\theta \, r \text{ cis } \theta$$
$$= r^3 \text{ cis } 3\theta$$

and so on. This leads us to the general result referred to as *De Moivre's Theorem*.

De Moivre's Theorem:

$$(r \text{ cis } \theta)^n = r^n \text{ cis } n\theta$$

or

$$[r(\cos \theta + i \sin \theta)]^n = r^n(\cos n\theta + i \sin n\theta), \text{ for } n \in N$$

The proof of De Moivre's theorem will be presented in Chapter 11.

Vectorially the result $(r \text{ cis } \theta)^n = r^n \text{ cis } n\theta$ is a multiple rotation of an original vector with the magnitude of the original vector taken to the *n*th power.

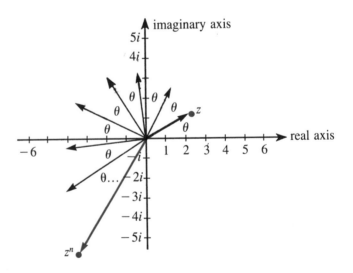

The resultant vector has argument $n\theta$. The resultant magnitude (modulus) is r^n.

In the opening statements to Section 10.4 we asked how to evaluate $(1 - i)^{11}$. We are now in a position to solve this problem.

Example 1   Use De Moivre's theorem to evaluate $(1 - i)^{11}$.

Solution   We express $1 - i$ in polar form and plot the number on the complex plane. We have $a = 1$ and $b = -1$, so $r = \sqrt{2}$ and $\theta = -\dfrac{\pi}{4}$. In polar form the number is $\sqrt{2}\operatorname{cis}\left(-\dfrac{\pi}{4}\right)$.

So,
$$(1 - i)^{11} = \left[\sqrt{2}\operatorname{cis}\left(-\frac{\pi}{4}\right)\right]^{11}$$
$$= (\sqrt{2})^{11}\operatorname{cis}\left[11\left(-\frac{\pi}{4}\right)\right]$$
$$= 32\sqrt{2}\operatorname{cis}\left(-\frac{11\pi}{4}\right)$$
$$= 32\sqrt{2}\operatorname{cis}\left(-\frac{3\pi}{4}\right)$$
$$= 32\sqrt{2}\left[\cos\left(-\frac{3\pi}{4}\right) + i\sin\left(-\frac{3\pi}{4}\right)\right]$$
$$= 32\sqrt{2}\left[-\frac{1}{\sqrt{2}} + i\left(-\frac{1}{\sqrt{2}}\right)\right]$$
$$= -32 - 32i$$

We can visualize the product $(1 - i)^{11}$ geometrically by picturing the complex number $1 - i$ with magnitude $\sqrt{2}$ being rotated 10 times through $-\dfrac{\pi}{4}$ and stretched to a magnitude of $(\sqrt{2})^{11}$ or $32\sqrt{2}$.

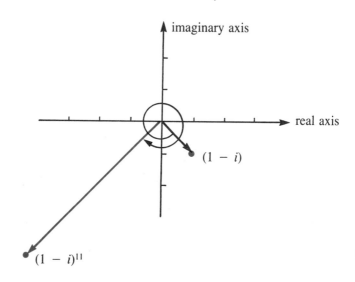

De Moivre's theorem has an interesting application to trigonometric identities. It enables us to relate terms like $\cos n\theta$ and $\sin n\theta$ to powers of $\cos \theta$ and $\sin \theta$.

Example 2 Develop a formula for $\cos 3\theta$ in terms of $\cos \theta$.

Solution We recognize that $\cos 3\theta$ is the *real part* of cis 3θ which, by De Moivre's theorem, equals $(\text{cis } \theta)^3$. We need only find the real part of $(\text{cis } \theta)^3$ (once it has been expanded) and this will be our formula for $\cos 3\theta$.

We know $(\text{cis } \theta)^3 = \text{cis } 3\theta$ (De Moivre's theorem)

and
$$
\begin{aligned}
(\text{cis } \theta)^3 &= (\cos \theta + i \sin \theta)^3 \\
&= (\cos \theta + i \sin \theta)(\cos \theta + i \sin \theta)(\cos \theta + i \sin \theta) \\
&= (\cos^2 \theta + i\, 2 \cos \theta \sin \theta - \sin^2 \theta)(\cos \theta + i \sin \theta) \\
&= \cos^3 \theta + i \cos^2 \theta \sin \theta + i\, 2 \cos^2 \theta \sin \theta \\
&\quad - 2 \cos \theta \sin^2 \theta - \cos \theta \sin^2 \theta - i \sin^3 \theta \\
&= (\cos^3 \theta - 3 \cos \theta \sin^2 \theta) + i(3 \cos^2 \theta \sin \theta - \sin^3 \theta)
\end{aligned}
$$

and $\quad \text{cis } 3\theta = \cos 3\theta + i \sin 3\theta$

Therefore,
$$
\begin{aligned}
\cos 3\theta &= \cos^3 \theta - 3 \cos \theta \sin^2 \theta \qquad \text{(real parts)} \\
&= \cos^3 \theta - 3 \cos \theta(1 - \cos^2 \theta) \\
&= \cos^3 \theta - 3 \cos \theta + 3 \cos^3 \theta \\
&= 4 \cos^3 \theta - 3 \cos \theta
\end{aligned}
$$

Notice that in the above example we could have also developed a formula for $\sin 3\theta$ in terms of $\sin \theta$. This result comes from the equality of the *imaginary parts* of $(\text{cis } \theta)^3$ and cis 3θ:

$$
\begin{aligned}
\sin 3\theta &= 3 \cos^2 \theta \sin \theta - \sin^3 \theta \\
&= 3(1 - \sin^2 \theta) \sin \theta - \sin^3 \theta \\
&= 3 \sin \theta - 4 \sin^3 \theta.
\end{aligned}
$$

PROBLEMS PLUS

Find the sum of

$$
\cos \frac{\pi}{4} + i \cos \frac{3\pi}{4} + \ldots +
$$
$$
i^n \cos \left(\frac{\pi}{4} + n\frac{\pi}{2}\right) + \ldots + i^{40} \cos \left(\frac{81\pi}{4}\right)
$$

EXERCISE 10.6

A **1.** Evaluate the following powers of complex numbers. Leave your answers in polar form.

(a) $\left(3 \text{ cis } \dfrac{\pi}{2}\right)^3$

(b) $(2 \text{ cis } \pi)^4$

(c) $\left(\text{cis } \dfrac{\pi}{3}\right)^6$

(d) $\left(2 \text{ cis } \dfrac{\pi}{4}\right)^8$

(e) $\left(\cos \dfrac{\pi}{4} + i \sin \dfrac{\pi}{4}\right)^8$

(f) $(2 \text{ cis } 0)^5$

(g) i^7

(h) 3^4

(i) $\left(\sqrt{2} \text{ cis } \dfrac{\pi}{4}\right)^8$

(j) $(\sqrt{3} \text{ cis } 1)^5$

B **2.** Evaluate the following expressions and leave your answers in polar form.

(a) $\dfrac{\left(3 \text{ cis } \dfrac{\pi}{2}\right)^4 \left(2 \text{ cis } \dfrac{\pi}{3}\right)^6}{(\sqrt{2} \text{ cis } \pi)^6}$

(b) $\dfrac{\left(2 \text{ cis } \dfrac{\pi}{4}\right)^7 \left(\sqrt{2} \text{ cis } \dfrac{\pi}{2}\right)^4}{\left(4 \text{ cis } \dfrac{\pi}{3}\right)^3 \left(8 \text{ cis } \dfrac{\pi}{2}\right)^2}$

(c) $\dfrac{(3 \text{ cis } 2)^3 (2 \text{ cis } 1.1)^4}{(2 \text{ cis } 1)^5 (4 \text{ cis } 1.5)^3}$

(d) $\dfrac{\left(\sqrt{2} \text{ cis } \dfrac{\pi}{4}\right)^{11} (\sqrt{2} \text{ cis } 0)^7}{\left(\sqrt{2} \text{ cis } \dfrac{\pi}{2}\right)^9}$

(e) $\dfrac{\left(\sqrt{3} \text{ cis } \dfrac{\pi}{3}\right)^6 \left(\sqrt{5} \text{ cis } \dfrac{\pi}{4}\right)^6}{\left(3 \text{ cis } \dfrac{\pi}{2}\right)^4 \left(5 \text{ cis } \dfrac{\pi}{3}\right)^3}$

3. Evaluate the following expressions making use of De Moivre's theorem. Express your answers in the form $a + bi$.

(a) $(-1 + i)^7$

(b) $(1 - i)^7$

(c) $(2\sqrt{3} - 2i)^6$

(d) $(1 - i\sqrt{3})^{13}$

(e) $(\sqrt{3} + i)^6(1 - i\sqrt{3})^7$

(f) $(3 - 2i)^9$

(g) $(5 + 2i)^5(4 - i)^4$

(h) $\dfrac{(1 - i)^7(-1 + i)^9}{(-1 - i)^4(1 + i)^8}$

(i) $\dfrac{(\sqrt{3} + i)^7(3\sqrt{3} - 3i)^4}{(-2\sqrt{3} + 2i)^5(-\sqrt{3} - i)^7}$

(j) $\dfrac{(3 + 2i)^6(2 - i)^4}{(1 + 3i)^5(-3 - 4i)^6}$

4. (a) Show that

$$(r \text{ cis } \theta)^{-n} = \frac{1}{r^n} \text{cis}(-n\theta)$$

(b) Evaluate the following expressions.

(i) $\left(2 \text{ cis } \dfrac{\pi}{4}\right)^{-3}$

(ii) $(\sqrt{2} \text{ cis } \pi)^{-7}$

(iii) $\dfrac{1}{\left(3 \text{ cis } \dfrac{\pi}{3}\right)^6}$

(c) If $z = \text{cis } \theta$ express $z^n - \dfrac{1}{z^n}$ in terms of $\sin n\theta$.

5. Use De Moivre's theorem to verify the identities:

$$\cos 2\theta = \cos^2 \theta - \sin^2 \theta \quad \text{and} \quad \sin 2\theta = 2 \sin \theta \cos \theta$$

6. (a) Develop formulas for $\cos 4\theta$ and $\sin 4\theta$ with the aid of De Moivre's theorem.

(b) Write a formula for $\cot 4\theta$ in terms of $\sin \theta$ and $\cos \theta$.

7. Develop a formula for $\tan 5\theta$ in terms of $\sin \theta$ and $\cos \theta$.

10.7 DE MOIVRE'S THEOREM: ROOTS OF COMPLEX NUMBERS

Let us now consider how roots are handled in the complex number system. The general definition of the square root of a number is that number when multiplied by itself yields the given number. Similarly the nth root of a number is that number whose nth power is the given number. The polar form reveals the roots of complex numbers readily.

De Moivre's theorem may be extended to enable us to determine the *roots* of complex numbers algebraically. That is,

$$(r \text{ cis } \theta)^{\frac{1}{q}} = r^{\frac{1}{q}} \text{cis}\left(\frac{\theta + 2k\pi}{q}\right), \text{ for any } k \in I$$

This result follows from the following argument.
Suppose

$$(\text{cis } \theta)^{\frac{1}{q}} = \text{cis } \beta$$

Raising both sides to a power of q:

$$\text{cis } \theta = (\text{cis } \beta)^q$$
$$= (\text{cis } q\beta) \qquad \text{(De Moivre's theorem)}$$

The real and imaginary parts must be equal, so

$$\cos \theta = \cos q\beta \quad \text{and} \quad \sin \theta = \sin q\beta$$

The angles θ and $q\beta$ must differ by a multiple of 2π, so

$$q\beta = \theta + 2k\pi$$
$$\beta = \frac{\theta + 2k\pi}{q}$$

Therefore we may conclude that $(\text{cis } \theta)^{\frac{1}{q}} = \text{cis}\left(\dfrac{\theta + 2k\pi}{q}\right)$.

So in general,

$$(r \text{ cis } \theta)^{\frac{1}{q}} = r^{\frac{1}{q}} \text{cis}\left(\frac{\theta + 2k\pi}{q}\right).$$

Example 1   Find (a)   the square roots of i,
   (b)   the cube roots of -8,
   (c)   the fourth roots of $-8 + 8\sqrt{3}i$.
Express the answers in rectangular form and illustrate the roots on the complex plane.

Solution   (a)   We need to determine $i^{\frac{1}{2}}$. We write the complex number in the general polar form in order to use De Moivre's theorem.

$$i = 1 \text{ cis}\left(\frac{\pi}{2} + 2k\pi\right)$$

Then $i^{\frac{1}{2}} = \left[1 \text{ cis}\left(\frac{\pi}{2} + 2k\pi\right)\right]^{\frac{1}{2}}$

$$= 1^{\frac{1}{2}} \text{ cis}\left(\frac{\frac{\pi}{2} + 2k\pi}{2}\right) \qquad \text{(De Moivre's theorem)}$$

$$= 1 \text{ cis}\left(\frac{\pi}{4} + k\pi\right)$$

To determine the roots we substitute for $k = 0, 1, 2, 3, \ldots$ and we denote the different roots by subscripts on z.

$k = 0, \quad z_0 = \text{cis}\left(\dfrac{\pi}{4}\right)$

$k = 1, \quad z_1 = \text{cis}\left(\dfrac{\pi}{4} + \pi\right) = \text{cis}\left(\dfrac{5\pi}{4}\right)$

$k = 2, \quad z_2 = \text{cis}\left(\dfrac{\pi}{4} + 2\pi\right) = \text{cis}\left(\dfrac{9\pi}{4}\right) = z_0$

$k = 3, \quad z_3 = \text{cis}\left(\dfrac{\pi}{4} + 3\pi\right) = \text{cis}\left(\dfrac{13\pi}{4}\right) = z_1$

and so on. Notice that there are only two unique roots z_0 and z_1.

For continuing values of k we are duplicating these roots. The original complex number was in the form $a + bi$ so we express the roots in the same form.

$$z_0 = \text{cis}\left(\frac{\pi}{4}\right) = \cos\frac{\pi}{4} + i \sin\frac{\pi}{4} = \frac{1}{\sqrt{2}} + \frac{1}{\sqrt{2}} i$$

and $$z_1 = \text{cis}\left(\frac{5\pi}{4}\right) = -\frac{1}{\sqrt{2}} - \frac{1}{\sqrt{2}} i$$

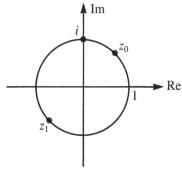

(b) $(-8)^{\frac{1}{3}} = [8 \text{ cis}(\pi + 2k\pi)]^{\frac{1}{3}}$

$$= 8^{\frac{1}{3}} \text{ cis}\left(\frac{\pi + 2k\pi}{3}\right) \qquad \text{(De Moivre's theorem)}$$

$$= 2 \text{ cis}\left(\frac{\pi + 2k\pi}{3}\right)$$

We list the roots.

$k = 0,$ $z_0 = 2 \text{ cis } \dfrac{\pi}{3}$

$k = 1,$ $z_1 = 2 \text{ cis } \pi$

$k = 2,$ $z_2 = 2 \text{ cis } \dfrac{5\pi}{3}$

$k = 3,$ $z_3 = 2 \text{ cis } \dfrac{7\pi}{3} = z_0$

and so on. There are only 3 distinct roots. In rectangular form the roots are:

$$z_0 = 2\left(\frac{1}{2} + \frac{\sqrt{3}}{2}i\right) = 1 + \sqrt{3}\, i$$

$$z_1 = 2(-1 + 0\, i) = -2$$

$$z_2 = 2\left(\frac{1}{2} - \frac{\sqrt{3}}{2}i\right) = 1 - \sqrt{3}\, i$$

(c) We express $-8 + 8\sqrt{3}\, i$ in polar form. We have $a = -8$ and $b = 8\sqrt{3}$ so $r = 16$ and $\theta = \dfrac{2\pi}{3}$.

So, $(-8 + 8\sqrt{3}\, i)^{\frac{1}{4}} = \left[16 \operatorname{cis}\left(\dfrac{2\pi}{3} + 2k\pi \right) \right]^{\frac{1}{4}}$

$$= 16^{\frac{1}{4}} \operatorname{cis}\left(\dfrac{\dfrac{2\pi}{3} + 2k\pi}{4} \right) \quad \text{(De Moivre's theorem)}$$

$$= 2 \operatorname{cis}\left(\dfrac{\pi}{6} + \dfrac{k\pi}{2} \right)$$

We list the roots.

$k = 0, \quad z_0 = 2 \operatorname{cis} \dfrac{\pi}{6}$

$k = 1, \quad z_1 = 2 \operatorname{cis}\left(\dfrac{\pi}{6} + \dfrac{\pi}{2} \right) = 2 \operatorname{cis} \dfrac{4\pi}{6}$

$k = 2, \quad z_2 = 2 \operatorname{cis}\left(\dfrac{\pi}{6} + \pi \right) = 2 \operatorname{cis} \dfrac{7\pi}{6}$

$k = 3, \quad z_3 = 2 \operatorname{cis}\left(\dfrac{\pi}{6} + \dfrac{3\pi}{2} \right) = 2 \operatorname{cis} \dfrac{10\pi}{6}$

$k = 4, \quad z_4 = 2 \operatorname{cis}\left(\dfrac{\pi}{6} + 2\pi \right) = z_0$

and so on. There are only 4 distinct roots.
In rectangular form the roots are:

$$z_0 = \sqrt{3} + i$$
$$z_1 = -1 + \sqrt{3}\, i$$
$$z_2 = -\sqrt{3} - i$$
$$z_3 = 1 - \sqrt{3}\, i$$

By recognizing the *periodic* nature of the term $\dfrac{2k\pi}{q}$ in the equation for the qth roots of a complex number, we can conclude that there are q *distinct* complex roots of $z^{\frac{1}{q}}$. Each one of the roots will be rotated by an angle of $\dfrac{2\pi}{q}$ from each other. This suggests that we can easily determine the q distinct roots if we can determine one root by inspection. The others may be found by rotating $q - 1$ times by $\dfrac{2\pi}{q}$.

Example 2   Determine the five fifth roots of the complex number 32. Leave the roots in polar form.

Solution   We need to determine $(32)^{\frac{1}{5}}$. By inspection, one of the fifth roots is 2 or $2 \operatorname{cis}(0)$. The remaining four roots are at an angle of $\dfrac{2\pi}{5}$ from each other. So they are:

$$2 \text{ cis}\left[0 + 1\left(\frac{2\pi}{5}\right)\right] = 2 \text{ cis } \frac{2\pi}{5}$$

$$2 \text{ cis}\left[0 + 2\left(\frac{2\pi}{5}\right)\right] = 2 \text{ cis } \frac{4\pi}{5}$$

$$2 \text{ cis}\left[0 + 3\left(\frac{2\pi}{5}\right)\right] = 2 \text{ cis } \frac{6\pi}{5}$$

$$2 \text{ cis}\left[0 + 4\left(\frac{2\pi}{5}\right)\right] = 2 \text{ cis } \frac{8\pi}{5} \cdot$$

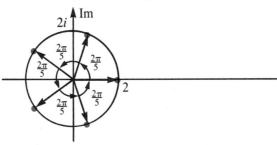

Example 3   Solve for the complex variable z in the equation $z^3 - 1 = 0$.

Solution
$$z^3 - 1 = 0$$
$$z^3 = 1$$
$$z = 1^{\frac{1}{3}}$$

We know one of the roots is 1 or 1 cis 0. The others are readily obtained by rotating through $\frac{2\pi}{3}$. The three roots are cis 0, cis $\frac{2\pi}{3}$ and cis $\frac{4\pi}{3}$. In rectangular form these roots are 1, $-\frac{1}{2} + \frac{\sqrt{3}}{2}i$, and $-\frac{1}{2} - \frac{\sqrt{3}}{2}i$.

Example 4   Solve for the complex variable z. Write the answers in the form $a + bi$.

$$z^2 + (1 + i)z - 2i = 0$$

Solution   We solve by completing the square.

$$z^2 + (1 + i)z - 2i = 0$$
$$z^2 + (1 + i)z = 2i$$
$$z^2 + (1 + i)z + \left(\frac{1 + i}{2}\right)^2 = 2i + \left(\frac{1 + i}{2}\right)^2$$
$$\left(z + \frac{1 + i}{2}\right)^2 = 2i + \frac{1 + 2i + i^2}{4}$$
$$\left(z + \frac{1 + i}{2}\right)^2 = 2i + \frac{2i}{4}$$
$$\left(z + \frac{1 + i}{2}\right)^2 = \frac{5}{2}i$$

So,
$$z + \frac{1+i}{2} = \left(\frac{5}{2}i\right)^{\frac{1}{2}}$$

$$z = -\frac{1+i}{2} + \left(\frac{5}{2}i\right)^{\frac{1}{2}}$$

We now determine the square roots of $\frac{5}{2}i$. We write $\frac{5}{2}i$ in polar form.

$$\frac{5}{2}i = \frac{5}{2}\operatorname{cis}\left(\frac{\pi}{2} + 2k\pi\right)$$

So, $\left[\frac{5}{2}\operatorname{cis}\left(\frac{\pi}{2} + 2k\pi\right)\right]^{\frac{1}{2}} = \sqrt{\frac{5}{2}}\operatorname{cis}\left(\dfrac{\dfrac{\pi}{2} + 2k\pi}{2}\right)$ (De Moivre's theorem)

$$= \sqrt{\frac{5}{2}}\operatorname{cis}\left(\frac{\pi}{4} + k\pi\right)$$

We substitute for $k = 0$ and $k = 1$ to obtain the two square roots of $\frac{5}{2}i$.

$k = 0$,   we have $\sqrt{\frac{5}{2}}\operatorname{cis}\dfrac{\pi}{4} = \sqrt{\frac{5}{2}}\left(\cos\dfrac{\pi}{4} + i\sin\dfrac{\pi}{4}\right)$

$$= \sqrt{\frac{5}{2}}\left(\frac{1}{\sqrt{2}} + \frac{1}{\sqrt{2}}i\right)$$

$$= \frac{\sqrt{5}}{2} + \frac{\sqrt{5}}{2}i$$

$k = 1$,   we have $\sqrt{\frac{5}{2}}\operatorname{cis}\dfrac{5\pi}{4} = \sqrt{\frac{5}{2}}\left(\cos\dfrac{5\pi}{4} + i\sin\dfrac{5\pi}{4}\right)$

$$= \sqrt{\frac{5}{2}}\left(\frac{-1}{\sqrt{2}} + \frac{-1}{\sqrt{2}}i\right)$$

$$= -\frac{\sqrt{5}}{2} - \frac{\sqrt{5}}{2}i$$

We can now express the roots of the given equation in the form $a + bi$. The solution of the equation is

$$z = -\frac{1+i}{2} + \left(\frac{5}{2}i\right)^{\frac{1}{2}}$$

So the roots are

$$z = -\frac{1+i}{2} + \frac{\sqrt{5}}{2} + \frac{\sqrt{5}}{2}i \quad \text{or} \quad z = -\frac{1+i}{2} - \frac{\sqrt{5}}{2} - \frac{\sqrt{5}}{2}i$$

$$= \frac{-1+\sqrt{5}}{2} + \frac{-1+\sqrt{5}}{2}i \qquad\qquad = \frac{-1-\sqrt{5}}{2} + \frac{-1-\sqrt{5}}{2}i$$

$$\doteq 0.6180 + 0.6180\,i \qquad\qquad\qquad \doteq -1.6180 - 1.6180\,i$$

EXERCISE 10.7

B **1.** Use De Moivre's theorem to determine the following.
   (a) the square roots of -9 (b) the cube roots of i
   (c) the square roots of -4 (d) the fifth roots of 1
   (e) the fourth roots of $16i$ (f) the square roots of $1 - i$
   (g) the square roots of $\sqrt{3} + i$ (h) the sixth roots of $-i$

2. In the following, determine one root by inspection and then find all other roots by using the geometric properties of roots of complex numbers. Illustrate your solutions in the complex plane.
   (a) cube roots of eight   (b) fourth roots of one
   (c) square roots of -1 (d) fifth roots of 243
   (e) cube roots of -27 (f) sixth roots of 729
   (g) square roots of -9 (h) fifth roots of $-\frac{1}{32}$
   (i) tenth roots of 1024   (j) fourth roots of $\frac{1}{16}$

3. Solve for the complex variable z in the following equations. Write your answers in the form $a + bi$.
   (a) $z^3 = 1$ (b) $z^2 + 9 = 0$
   (c) $z^4 + 16 = 0$ (d) $3z^3 - 81 = 0$
   (e) $z^2 + (\sqrt{3} + i) = 0$ (f) $z^5 - 32 = 0$
   (g) $(1 - i)z^3 + (-1 + i) = 0$
   (h) $\left(2 \text{ cis } \dfrac{\pi}{4}\right)z^3 - \left(4 \text{ cis } \dfrac{\pi}{2}\right) = 0$
   (i) $5z^5 - (5 + 5i) = -10 - 10i$
   (j) $3z^4 + i = 1 - 2i$
   (k) $(7 + i)z^3 - (3 + 2i) = 0$
   (l) $\sqrt{3}z^3 - \sqrt{6} = 0$

4. Determine the complex roots of the following quadratic equations. Write your answers in the form $a + bi$.
   (a) $3z^2 + 6z + 3i = 0$ (b) $\sqrt{3}z^2 + 2z - i = 0$
   (c) $iz^2 + 2z - 3 = 0$ (d) $(2 + i)z^2 - (1 + i)z + 2i = 0$

5. Explain what is meant by the statement, "the nth roots of a complex number form a regular n-gon on the complex plane."

PROBLEMS PLUS

If $z = \text{cis } \theta$, show that $z^n + \dfrac{1}{z^n} = 2 \cos n\theta$, and

$z^n - \dfrac{1}{z^n} = 2i \sin n\theta$.

Now, by expanding $\left(z + \dfrac{1}{z}\right)^3 \left(z - \dfrac{1}{z}\right)^3$ or otherwise, show that

$32 \sin^3 \theta \cos^3 \theta = 3 \sin 2\theta - \sin 6\theta$

10.8 EULER'S FORMULA

Leonard Euler
1707–1783

Euler's formula is a result that relates the function cis to an exponential function. When powers are multiplied, the exponents are added; when complex numbers in polar form are multiplied, the arguments are added. It is this similarity that led Euler to his formula. The statement of **Euler's formula** is:

$$\text{cis } \theta = e^{i\theta} \quad \text{or} \quad \cos \theta + i \sin \theta = e^{i\theta}, \text{ where } e \doteq 2.71828$$

The derivation of Euler's formula is based on the infinite series expansions of e^x, $\sin \theta$ and $\cos \theta$. By using advanced Calculus techniques it can be shown that:

$$\cos \theta = 1 - \frac{\theta^2}{2!} + \frac{\theta^4}{4!} - \frac{\theta^6}{6!} + \dots$$

$$\sin \theta = \theta - \frac{\theta^3}{3!} + \frac{\theta^5}{5!} - \frac{\theta^7}{7!} + \dots$$

and $$e^x = 1 + x + \frac{x^2}{2!} + \frac{x^3}{3!} + \frac{x^4}{4!} + \dots$$

So   cis $\theta = \cos \theta + i \sin \theta$

$$= \left(1 - \frac{\theta^2}{2!} + \frac{\theta^4}{4!} - \frac{\theta^6}{6!} + \dots\right) + i\left(\theta - \frac{\theta^3}{3!} + \frac{\theta^5}{5!} - \frac{\theta^7}{7!} + \dots\right)$$

$$= 1 + i\theta - \frac{\theta^2}{2!} - \frac{i\theta^3}{3!} + \frac{\theta^4}{4!} + \frac{i\theta^5}{5!} - \dots$$

$$= 1 + (i\theta) + \frac{(i\theta)^2}{2!} + \frac{(i\theta)^3}{3!} + \frac{(i\theta)^4}{4!} + \dots$$

$$= e^{i\theta}$$

Complex numbers expressed in polar form, can now be expressed in an **exponential form**. That is, if $z = r$ cis θ then $z = re^{i\theta}$.

Example 1   Write the following complex numbers in exponential form.

(a) 2 cis $\dfrac{\pi}{2}$

(b) $3 \cos \pi + 3i \sin \pi$

(c) $1 - i$

Solution   (a)   We can write cis $\dfrac{\pi}{2} = e^{\frac{i\pi}{2}}$ by Euler's formula. So,

$$2 \text{ cis } \frac{\pi}{2} = 2e^{\frac{i\pi}{2}}.$$

(b)   We write $3 \cos \pi + 3i \sin \pi = 3\text{cis } \pi$ which equals $3e^{i\pi}$ by Euler's formula.

(c) We express $1 - i$ in polar form. We have $a = 1$ and $b = -1$
so $r = \sqrt{2}$ and $\tan \theta = -1$, so $\theta = -\dfrac{\pi}{4}$.

Then $\quad 1 - i = \sqrt{2} \operatorname{cis} \left(-\dfrac{\pi}{4}\right) \qquad$ (polar form)

$\qquad\qquad = \sqrt{2}\, e^{-\frac{i\pi}{4}} \qquad$ (exponential form)

Example 2 Evaluate the following and leave your answers in the form $a + bi$:

(a) $e^{i\pi}$

(b) $3e^{2i}$

Solution (a) $e^{i\pi} = \operatorname{cis} \pi \qquad\qquad$ (Euler's formula)

$\qquad\qquad = \cos \pi + i \sin \pi$

$\qquad\qquad = -1$

(b) $3e^{2i} = 3 \operatorname{cis} 2 \qquad\qquad$ (Euler's formula)

$\qquad\qquad = 3(\cos 2 + i\sin 2)$

$\qquad\qquad \doteq -1.248 + 2.728i$

Example 3 Show that $e^{2i\pi} - 1 = 0$.

Solution We can express $e^{2i\pi}$ in an alternate form.

$e^{2i\pi} = \operatorname{cis} 2\pi \qquad\qquad$ (Euler's formula)

$\qquad = \cos 2\pi + i \sin 2\pi$

$\qquad = 1 + i(0) \qquad\qquad$ (rectangular form)

$\qquad = 1$

So the given equation is equivalent to $1 - 1 = 0$.

EXERCISE 10.8

A **1.** Express the following complex numbers in exponential form.

(a) $\operatorname{cis} \dfrac{\pi}{4}$

(b) $\operatorname{cis} 3$

(c) $2 \operatorname{cis} \dfrac{\pi}{2}$

(d) $3 \operatorname{cis} \pi$

(e) $\cos \pi + i \sin \pi$

(f) $4 \cos \dfrac{\pi}{4} + 4i \sin \dfrac{\pi}{4}$

(g) $2 \operatorname{cis} \dfrac{\pi}{6}$

(h) $5 \operatorname{cis} \dfrac{\pi}{3}$

(i) $2 \operatorname{cis} \dfrac{3\pi}{4}$

(j) $\operatorname{cis} 1$

(k) $\operatorname{cis} 2.35$

(l) $3 \operatorname{cis} 1.1$

(m) $4 \operatorname{cis}\left(-\dfrac{\pi}{3}\right)$

(n) $\sqrt{2} \operatorname{cis} \dfrac{\pi}{6}$

2. Express the following complex numbers in polar form.
    (a) $e^{2\pi i}$
    (b) $e^{\frac{i\pi}{3}}$
    (c) $3e^{i\pi}$
    (d) $2e^{2i}$
    (e) $e^{\frac{i\pi}{4}}$
    (f) e^{3i}
    (g) $5e^{i}$
    (h) $e^{\frac{3i\pi}{4}}$
    (i) $2e^{2i\pi}$
    (j) $e^{3i\pi}$

3. Explain why the usual interpretation of a power as the number of times a quantity is multiplied by itself does not apply to exponents that are complex numbers.

B 4. Express the following complex numbers in the form $a + bi$.
    (a) $e^{\frac{i\pi}{4}}$
    (b) $2e^{i\pi}$
    (c) $e^{\frac{i3\pi}{4}}$
    (d) $3e^{\frac{i5\pi}{3}}$
    (e) $e^{1.1i}$
    (f) $2.1e^{2.3i}$

5. Express the following complex numbers in the form $e^{i\theta}$.
    (a) $-1 - i$
    (b) $1 + i$
    (c) $\sqrt{2} - i\sqrt{2}$
    (d) $\sqrt{3} + i$
    (e) $1 - i\sqrt{3}$
    (f) $3\sqrt{3} + 3i$
    (g) $2 - i$
    (h) $5 + 7i$

6. Show that the following equations are true.
    (a) $e^{i\pi} + 1 = 0$
    (b) $e^{3i\pi} + e^{2i\pi} = 0$
    (c) $e^{\frac{i\pi}{2}} - i = 0$
    (d) $ie^{\frac{3i\pi}{2}} - 1 = 0$

7. (a) Show that $e^{-i\theta} = \cos\theta - i\sin\theta$.
    (b) Using the relationships $e^{-i\theta} = \cos\theta - i\sin\theta$ and $e^{i\theta} = \cos\theta + i\sin\theta$ develop formulas for $\cos\theta$ and $\sin\theta$ in terms of the exponential function.

10.9 REVIEW EXERCISE

B 1. Perform the indicated operations and leave your answers in the form in which the equation is presented.
    (a) $(3 \text{ cis } \pi)\left(4 \text{ cis } \dfrac{\pi}{2}\right)$
    (b) $(3 + 2i) + (-1 - i)$

    (c) $\dfrac{i}{2 + i}$
    (d) $\left(2 \text{ cis } \dfrac{\pi}{3}\right)^{3}$

    (e) $(\sqrt{2} + i)(2 - \sqrt{2}i)$
    (f) $\left(8 \text{ cis } \dfrac{\pi}{3}\right)^{\frac{1}{3}}$

    (g) $(3 - 4i)(2 + i)$
    (h) $\dfrac{\sqrt{3} + i}{\sqrt{3} - i}$

    (i) $\dfrac{16 \text{ cis } \pi}{2 \text{ cis } \dfrac{\pi}{2}}$
    (j) $i^{17} + i^{23}$

2. Solve for the complex variable z in the following equations.

   (a) $(2 - i)z = 3 + i$ (b) $(5 - i) - 3i = 2i + z$

   (c) $iz - 3z = (1 + i)z$ (d) $(1 + i)z = (4 - 2i)^2$

   (e) $z^2 - 2z + 2 = 0$ (f) $z^2 = 3z - 4$

   (g) $(z - 3 + i)^2 = -1$ (h) $z^3 - 64 = 0$

   (i) $z^5 + 1 = 0$ (j) $z^4 + i = 0$

   (k) $z^2 + 2z + i = 0$ (l) $3z^2 - 12z + 9i = 0$

3. Evaluate the following expressions.

   (a) $\dfrac{\left(4 \operatorname{cis} \dfrac{\pi}{3}\right)^2 (27 \operatorname{cis} \pi)^{\frac{1}{3}}}{\left(3 \operatorname{cis} \dfrac{\pi}{2}\right)^2 (2 \operatorname{cis} \pi)^3}$

   (b) $\dfrac{(-1 + \sqrt{3}\, i)^3}{(1 + i)^3 (\sqrt{3} - i)^4}$

4. Prove the identity:

   $$\overline{z_1 z_2 z_3} = \overline{z_1}\ \overline{z_2}\ \overline{z_3}$$

5. (a) Use De Moivre's theorem to develop the formula for $\sin 3\theta$ in terms of $\sin \theta$ and use this result to determine a formula for $\csc 3\theta$ in terms of $\csc \theta$.

   (b) Determine a formula for $\sec 3\theta$ in terms of $\sec \theta$.

6. Express the following complex numbers in exponential form.

   (a) $5 \operatorname{cis} \pi$ (b) $2 \operatorname{cis} \dfrac{\pi}{2}$ (c) $1 - i$

   (d) $\sqrt{3} - i$ (e) $3 - 2i$ (f) 1

7. Find the cube roots of the complex number $-1 - i$ and verify that the moduli of the roots are identical.

10.10 CHAPTER 10 TEST

1. On the following graphs, sketch the relative position of the related complex number.

   (a) $\bar{z}$:

   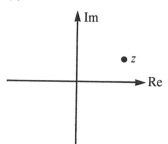

   (b) $3z$:

   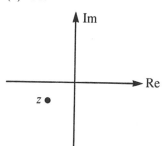

   (c) iz:

   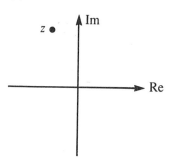

   (d) $\dfrac{1}{z}$:

   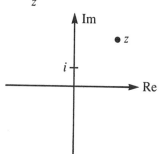

   (e) $z + w$:

   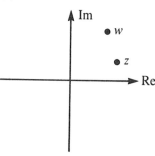

   (f) zw:

   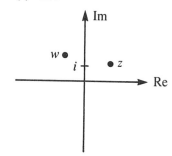

2. Perform the following complex number arithmetic. Leave answers in either rectangular or polar form.

   (a) $(2 - 5i)(3 + i)$

   (b) $\dfrac{2 - i}{3i}$

   (c) $\left(2\text{cis}\dfrac{\pi}{3}\right)\left(5\text{cis}\dfrac{2\pi}{3}\right)^2$

   (d) $3 + 2i - \dfrac{3}{5i}$

3. Solve for the complex variable z. Write your answers in rectangular form.

   (a) $(3 + 2i)z = (5 - i) + 2z$ (b) $z^2 + 6z = -13$

4. Use De Moivre's Theorem to:
   (a) evaluate $(-1 - i)^{11}$,
   (b) develop a formula for $\cos 4\theta$ in terms of $\cos \theta$.

5. (a) "We can easily determine q distinct roots of $z^{\frac{1}{q}}$ if we can find one root by inspection, then the others may be found by _____." Complete the statement.
   (b) Find the fourth roots of unity. Express your answers in the form $a + bi$.
   (c) Solve for z and leave your answers in polar form.
   $$z^5 + 243 = 0$$

6. Evaluate the following by converting each complex number into its polar form. Write your final answer in rectangular form.
   $$\frac{(-1 + i)^2(1 + i\sqrt{3})^2}{(-\sqrt{3} + i)^2(-1 - i\sqrt{3})^2}$$

7. Solve for z and leave your answers in rectangular form.
   $$z^2 + 2z - \sqrt{3}i = 0$$

8. Show that the following equation is true.
   $$3e^{4i\pi} - 3 = 0$$

9. If $z_1 = r_1 \operatorname{cis}\theta_1$ and $z_2 = r_2 \operatorname{cis}\theta_2$, prove that
   $$z_1z_2 = r_1r_2 \operatorname{cis}(\theta_1 + \theta_2)$$

PROBLEMS PLUS

Electronics

1. Complex numbers are widely used in electronics to describe voltages. A certain current called a *phasor* is made of two components: an in-phase component and an out-of-phase component called the *quadrature* component. The quadrature component is so named because it is always 90° out of phase. Thus a "complex" voltage can be specified as

$$V = V_{\text{in phase}} \pm i \, V_{\text{quadrature}}$$

Determine the magnitude of the current $85 - 5i$ kV.

2. In working with parallel circuits it is sometimes convenient to use the *admittance* concept. By definition, the admittance of a given circuit is the reciprocal of the *impedance* (the impedance is the total effect of *resistance* and *reactance* in ac circuits). Thus

$$Y = \frac{1}{Z}, \quad \text{where } Y \text{ is the admittance and } Z \text{ is the}$$

impedance.

The impedance is of the form $Z = R + iX$ where R is the resistance and X is the reactance of the circuit. Express the admittance, Y, in the form

$$Y = G + iB.$$

(*G* is called the *conductance* of the element and *B* is called the *susceptance* of the element.)

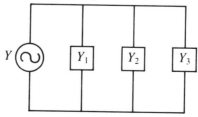

TWENTIETH CENTURY MATHEMATICIANS

David Hilbert was born in 1862 in Königsberg, Germany, and studied at the local university. In 1895 he was appointed professor at Göttingen, a position he held until his death in 1943. He played a leading role in establishing a mathematical institute at Göttingen that was, in its time, the most important in the world.

He worked in a great variety of areas of mathematics, including the foundations of geometry, algebraic number theory, the calculus of variations, theoretical physics, and the foundations of mathematics. But his impact on modern mathematics was far greater than the totality of his own research. He established an agenda for what is important in mathematics.

At the International Congress of Mathematicians held in Paris in 1900, Hilbert proposed 23 problems as targets for the mathematics of the twentieth century. Problem 6 was a challenge to axiomatize those physical sciences in which mathematics plays an important role; that is, to construct a small number of axioms and obtain the truths of those sciences deductively from these rules. Problem 7 was to investigate numbers such as $2^{\sqrt{2}}$ or e^{π}. A *transcendental* number is not the root of a polynomial with integer coefficients. Hilbert asked for a proof that $2^{\sqrt{2}}$ is a transcendental number and the Russian mathematician Gelfond was able to prove this in 1934. But Hilbert was asking for a general study, and this continues today.

Hilbert told his audience at the Paris meeting, "The problems mentioned are merely samples of problems; yet they are sufficient to show how rich, how manifold and how extensive mathematics is today. May the new century bring it gifted prophets and many zealous and enthusiastic disciples!"

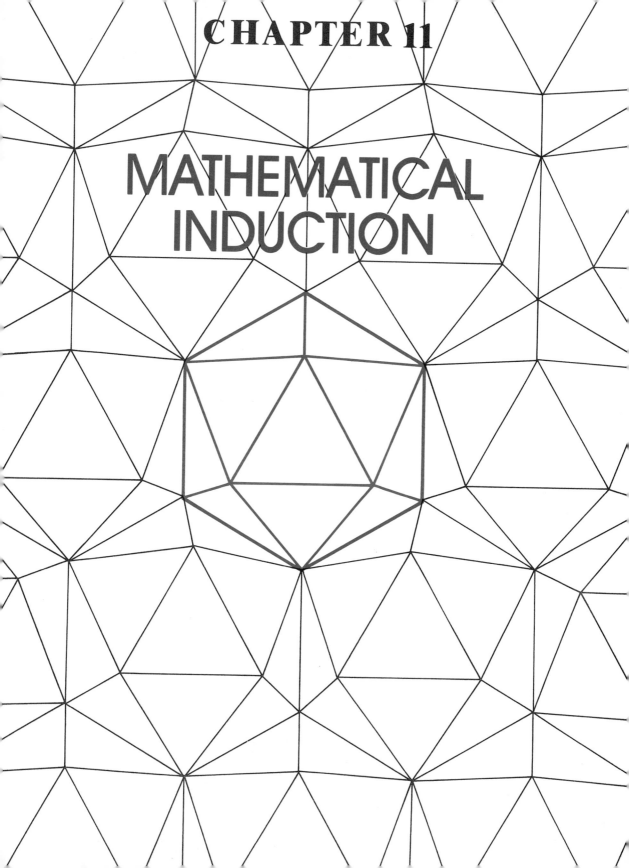

CHAPTER 11

MATHEMATICAL INDUCTION

REVIEW AND PREVIEW TO CHAPTER 11

Sigma Notation

Series can be described using the Greek letter Σ (sigma). For example,

$$3 + 5 + 7 + 9 + 11$$

can be written

$$\sum_{i=1}^{5}(2i + 1)$$

which is read "the sum of $2i + 1$ from $i = 1$ to $i = 5$."

Example 1 Write $\sum_{i=0}^{4}(2i^2 - i)$ in expanded form.

Solution
$$\begin{aligned}
\sum_{i=0}^{4}(2i^2 - i) &= [2(0)^2 - 0] + [2(1)^2 - 1] + [2(2)^2 - 2] \\
&\quad + [2(3)^2 - 3] + [2(4)^2 - 4] \\
&= 0 + 1 + 6 + 15 + 28
\end{aligned}$$

Example 2 Write $1 + 4 + 9 + \ldots + 64$ by using sigma notation.

Solution $1 + 4 + 9 + \ldots + 64 = (1)^2 + (2)^2 + (3)^2 + \ldots + (8)^2$

$$= \sum_{i=1}^{8} i^2$$

EXERCISE 1

1. Write each of the following in expanded form.

   (a) $\sum_{i=1}^{4}(2i - 3)$ (b) $\sum_{i=2}^{6}\dfrac{1}{i + 4}$

   (c) $\sum_{k=0}^{5}k(k + 1)$ (d) $\sum_{r=0}^{6}2^{r-1}$

   (e) $\sum_{r=0}^{4}\binom{4}{r}$ (f) $\sum_{r=0}^{7}(-1)^r\binom{7}{r}^2$

2. Write each of the following by using sigma notation.
   (a) $1 + 2 + 4 + 8 + 16 + 32 + 64 + 128$
   (b) $3x + 4x + 5x + 6x + 7x$
   (c) $a + a^2 + a^3 + a^4 + a^5 + a^6 + a^7$
   (d) $x - x^2 + x^3 - x^4 + x^5 - x^6$

(e) $\binom{7}{0} + \binom{7}{1} + \binom{7}{2} + \binom{7}{3} + \binom{7}{4} + \binom{7}{5} + \binom{7}{6} + \binom{7}{7}$

(f) $\binom{10}{0}^2 + \binom{10}{1}^2 + \binom{10}{2}^2 + \ldots + \binom{10}{10}^2$

(g) $\binom{9}{0} - \binom{9}{1} + \binom{9}{2} - \binom{9}{3} + \ldots - \binom{9}{9}$

(h) $\binom{n}{0} + \binom{n}{1} + \binom{n}{2} + \ldots + \binom{n}{n}$

(i) $\binom{n}{0}^2 - \binom{n}{1}^2 + \binom{n}{2}^2 - \binom{n}{3}^2 + \ldots + (-1)^n \binom{n}{n}^2$

Sequences

A **sequence** is an ordered list of numbers. Alternatively, a sequence is a function whose domain is a subset of the natural numbers. There are a number of ways of describing a sequence:

List   (i)   1, 3, 5, 7, 9, 11, ...

General Term   (ii) $t_n = 2n - 1$ $n \in N$

Function Value   (iii) $f(n) = 2n - 1$ $n \in N$

Arithmetic Sequences

Sequences such as 1, 3, 5, 7, ... where the difference between consecutive terms is constant are called **arithmetic sequences**. The general arithmetic sequence is

$$a, a + d, a + 2d, a + 3d, \ldots$$

where a is the **first term**, and d is the **common difference**. The nth term is given by

$$t_n = a + (n - 1)d, n \in N$$

EXERCISE 2

1. Find the first five terms for the following arithmetic sequences; find the relevant a, d.

    (a) $t_n = 3n + 2$ (b) $f(n) = 7 - 2n$

    (c) 1, 4, 7, ...   (d) 3, -1, -5, ...

2. Two of the terms of an arithmetic sequence are given. Find the general term.

    (a) $t_1 = 5, t_2 = 125$ (b) $t_3 = 2, t_5 = 3$

    (c) $t_{10} = 0, t_{19} = 9$ (d) $t_4 = -9, t_7 = -21$

3. The sum of the first two terms of an arithmetic sequence is 12, and the sum of the first three terms is also 12. Find the first term and the common difference.

Geometric Sequences

Sequences such as 3, 6, 12, 24, 48, ... where the ratio of consecutive terms is constant are called **geometric sequences**. The general geometric sequence is

$$a, \ ar, \ ar^2, \ ar^3, \ ...$$

where a is the **first term** and r is the **common ratio**. The general term is

$$t_n = ar^{n-1}, \ n \in N$$

Example 1 In a geometric sequence $t_3 = 75$ and $t_6 = 9375$. Find t_n.

Solution Since $t_6 = ar^5$, and $t_3 = ar^2$, by division we have $\dfrac{t_6}{t_3} = \dfrac{ar^5}{ar^2}$.

So $\dfrac{t_6}{t_3} = r^3$

But $\dfrac{t_6}{t_3} = \dfrac{9375}{75} = 125$

So we see that $r^3 = 125$, and thus $r = 5$.
From this we have $75 = t_3 = a(5)^2$, so $a = 3$. Hence the general term t_n is given by $t_n = 3(5)^{n-1}$.

EXERCISE 3

1. Find the first five terms for the following geometric sequences; find the values of a, r.
   (a) 1, 2, 4, 8, ...   (b) $f(n) = 3 \times 2^{n-1}$
   (c) $t_n = 2(3)^n$ (d) 1, $\frac{1}{3}$, $\frac{1}{9}$, $\frac{1}{27}$, ...

2. Two of the terms of a geometric sequence are given. Find the general term.
   (a) $t_1 = 5$, $t_{10} = 2560$ (b) $t_2 = 15$, $t_5 = 405$
   (c) $t_4 = -7$, $t_7 = \frac{1}{49}$ (d) $t_5 = 1875$, $t_7 = 46\ 875$

3. The product of the first two terms of a geometric sequence is 27, and the product of the first three terms is also 27. Find a, r.

4. The sequence t_1, t_2, t_3, ... is *both* a geometric sequence *and* an arithmetic sequence. Moreover $t_1 = 10$. Find t_n.

Recursion Formulas

We may describe the pattern of an arithmetic sequence $t_1, t_2, \ldots$ symbolically as follows.

The first term is a, so $t_1 = a$; the common difference is d, so $t_{n+1} - t_n = d$. We write this as a **recursion formula**.

General Arithmetic Sequence

$$t_1 = a$$
$$t_{n+1} = t_n + d \qquad n \in N$$

Example 1 Given that $t_1 = 3$, and $t_{n+1} = t_n - 1$, find t_2, t_3, t_4.

Solution
$$t_2 = t_1 - 1 = 3 - 1 = 2$$
$$t_3 = t_2 - 1 = 2 - 1 = 1$$
$$t_4 = t_3 - 1 = 1 - 1 = 0$$

A recursion formula for the geometric sequence with first term a and common ratio r is

General Geometric Sequence

$$t_1 = a$$
$$t_{n+1} = rt_n \qquad n \in N$$

Example 2 Given that $t_1 = 2$ and $t_{n+1} = 3t_n$, find t_2, t_3, t_4.

Solution
$$t_2 = 3t_1 = 3 \times 2 = 6$$
$$t_3 = 3t_2 = 3 \times 6 = 18$$
$$t_4 = 3t_3 = 3 \times 18 = 54$$

In the preceding examples t_{n+1} was evaluated in terms of constants and t_n. This need not be the case for recursion formulas in general.

An Arithmetico-Geometric Sequence

Example 3 Suppose $t_1 = 1$, $t_2 = 10$, and $t_{n+2} = 10t_{n+1} - 25t_n$, $n \in N$. Find t_3, t_4, t_5.

Solution
$$t_3 = 10t_2 - 25t_1 = 10 \times 10 - 25 \times 1 = 75$$
$$t_4 = 10t_3 - 25t_2 = 10 \times 75 - 25 \times 10 = 500$$
$$t_5 = 10t_4 - 25t_3 = 10 \times 500 - 25 \times 75 = 3125$$

EXERCISE 4

1. Find t_5 given that

   (a) $t_1 = 4$, $t_{n+1} = 6 + t_n$ (b) $t_1 = 7$, $t_{n+1} = \frac{1}{3} t_n$

2. Find t_5 given that $t_1 = 1$, $t_2 = 1$, $t_{n+2} = 6t_{n+1} - 9t_n$.

11.1 THE PRINCIPLE OF MATHEMATICAL INDUCTION

Propositions can be divided into general and particular. An example of a general proposition is:

All numbers ending with a 5 are divisible by 5.

A corresponding example of a particular proposition is:

The number 75 is divisible by 5.

The transition from general propositions to corresponding particular ones is called deduction. In the preceding we could write

(1)   all numbers ending with a 5 are divisible by 5,
(2)   75 ends in a 5,
(3)   75 is divisible by 5.

The transition from particular propositions to general ones is called *induction*, and is a cornerstone of the scientific method. However induction can lead to incorrect as well as correct conclusions. Here is an example of an *incorrect* induction:

(1)   75 is divisible by 5,
(2)   75 is a 2-digit number,
(3)   all 2-digit numbers are divisible by 5.

We see that (1) and (2) are true but (3) is false since we can find a 2-digit number, for example 11, which is not divisible by 5.

The principle of mathematical induction enables us to guarantee that an induction process yields a correct conclusion: it applies to general propositions that make assertions about natural numbers.

The Principle of Mathematical Induction

A proposition is true for every natural number n if:
(1)   it is true for $n = 1$, and
(2)   it follows from the truth of the proposition for $n = k$ that the proposition is true for $n = k + 1$, for an arbitrary natural number k.

The supposition that the proposition is true for $n = k$ is called the **induction hypothesis**.

The photograph illustrates induction in the following way: since the dominos are almost touching, to knock them all down it suffices to tip the first one over so that it knocks over the second, which in turn knocks over the third, and so on ...

Example 1   Prove that the nth term of the arithmetic sequence

$$a, a + d, a + 2d, \ldots$$
is given by $a + (n - 1)d$.

Solution   Let t_n denote the nth term of the given sequence. The general proposition we are to prove is

$$t_n = a + (n - 1)d$$

(1)   For $n = 1$ this proposition becomes

$$t_1 = a + (1 - 1)d = a$$

which is true since the first term is a.

(2)   We assume that the proposition is true for $n = k$, that is

$$t_k = a + (k - 1)d \;\; + \; d$$

With this induction hypothesis we have to prove that

$$t_{k+1} = a + (k + 1 - 1)d = a + kd$$

In an arithmetic sequence we know that each term is obtained from the preceding term by adding the common difference, in this case d. So

$$
\begin{aligned}
t_{k+1} &= t_k + d \\
&= a + (k - 1)d + d \\
&= a + kd - d + d \\
&= a + kd
\end{aligned}
$$

So $t_{k+1} = a + (k + 1 - 1)d$

as was to be proved.

Hence the proposition is true for every $n \in N$, by mathematical induction.

Example 1 shows the general pattern of proof by mathematical induction.

To use mathematical induction to prove a general proposition involving natural numbers

(1) we prove it true for $n = 1$, and

(2) assuming that it is true for $n = k$ (the induction hypothesis) we prove it for $n = k + 1$.

In step (2) we may use the properties of inequalities, or algebra, or any other valid method of proof.

Example 2   Prove that $2^n > n$ for every $n \in N$.

Solution   The proposition we prove states $2^n > n$.

(1) For $n = 1$, this proposition becomes

$$2^1 > 1$$

which is true.

(2) Assume the proposition is true for $n = k$; that is

$$2^k > k$$

We have to prove that it is true for $n = k + 1$; that is, we must prove that

$$2^{k+1} > k + 1$$

Now $2^{k+1} = 2 \times 2^k$

$$> 2 \times k \text{ (since } 2^k > k)$$
$$= 2k$$
$$= k + k$$
$$\geq k + 1 \text{ (since } k \in N)$$

So $2^{k+1} > k + 1$ is true.

By the principle of mathematical induction we have $2^n > n$, for $n \in N$.

Example 3   Prove that for every natural number n, $n^2 + n$ is even.

Solution   The general proposition is that $n^2 + n$ is even. In other words $n^2 + n$ is twice a natural number, for every $n \in N$.

(1) When $n = 1$ the proposition states that $1^2 + 1$ is even, which is true since $1^2 + 1 = 2$.

(2) The induction hypothesis states that $k^2 + k$ is even. We have to prove, using the induction hypothesis, that $(k + 1)^2 + (k + 1)$ is even.

Now

$$(k + 1)^2 + (k + 1) = k^2 + 2k + 1 + k + 1$$
$$= k^2 + 3k + 2$$

In order to use the assumption that $k^2 + k$ is even we regroup the expression $k^2 + 3k + 2 = k^2 + k + 2k + 2$. Since $k^2 + k$ is even, (induction hypothesis) and $2k + 2$ is even, and the sum of even numbers is even we conclude that $(k + 1)^2 + k + 1$ is even.

By mathematical induction, we have shown that $n^2 + n$ is always even, for $n \in N$.

Sequences given by a recursion formula are well adapted to mathematical induction.

Example 4   Let $t_1, t_2, \ldots$ be the sequence given by

$$t_1 = 4$$
$$t_{n+1} = 3t_n + 2 \qquad n \in N$$

Prove that

$$t_n = 5(3)^{n-1} - 1$$

Solution   (1)   The proposition is true for $n = 1$ since

$$5(3)^{1-1} - 1 = 4 = t_1$$

(2)   The induction hypothesis is that

$$t_k = 5(3)^{k-1} - 1.$$

We have to prove that

$$t_{k+1} = 5(3)^{k+1-1} - 1 = 5(3)^k - 1.$$

Now $t_{k+1} = 3t_k + 2$ \qquad (recursion formula)
$$= 3[5(3)^{k-1} - 1] + 2$$
$$= 5(3)^k - 3 + 2,$$

so $t_{k+1} = 5(3)^k - 1,$

as was to be shown.

The result follows by induction.

PROBLEMS PLUS

Let a_n be the number of binomial coefficients $\binom{n}{r}$ $(0 \leqslant r \leqslant n)$ that leave remainder 1 on division by 3, and let b_n be the number which leave remainder 2. Prove that $a_n > b_n$ for all natural numbers n.

EXERCISE 11.1

Use the principle of mathematical induction in each of the following.

B **1.** Prove that the nth term of the geometric series $a, ar, ar^2, \ldots$ is ar^{n-1}.

2. Let $x > 1$. Prove $x^n > 1$, $n \in N$.

3. Let $x > -1$. Prove $(1 + x)^n \geq 1 + nx$.

4. Prove $n^3 - n$ is divisible by 3.

5. Prove $n^3 + (n + 1)^3 + (n + 2)^3$ is divisible by 9.

6. Prove $11^{n+2} + 12^{2n+1}$ is divisible by 133.

7. If $t_1 = 4$ and $t_{n+1} = 3t_n - 8$ ($n \in N$) then prove that $t_n = 4$ for every $n \in N$.

8. If $t_1 = 4$ and $t_{n+1} = 3t_n$ then prove that $t_n = 4 \times 3^{n-1}$.

9. If $t_1 = 4$ and $t_{n+1} = 3t_n + 4$ then prove that $t_n = 2 \times 3^{n-1} + 2$.

C **10.** If $t_1 = a$ and $t_{n+1} = 3t_n + c$ ($n \in N$) then prove that
$$t_n = \left(a + \frac{c}{2}\right)3^{n-1} - \frac{c}{2}.$$

11. If $t_1 = a$ and $t_{n+1} = bt_n + c$ ($n \in N$) where $a, b, c, \in R$ are given, then prove that
$$t_n = \left(a + \frac{c}{b - 1}\right)b^{n-1} + \frac{c}{1 - b} \qquad (b \neq 1)$$

12. If $t_1 = 1$ and $t_{n+1} = t_n + 2n + 1$ then prove that $t_n = n^2$.

13. If $t_1 = 3$, $t_2 = 4$, and $t_{n+1} \leq t_n + 2$ for $n \geq 2$ then prove that $t_n \leq 2n$ for $n \geq 2$.

14. Prove that $n^7 - n$ is divisible by 42.

11.2 FORMULAS FOR SUMS

For certain sequences $t_1, t_2, t_3, \ldots$ it is possible to obtain a formula for
$$S_n = \sum_{i=1}^{n} t_i \qquad (n \in N)$$

that can be proved by mathematical induction. The sum of $n + 1$ terms can be regrouped as follows:
$$\begin{aligned} S_{n+1} &= t_1 + t_2 + \ldots + t_n + t_{n+1} \\ &= (t_1 + t_2 + \ldots + t_n) + t_{n+1} \\ &= S_n + t_{n+1} \end{aligned}$$

This gives us the **basic observation**

$$\boxed{S_{n+1} = S_n + t_{n+1}}$$

Example 1   Prove that, for each natural number n

$$\sum_{i=1}^{n} \frac{1}{i(i + 1)} = \frac{n}{n + 1}$$

Solution   Let $S_n = \sum_{i=1}^{n} \frac{1}{i(i + 1)}$

Then we have to prove the general proposition that, for every $n \in N$,

$$S_n = \frac{n}{n + 1}$$

(1)   This is true for $n = 1$ since

$$S_1 = \sum_{i=1}^{1} \frac{1}{i(i + 1)} = \frac{1}{1 \times 2} = \frac{1}{2} = \frac{1}{1 + 1}.$$

(2)   The induction hypothesis is that

$$S_k = \frac{k}{k + 1}$$

from which we have to prove that

$$S_{k+1} = \frac{k + 1}{k + 1 + 1} = \frac{k + 1}{k + 2}$$

Now $S_{k+1} = S_k + t_{k+1}$ (basic observation)

$$= S_k + \frac{1}{(k + 1)(k + 2)} \qquad \left(t_1 = \frac{1}{i(i + 1)} \right)$$

$$= \frac{k}{k + 1} + \frac{1}{(k + 1)(k + 2)} \qquad \text{(induction hypothesis)}$$

$$= \frac{k(k + 2)}{(k + 1)(k + 2)} + \frac{1}{(k + 1)(k + 2)}$$

$$= \frac{k^2 + 2k + 1}{(k + 1)(k + 2)}$$

$$= \frac{(k + 1)^2}{(k + 1)(k + 2)}$$

So $S_{k+1} = \dfrac{k + 1}{k + 2}$

which is what we had to prove for the induction step.

Thus $\sum_{i=1}^{n} \dfrac{1}{i(i + 1)} = \dfrac{n}{n + 1}$ as required.

Example 2   Prove that the sum of the first n natural numbers is $\dfrac{n(n+1)}{2}$

Solution   We write the sum of the first n natural numbers using sigma notation.

Let $S_n = \displaystyle\sum_{i=1}^{n} i$. We have to prove the general proposition that

$$S_n = \frac{n(n+1)}{2}$$

(1)   This is true for $n = 1$ since $S_1 = 1 = \dfrac{1(1+1)}{2}$.

(2)   The induction hypothesis is that

$$S_k = \frac{k(k+1)}{2}$$

We have to prove that

$$S_{k+1} = \frac{(k+1)(k+1+1)}{2} = \frac{(k+1)(k+2)}{2}$$

Now $\begin{aligned} S_{k+1} &= S_k + t_{k+1} & \text{(basic observation)} \\ &= S_k + k + 1 & (t_i = i) \\ &= \frac{k(k+1)}{2} + k + 1 & \text{(induction hypothesis)} \\ &= (k+1)\left(\frac{k}{2} + 1\right) & \text{(common factor)} \\ &= (k+1)\left(\frac{k+2}{2}\right) \end{aligned}$

So $S_{k+1} = \dfrac{(k+1)(k+2)}{2}$

Hence we have proved that the sum of the first n natural numbers is $\dfrac{n(n+1)}{2}$ for every natural number n, by the principle of mathematical induction.   ⬡

Example 3   Prove that

$$1 + r + r^2 + \ldots + r^{n-1} = \frac{1 - r^n}{1 - r}, \text{ if } r \neq 1.$$

Solution   Let $S_n = r^0 + r^1 + r^2 + \ldots + r^{n-1}$. We have to prove that

$$S_n = \frac{1 - r^n}{1 - r}$$

(1) The case $n = 1$ of this proposition asserts that

$$S_1 = \frac{1 - r^1}{1 - r} = 1$$

which is true since, by definition

$$S_1 = r^0 = 1$$

(2) Assume that the proposition is true for $n = k$; that is

$$S_k = \frac{1 - r^k}{1 - r}$$

We have to prove, using this, that

$$S_{k+1} = \frac{1 - r^{k+1}}{1 - r}$$

Now $S_{k+1} = S_k + t_{k+1}$ (basic observation)

$\qquad\quad = S_k + r^{k+1-1}$ ($t_i = r^{i-1}$)

$\qquad\quad = \dfrac{1 - r^k}{1 - r} + r^k$ (induction hypothesis)

$\qquad\quad = \dfrac{1 - r^k + r^k(1 - r)}{1 - r}$

$\qquad\quad = \dfrac{1 - r^k + r^k - r^{k+1}}{1 - r}$

So $S_{k+1} = \dfrac{1 - r^{k+1}}{1 - r}$,

as was to be proved.

EXERCISE 11.2

Prove the following sum-formulas using mathematical induction.

B **1.** $\displaystyle\sum_{i=1}^{n}(2i - 1)^2 = \frac{4n^3 - n}{3}$

2. $\displaystyle\sum_{i=1}^{n} i(i + 1) = \frac{n(n + 1)(n + 2)}{3}$

3. $2 \times 5 + 3 \times 6 + 4 \times 7 + \ldots + (n + 1)(n + 4)$

$\quad = \dfrac{n(n + 4)(n + 5)}{3}$

4. $\displaystyle\sum_{i=1}^{n} i^3 = \left(\frac{n^2 + n}{2}\right)^2$

5. $1 \times 3 + 2 \times 3^2 + 3 \times 3^3 + \ldots + n \times 3^n = \dfrac{(2n - 1)3^{n+1} + 3}{4}$

6. $\displaystyle\sum_{j=1}^{n} \frac{1}{(3j - 2)(3j + 1)} = \frac{n}{3n + 1}$

7. $\displaystyle\sum_{k=1}^{n} \frac{k^2}{4k^2 - 1} = \frac{n^2 + n}{4n + 2}$

C 8. $\displaystyle\sum_{j=1}^{n} j \, r^{j-1} = \frac{1 - r^n}{(1 - r)^2} - \frac{nr^n}{1 - r}$ if $r \neq 1$

9. Let $m \in N$. For $x \in R$ define the notation $x^{(m)}$ by
$x^{(m)} = x(x - 1) \ldots (x - (m - 1))$.
So $x^{(1)} = x$, $x^{(2)} = x(x - 1)$, $x^{(3)} = x(x - 1)(x - 2)$, and so on.
Prove that $\displaystyle\sum_{j=1}^{n} j^{(m)} = \frac{(n + 1)^{(m + 1)}}{(m + 1)}$

10. Prove that $\displaystyle\sum_{j=1}^{n} \frac{1}{(x(j - 1) + 1)(xj + 1)} = \frac{n}{xn + 1}$ if $x \neq -\dfrac{1}{k}$ for any $k \in N$.

11. Prove that $\displaystyle\sum_{i=1}^{n} \frac{1}{(x + i - 1)(x + i)} = \frac{n}{x^2 + xn}$, if $x \neq 0$. $x \neq -k$ for any $k \in N$.

11.3 GUESSING FORMULAS

In the preceding sections of this chapter we pulled general propositions "out of thin air" and proved them by mathematical induction. In this section we illustrate the power of mathematical induction by stressing the *induction* component, that is, by looking at patterns we make a guess at a general proposition that we then attempt to prove by mathematical induction.

Example 1   For each natural number n

$$S_n = \sum_{i=1}^{n} \frac{1}{4i^2 - 1}$$

Part (b) is induction.

(a) Calculate S_1, S_2, S_3, S_4, and S_5.
(b) Guess a formula for S_n from (a).
(c) Prove that the guess is correct.

Solution   (a) $S_1 = \dfrac{1}{4(1)^2 - 1} \qquad\qquad = \dfrac{1}{3}$

$$S_2 = S_1 + \dfrac{1}{4(2)^2 - 1} = \dfrac{1}{3} + \dfrac{1}{15} = \dfrac{2}{5}$$

$$S_3 = S_2 + \dfrac{1}{4(3)^2 - 1} = \dfrac{2}{5} + \dfrac{1}{35} = \dfrac{3}{7}$$

$$S_4 = S_3 + \dfrac{1}{4(4)^2 - 1} = \dfrac{3}{7} + \dfrac{1}{63} = \dfrac{4}{9}$$

$$S_5 = S_4 + \dfrac{1}{4(5)^2 - 1} = \dfrac{4}{9} + \dfrac{1}{99} = \dfrac{5}{11}$$

We tabulate these results:

n	1	2	3	4	5
S_n	$\frac{1}{3}$	$\frac{2}{5}$	$\frac{3}{7}$	$\frac{4}{9}$	$\frac{5}{11}$

**FINDING A
PATTERN**

(b)   Looking at this table we see that the numerator of S_n is n, for $n = 1, 2, 3, 4, 5$. The denominator of S_n follows the sequence 3, 5, 7, 9, 11 which is an arithmetic sequence with first term 3, and common difference 2. So we guess that the denominator of S_n is $3 + (n - 1)2 = 2n + 1$. Putting the numerators and denominators together we guess

$$S_n = \dfrac{n}{2n + 1}$$

(c)   We now prove our guess by mathematical induction.

    (1) $S_1 = \frac{1}{3}$ is true. $(n = 1)$

    (2)   The induction hypothesis is that

$$S_k = \dfrac{k}{2k + 1}.$$

From this we have to prove that

$$S_{k+1} = \dfrac{k + 1}{2(k + 1) + 1} = \dfrac{k + 1}{2k + 3}$$

Now $S_{k+1} = S_k + t_{k+1}$ by the basic observation.

Since $t_i = \dfrac{1}{4i^2 - 1}$ for all i

$$t_{k+1} = \dfrac{1}{4(k + 1)^2 - 1}$$

$$= \dfrac{1}{(2(k + 1) - 1)(2(k + 1) + 1)} \quad \text{(difference of squares)}$$

$$= \dfrac{1}{(2k + 1)(2k + 3)}$$

So $S_{k+1} = S_k + \dfrac{1}{(2k + 1)(2k + 3)}$

$= \dfrac{k}{2k + 1} + \dfrac{1}{(2k + 1)(2k + 3)}$ (induction hypothesis)

$= \dfrac{k(2k + 3) + 1}{(2k + 1)(2k + 3)}$

$= \dfrac{2k^2 + 3k + 1}{(2k + 1)(2k + 3)}$

$= \dfrac{(2k + 1)(k + 1)}{(2k + 1)(2k + 3)}$

So $S_{k+1} = \dfrac{k + 1}{2k + 3}$

which is what we had to prove.

Hence $S_n = \dfrac{n}{2n + 1}$ is true for all $n \in N$, by mathematical induction.

EXERCISE 11.3

B   Use Example 1 as a guide to find and prove a formula for the following:

1. $\displaystyle\sum_{j=1}^{n} \dfrac{1}{9j^2 - 3j - 2}$

2. $\displaystyle\sum_{i=1}^{n} i(i + 1)$

3. $\displaystyle\sum_{i=1}^{n} (2i - 1)3^{i-1}$

4. $1^3 + 3^3 + 5^3 + \ldots + (2n - 1)^3$.

C **5.** Find the least number of guesses needed to determine a given integer between 1 and $2^n - 1$, where with each incorrect guess the guesser is told whether the guess is high or low.

11.4 THE BINOMIAL THEOREM

When binomials are expanded we notice some patterns:

$$(x + y)^2 = x^2 + 2xy + y^2$$
$$(x + y)^3 = x^3 + 3x^2y + 3xy^2 + y^3$$
$$(x + y)^4 = x^4 + 4x^3y + 6x^2y^2 + 4xy^3 + y^4$$

In general it appears that

$$(x + y)^n = x^n + nx^{n-1}y + \ldots + nxy^{n-1} + y^n$$

and that the omitted terms denoted by ... are of the form

$$\text{(coefficient) } x^{n-j}\, y^j \text{ where } 2 \leqslant j \leqslant n - 2.$$

We define, for $n \in N$, $n!$ (read as **factorial** n, or n factorial) to be the product of the first n natural numbers; so

$$n! = n \times (n - 1) \times (n - 2) \dots \times 3 \times 2 \times 1 = n(n - 1)!$$

We supplement this definition by setting $0! = 1$.

We use factorials to define the **binomial coefficients** $\binom{n}{j}$ (read as n choose j) by

$$\binom{n}{j} = \frac{n!}{j!(n - j)!}$$

Example 1   (a)   Evaluate $\binom{3}{j}$, $j = 0, 1, 2, 3$.

(b)   Evaluate $\binom{4}{j}$, $j = 0, 1, 2, 3, 4$.

Solution   (a) $\binom{3}{0} = \dfrac{3!}{0!(3 - 0)!} = \dfrac{3!}{1 \times 3!} = 1$

$\binom{3}{1} = \dfrac{3!}{1(3 - 1)!} = \dfrac{3!}{1!2!} = \dfrac{6}{1 \times 2} = 3$

$\binom{3}{2} = \dfrac{3!}{2!(3 - 2)!} = \dfrac{3!}{2!1!} = \dfrac{6}{2 \times 1} = 3$

$\binom{3}{3} = \dfrac{3!}{3!(3 - 3)!} = \dfrac{3!}{3!0!} = \dfrac{3!}{3! \times 1} = 1$

(b) $\binom{4}{0} = \dfrac{4!}{0!(4 - 0)!} = \dfrac{4!}{1 \times 4!} = 1$

$\binom{4}{1} = \dfrac{4!}{1!(4 - 1)!} = \dfrac{4!}{1 \times 3!} = \dfrac{24}{1 \times 6} = 6$

$\binom{4}{2} = \dfrac{4!}{2!(4 - 2)!} = \dfrac{4!}{2!2!} = \dfrac{24}{2 \times 2} = 6$

$\binom{4}{3} = \dfrac{4!}{3!(4 - 3)!} = \dfrac{4!}{3!1!} = \dfrac{24}{6 \times 1} = 4$

$\binom{4}{4} = \dfrac{4!}{4!(4 - 4)!} = \dfrac{4!}{4!0!} = \dfrac{4!}{4! \times 1} = 1$

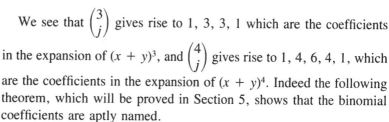

We see that $\binom{3}{j}$ gives rise to 1, 3, 3, 1 which are the coefficients in the expansion of $(x + y)^3$, and $\binom{4}{j}$ gives rise to 1, 4, 6, 4, 1, which are the coefficients in the expansion of $(x + y)^4$. Indeed the following theorem, which will be proved in Section 5, shows that the binomial coefficients are aptly named.

> ### The Binomial Theorem
>
> For all numbers x, y and all $n \in N$,
>
> $$(x + y)^n = \sum_{j=0}^{n} \binom{n}{j} x^{n-j} y^j.$$

Example 2 Expand and simplify the following using the binomial theorem.

(a) $(a + 2b)^5$

(b) $\left(x + \dfrac{1}{x}\right)^4$

Solution (a) $(a + 2b)^5 = \displaystyle\sum_{j=0}^{n} \binom{5}{j} a^{5-j} (2b)^j$

$$= \binom{5}{0} a^5 (2b)^0 + \binom{5}{1} a^4 (2b)^1$$

$$+ \binom{5}{2} a^3 (2b)^2 + \binom{5}{3} a^2 (2b)^3 + \binom{5}{4} a(2b)^4 + \binom{5}{5} a^0 (2b)^5$$

$$= 1\, a^5(1) + 5(a^4)(2b) + 10a^3(4b^2) + 10a^2(8b^3)$$
$$+ 5a(16b^4) + 1(1)32b^5$$

$$= a^5 + 10a^4 b + 40a^3 b^2 + 80a^2 b^3 + 80ab^4 + 32b^5$$

(b) $\left(x + \dfrac{1}{x}\right)^4 = \displaystyle\sum_{j=0}^{n} \binom{4}{j} x^{4-j} \left(\dfrac{1}{x}\right)^j$

$$= \binom{4}{0} x^4 \left(\frac{1}{x}\right)^0 + \binom{4}{1} x^3 \left(\frac{1}{x}\right)^1 + \binom{4}{2} x^2 \left(\frac{1}{x}\right)^2 + \binom{4}{3} x \left(\frac{1}{x}\right)^3$$

$$+ \binom{4}{4} x^0 \left(\frac{1}{x}\right)^4$$

$$= x^4 + 4x^3 \frac{1}{x} + 6x^2 \frac{1}{x^2} + 4x \frac{1}{x^3} + \frac{1}{x^4}$$

$$= x^4 + 4x^2 + 6 + \frac{4}{x^2} + \frac{1}{x^4}$$

Example 3 Use the binomial theorem to show that

(a) $\displaystyle\sum_{j=0}^{n} \binom{n}{j} = 2^n$

(b) $\displaystyle\sum_{j=0}^{n} (-1)^j \binom{n}{j} = 0$

Solution (a) We recognize $\displaystyle\sum_{j=0}^{n} \binom{n}{j}$ as a simplified form of $\displaystyle\sum_{j=0}^{n} \binom{n}{j} 1^{n-j} 1^j$ which, by the binomial theorem is equal to $(1 + 1)^n$. Hence $\displaystyle\sum_{j=0}^{n} \binom{n}{j} = 2^n$.

(b) We rewrite

$$\sum_{j=0}^{n} (-1)^j \binom{n}{j} = \sum_{j=0}^{n} \binom{n}{j} 1^{n-j} (-1)^j$$

$$= (1 + (-1))^n$$

$$= 0$$

EXERCISE 11.4

B **1.** From the definition of the binomial coefficients prove, for $n \in N$.

(a) $\displaystyle \binom{n}{j} = \binom{n}{n-j}$ $\qquad j = 0, 1, \ldots, n$

(b) $\displaystyle \binom{2n}{n-1} < \binom{2n}{n}$

2. Expand and simplify each of the following.

(a) $(1 + x^2)^6$ $\qquad\qquad$ (b) $(a - 2b)^4$

(c) $\displaystyle \left(x - \frac{1}{x} \right)$ $\qquad\qquad$ (d) $\displaystyle \left(x + \frac{1}{x} \right)^6$

(e) $\displaystyle \left(x^2 + \frac{3y}{x} \right)^4$ $\qquad\qquad$ (f) $(2x^3 + \sqrt{y})^4$

3. In the expansion of $(1 + x)^n$ the first three terms are $1, -18$ and 144. Find the values of x and n.

4. Evaluate:

(a) $\displaystyle 1 + n + \binom{n}{2} + \binom{n}{3} + \ldots + \binom{n}{n-1} + \binom{n}{n}$

(b) $\displaystyle 1 - n + \binom{n}{2} - \binom{n}{3} + \ldots + (-1)^{n-1} \binom{n}{n-1} + (-1)^n \binom{n}{n}$

5. Evaluate:

(a) $\displaystyle \sum_{j=0}^{n} \frac{1}{2^j} \binom{n}{j}$

(b) $\displaystyle \sum_{j=0}^{n} (-1)^j 2^j \binom{n}{j}$

6. Prove that $\displaystyle \sum_{j=1}^{n} j \binom{n}{j} = n2^{n-1}$ using the definition of $\displaystyle \binom{n}{j}$

7. Show that $\displaystyle \sum_{j=0}^{n} \frac{1}{j+1} \binom{n}{j} = \frac{2^{n+1} - 1}{n+1}$.

8. Prove that for all $n \in N$

(a) $\displaystyle \binom{2n+2}{n+1} < 4\binom{2n}{n}$ $\qquad\qquad$ (b) $\displaystyle \binom{2n+2}{n+1} > \binom{2n}{n}$

C **9.** Prove that

$$\sum_{j=0}^{l} \binom{m}{j} \binom{n}{l-j} = \binom{m+n}{l}$$

using the binomial theorem and the equation

$$(1 + x)^m (1 + x)^n = (1 + x)^{m+n}.$$

10. Let $\displaystyle A = \sum_{\substack{k=0 \\ k \text{ even}}}^{n} \binom{n}{k} x^{n-k} y^k$, and

$$B = \sum_{\substack{k=1 \\ k \text{ odd}}}^{n} \binom{n}{k} x^{n-k} y^k.$$

Prove that k odd $A^2 - B^2 = (x^2 - y^2)^n$

11. Show that
$$\binom{2n}{n} = \sum_{j=0}^{n} \binom{n}{j}^2$$

12. (a) For $j = 0, 1, 2, \ldots$ show that
$$\binom{n}{j} \leq \frac{n^j}{j!}$$

(b) Prove that $\left(1 + \dfrac{1}{n}\right)^n \leq \displaystyle\sum_{j=0}^{n} \dfrac{1}{j!}$

(c) Prove that $\dfrac{1}{2!} + \dfrac{1}{3!} + \dfrac{1}{4!} + + \dfrac{1}{n!} < \dfrac{1}{1 \times 2} + \dfrac{1}{2 \times 3} + \dfrac{1}{3 \times 4}$

$+ \ldots + \dfrac{1}{(n-1)n}$

for $n \geq 4$

(d) Recall that $\displaystyle\sum_{j=1}^{n} \dfrac{1}{j(j+1)} = \dfrac{n}{n+1} < 1$ for all n to prove that

$\left(1 + \dfrac{1}{n}\right)^n < 3$ for all n.

11.5 PROOF OF THE BINOMIAL THEOREM

In the preceding section we stated and used the binomial theorem. In this section we prove it, using the following result:

Pascal's Theorem

For all $n \in N$, and $j \in N$ with $j \leq n$

$$\binom{n}{j} + \binom{n}{j-1} = \binom{n+1}{j}$$

Proof

$$\binom{n}{j} + \binom{n}{j-1} = \frac{n!}{j!(n-j)!} + \frac{n!}{(j-1)!(n-j+1)!}$$

$$= n!\left(\frac{1}{j!(n-j)!} + \frac{1}{(j-1)!(n-j+1)!}\right)$$

$$= n!\left(\frac{(n-j+1)}{j!(n-j+1)(n-j)!} + \frac{j}{j(j-1)!(n-j+1)!}\right)$$

$$= n!\left(\frac{n-j+1}{j!(n-j+1)!} + \frac{j}{j!(n-j+1)!}\right)$$

$$= \frac{n!(n+1)}{j!(n+1-j)!}$$

$$= \frac{(n+1)!}{j!(n+1-j)!}$$

$$= \binom{n+1}{j}$$

This result is easily recalled if the binomial coefficients are laid out in a triangular array, called **Pascal's triangle**.

$$
\begin{array}{ccccc}
1 & & 1 & & \\
& 1 & 2 & 1 & \\
1 & 3 & 3 & 1 & \\
1 & 4 & 6 & 4 & 1
\end{array}
\qquad
\begin{array}{ccccc}
& & \binom{1}{0} & \binom{1}{1} & \\
& \binom{2}{0} & \binom{2}{1} & \binom{2}{2} & \\
\binom{3}{0} & \binom{3}{1} & \binom{3}{2} & \binom{3}{3} & \\
\binom{4}{0} & \binom{4}{1} & \binom{4}{2} & \binom{4}{3} & \binom{4}{4}
\end{array}
$$

For example,
$$6 = \binom{4}{2} = \binom{3}{2} + \binom{3}{1} = 3 + 3$$

Example 1   Using Pascal's Theorem prove that

$$\binom{n+2}{j} = \binom{n}{j} + 2\binom{n}{j-1} + \binom{n}{j-2} \quad \text{for } j = 2, 3, \ldots, n.$$

Solution
$$
\begin{aligned}
\binom{n+2}{j} &= \binom{n+1+1}{j} \\
&= \binom{n+1}{j} + \binom{n+1}{j-1}
\end{aligned}
$$

by Pascal's Theorem applied to $n + 1$ and j. Next we observe that

$$\binom{n+1}{j} = \binom{n}{j} + \binom{n}{j-1}$$

$$
\begin{aligned}
\binom{n+1}{j-1} &= \binom{n}{j-1} + \binom{n}{j-1-1} \\
&= \binom{n}{j-1} + \binom{n}{j-2}.
\end{aligned}
$$

and

So
$$
\begin{aligned}
\binom{n+2}{j} &= \binom{n+1}{j} + \binom{n+1}{j-1} \\
&= \binom{n}{j} + \binom{n}{j-1} + \binom{n}{j-1} + \binom{n}{j-2}
\end{aligned}
$$

We recall that the Binomial Theorem asserts that

$$(x + y)^n = \sum_{j=0}^{n} \binom{n}{j} x^{n-j} y^j$$

We proceed to prove this by induction on n.

Proof

(1) For $n = 1$ the theorem (our general proposition) states that

$$(x + y)^1 = \sum_{j=0}^{1} \binom{1}{j} x^{1-j} y^j$$
$$= \binom{1}{0} x^{1-0} y^0 + \binom{1}{1} x^{1-1} y^1$$
$$= 1 x^1 y^0 + 1 x^0 y^1$$
$$= x + y$$

which is true.

(2) Assume the result is true for $n = k$; so we have

$$(x + y)^k = \sum_{j=0}^{k} \binom{k}{j} x^{k-j} y^j$$

We have to deduce that

$$(x + y)^{k+1} = \sum_{j=0}^{k+1} \binom{k+1}{j} x^{k+1-j} y^j$$

Now
$$(x + y)^{k+1} = (x + y)(x + y)^k$$
$$= x(x + y)^k + y(x + y)^k$$
$$= x\left[x^k + \binom{k}{1} x^{k-1} y + \ldots \binom{k}{j} x^{k-j} y^j + \ldots + y^k \right]$$
$$+ \left[x^k + \binom{k}{1} x^{k-1} y + \ldots + y^k \right] y$$
$$= \binom{k}{0} x^{k+1} + \binom{k}{1} x^k y + \ldots + \binom{k}{j} x^{k+1-j} y^j$$
$$+ \ldots + \binom{k}{k} xy^k + x^k y + \ldots + \binom{k}{j-1} x^{k-(j-1)} y^j$$
$$+ \ldots + \binom{k}{k-1} xy^k + y^{k+1}$$
$$= x^{k+1} + \sum_{j=1}^{k} \left[\binom{k}{j} + \binom{k}{j-1} \right] x^{k+1-j} y + y^{k+1}$$
$$= x^{k+1} + \sum_{j=1}^{k} \binom{k+1}{j} x^{k+1-j} y^j + y^{k+1}$$

(by Pascal's Theorem)

$$(x + y)^{k+1} = \sum_{j=0}^{k} \binom{k+1}{j} x^{k+1-j} y^j,$$

So

which is what we had to prove.

By mathematical induction, the theorem is true.

EXERCISE 11.5

B **1.** Using Pascal's Theorem prove that

(a) $\binom{n+3}{j} = \binom{n}{j} + 3\binom{n}{j-1} + 3\binom{n}{j-2} + \binom{n}{j-3}$

$j = 3, 4, ..., n$

(b) $\binom{2n+2}{n+1} = 2\binom{2n}{n} + 2\binom{2n}{n-1}$

2. Prove that $\binom{2n}{j+1} > \binom{2n}{j}$ for $j = 0, 1, ..., n-1$.

3. Prove that $\binom{2n-1}{j+1} > \binom{2n-1}{j}$

for $j = 0, 1, ..., n-2$.

4. Which rows of the Pascal triangle contain only odd numbers?

11.6 PROOF OF DE MOIVRE'S THEOREM

We stated De Moivre's theorem in Chapter 10: for each n

$$(r \text{ cis } \theta)^n = r^n \text{ cis}(n\theta)$$

where $r \in R$, $r \geq 0$ and cis $\theta = \cos \theta + i \sin \theta$.
We also showed there that

$$\text{cis } \theta \text{ cis } \phi = \text{cis}(\theta + \phi)$$

We now prove the difficult part of De Moivre's theorem.

> **Theorem**
>
> $(\text{cis } \theta)^n = \text{cis}(n\theta)$, $n \in N$, $\theta \in R$.

Proof

We proceed by induction
(1) For $n = 1$ the theorem states that $(\text{cis } \theta)^1 = \text{cis}(1\theta)$, which is true.
(2) Assume the result is true for $n = k$; so that we have

$$(\text{cis } \theta)^k = \text{cis}(k\theta)$$

We have to prove that $(\text{cis } \theta)^{k+1} = \text{cis}((k+1)\theta)$

Now $(\text{cis } \theta)^{k+1} = (\text{cis } \theta)(\text{cis}(\theta))^k$

$= \text{cis } \theta \text{ cis}(k\theta)$

$= \text{cis}(\theta + k\theta)$

So $(\text{cis } \theta)^{k+1} = \text{cis}((k + 1)\theta)$

and the induction step is verified. Hence, by the principle of mathematical induction, the theorem is true.

We can find interesting results by combining De Moivre's Theorem with the binomial theorem.

Example 1 Show that, for each $n \in N$,

$$\cos n\theta = \binom{n}{0} (\cos \theta)^n - \binom{n}{2} (\cos \theta)^{n-2} (\sin \theta)^2$$
$$+ \binom{n}{4} (\cos \theta)^{n-4} (\sin \theta)^4 + \dots$$

Solution $\cos (n\theta)$ is the real part of cis $(n\theta)$, which by De Moivre's Theorem is $(\text{cis } \theta)^n$.

Now $(\text{cis } \theta)^n = (\cos \theta + i \sin \theta)^n$
$$= \sum_{j=0}^{n} \binom{n}{j} (\cos \theta)^{n-j} i^j (\sin \theta)^j$$

If j is odd the real part of $\binom{n}{j} (\cos \theta)^{n-j} i^j (\sin \theta)^j$ is 0. So

$$\cos (n\theta) = \text{Re (cis } n\theta)$$
$$= \sum_{\substack{j=0 \\ j \text{ even}}}^{n} j (\cos \theta)^{n-j} (-1)^{\frac{j}{2}} (\sin \theta)^j$$

Example 2 Prove that

$$\cos (3\theta) = 4 \cos^3 \theta - 3 \cos \theta$$

Solution From Example 1,

$$\cos (3\theta) = \binom{3}{0} \cos^3\theta - \binom{3}{2} \cos \theta \sin^2 \theta$$
$$= \cos^3 \theta - 3 \cos \theta (1 - \cos^2 \theta)$$
$$= 4 \cos^3 \theta - 3 \cos \theta$$

There is another method that we can apply to the solution of Example 2.

Example 3 Using the fact that

cis θ + cis $(-\theta)$
= cis θ + $i \sin \theta$
+ cis θ − $i \sin \theta$
= 2 cos θ

$$\cos \theta = \frac{\text{cis } \theta + \text{cis}(-\theta)}{2}$$

prove that $\cos(3\theta) = 4 \cos^3 \theta - 3 \cos \theta$

Solution

$$\cos^3 \theta = \left(\frac{\text{cis } \theta + \text{cis}(-\theta)}{2} \right)^3$$

$$= \frac{1}{8} \sum_{j=0}^{3} \binom{3}{j} (\text{cis } \theta)^{3-j} (\text{cis } (-\theta))^j$$

$$= \frac{1}{8} \sum_{j=0}^{3} \binom{3}{j} (\text{cis } ((3-j)\,\theta) \text{ cis}(-j\theta)$$

$$= \frac{1}{8} \sum_{j=0}^{3} \binom{3}{j} \text{cis } (3-2j)\theta$$

$$= \frac{1}{8} [\text{cis } (3\theta) + 3 \text{ cis } \theta + 3 \text{ cis}(-\theta) + \text{cis } (-3\theta)]$$

$$= \frac{1}{8} (\text{cis } (3\theta) + \text{cis}(-3\theta)) + \frac{3}{8} (\text{cis } \theta + \text{cis } (-\theta))$$

$$= \frac{1}{8} (2 \cos (3\theta)) + \frac{3}{8} (2 \cos \theta)$$

So $\cos^3 \theta = \frac{1}{4} \cos 3\theta + \frac{3}{4} \cos \theta$

Hence $\cos (3\theta) = 4 \cos^3 \theta - 3 \cos \theta$.

EXERCISE 11.6

B **1.** Prove that $\sin (n\theta) = \displaystyle\sum_{\substack{j=1 \\ j \text{ odd}}}^{n} (-1)^{\frac{j-1}{2}} \binom{n}{j} \cos^{n-j} \theta \sin^j \theta$

2. Show that $\sin (3\theta) = 3 \sin \theta - 4 \sin^3 \theta$.

3. Using the fact that $\sin \theta = \dfrac{\text{cis } \theta - \text{cis}(-\theta)}{2i}$ show that
$16 \sin^5 \theta = \sin(5\theta) - 5 \sin (3\theta) + 10 \sin \theta$.

C **4.** Prove that if $n \in N$ is even then

$$\cos^n \theta = \frac{1}{2^{n-1}} \sum_{j=0}^{\frac{n}{2}} \binom{n}{j} \cos((n - 2j)\theta) - \frac{1}{2^n} \binom{n}{\frac{n}{2}}$$

5. Show that (a) $\cos \dfrac{\pi}{8} = \dfrac{\sqrt{2 + \sqrt{2}}}{2}$ using $\cos^2 \theta = \dfrac{\cos 2\theta + 1}{2}$, and

(b) $\cos \dfrac{\pi}{8} = \left(\dfrac{3 + 2\sqrt{2}}{8} \right)^{\frac{1}{4}}$ using

$$\cos^4 \theta = \frac{\cos 4\theta + 4 \cos 2\theta + 3}{8}$$

PROBLEMS PLUS

Prove that the number of people who have shaken hands with an odd number of people is an even number.

11.7 FALLACIES

The form in which we use mathematical induction is
(1) prove P_1
(2) assume P_k is true, where $k \geqslant 1$ and from this deduce P_{k+1}.
Then we conclude P_n is true for all $n \in N$. If (1) or (2) is violated then we have not proved P_n. Here are some flawed proofs and fallacies.

Example 1 Show that $n = n + 1$ for all $n \in N$.

Solution Assume true for $n = k$. Then $k = k + 1$. We have to prove that $k + 1 = k + 2$.

Now $k + 1 = (k + 1) + 1$ ($k = k + 1$ by induction hypothesis)
So $k + 1 = k + 2$

This proves the induction step (2). But step (1) is false since $1 \neq 1 + 1$.

Example 2 Any n people have eyes of the same colour.

Solution (1) This is true for $n = 1$.
(2) Assume true for k. Hence any k people have eyes of the same colour. We have to prove that any $(k + 1)$ people have eyes of the same colour. Let $(k + 1)$ people be given. Line them up in a row.

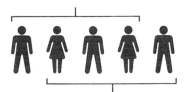

The first k people all have eyes of the same colour, and the last k people have eyes of the same colour, by the induction hypothesis. So the first person, and the last person have the same eye colour as any person in the middle, so they all have the same eye colour.

Since steps (1) and (2) have been verified the result is true by mathematical induction!

The gap in the reasoning occurs in going from k to $k + 1$ when $k = 1$, for then there is no person in the middle; $k + 1 = 2$, so the lineup is ...,

and so there is no link between first and last.

Sometimes the evidence seems so overwhelming that we are lazy about the induction step.

Example 3 $n^2 - n + 41$ is prime for all $n \in N$.

Solution   True for $n = 1$, since 41 is prime and for $n = 2$ since 43 is prime.

In fact it is true for $n = 1, 2, 3, \ldots, 40$. So it seems to be true always.
    But for $n = 41$ we have $41^2 - 41 + 41 = 41^2$ which is *not* prime.

n	$n^2 - n + 41$
1	41
2	43
3	47
4	53
5	61
6	71
7	83
8	97

We can present a more mathematical example using the function max.

For $m, n \in N$ we set

$$\max (m, n) = p \text{ where } p \text{ is the larger of } m \text{ and } n.$$

So, for example, $\max (3, 8) = 8$ and $\max (7, 7) = 7$.

Example 4   For each triple of natural numbers a, b, n if the bigger of a and b is n, then a and b are equal to n. Symbolically, for each $n \in N$ if $\max (a, b) = n$ then $a = b = n$ $(a, b \in N)$.

Solution   (1)   This is true for $n = 1$. If $\max (a, b) = 1$ then $1 \geq a$, $1 \geq b$; but $a, b \in N$ so $a \geq 1$, $b \geq 1$. Hence $a = 1$ and $b = 1$.

(2)   Assume true for $n = k$. Thus $\max (a, b) = k$ implies $a = b = k$. Now suppose $\max (c, d) = k + 1$. We have to prove that $c = d = k + 1$.
    Set $c = a + 1$, $d = b + 1$ Then

$$\begin{aligned}
k + 1 &= \max (c, d) \\
&= \max (a+1, b+1) \\
&= \max (a, b) + 1
\end{aligned}$$

for if a, b are both increased by 1 so is their maximum.
    Hence $\max (a, b) = k$. By the induction hypothesis $a = b = k$, so $a + 1 = b + 1 = k + 1$. That is: $c = d = k + 1$. This proves the induction step.
    So by mathematical induction the result is true for all n.
    There must be an error since $\max (3, 8) = 8$ but $3 \neq 8$. Let us look at the step from 1 to 2

$$\begin{aligned}
\max (1, 2) &= 2 \\
\max (0+1, 1+1) &= 1 + 1 \\
\max (0, 1) + 1 &= 1 + 1 \\
\max (0, 1) &= 1
\end{aligned}$$

We now conclude that $0 = 1 = 1$ which is false. The flaw here is that 0 is not a natural number. We proved that if $\max (a, b) = 1$, and a, b are natural numbers then $a = b = 1$. This does not apply here since $0 \notin N$.

Example 5   There is no such thing as a heap of sand. More precisely for each $n \in N$ it is false that n grains of sand form a heap.

Solution   (1)   True for $n = 1$; no one would say that 1 grain of sand is a heap.
(2)   Assume true for $n = k$. So we assume that no heap of sand contains k grains. Consider now $n = k + 1$. If you don't have a heap, adding 1 grain will not make it a heap. So true for $n = k + 1$.

Where is the flaw here? It probably lies in the imprecise term heap, not in the mathematics at all!   ⬡

EXERCISE 11.7

B **1.**   If parallel lines are regarded as intersecting at infinity the statement "Any n lines in a plane have a common point" is true for $n = 1$ and for $n = 2$. Construct a fallacious proof of the general statement by mathematical induction.

2.   Which of the following is a valid general proposition for all natural numbers? If the proposition is false explain which step fails in a proof by mathematical induction.

(a) $1000n \geqslant n^3$

(b) $n^3 \geqslant 1000n$

(c)   The nth odd number is $2n + 1$

(d) $\displaystyle\sum_{j=1}^{n} 2^j = 2^{n+1}$

(e) $\displaystyle\sum_{j=1}^{n} 4j = n(2n + 2)$

(f) $n^2 - 79n + 1601$ is prime.

*11.8   THE FIBONACCI SEQUENCE

The mathematician Leonardo Pisano, known as Fibonacci, in his book Liber Abaci published in 1202, introduced the Fibonacci sequence as the solution to a problem in population growth.

The problem is this: how many pairs of rabbits will be produced in a year if in every month each pair bears a new pair which becomes productive in the second month?

Let a_n denote the number of pairs of adult rabbits in the nth month, b_n denote the number of pairs of baby rabbits, and f_n denote the total number of pairs of rabbits, that is

$$f_n = a_n + b_n$$

We observe the following relationships

$$\text{(i)} \quad a_{n+1} = a_n + b_n$$

since baby rabbits are babies only in the month in which they are born.

$$\text{(ii)} \quad b_{n+1} = a_n,$$

since adults bear new rabbits in the next month.

$$\text{(iii)} \quad f_{n+2} = f_{n+1} + f_n,$$

since

$$
\begin{aligned}
f_{n+2} &= a_{n+2} + b_{n+2} \\
&= a_{n+1} + b_{n+1} + b_{n+2} && \text{(by (ii))} \\
&= f_{n+1} + b_{n+2} \\
&= f_{n+1} + a_{n+1} && \text{(by (ii))} \\
&= f_{n+1} + a_n + b_n && \text{(by (ii))} \\
&= f_{n+1} + f_n
\end{aligned}
$$

$$\text{(iv)} \quad f_1 = 1, f_2 = 1$$

since one pair of baby rabbits is present initially (first month) and this pair becomes adult in the second month.

The Fibonacci sequence $f_1, f_2, f_3, \ldots$ is completely determined by the recursion formula (iii)

$$f_{n+2} = f_{n+1} + f_n \qquad n \in N$$

and, $f_1 = 1, f_2 = 1,$

the initial conditions.

We compute a table for the sequence.

n	1	2	3	4	5	6	7	8	9	10	11	12
f_n	1	1	2	3	5	8	13	21	34	55	89	144

We see from this table that the solution to the problem is: 144 pairs of rabbits will be produced in a year.

It is commonly accepted that population grows geometrically in suitable circumstances. The Fibonacci sequence shows this.

Example 1 Prove that for all $n \in N$

$$\frac{2}{3}\left(\frac{3}{2}\right)^{n-1} \leq f_n \leq 1 \, (2)^{n-1}$$

Remark This shows that the Fibonacci sequence is bounded by geometric sequences.

Solution We have to prove two general propositions:

$$f_n \geq \frac{2}{3}\left(\frac{3}{2}\right)^{n-1}, \quad f_n \leq 2^{n-1}.$$

We assert the following form of the first inequality.

$$f_j \geq \frac{2}{3}\left(\frac{3}{2}\right)^{j-1} \text{ for } j = 1, 2, \ldots, n.$$

Call this proposition P_n. We prove P_n by induction.

(1) P_1 is true since $f_1 = 1 \geq \frac{2}{3}\left(\frac{3}{2}\right)^{1-1}$.

P_2 is true since $f_1 \geq \frac{2}{3}\left(\frac{3}{2}\right)^{1-1}$ and $f_2 = 1 \geq \frac{2}{3}\left(\frac{3}{2}\right)^{2-1} = 1$.

(2) Now assume that P_n is true for $n = k$ where $k \geq 2$. So we assume that

$$f_1 \geq \frac{2}{3}, f_2 \geq 1, f_3 \geq \frac{3}{2}, \ldots, f_k \geq \frac{2}{3}\left(\frac{3}{2}\right)^{k-1}$$

We have to prove that P_{k+1} is true:

$$f_1 \geq \frac{2}{3}, f_2 \geq 1, \ldots, f_k \geq \frac{2}{3}\left(\frac{3}{2}\right)^{k-1}, f_{k+1} \geq \frac{2}{3}\left(\frac{3}{2}\right)^{k+1-1}$$

in other words, we have to prove the inequality $f_{k+1} \geq \frac{2}{3}\left(\frac{3}{2}\right)^{k}$.

Now $\quad f_{k+1} = f_k + f_{k-1} \qquad (k, k-1 \in N)$

$$\geq \frac{2}{3}\left(\frac{3}{2}\right)^{k-1} + \frac{2}{3}\left(\frac{3}{2}\right)^{k-2}$$

$$= \frac{2}{3}\left(\frac{3}{2}\right)^{k-2}\left(\frac{3}{2} + 1\right)$$

$$\geq \frac{2}{3}\left(\frac{3}{2}\right)^{k-2}\left(\frac{3}{2}\right)^{2} \qquad \left(\text{since } \frac{3}{2} + 1 > \left(\frac{3}{2}\right)^{2}\right)$$

So $\quad f_{k+1} \geq \frac{2}{3}\left(\frac{3}{2}\right)^{k}$

as was to be shown.

Hence the proposition is true for all natural numbers, by the principle of mathematical induction.

Let Q_n be the proposition that $f_j \leq 2^{j-1}$, for $j = 1, 2, \ldots, n$. Then we can prove by induction that Q_n is true for all $n \in N$ by a process very similar to that used for P_n. (see Question 1 in Exercise 11.8).

The Fibonacci sequence has interesting arithmetical patterns as well. We notice that the 3rd, 6th, 9th, ... terms in the table are even.

Example 2 Prove that f_{3n} is even.

Solution We proceed by induction.

(1) $f_3 = 2$ is even. So the case $n = 1$ is true.

(2) The induction hypothesis is that f_{3k} is even. We have to prove that $f_{3(k+1)} = f_{3k+3}$ is even.

Now $f_{3k+3} = f_{3k+2} + f_{3k+1}$ (recursion formula for Fibonacci sequence)

$= f_{3k+1} + f_{3k} + f_{3k+1}.$

So $f_{3k+3} = 2f_{3k+1} + f_{3k}.$

Since $2f_{3k+1}$ is even, and f_{3k} is even by the induction hypothesis, f_{3k+3} is even. This proves the induction step, and so the proposition is true for all $n \in N$.

The converse of this result seems to be true also: if f_n is even then n is divisible by 3. We will prove this by introducing a principle that is equivalent to the principle of mathematical induction.

Well-order principle

Each non-empty subset of the natural numbers has a least element.

Example 3 Prove: if f_n is even then n is divisible by 3.

Solution Let $S = \{n \in N: f_n$ is even and n is *not* divisible by 3$\}$.

We will prove, using the well order principle that S is empty. For suppose that S is non-empty. Then by the well-order principle S has a least element, call it m.

Then $m \neq 1$ since $f_1 = 1$ is not even and $m \neq 2$ since $f_2 = 1$ is not even. Also $m \neq 3$ since $m \in S$ requires that m be not divisible by 3. Hence $m \geqslant 4$.

Now $f_m = f_{m-1} + f_{m-2}$

$= f_{m-2} + f_{m-3} + f_{m-2}.$

So $f_m = 2f_{m-2} + f_{m-3}$

(Note that $m - 3 \in N$ since $m \geqslant 4$)

Since $m \in S$, f_m is even, and so f_{m-3} is even as it differs from f_m by $2f_{m-2}$ which is an even number. Also $m - 3$ is not divisible by 3: else $m = m - 3 + 3$ would be divisible by 3. So f_{m-3} is even, and $m - 3$ is not divisible by 3, hence $m - 3 \in S$. But $m - 3 < m$ and m was chosen to be the least element of S. This is a contradiction, so S has no least element, so S is empty.

We conclude that there are no natural numbers n with the property that f_n is even and n is not divisible by 3. So it is true that if f_n is even then N is divisible by 3.

EXERCISE 11.8

B **1.** Complete the proof of Example 1: Q_n is true for all $n \in N$.

2. Using the technique of example 1, prove that

(a) $f_n \geqslant \frac{5}{8} \left(\frac{8}{5}\right)^{n-1}$,

(b) $f_n \leqslant \left(\frac{5}{3}\right)^{n-1}$

3. Suppose that $t \in R$ satisfies $t > 1$ and $1 + t \leqslant t^2$. Prove that $f_n \leqslant t^{n-1}$.

4. Suppose that $s \in R$ satisfies $1 + s \geqslant s^2$ and $s > 1$. Prove that $f_n \geqslant \dfrac{1}{s} s^{n-1}$.

5. Suppose we toss a coin n times. There are 2^n possible outcomes of heads and tails. Let t_n denote the number of sequences in which heads never appear on successive tosses. Show that

(a) $t_{n+2} = t_{n+1} + t_n$

(b) $t_1 = 2, t_2 = 3$

(c) $t_n = f_{n+2}, \qquad n \in N$

6. How many n-digit binary sequences (sequences of zeros and ones) are there that have no adjacent zeros?

7. Using the technique of Example 2 prove that f_{5n} is divisible by 5.

8. Prove that f_{4n} is divisible by 3 for all $n \in N$.

9. Using the technique of Example 3 prove that if f_n is divisible by 5, then n is divisible by 5.

10. Prove that if f_n is divisible by 3 then n is divisible by 4.

C **11.** Let $\alpha = \dfrac{1 + \sqrt{5}}{2}, \beta = \dfrac{1 - \sqrt{5}}{2}$. Prove by induction that, for all $n \in N$,

$$f_n = \frac{\alpha^n - \beta^n}{\sqrt{5}}$$

PROBLEMS PLUS

Show that

$$1 - \frac{1}{2} + \frac{1}{3} - \frac{1}{4} + \ldots + \frac{1}{1999} - \frac{1}{2000}$$

$$= \frac{1}{1001} + \frac{1}{1002} + \ldots + \frac{1}{2000}.$$

11.9 REVIEW EXERCISE

1. Prove by mathematical induction:
   (a) If $t_1 = a$ and $t_{n+1} = t_n + d$ then $t_n = a + (n-1)d$
   (b) If $t_1 = a$ and $t_{n+1} = rt_n$ then $t_n = ar^{n-1}$

2. Use the principle of mathematical induction to prove the following results true for each $n \in N$.
   (a) $n^4 - n$ is even
   (b) $n(n + 3)$ is even
   (c) $9^n - 1$ is divisible by 8
   (d) $9^n - 8n - 1$ is divisible by 64

3. Prove that $(1 + x^2)^n \geq 1 + nx^2$ for all $n \in N$.

4. Prove that $\dfrac{1}{\sqrt{1}} + \dfrac{1}{\sqrt{2}} + \ldots + \dfrac{1}{\sqrt{n}} \geq \sqrt{n}$.

5. Prove each of the following formulas by induction.
   (a) $\displaystyle\sum_{k=1}^{n} 2^k = 2^{n+1} - 2$
   (b) $\displaystyle\sum_{j=1}^{n} j\, 2^{j-1} = (n-1)2^n + 1$
   (c) $\displaystyle\sum_{j=1}^{n} \binom{j+1}{2} = \binom{n+2}{3}$
   (d) $\displaystyle\sum_{k=1}^{n} k\, 3^{k-1} = \dfrac{(2n-1)3^n + 1}{4}$

6. Prove that the sum of the cubes of the first n odd natural numbers is equal to $n^2(2n^2 - 1)$.

7. Find and prove the truth of a formula for each of the following:
   (a) $\displaystyle\sum_{k=1}^{n} k\,(k!)$
   (b) $\displaystyle\sum_{k=1}^{n} \tfrac{1}{2}\binom{j+1}{2}^{-1}$
   (c) $\displaystyle\sum_{j=1}^{n} (2j-1)\, 2^{-j}$
   (d) $\displaystyle\sum_{k=1}^{n} \dfrac{k}{(k+1)!}$

8. How many terms are there in the expansion of each of the following?
   (a) $(a + b)^{12}$
   (b) $(2x - x^{-1})^{10}$

9. Write down the binomial expansions for
   (a) $(1 + x)^8$
   (b) $(2 - x)^7$
   (c) $(3 - 2x)^6$
   (d) $(2x - 3)^6$

10. Expand and simplify
    (a) $\left(\dfrac{a}{b} + \dfrac{b}{a}\right)^3$
    (b) $(\sqrt{x} - \sqrt{y})^6$
    (c) $(2a + b)^4$
    (d) $(ab - cd)^5$

11. Find the coefficient of x^9 in the expansion of
    (a) $(1 + x)^{11}$
    (b) $\left(2 + \dfrac{x}{2}\right)^{11}$

12. Find the coefficient of x^3 in the expansion of
    (a) $(x - 1)^5\left(1 - \dfrac{1}{x}\right)^4$
    (b) $(1 + x + x^2)^4$

13. Find n, r such that each of the following is true.

(a) $\dbinom{100}{50} + \dbinom{100}{49} = \dbinom{n}{r}$ (b) $\dbinom{m-1}{j} + \dbinom{m-1}{j-1} = \dbinom{n}{r}$

14. Using Pascal's Theorem prove that

$$\dbinom{n+4}{r} = \dbinom{n}{r} + 4\dbinom{n}{r-1} + 6\dbinom{n}{r-2} + 4\dbinom{n}{r-3} + \dbinom{n}{r-4}$$

for $r = 4, 5, \ldots, n$.

15. Which of the following is a valid general proposition concerning the natural numbers? If the proposition is false, explain which step fails in an attempted proof by mathematical induction.

(a) $2^n > 2n + 1$ (b) $2^n > n^2$

(c) $\dfrac{1}{n+1} + \dfrac{1}{n+2} + \ldots + \dfrac{1}{2n} > \dfrac{1}{2}$

(d) $\dfrac{4^n}{n+1} \leqslant \dbinom{2n}{n}$

11.10 CHAPTER 11 TEST

1. Prove by induction that $3^n \geq 2n^2 + 1$.

2. Using mathematical induction prove that the sum of the first n odd natural numbers is equal to n^2.

3. (a) Define the binomial coefficients $\binom{n}{j}$.

    (b) State and prove Pascal's Theorem.

4. (a) State the Binomial Theorem.

    (b) Evaluate $\sum_{j=0}^{n} (-1)^j \binom{n}{j}$.

5. Prove, by induction, that
    $$(\text{cis } \theta)^n = \text{cis } n\theta \qquad (n \in N).$$

ANSWERS

CHAPTER 1 GEOMETRIC VECTORS

REVIEW AND PREVIEW TO CHAPTER 1

EXERCISE 1

1. (a) $\angle A = 52°$ $b = 93.8$ $c = 152.3$
   (b) $\angle B = 38°$ $\angle C = 52°$ $b = 71.6$
   (c) $\angle C = 23°$ $a = 25.6$ $b = 23.6$
   (d) $\angle B = 45°$ $\angle C = 45°$ $b = 999.7$
   (e) $\angle A = 20°$ $a = 45.5$ $c = 133.0$
   (f) $\angle C = 52°$ $a = 905.0$ $c = 1158.4$

2. (a) $b = 10.7$ $\angle A = 76°$ $\angle C = 56°$
   (b) $a = 14.7$ $\angle C = 71°$ $b = 10.4$
   (c) $\angle A = 47°$ $\angle B = 72°$ $\angle C = 61°$
   (d) $a = 27.1$ $b = 15.5$ $\angle C = 27°$
   (e) $a = 50.5$ $b = 37.6$ $\angle C = 92°$
   (f) $\angle A = 60°$ $\angle B = 72°$ $\angle C = 48°$

EXERCISE 1.1

1. (b), (c), (d)

2. (a) (i) X (ii) B (b) (i) Y (ii) A

3. (a) $\overrightarrow{PQ} = \overrightarrow{SR} = \overrightarrow{FE}$, $\overrightarrow{PF} = \overrightarrow{FS} = \overrightarrow{QE} = \overrightarrow{ER}$,
   $\overrightarrow{PS} = \overrightarrow{QR}$ (and $\overrightarrow{QP} = \overrightarrow{RS}$ etc.)
   (b) $\overrightarrow{AE} = \overrightarrow{BD}$, $\overrightarrow{AB} = \overrightarrow{FC} = \overrightarrow{ED}$, $\overrightarrow{AF} = \overrightarrow{BC}$,
   $\overrightarrow{FE} = \overrightarrow{CD}$ (and $\overrightarrow{EA} = \overrightarrow{DB}$ etc.)
   (c) $\overrightarrow{JK} = \overrightarrow{NL}$, $\overrightarrow{JN} = \overrightarrow{KL}$ (and $\overrightarrow{KJ} = \overrightarrow{LN}$ etc.)

4.
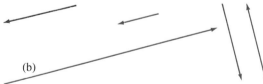
(a)   (c)
(b)

5. (a) $\overrightarrow{XU} = \overrightarrow{UY} = \overrightarrow{WV}$, $\overrightarrow{YV} = \overrightarrow{VZ}$, $\overrightarrow{XW} = \overrightarrow{WZ}$
   (b) $\overrightarrow{PQ} = \overrightarrow{SR}$, $\overrightarrow{PS} = \overrightarrow{QR}$, $\overrightarrow{PX} = \overrightarrow{XR}$,
   $\overrightarrow{QX} = \overrightarrow{XS}$
   (c) $\overrightarrow{HI} = \overrightarrow{ML}$, $\overrightarrow{GH} = \overrightarrow{LK}$, $\overrightarrow{GN} = \overrightarrow{JK}$,
   $\overrightarrow{NM} = \overrightarrow{IJ}$
   (d) $\overrightarrow{AB} = \overrightarrow{DC} = \overrightarrow{EF} = \overrightarrow{HG}$,
   $\overrightarrow{AE} = \overrightarrow{BF} = \overrightarrow{CG} = \overrightarrow{DH}$,
   $\overrightarrow{AD} = \overrightarrow{BC} = \overrightarrow{EH} = \overrightarrow{FG}$

6. (a) $\frac{20}{3} \doteq 6.7$ (b) 12   (c) 9.4   (d) 7.4
   (e) 147.4

7. (a) same length   (b) no indication of direction

EXERCISE 1.2

1. (a) $\vec{u} = \vec{v} + \vec{w}$, $\vec{v} = \vec{u} - \vec{w}$, $\vec{w} = \vec{u} - \vec{v}$
   (b) $\overrightarrow{AB} = \overrightarrow{AC} - \overrightarrow{CB}$, $\overrightarrow{AC} = \overrightarrow{AB} + \overrightarrow{BC}$,
   $\overrightarrow{BC} = \overrightarrow{AC} - \overrightarrow{AB}$
   (c) $\overrightarrow{PR} = \overrightarrow{PQ} - \overrightarrow{RQ}$, $\overrightarrow{PQ} = \overrightarrow{PR} + \overrightarrow{RQ}$,
   $\overrightarrow{RQ} = \overrightarrow{PQ} - \overrightarrow{PR}$
   (d) $\vec{e} = \vec{v} - \vec{f}$, $\vec{f} = \vec{v} - \vec{e}$, $\vec{g} = \vec{v} + \vec{h}$,
   $\vec{h} = \vec{g} - \vec{v}$, $\vec{v} = \vec{e} + \vec{f} = \vec{g} - \vec{h}$

2. (a) $\overrightarrow{AC}$ (b) $\overrightarrow{AD}$ (c) $\overrightarrow{CA}$ (d) $\overrightarrow{BD}$ (e) $\overrightarrow{AD}$

3. (a) $\vec{w} + \vec{s} + \vec{r} + \vec{u}$
   (b) $\vec{u} + (-\vec{w}) + \vec{c} + \vec{d} + \vec{e} + (-\vec{m}) + \vec{n}$

4. (a) $\overrightarrow{BC}$ (b) $\overrightarrow{BE}$ (c) $\overrightarrow{EC}$ (d) $\overrightarrow{BA}$ (e) $\overrightarrow{AB}$
   (f) $\overrightarrow{BD}$ (g) $\overrightarrow{AC}$ (h) $\overrightarrow{BD}$ (i) $\overrightarrow{BC}$

5. (a)   (b)   (c)
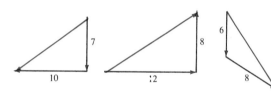

(d)
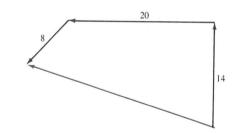

7. (a) (i)   (ii)
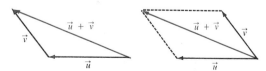

7. (b) (i)

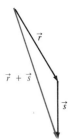

$\vec{x} + \vec{y}$

$\vec{y}$

$\vec{x}$

(ii)

$\vec{x} + \vec{y}$

$\vec{y}$

$\vec{x}$

(c) (i)

$\vec{r}$

$\vec{r} + \vec{s}$

$\vec{s}$

(ii)

$\vec{s}$ $\vec{r}$

$\vec{r} + \vec{s}$

8. (a)

$-\vec{v}$

$\vec{u} - \vec{v}$

$\vec{u}$

(b)

$\vec{u} - \vec{v}$

$\vec{u}$

$-\vec{v}$

(c)

$\vec{u} - \vec{v}$

$\vec{u}$

$-\vec{v}$

9.

$\vec{x}$

$-\vec{w}$

$\vec{u} + \vec{v} - \vec{w} + \vec{x}$

$\vec{v}$

$\vec{u}$

10. (b) if $\vec{u}$ and $\vec{v}$ have same direction

11. (a) $\overrightarrow{AC}$ (b) $\overrightarrow{GB}$ (c) $\overrightarrow{AC}$ (d) $\overrightarrow{HC}$ (e) $\overrightarrow{EB}$
(f) $\overrightarrow{AG}$ (g) $\overrightarrow{DF}$ (h) $\overrightarrow{FH}$ (i) $\overrightarrow{AC}$

12. (a) 58 m   (b) 60 m, 20° from sideline

13. (a) $\sqrt{|\vec{u}|^2 + |\vec{v}|^2}$ (b) $\sqrt{|\vec{u}|^2 + |\vec{v}|^2}$

EXERCISE 1.3

1. (a) 4 N right   (b) 9 N right   (c) 6 N left
   (d) 0 N

2. (a) 3 N right   (b) 1 N right

3. (a) 5 km/h E   (b) 200 km/h W   (c) 15 km/h E
   (d) 15 km/h W   (e) 210 km/h E
   (f) 215 km/h E   (g) 5 km/h W

4. (a) 11 N at 49° to 7 N force   (b) 96 N at 34° to
   48 N force   (c) 21 N at 42° to 12 N force

5. (a) 89 N at 168° from 55 N force away from the
   37 N force   (b) 11 N at 109° from 9 N force
   away from the 12 N force   (c) 25 N at 160°
   from 11 N force away from the 15 N force

6. 450 km/h, N71°E   **7.** 410 km/h, S54°W

8. 300 km/h, N70°W

9. (a) 11 kn, S4°E   (b) behind   **10.** 22 N

11. 7955 N

12. 18 kn, NE   **13.** 550 km h, S6°E

14. 28 N, 37 N

15. 227 km/h, S20°E   **16.** N42°E   **17.** 52 N

18. (a) 44° from shore   (b) 20 min

EXERCISE 1.4

1. (a) $-0.6\vec{v}$ (b) not possible   (c) $2\vec{v}$ (d) not
   possible

2.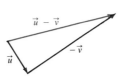

$\vec{u}$

$\vec{v}$

(a) $\frac{1}{2}\vec{u}$

(b)

$-3\vec{v}$

(c)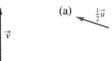

$5.2\vec{u}$

(d)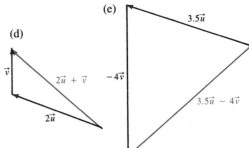

$\vec{v}$

$2\vec{u} + \vec{v}$

$2\vec{u}$

$-4\vec{v}$

(e)

$3.5\vec{u}$

$3.5\vec{u} - 4\vec{v}$

2. (f)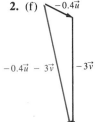

3.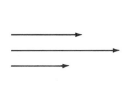

5. (a) 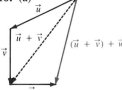 (b)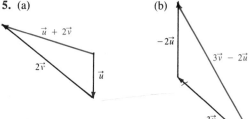

6. 1   **7.** (a) 75 N (b) 14 N

8. (a) 17 N to left (b) 23 N at 145° from 12 N force away from 15 N force

9. (a) 29 m/s at N78°E (b) 11 km/h at N49°E

10. (a) $-11\vec{u}$ (b) $6\vec{u} - 4\vec{v}$ (c) $5\vec{u} + 8\vec{v}$
(d) $-15\vec{u} + 3\vec{v}$ (e) $2\vec{v}$

11. 7 N at 31° to the resultant   **12.** 22 N

13. 288 km/h at N58°W   **14.** (a) 10 kn at S13°E
(b) in front

15. (a) $\sqrt{|\vec{x}|^2 + |\vec{y}|^2}$ (b) $\sqrt{|\vec{x}|^2 + |\vec{y}|^2}$
(c) $\sqrt{4|\vec{x}|^2 + 25|\vec{y}|^2}$ (d) $\sqrt{9|\vec{y}|^2 + |\vec{x}|^2}$

16. (a)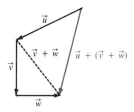

5. (a) $2\vec{v}$ (b) $\vec{u}$ (c) $2\vec{u}$ (d) $\vec{u} + \vec{v}$
(e) $2\vec{u} + 2\vec{v}$ (f) $\vec{u} + 2\vec{v}$ (g) $2\vec{v} - 2\vec{u}$

6. 1

8. (a) $\sqrt{|\vec{u}|^2 + 9|\vec{v}|^2}$ (b) $2\sqrt{4|\vec{u}|^2 + |\vec{v}|^2}$
(c) $\sqrt{\frac{1}{4}|\vec{v}|^2 + 25|\vec{u}|^2}$ (d) $\sqrt{2}|\vec{u}||\vec{v}|$

EXERCISE 1.5

1. (a) yes (b) yes (c) yes

3.

(b)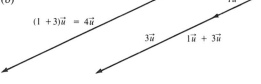

5. (a)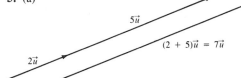

(c)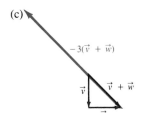

7. (a) $-7\vec{u} + 4\vec{v}$ (b) $7\vec{u} - 5\vec{v}$ (c) $7\vec{v} + \vec{w}$
(d) $-8\vec{u} + 17\vec{v} + \vec{w}$ (e) $6\vec{u}$

8. $\vec{u} = -2\vec{i}, \vec{v} = 7\vec{i} + \vec{j}, \vec{u} + \vec{v} = 5\vec{i} + \vec{j},$
$\vec{u} - \vec{v} = -9\vec{i} - \vec{j}$

10. (Let $\vec{w} = -\vec{u} - \vec{v}$.)

1.6 REVIEW EXERCISE

1. (b), (c), (d), and (e)

2. (a) $-\vec{r} + \vec{q} - \vec{w} - \vec{v}$ (b) $\vec{z} + 0\vec{w} - \vec{v}$
(c) $-\vec{y} - \vec{x} - \vec{q} - \vec{p} - \vec{v}$

3. $\overrightarrow{AD} = \overrightarrow{DB} = \overrightarrow{FE}, \overrightarrow{AF} = \overrightarrow{FC} = \overrightarrow{DE},$
$\overrightarrow{CE} = \overrightarrow{EB} = \overrightarrow{FD}$

4. (a)   (b)

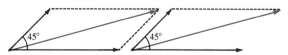

1.7 CHAPTER 1 TEST

1. when $\vec{u}$ and $\vec{v}$ have same direction

2. (a) $\frac{1}{2}\overrightarrow{AC}$ (b) $\overrightarrow{AB} + \frac{1}{2}\overrightarrow{BC}$ (c) $2\overrightarrow{AF} - 2\overrightarrow{EC}$

3. $-\vec{u} + 3\vec{v}$

5. 23 N   **6.** (a) S25°E (b) 540 km/h

7. $13\vec{u}$ **8.** 10 N, 7 N

CHAPTER 2 LINEAR COMBINATIONS OF VECTORS

REVIEW AND PREVIEW TO CHAPTER 2

EXERCISE 1

1. (a) 5:2, internally   (b) 6:5, externally
(c) 3:1, internally   (d) 2:5, externally
(e) 6:5 internally

2. (a) 1:3   (b) 2:9   (c) 17:7

3. $CQ = \frac{27}{4}$ cm, $QD = \frac{45}{4}$ cm

4. $AP = \frac{70}{3}$ cm, $PB = \frac{40}{3}$ cm

EXERCISE 2

1. $a = 2, b = 3, c = -6$

2. $a = 0, b = 1, c = 2$

3. $a = 1, b = 3, c = -2$

4. $a = -1, b = \frac{3}{4}, c = 2$

5. $a = b = 1, c = -1, d = 2$

6. $a = 1, b = 0, c = 3, d = 2$

EXERCISE 2.1

1. $\vec{u} = -\frac{1}{5}\vec{v} + \frac{7}{5}\vec{w} - \frac{7}{10}\vec{z}$,
$\vec{v} = -5\vec{u} + 7\vec{w} - 3.5\vec{z}$,
$\vec{w} = \frac{5}{7}\vec{u} + \frac{1}{7}\vec{v} + \frac{1}{2}\vec{z}$, $\vec{z} = -\frac{10}{7}\vec{u} - \frac{2}{7}\vec{v} + 2\vec{w}$

2. (a) $\vec{a} = 2\vec{c} - \vec{b}$ (b) $\vec{a} = \vec{c} - \vec{d}$
(c) $\vec{b} = 0\vec{a} + \vec{c} + \vec{d}$

3. (a)   (b)

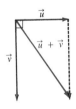

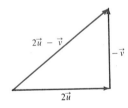

(c)

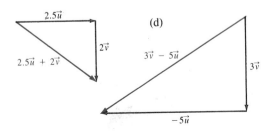

(d)

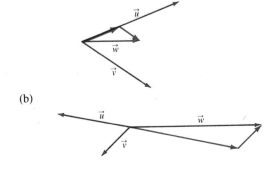

4. (a)   (b)

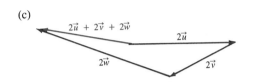

(c)

(d)

5. (a) $\vec{w} = \sqrt{3}\,\vec{u} + \frac{2}{3}\vec{v} \doteq 1.7\vec{u} + 0.7\vec{v}$

(b) $\vec{u} = \frac{1}{\sqrt{3}}\vec{w} - \frac{2\sqrt{3}}{9}\vec{v} \doteq 0.6\vec{w} - 0.4\vec{v}$

6. $\vec{w} = -\frac{8}{\sqrt{3}}\vec{u} - \frac{8}{5\sqrt{3}}\vec{v}$
$\doteq -4.6\vec{u} - 0.9\vec{v}$

7. (a) $\vec{z} \doteq -0.3\vec{x} - 0.6\vec{y}$
(b) $\vec{x} \doteq -2\vec{y} - 3.3\vec{z}$

8. (a) $-\frac{1}{2}(\vec{u} + \vec{v}) + \frac{7}{2}(\vec{u} - \vec{v})$ (b) coplanar

9. (c) 4 linearly dependent vectors   **12.** (b) $\vec{O}$

EXERCISE 2.2

1. (a) parallel   (b) not coplanar

2. (a) $a = -2, b = 3$ (b) not possible
(c) $a = -1$

3. (a) $\overrightarrow{AD}$, $\overrightarrow{BC}$ dependent; $\overrightarrow{AB}$, $\overrightarrow{DC}$ independent
(b) $\overrightarrow{PT}$, $\overrightarrow{TS}$ dependent; $\overrightarrow{QT}$, $\overrightarrow{TR}$ independent

4. (a)

(b)

4. (c) not possible because $\vec{u}$ and $\vec{v}$ are dependent (parallel)

(d)

5. (a) $\vec{u}, \vec{v}$ parallel

(b) $\vec{u}, \vec{v}$, and $\vec{w}$ coplanar

(c) $\vec{u}, \vec{v}$ parallel $\vec{u}, \vec{v}, \vec{w}$ coplanar

(d) $\vec{u}, \vec{v}, \vec{w}$ coplanar

6. (a) $a = \frac{2}{3}, b = -\frac{3}{4}$

(b) $a = -\frac{1}{2}, b = \frac{5}{12}, c = 0$

(c) $m = k = 1$ (d) $a = m = \frac{1}{2}$

EXERCISE 2.3

1. (a) $3:7$ (b) $2:-5$ (c) $11:-2$ (d) $5:4$

2. (a) (i) X divides $\overrightarrow{YZ}$ in ratio $3:7$ (ii) Y divides $\overrightarrow{XZ}$ in ratio $3:-10$ (b) (i) Y divides $\overrightarrow{XZ}$ in ratio $2:3$ (ii) X divides $\overrightarrow{YZ}$ in ratio $2:-5$ (c) (i) Z divides $\overrightarrow{XY}$ in ratio $2:9$ (ii) X divides $\overrightarrow{ZY}$ in ratio $2:-11$ (d) (i) X divides $\overrightarrow{ZY}$ in ratio $4:5$ ii) Z divides $\overrightarrow{XY}$ in ratio $4:-9$

3. (a)

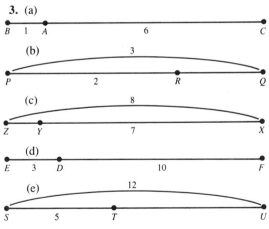

4. (a) $-\frac{3}{14}$ (b) $\frac{11}{14}$ (c) $\frac{11}{3}$

5. (a) $\overrightarrow{XZ} = \frac{7}{10}\overrightarrow{YZ}$ (b) $\overrightarrow{YZ} = \frac{3}{5}\overrightarrow{XZ}$

(c) $\overrightarrow{ZY} = \frac{9}{11}\overrightarrow{XY}$ (d) $\overrightarrow{XY} = \frac{5}{9}\overrightarrow{ZY}$

6. (a) $\overrightarrow{XZ} = \frac{7}{3}\overrightarrow{YX}$ (b) $\overrightarrow{YZ} = \frac{3}{2}\overrightarrow{XY}$

(c) $\overrightarrow{ZY} = \frac{9}{2}\overrightarrow{XZ}$ (d) $\overrightarrow{XY} = \frac{5}{4}\overrightarrow{ZX}$

8. (a)

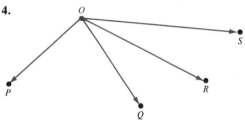

(b) $3:-38$ (c) $\overrightarrow{CD} = -\frac{2}{19}\overrightarrow{BD}$ **9.** $4:-5$

10. $5:-4$ **11.** $3:-4$

12.

13. Z divides $\overrightarrow{XY}$ in ratio $1 + c:-1$

EXERCISE 2.4

1. (a) internally   (b) externally   (c) externally

(d) internally

2. (a) $1:5$ (b) $11:-2$ (c) $-5:11$ (d) $1:1$

3. (a) $\frac{2}{7}\overrightarrow{OY} + \frac{5}{7}\overrightarrow{OZ}$ (b) $\frac{5}{4}\overrightarrow{OY} - \frac{1}{4}\overrightarrow{OZ}$

(c) $\frac{4}{13}\overrightarrow{OY} + \frac{9}{13}\overrightarrow{OZ}$ (d) $-\frac{2}{5}\overrightarrow{OY} + \frac{7}{5}\overrightarrow{OZ}$

4.

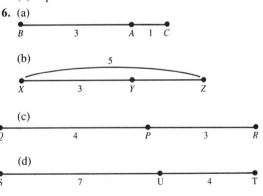

5. (a) coplanar   (b) collinear   (c) collinear

(d) coplanar

6. (a)

(b)

(c)

(d)

7. (a) $\frac{7}{10}\overrightarrow{OY} + \frac{3}{10}\overrightarrow{OZ}$ (b) $-\frac{2}{5}\overrightarrow{OY} + \frac{7}{5}\overrightarrow{OZ}$

8. (a) $-2\overrightarrow{OB} + 3\overrightarrow{OC}$ (b) $\frac{2}{3}\overrightarrow{OB} + \frac{1}{3}\overrightarrow{OC}$

(c) $\frac{9}{5}\overrightarrow{OB} - \frac{4}{5}\overrightarrow{OC}$ (d) $-\frac{2}{9}\overrightarrow{OB} + \frac{11}{9}\overrightarrow{OC}$

13. (a) $\overrightarrow{OA} = \frac{11}{5}\overrightarrow{OC} - \frac{6}{5}\overrightarrow{OD}$

(b) $\overrightarrow{OC} = \frac{5}{9}\overrightarrow{OB} + \frac{4}{9}\overrightarrow{OD}$

EXERCISE 2.5

1. (a) $\frac{7}{11}\overrightarrow{OB} + \frac{4}{11}\overrightarrow{OC}$ (b) $\frac{7}{4}\overrightarrow{OX} - \frac{3}{4}\overrightarrow{OY}$

(c)$\frac{3}{2}\overrightarrow{OP} - \frac{1}{2}\overrightarrow{OB}$ (d) $\frac{5}{7}\overrightarrow{OF} + \frac{2}{7}\overrightarrow{OB}$

(e) $2\overrightarrow{OM} - \overrightarrow{OB}$

2. (a) $a = c = \frac{1}{3}$, $b = d = \frac{2}{3}$

(b) $k = n = \frac{4}{11}$, $l = m = \frac{7}{11}$

12. $1:2$ **13.** G divides $\overrightarrow{AF}$ in ratio $25:7$;
G divides $\overrightarrow{BE}$ in ratio $7:32$.

14. (b) $|\overrightarrow{XY}| = \left|\frac{m}{m+n}\right| |\overrightarrow{QR}|$

2.6 REVIEW EXERCISE

1. (a) $\vec{v} = -\frac{2}{3}\vec{u} + \frac{5}{3}\vec{w}$ (b) $\vec{x} = -\vec{y} + \frac{1}{2}\vec{z}$

(c) $\vec{a} = \frac{5\sqrt{3}}{4}\vec{b} + \frac{5}{3}\vec{c} \doteq 2.2\vec{b} + 1.7\vec{c}$

(d) $2\vec{v} - \vec{u} = \frac{1}{2}(\vec{u} + \vec{v}) - \frac{3}{2}(\vec{u} - \vec{v})$

(e) $\overrightarrow{OA} = \frac{1}{3}\overrightarrow{OB} + \frac{2}{3}\overrightarrow{OC}$

(f) $\overrightarrow{OX} = 3\overrightarrow{OY} - 2\overrightarrow{OZ}$

(g) $\overrightarrow{OQ} = \frac{2}{7}\overrightarrow{OP} + \frac{5}{7}\overrightarrow{OR}$

3. (a) not parallel   (b) coplanar

4. (a) $c = 3$, $d = \frac{4}{5}$ (b) $a = \frac{3}{5}$, $b = \frac{2}{3}$

5. (a)

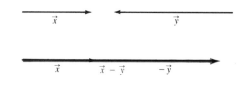

(b)   (i)

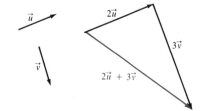

5. (b)   (ii)   (c)

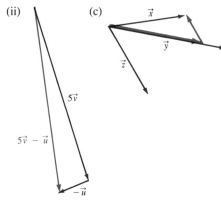

6. (a) $\vec{u}$, $\vec{v}$ parallel   (b) $\vec{x}$, $\vec{u}$, and $\vec{v}$ coplanar

10. (a) $5:4$ (b) $4: -7$

(c) $2:3$

(d) $2: -9$

12. (a)

(b) $\overrightarrow{OT} = \frac{2}{7}\overrightarrow{OX} + \frac{5}{7}\overrightarrow{OZ}$

13. (a) no conclusion possible   (b) coplanar

15. $6:1$

2.7 CHAPTER 2 TEST

1. $9\vec{x} - 3\vec{y}$

2.

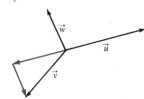

3. $c = 2$, $d = 3$

5. (a) coplanar   (b) no conclusion possible

6. (a)

(b) $\overrightarrow{OC} = \frac{1}{3}\overrightarrow{OA} + \frac{2}{3}\overrightarrow{OB}$

CHAPTER 3 PRODUCTS OF VECTORS

REVIEW AND PREVIEW TO CHAPTER 3

EXERCISE 1

1. (a) $\sin \theta = \dfrac{4}{5}$ $\cos \theta = \dfrac{3}{5}$ $\tan \theta = \dfrac{4}{3}$

$\csc \theta = \dfrac{5}{4}$ $\sec \theta = \dfrac{5}{3}$ $\cot \theta = \dfrac{3}{4}$

(b) $\sin \theta = \dfrac{5}{13}$ $\cos \theta = -\dfrac{12}{13}$ $\tan \theta = -\dfrac{5}{12}$

$\csc \theta = \dfrac{13}{5}$ $\sec \theta = -\dfrac{13}{12}$ $\cot \theta = -\dfrac{12}{5}$

(c) $\sin \theta = -\dfrac{2}{\sqrt{13}}$ $\cos \theta = -\dfrac{3}{\sqrt{13}}$ $\tan \theta = \dfrac{2}{3}$

$\csc \theta = -\dfrac{\sqrt{13}}{2}$ $\sec \theta = -\dfrac{\sqrt{13}}{3}$ $\cot \theta = \dfrac{3}{2}$

(d) $\sin \theta = -\dfrac{1}{\sqrt{2}}$ $\cos \theta = \dfrac{1}{\sqrt{2}}$ $\tan \theta = -1$

$\csc \theta = -\sqrt{2}$ $\sec \theta = \sqrt{2}$ $\cot \theta = -1$

2. (a) $\sin \theta = \dfrac{4}{5}$ $\cos \theta = -\dfrac{3}{5}$ $\tan \theta = -\dfrac{4}{3}$

$\csc \theta = \dfrac{5}{4}$ $\sec \theta = -\dfrac{5}{3}$ $\cot \theta = -\dfrac{3}{4}$

(b) $\sin \theta = -\dfrac{2}{\sqrt{29}}$ $\cos \theta = \dfrac{5}{\sqrt{29}}$ $\tan \theta = -\dfrac{2}{5}$

$\csc \theta = -\dfrac{\sqrt{29}}{2}$ $\sec \theta = \dfrac{\sqrt{29}}{5}$ $\cot \theta = -\dfrac{5}{2}$

(c) $\sin \theta = -\dfrac{5}{\sqrt{29}}$ $\cos \theta = -\dfrac{2}{\sqrt{29}}$ $\tan \theta = \dfrac{5}{2}$

$\csc \theta = -\dfrac{\sqrt{29}}{5}$ $\sec \theta = -\dfrac{\sqrt{29}}{2}$ $\cot \theta = \dfrac{2}{5}$

(d) $\sin \theta = -1$ $\cos \theta = 0$ $\tan \theta$ is undefined $\csc \theta = -1$ $\sec \theta$ is undefined $\cot \theta = 0$

4. (a) $\sin 0° = 0$ $\cos 0° = 1$ $\tan 0° = 0$ $\csc 0°$ is undefined $\sec 0° = 1$ $\cot 0° =$ is undefined
(b) $\sin 90° = 1$ $\cos 90° = 0$ $\tan 90°$ is undefined $\csc 90° = 1$ $\sec 90°$ is undefined $\cot 90° = 0$
(c) $\sin 180° = 0$ $\cos 180° = -1$ $\tan 180° = 0$ $\csc 180°$ is undefined $\sec 180° = -1$ $\cot 180°$ is undefined
(d) $\sin 270° = -1$ $\cos 270° = 0$ $\tan 270°$ is undefined $\csc 270° = -1$ $\sec 270°$ is undefined $\cot 270° = 0$

EXERCISE 2

1. (a) $\dfrac{1}{\sqrt{2}}$ (b) $\dfrac{\sqrt{3}}{2}$ (c) $\sqrt{3}$ (d) $-\dfrac{1}{\sqrt{2}}$ (e) 1

(f) $-\dfrac{1}{2}$ (g) $\dfrac{1 + \sqrt{2}}{\sqrt{2}}$ (h) $\dfrac{1 - \sqrt{3}}{2}$

EXERCISE 3

1. (a) $\dfrac{\sqrt{3}}{2}$ (b) $\dfrac{1}{\sqrt{2}}$ (c) $\dfrac{1}{\sqrt{3}}$ (d) $-\dfrac{1}{2}$ (e) 0 (f) 1
(g) 0 (h) $\dfrac{1}{2}$

EXERCISE 3.1

1. (a) 50 N and 42 N (b) 39 N and 17 N
(c) 750 N and 650 N
2. 57° and 29°
3. (a) $25\sqrt{3}$ and 25 (b) 192 and 161
(c) 0 and 110
4. 27 N and 63° **5.** 384 N and 507 N
6. (a) 2.6 kN and 29.9 kN (b) The component parallel to the ground moves the helicopter forward. The component perpendicular to the ground lifts the helicopter.
7. 1350 N and 1350 N **8.** 434 N and 377 N
9. 215 N and 215 N **10.** 840 N and 840 N
11. 8.9 N and 4.7 N **12.** 3900 N and 3380 N

EXERCISE 3.2

1. $14.1\hat{v}$ **2.** (a) $-9.6\hat{b}$ (b) -12.9
3. $-7.6\hat{v}$
4. (a) $\vec{u}$ (b) 0, 0 (c) $\vec{u}$, $-|\vec{u}$
5. (a) When $|\vec{u}| = |\vec{v}|$ or $\vec{u} \perp \vec{v}$
(b) When $\vec{u} = \vec{v}$ or $\vec{u} \perp \vec{v}$
6. 45° or 135° **7.** 710 km/h, 3170 m/min
8. 303 N, 212 N **9.** 96 N **10.** 108 N
11. 1880 m/min, 421 km/h **12.** 30 N
13. 105 N **14.** 30°

EXERCISE 3.3

1. (a) vector (b) scalar (c) scalar (d) vector
(e) vector (f) scalar (g) vector (h) scalar
(i) vector (j) scalar (k) scalar (l) scalar
2. (a) no meaning (b) meaning (c) meaning
(d) no meaning (e) meaning (f) meaning
(g) no meaning (h) no meaning
3. (a) $30\sqrt{3}$ (b) -225 (c) -77.7 (d) 0
(e) 21 200 000 (f) -456 (g) $-\dfrac{1}{2}$
4. (a) $\dfrac{1}{2}$ (b) $\dfrac{1}{2}$ (c) -0.31 (d) 0.81
5. (a) $k|\vec{u}|^2 + \vec{u}\cdot\vec{v}$
(b) $kl(\vec{u}\cdot\vec{v}) - l|\vec{v}|^2$
(c) $|\vec{u}|^2 - |\vec{v}|^2$
(d) $\vec{u}\cdot\vec{w} + \vec{u}\cdot\vec{x} + \vec{v}\cdot\vec{w} + \vec{v}\cdot\vec{x}$
6. (a) $-8 \leqslant \vec{u}\cdot\vec{v} \leqslant 8$ **7.** no **9.** 2

EXERCISE 3.4

6. 9020 J   **7.** 2040 J   **8.** 303 J

EXERCISE 3.5

1. (a) scalar (b) no meaning (c) vector
   (d) no meaning (e) vector (f) no meaning
   (g) scalar

2. (a) into the page (b) into the page
   (c) out of the page

3. (a) $25\sqrt{3}$ into the page (b) 36 out of the page
   (c) 14 800 out of the page

4. (a) 3 N·m (b) 17 N·m (c) 128 N·m

5. 11 N·m   **6.** 5300 N·m, 5340 N·m

7. (a) 287 (b) 257

11. $\vec{u}, \vec{u} \times \vec{v}, \vec{u} \times (\vec{u} \times \vec{v})$

3.6 REVIEW EXERCISE

1. (a) 17.3 N and 9.9 N (b) 8.8 N and 3.0 N

2. 1140 N and 654 N

3. 329 N and 247 N   **4.** (a) $-14\hat{v}$ (b) 21.5

5. 93 N   **6.** 587 km/h and 3560 m/min

7. (a) scalar (b) vector (c) scalar (d) vector
   (e) vector

8. (a) no meaning (b) meaning (c) no meaning

9. (a) 138 (b) $-\dfrac{11\ 875}{\sqrt{2}}$ (c) -46.1 **10.** 1

11. (a) $\vec{u} \cdot \vec{w} - \vec{u} \cdot \vec{x} - \vec{v} \cdot \vec{w} + \vec{v} \cdot \vec{x}$
    (b) $k^2|\vec{u}|^2 + k\vec{v} \cdot \vec{u}$

13. 2320 J   **14.** 1740 J

15. (a) 261 N·m into the page
    (b) 279 N·m into the page

16. (a) 1.5 N·m (b) 0.96 N·m

17. (a) $64\sqrt{3}$ (b) 78.8   **18.** 550 N·m

19. (a) true (b) false (c) true (d) true (e) true
    (f) true (g) true (h) false (i) true (j) true

20. (a) $3.6\hat{v}$ (b) 2.6 (c) 36.2
    (d) 36.2 (e) $135\ \hat{n}$ (where $\hat{n}$ is directed into the page)
    (f) $-135\ \hat{n}$

3.7 CHAPTER 3 TEST

1. (a) $-2\hat{v}$ (b) -4.5 (c) -18 (d) $18\sqrt{3}$

2. (a) $\vec{w}$ (b) $\vec{u}$ (c) $-\vec{v}$ **3.** 1

4. 767 N and 718 N   **5.** 29.4 N   **6.** 1420 J

8. when the shaft of the pedal is in the horizontal position

CUMULATIVE REVIEW FOR CHAPTERS 1 TO 3

1. (a)   (b)

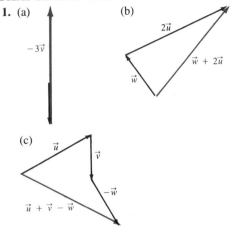

2. (a) magnitude 16 at 33° from vector with magnitude 7 (b) magnitude 42 at 98° from vector with magnitude 65 (c) magnitude 21 at N48°E

3. if $\vec{u}$ and $\vec{v}$ have same direction

4. (a) 21 N (b) 41 N (c) 205 N

5. (a) 2 N left (b) 79 N at 154° to 105 N force away from 48 N force (c) 66 N at 166° to 56 N force away from 18 N force

6. (a) $\overrightarrow{AB} = \overrightarrow{FE} = \dfrac{\vec{u} + \vec{v}}{\sqrt{2}}$,
    $\overrightarrow{CD} = \overrightarrow{HG} = \dfrac{\vec{u} - \vec{v}}{\sqrt{2}}$, $\overrightarrow{BC} = \overrightarrow{GF} = \vec{u}$,
    $\overrightarrow{HA} = \overrightarrow{ED} = \vec{v}$
    (b) $\overrightarrow{GA} = \dfrac{-\vec{u} + (\sqrt{2} + 1)\vec{v}}{\sqrt{2}}$,
    $\overrightarrow{GB} = \dfrac{(\sqrt{2} + 2)\vec{v}}{\sqrt{2}}$,
    $\overrightarrow{GC} = \dfrac{\sqrt{2}\vec{u} + (\sqrt{2} + 2)\vec{v}}{\sqrt{2}}$,
    $\overrightarrow{GD} = \dfrac{(\sqrt{2} + 1)\vec{u} + (\sqrt{2} + 1)\vec{v}}{\sqrt{2}}$,
    $\overrightarrow{GE} = \dfrac{(\sqrt{2} + 1)\vec{u} + \vec{v}}{\sqrt{2}}$

7. 20 N   **8.** 23 knots N25°W

9. S13°E, 1 hour 13 minutes   **10.** 12 km/h

12. (a) $-12\vec{u} + 3\vec{v}$ (b) $2\vec{u} + 10\vec{v} + 2\vec{w}$

13. (a) $\vec{u} = \vec{x} + 0\vec{y} + \vec{z} + \vec{w}$
    (b) $\vec{u} = 0.32\vec{v} + 0.17\vec{w}$
    (c) $\overrightarrow{AX} = \frac{1}{2}\overrightarrow{AD} + \frac{1}{2}\overrightarrow{DC} = \frac{1}{2}\overrightarrow{AB} + \frac{1}{2}\overrightarrow{BC}$
    (d) $\overrightarrow{OA} = \frac{4}{7}\overrightarrow{OB} + \frac{3}{7}\overrightarrow{OC}$

14. (a) two parallel vectors   (b) three non-coplanar vectors (basis for space)

16. linearly dependent

17. (a) $a = -\frac{1}{2}$, $b = -1$, $c = \frac{2}{3}$ (b) no such m

19. (a)

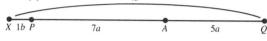

(b) 28:15

20. $(k + 1) : -1$

21. (a)

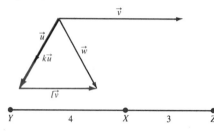

(b)

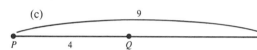

(c)

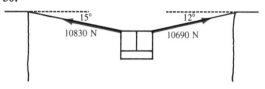

23. (a) $\overrightarrow{OA} = \frac{7}{5}\overrightarrow{OB} - \frac{2}{5}\overrightarrow{OC}$

   (b) $\overrightarrow{OC} = \frac{1}{8}\overrightarrow{OA} + \frac{7}{8}\overrightarrow{OD}$ **24.** 8 : 5

28. (a)

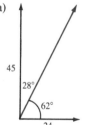

(b)

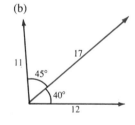

28. (c)

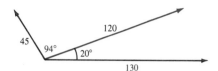

(d)

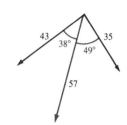

29. tension 92 N, force exerted by hinge 62 N

30.

31. (a) (i) $1.5\vec{v}$ (ii) 6   (b) (i) $1.3\vec{v}$ (ii) -32

32. groundspeed 264 km/h, rate of climb 3958 m/min

33. (a) 101 N   (b) 108 N

34. (a) 75 315   (b) -228 (c) $\sqrt{2}$ (d) 419

35. (a) 41 748   (b) $228\sqrt{3} \doteq 395$ (c) $\sqrt{2}$
   (d) 294

37. (a) 900 J   (b) 1300 J   (c) 2100 J

38. (a) 99   (b) 3964

39. (a) 200 Nm   (b) 68 Nm   (c) 68 Nm

CHAPTER 4 ALGEBRAIC VECTORS

REVIEW AND PREVIEW TO CHAPTER 4

EXERCISE 1

1. $x = -2$
   $y = 1$

2. $k = 3$
   $l = 3$

3. $m = \frac{30}{12}$
   $n = \frac{6}{13}$

4. $k = -\frac{2}{5}$
   $l = \frac{23}{10}$

EXERCISE 2

1. $k = 2$
   $l = -3$

2. no solution

3. $x = -1$
   $y = 2$

4. no solution

EXERCISE 3

1. $k = 2$
   $l = -1$
   $m = 0$

2. $k = 2$
   $l = -1$
   $m = 0$

3. $x = 4$
   $y = -5$
   $z = 3$

4. $r = 2$
   $s = -2$
   $t = 1$

EXERCISE 4.1

1. (a) $3\vec{i} - 5\vec{j}$ (b) $-3\vec{i} - 6\vec{j} + 9\vec{k}$
   (c) $5\vec{i} - 7\vec{k}$

2. (a) $(3, 8)$ or $(3, 8, 0)$ (b) $(-5, 0, -2)$
   (c) $(7, -4, 9)$

3. (a) $(2, -3)$ (b) $(-5, 4, 0)$ (c) $(5, -4, 5)$
   (d) $(-6, -8, -2)$

5. (a)

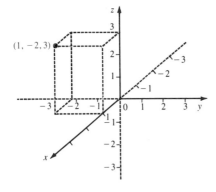

(b)

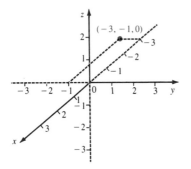

(c)

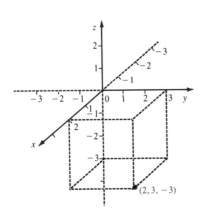

6. (a)

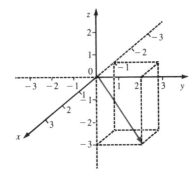

(b)

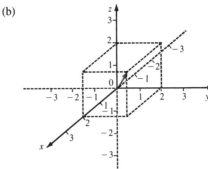

(c)

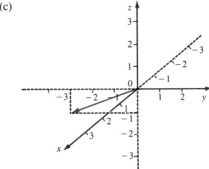

7. (a) collinear vectors lying on the y-axis
   (b) coplanar vectors lying in the xy-plane
   (c) coplanar vectors lying in the yz-plane
   (c) coplanar vectors lying in the xz-plane

8. (a) $\vec{u} = (3, 3)$ (b) $\vec{u} = (7, -6)$
   (c) $\vec{u} = (-7, -8, 3)$

9. (a) $a = -\frac{7}{2}$ (b) $a = 2, b = -24$
   (c) $a = 1, b = 0$

10. $c = 9, b = -3a$

EXERCISE 4.2

1. (a) $(5, -7)$ (b) $(4, 5, -12)$ (c) $(-12, 27)$
   (d) $(-10, 15, -5)$

2. (a) $(-13, 2)$ (b) $(3, -13, 19)$
   (c) $-4\vec{i} + 11\vec{j}$ or $(-4, 11)$
   (d) $3\vec{i} - 9\vec{j} + \vec{k}$ or $(3, -9, 1)$ (e) $\sqrt{29}$
   (f) $\sqrt{34}$

3. (a) $(-4, 1)$ (b) $(-14, 29)$ (c) $(5, -31)$
   (d) $(8, -51)$ (e) $\sqrt{17}$ (f) $\sqrt{85}$

4. (a) $(-8, 2, 4)$ (b) $(-14, -44, 62)$
   (c) $(-17, 27, -16)$ (d) $\sqrt{586}$

5. $\sqrt{1979}$ 6. (a) $(-4, 2)$ (b) $3\sqrt{2}$
   (c) $3\sqrt{2} + 2\sqrt{5} + \sqrt{26}$

7. (a) $(10, 3, -4)$ (b) 11
   (c) $5\sqrt{5} + 11 + \sqrt{66}$

8. (a) $\left(-\dfrac{1}{\sqrt{17}}, \dfrac{4}{\sqrt{17}}\right)$

   (b) $\left(\dfrac{2}{\sqrt{33}}, -\dfrac{2}{\sqrt{33}}, -\dfrac{5}{\sqrt{33}}\right)$

EXERCISE 4.3

1. (a) 11 (b) 17 (c) 0 (d) -1 (e) 0

2. (a) 8 (b) -20 (c) 0 (d) 0

4. (a) $25°$ (b) $112°$ (c) $107°$ (d) $180°$ (e) $52°$
   (f) $90°$ (g) $90°$ (h) $66°$

5. (a) $\frac{3}{2}$ (b) $-\frac{32}{3}$ (c) $\frac{4}{3}$

6. any scalar multiple of $(3, -2)$

7. $(3, -2, 0)$ and $(2, 0, -1)$ [Note: Other answers are possible.]

8. (a) $(0, 0, -2)$ (b) $47°$ and $133°$
   (c) $71°$ and $109°$ 9. (a) $71°$ and $109°$

11. $\left(\dfrac{1}{\sqrt{6}}, -\dfrac{2}{\sqrt{6}}, -\dfrac{1}{\sqrt{6}}\right)$ or $\left(-\dfrac{1}{\sqrt{6}}, \dfrac{2}{\sqrt{6}}, \dfrac{1}{\sqrt{6}}\right)$

EXERCISE 4.4

1. (a) $(-6, 7, 10)$ (b) $(-15, -35, -2)$
   (c) $(0, 0, 0)$ (d) $(-15, 29, 21)$ (e) $(0, 0, 0)$
   (f) $(-12, 26, -18)$

4. $\left(-\dfrac{1}{\sqrt{26}}, \dfrac{4}{\sqrt{26}}, -\dfrac{3}{\sqrt{26}}\right)$ or

   $\left(\dfrac{1}{\sqrt{26}}, -\dfrac{4}{\sqrt{26}}, \dfrac{3}{\sqrt{26}}\right)$

5. (a) $PQRS$ is a parallelogram with area $2\sqrt{10}$
   (b) $PQRS$ is not a parallelogram (c) $PQRS$ is a parallelogram with area $\sqrt{1261}$

6. (a) $5\sqrt{3}$ (b) $\sqrt{586}$ (c) $\dfrac{\sqrt{3}}{2}$

9. (a) 11 (b) -11 (c) $(14, -8, 2)$
   (d) $(7, -11, 3)$

10. (a) -18 (b) -18 (c) $(-1, -2, -7)$
    (d) $(-48, -24, 6)$

EXERCISE 4.5

1. (a) collinear (b) non-collinear
   (c) non-collinear (d) non-collinear
   (e) collinear (f) non-collinear

2. $a = \frac{16}{25}$ 3. $a = -\frac{3}{4}$ and $b = 24$

4. (a) coplanar (b) coplanar (c) non-coplanar

5. (a) not a basis (b) basis (c) not a basis

6. (a) $\vec{u}$ and $\vec{x}$ are collinear. $\vec{v}$ and $\vec{w}$ are collinear. $\vec{u}$, $\vec{v}$, $\vec{w}$, and $\vec{x}$ are coplanar.
   (b) No two vectors are collinear. No three vectors are coplanar.
   (c) No two vectors are collinear. $\vec{u}$, $\vec{v}$, and $\vec{x}$ are coplanar and $\vec{w}$ does not lie in this plane.
   (d) No two vectors are collinear. No three vectors are coplanar.

7. (a) $\vec{u}$, $\vec{v}$, and $\vec{x}$ form a basis and
   $\vec{w} = -\vec{u} + 0\vec{v} + 0\vec{x}$.
   (b) $\vec{u}$, $\vec{v}$, and $\vec{x}$ form a basis and
   $\vec{w} = \vec{u} + 2\vec{v} + 0\vec{x}$.
   (c) No three vectors form a basis.
   (d) $\vec{u}$, $\vec{v}$, and $\vec{w}$ form a basis and
   $\vec{x} = -\vec{u} - \vec{v} - \vec{w}$.

8. $a = b$

4.6 REVIEW EXERCISE

1. (a)

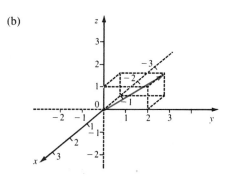

(b)

1. (c)

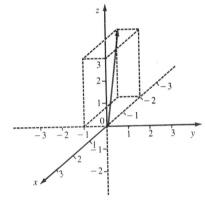

2. (a) collinear vectors lying on the z-axis
(b) coplanar vectors lying in the xz-plane

3. $c = \frac{15}{2}$ and $b = -\frac{5}{2}a$

4. (a) $(0, -13, 26)$ (b) $-3\vec{i} - 7\vec{j} + 10\vec{k}$ or
$(-3, -7, 10)$ (c) $\sqrt{29}$ (d) $2\sqrt{85}$

5. (a) $(-14, 21, -13)$ (b) 7

6. $\sqrt{29} + \sqrt{51} + \sqrt{42}$

7. $\left(-\dfrac{2}{\sqrt{22}}, \dfrac{3}{\sqrt{22}}, -\dfrac{3}{\sqrt{22}}\right)$ or
$\left(\dfrac{2}{\sqrt{22}}, -\dfrac{3}{\sqrt{22}}, \dfrac{3}{\sqrt{22}}\right)$

9. (a) 37   (b) -92 (c) -19 (d) -9

10. (a) $180°$ (b) $69°$ (c) $0°$ (d) $120°$

11. $4a - 3b = 12$

13. (a) $(12, 2, 28)$ (b) $(0, 0, 0)$ (c) $(-5, -11, 2)$

14. $\left(-\dfrac{1}{\sqrt{2}}, 0, \dfrac{1}{\sqrt{2}}\right)$ or $\left(\dfrac{1}{\sqrt{2}}, 0, -\dfrac{1}{\sqrt{2}}\right)$

15. (a) $(0, 0, 8)$ (b) $79°$ and $101°$ (c) $5\sqrt{38}$

16. (a) 3   (b) $(11, -8, 14)$ (c) They are not
coplanar.

17. (a) -1 (b) $(32, -17, -11)$ (c) They are not
coplanar.

18. (a) coplanar   (b) non-coplanar
(c) non-coplanar

19. (a) not a basis   (b) not a basis   (c) basis

20. (a) $\vec{u}$ and $\vec{x}$ are collinear. $\vec{u}, \vec{v}, \vec{w}$ and $\vec{x}$ are
coplanar.   (b) No two vectors are collinear.
$\vec{u}, \vec{w}$, and $\vec{x}$ are coplanar and $\vec{v}$ does not lie in
this plane.   (c) No two vectors are collinear.
No three vectors are coplanar.

21. (a) $\vec{u}, \vec{v}$, and $\vec{x}$ form a basis and
$\vec{w} = 2\vec{u} + \vec{v} + 0\vec{x}$.
(b) $\vec{u}, \vec{v}$, and $\vec{w}$ form a basis and
$\vec{x} = 0\vec{u} - 2\vec{v} + 0\vec{w}$.
(c) $\vec{u}, \vec{v}$, and $\vec{w}$ form a basis and
$\vec{x} = \frac{1}{2}\vec{u} + \frac{1}{2}\vec{v} + 0\vec{w}$.

4.7 CHAPTER 4 TEST

1.

2. (a) $(-10, -3, 5)$ (b) $\sqrt{91}$
(c) $\left(\dfrac{2}{\sqrt{14}}, -\dfrac{3}{\sqrt{14}}, -\dfrac{1}{\sqrt{14}}\right)$ (d) 4
(e) $(6, 0, 12)$

3. (a) $(0, -2, 1)$ (b) $51°$ and $129°$ (c) $\sqrt{185}$

4. $\left(\dfrac{1}{\sqrt{2}}, \dfrac{1}{\sqrt{2}}, 0\right)$ or $\left(-\dfrac{1}{\sqrt{2}}, -\dfrac{1}{\sqrt{2}}, 0\right)$

6. (a) -38 (b) $(21, -22, 19)$

7. No two vectors are collinear. $\vec{u}, \vec{v}$, and $\vec{w}$ are
coplanar and $\vec{x}$ does not lie in this plane.

8. $\vec{x} = 2\vec{u} - \vec{v} + 0\vec{w}$, $\vec{x}$ is coplanar with $\vec{u}$
and $\vec{v}$.

CHAPTER 5 EQUATIONS OF LINES

REVIEW AND PREVIEW TO CHAPTER 5

EXERCISE 1

1. (a) $y = -2x + 13$ (b) $y = 5$
(c) $y = 3x - 7$

2. (a) $5x - 2y - 7 = 0$
(b) $4x - 9y - 38 = 0$
(c) $12x + 5y - 1 = 0$ (d) $x + 2y = 0$

3. (a) undefined   (b) because slope is undefined
(c) $x = k$

EXERCISE 2

1. (a) $(-1, 2)$ (b) $\left(\frac{5}{2}, -5\right)$ (c) $\left(\frac{1}{2}, \frac{1}{3}\right)$
(d) $(-5, -1)$

EXERCISE 3

1. (a) a line in the plane 1 unit below *x*-axis
(b) a line in the plane 2 units right of *y*-axis
(c) *y*-axis   (d) a line in space 2 units right of
xz-plane, 1 unit below *xy*-plane   (e) a line in
space on *xy*-plane 2 units in front of *yz*-plane
(f) a line in space 3 units behind *yz*-plane,
4 units right of *xz*-plane

2. (a) a plane parallel to and 2 units in front of the
yz-plane   (b) a plane parallel to and 3 units to
the left of the *xz*-plane   (c) the *xy*-plane

3. (a) $(x, -2)$ (b) $(3, y)$ (c) $(x, 4.5, -1)$

4. (a)

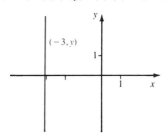

(b)

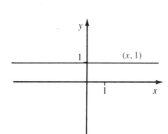

(c)

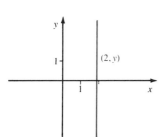

(d)

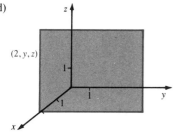

(e)

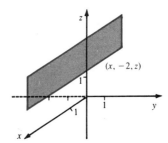

(f)

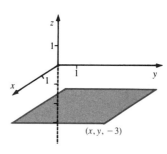

(g)

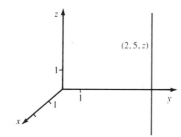

(h)

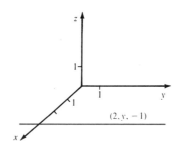

(i)

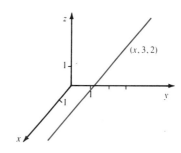

4. (j)

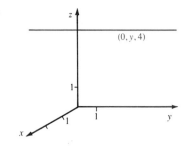

$(0, y, 4)$

EXERCISE 5.1

1. (a) $(5, -1)$ (b) $(-3, 4)$ (c) $(4, -1)$
   (d) $(5, 3)$ **2.** (a) 5, 1   (b) 2, 4

3. (a) $(2, 0)$, $(7, 3)$ (b) $(3, 0)$, $(-1, 2)$
   (c) $(3, -1)$, $(8, 0)$ (d) $(7, 2)$, $(12, 5)$

4. (a) $x = 2 + 3t$ (b) $x = 7 + 5t$
       $y = 5t$ $y = 2 + 3t$
   (c) $x = 3 + 5r$ (d) $x = 4$
       $y = -1 + r$ $y = -0.5 + 0.75s$

5. (a) $(x - 7, y - 2) = s(5, 3)$
   (b) $(x - 3, y) = t(-4, 2)$

6. (a) $\dfrac{x - 2}{5} = \dfrac{y}{3}$ (b) $\dfrac{3 - x}{4} = \dfrac{y}{2}$

7. (a) $(x - 2, y) = t(5, 3)$
   (b) $(x - 3, y) = t(-4, 2)$
   (c) $(x - 7, y - 2) = s(5, 3)$
   (d) $(x - 3, y + 1) = r(5, 1)$

8. (a) $\dfrac{x - 3}{2} = \dfrac{y + 7}{5}$ (b) $\dfrac{x + 4}{-2} = \dfrac{y}{3}$

   (c) $\dfrac{x}{2} = \dfrac{y}{-5}$ (d) $x - 5 = \dfrac{y - 6}{9}$

9. (a) no   (b) yes   (c) yes   (d) no

10. (a) $\overrightarrow{OP} = (2, 5) + t(1, 3)$
   (b) $\overrightarrow{OP} = (1, -3) + r(8, 5)$
   (c) $\overrightarrow{OP} = (3, -2) + s(0, 1)$
   (d) $\overrightarrow{OP} = t(1, 1)$

11. (a) $x = 3t$ (b) $x = 1$
       $y = -2t$ $y = 7 + 4t$
   (c) $x = 2 + 4s$ (d) $x = t$
       $y = 5 - 6s$ $y = 5 + 2t$

12. (a) $x - 1 = \dfrac{6 - y}{7}$ (b) $\dfrac{x}{3} = \dfrac{y + 5}{-4}$

   (c) no symmetric equations   (d) $\dfrac{x - \frac{5}{3}}{4} = \dfrac{y}{3}$

13. (b) parallel to x- or y-axis

14. $(x - 3, y + 5) = t(-1, 3)$,
   $x = 3 - t$, $y = -5 + 3t$
   $3 - x = \dfrac{y + 5}{3}$

15. $(x - 1, y - 2) = r(1, -3)$,
   $x = 1 + r$, $y = 2 - 3r$
   $x - 1 = \dfrac{2 - y}{3}$

16. (a) $3x + 5y - 16 = 0$

17. (a)

X Y P

(b) midpoint; P divides XY in ratio $3:2$;
P divides XY in ratio $2: -3$; P is X.
(c) $2:1$; $3: -4$; $5: -1$

18. (a) $\left(\frac{8}{5}, -\frac{6}{5}\right)$ (b) $\left(\frac{15}{11}, \frac{5}{11}\right)$ (c) $\left(\frac{1}{3}, \frac{23}{3}\right)$

EXERCISE 5.2

1. (a) $(5, -1, -3)$ (b) $(-3, 4, 0)$ (c) $(5, 3, 1)$

2. (a) $(5, 1, -3)$ (b) $(-1, 2, 3)$ (c) $(2, -3, -2)$

3. (a) $(2, 0, -1)$, $(7, 3, 3)$ (b) $(3, 0, 1)$, $(-1, 2, 6)$
   (c) $(3, -1, 4)$, $(8, 0, 4)$ (d) $(7, 2, -1)$,
   $(12, 5, 1)$

4. (a) $x = 2 + 3t$ (b) $x = 7 + 5t$
       $y = 5t$ $y = 2 + 3t$
       $z = -2 + t$ $z = -1 + 2t$
   (c) $x = 3 + 5r$ (d) $x = 4$
       $y = -1 + r$ $y = -0.5 + 0.75s$
       $z = 4$ $z = 1 + 2.0s$

5. (a) $(x - 7, y - 2, z + 1) = t(5, 3, 2)$
   (b) $(x - 3, y, z - 1) = t(-4, 2, 5)$

6. (a) $\dfrac{x - 2}{3} = \dfrac{y}{5} = z + 2$ (b) $\dfrac{3 - x}{4} = \dfrac{y}{2} = \dfrac{z - 1}{5}$

7. (a) $(x - 2, y, z + 2) = t(3, 5, 1)$
   (b) $(x - 3, y, z - 1) = t(-4, 2, 5)$
   (c) $(x - 7, y - 2, z + 1) = s(5, 3, 2)$
   (d) $(x - 3, y + 1, z - 4) = r(5, 1, 0)$

8. (a) $x - 3 = \dfrac{y + 2}{5} = -(z + 1)$

   (b) $\dfrac{x}{2} = \dfrac{y + 1}{3} = 1 - z$

9. (a) no   (b) yes   (c) yes   (d) no

10. (a) $(x, y, z) = t(3, -2, 7)$
   $x = 3t$, $y = -2t$, $z = 7t$
   (b) $(x - 1, y + 3, z - 2) = t(8, 5, -2)$
   $x = 1 + 8t$, $y = -3 + 5t$,
   $z = 2 - 2t$
   (c) $(x - 1, y - 3, z - 5) = t(0, 1, 0)$
   $x = 1$, $y = 3 + t$, $z = 5$
   (d) $(x, y, z - 4) = t(0, 1, 1)$
   $x = 0$, $y = t$, $z = 4 + t$

11. (a) $x - 1 = \dfrac{6 - y}{7} = \dfrac{z - 2}{3}$

(b) $x = -y = z - 5$ **12.** (b) parallel to

$x-$, $y-$, or z-axis

13. (a)$(x-3,\ y+5,\ z-1) = r\,(3,1,1)$

$x = 3 + 3r$

$y = -5 + r$

$z = 1 + r$

$\dfrac{x-3}{3} = y + 5 = z - 1$

14. (a) $\left(\frac{8}{5},\ -\frac{6}{5},\ \frac{28}{5}\right)$ (b) $\left(\frac{15}{11},\ \frac{5}{11},\ \frac{59}{11}\right)$ (c) $\left(\frac{1}{3},\ \frac{23}{3},\ \frac{13}{3}\right)$

EXERCISE 5.3

1.

	$\cos \alpha$	$\cos \beta$	$\cos \gamma$
(a)	1	0	0
(b)	0	1	0
(c)	0	0	1

2. (a) $\dfrac{2}{\sqrt{5}},\ \dfrac{1}{\sqrt{5}}$ (b) $-\dfrac{2}{\sqrt{29}},\ \dfrac{5}{\sqrt{29}}$

(c) $\dfrac{2}{\sqrt{30}},\ -\dfrac{1}{\sqrt{30}},\ \dfrac{5}{\sqrt{30}}$

3. (a) $-\dfrac{1}{\sqrt{5}},\ \dfrac{2}{\sqrt{5}}$ (b) $\dfrac{3}{\sqrt{13}},\ \dfrac{2}{\sqrt{13}}$

(c) $0,\ \dfrac{3}{\sqrt{13}},\ \dfrac{2}{\sqrt{13}}$ (d) $-\dfrac{3}{\sqrt{10}},\ \dfrac{1}{\sqrt{10}}$

(e) $\dfrac{2}{\sqrt{30}},\ \dfrac{5}{\sqrt{30}},\ \dfrac{1}{\sqrt{30}}$

4. (a) $\alpha = 34°,\ \beta = 56°$

(b) $\alpha = 97°,\ \beta = 125°,\ \gamma = 36°$

(c) $\alpha = 162°,\ \beta = 72°,\ \gamma = 90°$

5.

	$\cos \alpha$	α	$\cos \beta$	β	$\cos \gamma$	γ
(a)	$-\dfrac{5}{\sqrt{29}}$	158°	$\dfrac{2}{\sqrt{29}}$	68°	—	—
(b)	$-\frac{2}{7}$	107°	$\frac{3}{7}$	65°	$\frac{6}{7}$	31°

6. (a) $\dfrac{x-3}{2} = y$ (b) $\dfrac{x}{5} = -\dfrac{y}{2} = z$

9. $x = -2s,\ y = 1 - 4s,\ z = 5 + s$

11. (a) (i) $\alpha + \beta = 90°$ (ii) $\beta - \alpha = 90°$

(b) $\cos \beta = \pm \sin \alpha$

EXERCISE 5.4

1. (a) $(3, 2)$ (b) $(1, 1)$ (c) $(-3, 1)$ (d) $(1, 0)$

(e) $(5, -2)$ (f) $(0, 1)$

2. (a) $\left(\dfrac{3}{\sqrt{13}},\ \dfrac{2}{\sqrt{13}}\right)$ (b) $\left(\dfrac{1}{\sqrt{2}},\ \dfrac{1}{\sqrt{2}}\right)$

(c) $\left(-\dfrac{3}{\sqrt{10}},\ \dfrac{1}{\sqrt{10}}\right)$ (d) $(1, 0)$

2. (e) $\left(\dfrac{5}{\sqrt{29}},\ -\dfrac{2}{\sqrt{29}}\right)$ (f) $(0, 1)$

3. (a) parallel (b) perpendicular

4. (a) $5x + 7y - 3 = 0$ (b) $2x - 3y = 0$

(c) $5x - y - 11 = 0$ (d) $x = 4$

(e) $2x + y = 0$ (f) $10x - y - 13 = 0$

5. (a) $y = 2$ (b) $3x - 5y - 15 = 0$

(c) $x - 3y + 17 = 0$ (d) $3x - y - 10 = 0$

(e) $2x - 5y = 0$ (f) $x + 6y - 10 = 0$

6. (a) $x = 1$ (b) $5x + 3y + 9 = 0$

(c) $3x + y + 1 = 0$ (d) $x + 3y + 10 = 0$

(e) $5x + 2y = 0$ (f) $6x - y - 41.5 = 0$

7. (a) $x + y - 1 = 0$ (b) $x - 5y + 13 = 0$

(c) $5x - 2y - 17 = 0$

(d) $2x + 7y + 1 = 0$

8. (a) $(x+1, y+1) = r(2, -1)$

$x = -1 + 2r,\ y = -1 - r$

$\dfrac{x+1}{2} = -(y+1)$

(b) $(x-1, y+5) = r(1, 0)$

$x = 1 + r,\ y = -5$

no symmetric equations

(c) $(x-1, y-1) = r(1, 4)$

$x = 1 + r,\ y = 1 + 4r$

$x - 1 = \dfrac{y-1}{4}$

(d) $(x-3, y+2) = r(1, -3)$

$x = 3 + r,\ y = -2 - 3r$

$x - 3 = \dfrac{y+2}{-3}$

12. (a) $2x - y - 6 = 0$ (b) $2x - y + 5 = 0$

(c) parallel but distinct (d) parallel

EXERCISE 5.5

1. In (a) and (c) lines are parallel

2. Lines in 1.(a) are parallel, not identical.

3. $(-14, -20)$

4. (a) parallel so no intersection (b) $(-5, -7)$

(c) $(1, 7)$ (d) $\left(\frac{29}{14},\ \frac{19}{2}\right)$ **5.** $(1, 3, 0)$

6. (a) no intersection (b) no intersection

(c) no intersection (d) $(9, 8, 22)$

7. (intersect at $(-3, 6, 6)$)

8. (a) $k = 1$ (b) $k \in R$

EXERCISE 5.6

1. (a) $(2, -5)$ (b) $(1, 3)$ (c) $(-1, 0, 2)$

(d) $(-5, 0, 3)$

2. (a) $(-35, -11, 7)$ (b) $(17, -10, 4)$

3. (a) $\sqrt{\frac{57}{2}} \doteq 5.3$ (b) $\sqrt{\frac{172}{15}} \doteq 3.4$ (c) $\sqrt{\frac{465}{29}} \doteq 4.0$

4. (a) $X(3, 1)$ (b) $\dfrac{7}{\sqrt{10}}$

(c) (d) (e) $\dfrac{9}{\sqrt{10}} \doteq 2.8$

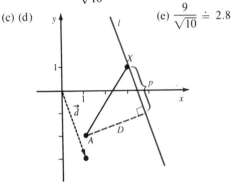

5. (a) $\dfrac{16}{\sqrt{34}} \doteq 2.7$ (b) $\dfrac{2}{\sqrt{2}} \doteq 1.4$ (c) 0

6. (a) $(2, -3)$ (b) $X(1, -1)$

(c)

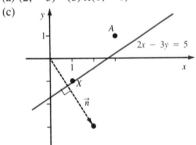

(d) $\dfrac{2}{\sqrt{13}}$ (e) same

7. (a) $\dfrac{2}{\sqrt{5}} \doteq 0.9$ (b) $\dfrac{2}{\sqrt{10}} \doteq 0.6$ (c) 0 (d) 4

8. (a) $\sqrt{\frac{464}{13}} \doteq 6.0$ (b) $\dfrac{3}{\sqrt{2}} \doteq 2.1$

(c) $\sqrt{13} \doteq 3.6$

9. (a) $X(2, -1)$ (b) 2

10. (a) (i) skew lines (ii) $\dfrac{158}{\sqrt{2214}} \doteq 3.4$

(b) (i) skew lines (ii) $\dfrac{234}{\sqrt{602}} \doteq 9.5$

11. (a) 0 (b) $\dfrac{98}{\sqrt{13169}} \doteq 0.9$ (c) $\dfrac{84}{\sqrt{390}} \doteq 4.3$

(d) $\dfrac{3}{\sqrt{2}} \doteq 2.1$

13. (b) (i) $3x + 5y - 2 = 0$, $3x + 5y + 2 = 0$
(ii) $x - 2 = 0$, $x + 2 = 0$

5.7 REVIEW EXERCISE

1. (a) $(1, -9)$ (b) $(7, 3)$ (c) $(3, -5, 9)$

2. (a) $(x-2, y, z-5) = t(1, 6, -6)$;
$x - 2 = \dfrac{y}{6} = \dfrac{5-z}{6}$ (b) $(x+5, y) = t(-2, 1)$;
$\dfrac{x+5}{-2} = y$

3. (a) $x = 2 + 5t$, $y = -7 + 3t$, $z = 1 - 2t$
(b) $x = t$, $y = 9 + 2t$

4. (a) $(3, -2)$ (b) $(5, 2)$

5. (a) $6x - y = 0$ (b) $x + 4y - \frac{6}{5} = 0$ or
$5x + 20y - 6 = 0$ (c) $3x + y - 7 = 0$

6. (a) $(x-2, y+4) = t(3, -1)$; $x + 3y + 10 = 0$
(b) $(x-2, y-7) = t(3, -5)$;
$5x + 3y - 31 = 0$

7. (a) $(2, -3, -4)$, $(3, -5, 3)$ (b) $(-1, 1)$, $(0, \frac{2}{5})$
(c) $(2, -1, -3)$, $(3, -1, 2)$ (d) $(-3, 2, 11)$,
$(-1, 1, 8)$

8. (a) no (b) no (c) no (d) no

9.

	$\cos \alpha$	α	$\cos \beta$	β	$\cos \gamma$	γ
(a)	$\dfrac{3}{\sqrt{10}}$	$18°$	$\dfrac{1}{\sqrt{10}}$	$72°$	0	$90°$
(b)	$\dfrac{3}{\sqrt{38}}$	$61°$	$-\dfrac{5}{\sqrt{38}}$	$144°$	$\dfrac{2}{\sqrt{38}}$	$71°$
(c)	$-\dfrac{5}{\sqrt{34}}$	$149°$	$\dfrac{3}{\sqrt{34}}$	$59°$	—	—

10. $x = 2 - \frac{1}{2}t$, $y = -1 + \frac{1}{2}t$, $z = 5 + \dfrac{1}{\sqrt{2}}t$

11. (a) $(4, 1)$ (b) $(-2, -5, -7)$
(c) no intersection

12. (intersect at $(-2, 4, -1)$)

13. (a) $\frac{9}{10} = 0.9$ (b) $3\sqrt{2} \doteq 4.2$ (c) $\dfrac{4}{\sqrt{3}} \doteq 2.3$

14. (a) $\dfrac{1}{2\sqrt{2}} \doteq 0.4$ (b) $\dfrac{52}{\sqrt{510}} \doteq 2.3$
(c) $\sqrt{\frac{1555}{74}} \doteq 4.6$

5.8 CHAPTER 5 TEST

1. $(x-4, y-1) = t(2, 7)$, $7x - 2y - 26 = 0$
2. $x = 3 - t$, $y = -1 + 12t$, $z = -5t$
3. not same line **4.** $3x + 2y - \frac{9}{4} = 0$ or
$12x + 8y - 9 = 0$
5. $\alpha \doteq 124°$, $\beta \doteq 42°$, $\gamma \doteq 68°$
6. no intersection (skew lines)
7. (a) $3\sqrt{3} \doteq 5.2$ (b) $\sqrt{41} \doteq 6.4$

CHAPTER 6 EQUATIONS OF PLANES

REVIEW AND PREVIEW TO CHAPTER 6

EXERCISE 1
1. (a) Yes (b) Yes (c) No (d) Yes
2. (a) Yes (b) No (c) Yes (d) Yes

EXERCISE 2
1. (a) Not collinear (b) Collinear (c) Collinear
(d) Collinear
2. (a) Coplanar (b) Coplanar (c) Not Coplanar
(d) Coplanar
3. (a) Not Coplanar (b) Coplanar

EXERCISE 6.1
1. (a) $(-1, -1, -4)$, $(5, -1, -3)$
(b) $(-3, 4, 0)$, $(2, -1, 3)$ (c) $(3, -1, 2)$,
$(1, -5, 3)$ (d) $(-2, 0, 1)$, $(-1, -2, 4)$
(e) $\vec{i}, \vec{k}$
2. (a) $(2, 0, -1)$, $(2, 2, -2)$ (b) $(3, 0, 1)$, $(1, 1, 2)$
(c) $(3, -1, 4)$, $(8, 0, 4)$
3. (a) Line (b) Plane (c) Plane (d) Line
(e) Line
4. (a) $x = 2 + 3t$, $y = s + 5t$,
$z = -2 - 2s + t$
(b) $x = 3 + 5r + s$, $y = -1 + r$,
$z = 4 + 3s$
(c) $x = 4 + t$, $y = -0.5 + 0.75s + 2.5t$,
$z = 1 + 2s - t$
5. $(x-3, y, z - 1) = s(-1, 0, 4) + t(4, 2, -5)$
6. (a) $(x-2, y, z+2) = s(0, 3, -1) + t(3, 5, 1)$
(b) $(x-3, y, z-1) = s(-2, 0, 5) + t(4, 2, 0)$
(c) $(x-3, y+1, z-4) = r(5, 1, 0)$
$+ s(-1, 2, 5)$
8. (a) $(-1, -1, 1)$ (b) $(-8, -5, -4)$
9. (a) Yes (b) Yes (c) No (d) Yes
10. (a) $(x, y, z) = s(3, -2, 7) + t(0, 1, -2)$
$x = 3s$, $y = -2s + t$, $z = 7s - 2t$
(b) $(x-1, y+3, z-2) = s(-1, 4, -4)$
$+ t(8, 5, -2)$ $x = 1 - s + 8t$,
$y = -3 + 4s + 5t$, $z = 2 - 4s - 2t$
(c) $(x-1, y-3, z-5) = s(1, 0, 0) + t(0, 1, 0)$
$x = 1 + s$, $y = 3 + t$, $z = 5$
(d) $(x, y, z-4) = s(1, 3, 0) + t(0, -1, 1)$
$x = s$, $y = 3s - t$, $z = 4 + t$
11. $(x-3, y+5, z-1) = s(1, 1, 1) + t(3, -1, 1)$
$x = 3 + s + 3t$, $y = -5 + s - t$,
$z = 1 + s + t$

12. (a) $(x-4, y-1, z+1) = s(-4, 0, 3)$
$+ t(-3, 0, 0)$ $x = 4 - 4s - 3t$, $y = 1$,
$z = -1 + 3s$
(b) $(x-4, y-1, z+1) = r(1, 0, 1) + s(2, 1, 0)$
$x = 4 + r + 2s$, $y = 1 + s$, $z = -1 + r$
(c) $(x-4, y-1, z+1) = s(-4, -1, 1)$
$+ t(-4, -1, 2)$
$x = 4 - 4s - 4t$,
$y = 1 - s - t$, $z = -1 + s + 2t$
(d) $(x-4, y-1, z+1) = s(1, 0, 1) + t(1, 0, 2)$
$x = 4 + s + t$, $y = 1$, $z = -1 + 2t$

EXERCISE 6.2
1. (a) $(3, 2, 1)$ (b) $(1, 1, 1)$ (c) $(-3, 1, 0)$
(d) $(1, 0, 2)$ (e) $(5, -2, -3)$ (f) $(0, 0, 1)$
2. (a) The normals of parallel planes are parallel.
(b) The normals of perpendicular planes are
perpendicular.
3. (a) Parallel (b) Perpendicular
(c) Perpendicular (d) Parallel
4. (a) $5x + 7y - 3 = 0$ (b) $2x - 3y + z = 0$
(c) $5x - y - 11 = 0$ (d) $z - 5 = 0$
(e) $6x - y + 4z - 9 = 0$
(f) $4x + 6y - 12z - 34 = 0$
(g) $3x - 2y + 4z + 8 = 0$
5. (a) $y - 2 = 0$ (b) $3x - y - 6z + 21 = 0$
(c) $3x - y - z - 9 = 0$
(d) $16x + 13y + 4z = 0$
(e) $x + 6y + 2z - 12 = 0$
6. (a) $x + y - 1 = 0$
(b) $-x - 8y + 3z + 26 = 0$
(c) $-4x + 2y + 14 = 0$
(d) $x - 2y + 5z - 5 = 0$
7. (a) $(x-3, y, z) = s(-3, \frac{3}{2}, 0) + t(-3, 0, \frac{3}{7})$
$x = 3 - 3s - 3t$, $y = \frac{3}{2}s$, $z = \frac{3}{7}t$
(b) $(x, y+5, z) = s(0, 5, 5) + t(1, 5, 5)$
$x = t$, $y = -5 + 5s + 5t$, $z = 5s + 5t$
(c) $(x-\frac{3}{4}, y, z) = s(-\frac{3}{4}, -3, 0) + t(-\frac{3}{4}, 0, \frac{1}{3})$
$x = \frac{3}{4} - \frac{3}{4}s - \frac{3}{4}t$, $y = -3s$, $z = \frac{1}{3}t$
(d) $(x-\frac{2}{3}, y, z) = s(-\frac{2}{3}, 2, 0) + t(-\frac{2}{3}, 0, -\frac{2}{5})$
$x = \frac{2}{3} - \frac{2}{3}s - \frac{2}{3}t$, $y = 2s$, $z = -\frac{2}{5}t$
9. (a) $\dfrac{3}{\sqrt{11}}$ (b) $\frac{9}{7}$ (c) 0 (d) $\dfrac{21}{\sqrt{83}}$ **10.** $\dfrac{13}{\sqrt{90}}$

15. (a) $\dfrac{6}{\sqrt{30}}$ (b) $\dfrac{5}{\sqrt{30}}$ (c) Planes are parallel and $\dfrac{11}{\sqrt{30}}$ units apart   (d) All planes are parallel to each other.   (e) $2x - 3y + 6z + 14 = 0$, $2x - 3y + 6z - 14 = 0$

EXERCISE 6.3

1. (a) The origin   (b) The origin

2. (a) $x = y = z$ (b) $x + y = 1$ (c) $\left(\frac{1}{2}, \frac{1}{2}, \frac{1}{2}\right)$
[The diagonals of a cube bisect each other.]

3. (a) $(-13, -10, -9)$ (b) $\left(\frac{31}{13}, \frac{20}{13}, -\frac{17}{13}\right)$

4. (a) $\left(\frac{43}{3}, 29, -\frac{70}{3}\right)$ (b) $\left(\frac{4}{7}, \frac{5}{7}, -\frac{6}{7}\right)$

5. (a) $(2, -3, 1)$ (b) None   (c) The whole line

6. (a) None   (b) $\left(\frac{379}{17}, \frac{147}{17}, \frac{280}{17}\right)$ (c) $(-49, 140, 93)$

7. (a) The whole line   (b) None   (c) $(27, 59, 44)$

8. (a) $(-16, 3, -11)$ (b) None
(c) $(-11, 3, -16)$ (d) The whole line

EXERCISE 6.4

1. (a) The y-axis   (b) The x-axis   (c) The z-axis

2. (a) $x - 1 = 0$ and $y - 2 = 0$
(b) $y - 3 = 0$ and $z + 2 = 0$

3. (a) $\dfrac{x + 16}{2} = \dfrac{y + 28}{1} = \dfrac{z}{1}$

(b) $\dfrac{x - 35.5}{7} = \dfrac{y - 21.5}{5} = \dfrac{z}{2}$

4. (a) $x = 1.3 - 7t$
$y = -1.2 - 12t$
$z = 10t$
(b) $\vec{d} = (-7, -12, 10)$
$\vec{n}_1 \times \vec{n}_2 = (7, 12, -10) = -\vec{d}$

5. (a) $x = 41.75 + 3t$ (b) $\vec{d} = (3, -1, 4)$
$y = 29.75 - t$ $\vec{n}_1 \times \vec{n}_2 = \vec{d}$
$z = 4t$

6. (a) The planes are parallel and distinct; empty intersection.
(b) $x = \frac{2}{11} - 5t$
$y = -\frac{5}{11} - 15t$
$z = 11t$
(c) The planes are identical.

7. (a) $x = \frac{11}{7} + 3t$, $y = -\frac{44}{7} + 23t$, $z = 7t$
(b) $\vec{n}_1 = (53, 15, -72)$, $\vec{d} = (3, 23, 7)$
(c) $(-3, -23, -7)$ With our choice of $\vec{d}$, $k = -1$.

EXERCISE 6.5

1. (a) $(0, 0, 0)$ (b) $(1, 2, -1)$ (c) $(0, 0, 1)$
(d) $(0, 1, 0)$

2. (a) Collinear   (c) Not collinear
(c) Not collinear   (d) Not collinear

3. (a) Two   (b) Three   (c) Two   (d) One

4. (a) IV   (b) IV   (c) II   (d) III   (e) IV   (f) I
(g) III   (h) I

5. (a) IV if $k \neq 0$ and III if $k = 0$ (b) IV if $k \neq \frac{13}{3}$ and III if $k = \frac{13}{3}$ (c) II if $k \neq 0$ and I if $k = 0$ (d) IV if $k \neq 1$ and III if $k = 1$

6. (a) $k = 7$ (b) $k = 1$

EXERCISE 6.6

1. (a) $x = 0$, $y = s$, $z = t$; $s, t \in R$
(b) $x = 0$, $y = 0$, $z = t$; $t \in R$
(c) $x = 0$, $y = 0$, $z = 0$ or $(0, 0, 0)$

2. (a) $x = 1$ (b) $x = 2$
$y = 0$ $y = -1$
$z = 0$ $z = 3$

3. (a) $x = -7$, $y = 0$, $z = 10$ (b) No solution
(c) $x = \frac{27}{4}$, $y = -\frac{15}{4}$, $z = -\frac{25}{4}$
(d) No solution   (e) $x = -514$, $y = -326$, $z = 473$ (f) No solution   (g) No solution
(h) $x = 2 + t$, $y = -3 - 2t$, $z = t$

4. (a) $k = -1$. Then $x = -1 - t$, $y = t$, $z = -2$
(b) $k = 10$. Then $x = 2 + t$, $y = -3 - 2t$, $z = t$
(c) $k = -6$. Then $x = -\frac{7}{13} + t$, $y = -\frac{17}{13} + 34t$, $z = 13t$
(d) $k = -23$. Then $x = -\frac{7}{13} + t$, $y = -\frac{17}{13} + 34t$, $z = 13t$

5. (a) $x = -4k + 4l - m$, $y = 5k - 7l + 2m$, $z = -2k + 3l - m$
(b) If $2k - 3l + m \neq 0$, there are no solutions. If $2k - 3l + m = 0$, there are infinitely many solutions: $x = -2k + l + t$, $y = k - l - 2t$, $z = t$ (c) $x = -2l + m$, $y = -3k + 5l - 2m$, $z = 2k - 3l + m$
(d) If $n = 7$, see part (b). If $n \neq 7$, the system has a unique solution.
$$x = -2k + l + \frac{-2k + 3l - m}{n - 7}$$
$$y = k - l + \frac{4k - 6l + 2m}{n - 7}$$
$$z = \frac{-2k + 3l - m}{n - 7}$$

EXERCISE 6.7

1. (a) Linear   (b) Non-linear   (c) Non-linear
   (d) Non-linear

2. (a) Point   (b) Line   (c) Plane

3. (a) $(x, y) = (41, -17)$: consistent and
   independent   (b) $(x, y) = (3.5 - 2.5t, t)$:
   consistent and dependent   (c) inconsistent
   (d) $(x, y) = (351, 152)$: consistent and
   independent

4. (a) Inconsistent   (b) $(x, y, z) = \left(-\frac{29}{7}, \frac{40}{7}, \frac{10}{7}\right)$:
   consistent and independent
   (c) $(x, y, z) = (-4.3, -4.7, 8.5)$: consistent and
   independent   (d) inconsistent
   (e) $(x, y, z) = \left(-\frac{25}{9}, \frac{37}{14}, -\frac{215}{126}\right)$: consistent and
   independent   (f) Inconsistent   (g) Inconsistent
   (h) $(x, y, z) = (-14 - t, -9, t)$: consistent and
   dependent

5. (a) For $k \neq 0$, the system is consistent and
   independent. For $k = 0$, the system is
   inconsistent.
   (b) For $k \neq -\frac{13}{3}$, the system is consistent and
   independent. For $k = -\frac{13}{3}$, the system is
   inconsistent.
   (c) The system is inconsistent for each value
   of k.
   (d) For $k \neq 9$, the system is consistent and
   dependent. For $k = 9$, the system is
   inconsistent.

6.8 REVIEW EXERCISE

1. Vector Equation:
   $(x+1, y+3, z-7) = s(-1, -2, 1)$
   $+ t(-3, 1, -4)$
   Parametric Equations: $x = -1 - s - 3t$
   $\qquad\qquad\qquad\qquad y = -3 - 2s + t$
   $\qquad\qquad\qquad\qquad z = 7 + s - 4t$
   Scalar Equation: $x - y - z + 5 = 0$

2. $x = \frac{1}{3} - \frac{1}{3}s - \frac{1}{3}t$
   $y = -s$
   $z = -t$

3. Yes, and the planes are distinct.

4. (a) $\dfrac{8}{\sqrt{18}}$ (b) $\dfrac{22}{\sqrt{18}}$ (c) $\dfrac{19}{\sqrt{2826}}$

5. (a) $\frac{1}{2}$ (b) 1   (c) $\dfrac{9}{2\sqrt{3}}$ (d) $\dfrac{15}{\sqrt{14}}$

6. The point $(-10, -9, -13)$.

7. The point $(3, -11, -16)$.

8. $x + 20 = y - 8 = \dfrac{z}{2}$

10. (a) IV   (b) III   (c) III   (d) II   (e) I

11. (a) $(x, y, z) = (1, 2, 3)$: consistent and
    independent   (b) $(x, y, z) = (-3 + t, -1 + t, t)$:
    consistent and dependent   (c) Inconsistent
    (d) Inconsistent   (e) Inconsistent

12. $(2, 3.5, -2.5)$

13. (a) Consistent and independent for every k.
    (b) consistent and dependent for every k.

6.9 CHAPTER 6 TEST

1. (a) $(2, -5, 1)$ and $(-3, 6, 1)$ (b) $(11, 5, 3)$
   (c) $11x + 5y + 3z - 15 = 0$
   (d) $11x + 5y + 3z = 0$

2. (a) $(1, 5, 7)$ (c) $\dfrac{5}{\sqrt{30}}$ 3. (b) $k = 7$

4. $(x, y, z) = (-2 - 2.2t, 3 - 0.4t, t)$, $t \in R$
   The system is consistent and dependent.

CUMULATIVE REVIEW FOR CHAPTERS 4 TO 6

1. (a)

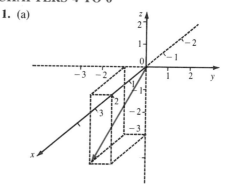

(b)

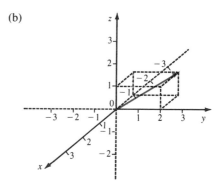

2. $\vec{u} = (-9, 8, 3)$

3. $b = -\frac{8}{5}$,

$c = \frac{5}{2}a$

4. (a) $(13, -10, 8)$ (b) $2\sqrt{139}$

(c) $\left(-\dfrac{2}{\sqrt{14}}, \dfrac{1}{\sqrt{14}}, \dfrac{3}{\sqrt{14}}\right)$ and

$\left(\dfrac{2}{\sqrt{14}}, -\dfrac{1}{\sqrt{14}}, -\dfrac{3}{\sqrt{14}}\right)$

(d) $(0, 0, 0)$ (e) 2 (f) $(-16, 8, 24)$

5. (a) $(-16, 5, -11)$ (b) $\sqrt{29}$ (c) -18

(d) $(11, 14, 9)$ (e) $(-34, 18, -32)$

6. (a) $117°$ (b) $90°$ (c) $102°$

7. (a) $(3, 2, 1)$ (b) $3\sqrt{5}$

(c) $\sqrt{14} + 3\sqrt{5} + \sqrt{43}$ (d) $\dfrac{\sqrt{566}}{2}$

8. (a) $(6, 0, 2)$ (b) $85°$ and $95°$ (c) $66°$ and $114°$

(d) $11\sqrt{33}$ 9. $-\frac{11}{3}$

10. (a) non-coplanar   (b) coplanar   11. (a) not a
basis   (b) basis

12. (a) $\vec{u}$ and $\vec{x}$ are collinear. The vectors $\vec{u}$, $\vec{v}$, and $\vec{w}$ are non-coplanar.   (b) No two vectors are collinear. No three vectors are coplanar.   (c) No two vectors are collinear. $\vec{u}$, $\vec{w}$, and $\vec{x}$ are coplanar and $\vec{v}$ does not lie in this plane.

13. (a) $\vec{u}$, $\vec{v}$, and $\vec{w}$ form a basis and
$\vec{x} = \frac{1}{2}\vec{u} + \frac{1}{2}\vec{v} + \frac{1}{2}\vec{w}$ (b) $\vec{u}$, $\vec{v}$, and $\vec{x}$ form a
basis and $\vec{w} = 2\vec{u} + 5\vec{v} + 0\vec{x}$ (c) $\vec{u}$, $\vec{v}$, and
$\vec{w}$ form a basis and $\vec{x} = \frac{1}{2}\vec{u} - \frac{19}{14}\vec{v} - \frac{6}{7}\vec{w}$

14. (a) any scalar multiple of $(6, -7)$
(b) any scalar multiple of $(-4, 3, -5)$
(c) any scalar multiple of $(5, 2)$

15. (a) $(-5, -1)$ and $(-6, 1)$ (b) $(-1, 2, 0)$ and
$(0, 2, -3)$ (c) $(-2, -3, 1)$ and $(-1, -8, 4)$

16. (a) $x = -1 + 3t$ (b) $x = -3 - 3r$
$\quad\;\; y = 2 - t$ $\qquad\quad\; y = 2 - 4r$
$\qquad\qquad\qquad\qquad\;\; z = 5r$

(c) $x = -10 + 6t$
$\;\;\; y = 12 - 7t$
$\;\;\; z = -2 - 3t$

17. (a) $\dfrac{x-2}{-1} = \dfrac{y-3}{2}$ (b) $\dfrac{x-2}{-3} = \dfrac{y}{2} = \dfrac{z+1}{1}$

18. (a) $(x-2, y+5, z+2) = t(1, 11, 6)$
(b) $(x+3, y+5) = t(3, 2)$
(c) $(x, y+4, z) = t(1, 0, 0)$

19. (a) $x = -4 + 5t$ (b) $x = 2 + t$
$\quad\;\; y = 7 - 11t$ $\qquad\;\; y = -5 + 6t$
$\qquad\qquad\qquad\qquad\;\; z = 4 - t$

19. (c) $x = 7 - 5t$
$\quad\;\; y = t$
$\quad\;\; z = 2t$

20. Vector
$(x-3, y) = t(3, -2)$

Parametric	Symmetric
$x = 3 + 3t$	$\dfrac{x-3}{3} = \dfrac{y}{-2}$
$y = -2t$	

21. Vector
$(x+1, y-2, z+1) = t(3, -1, -3)$

Parametric	Symmetric
$x = -1 + 3t$	$\dfrac{x+1}{3} = \dfrac{y-2}{-1} = \dfrac{x+1}{-3}$
$y = 2 - t$	
$z = -1 - 3t$	

22. (a) $a = 2$, $b = 0$; $\cos\alpha = 1$, $\cos\beta = 0$;
$\alpha = 0°$, $\beta = 90°$ (b) $a = -1$, $b = 3$;

$\cos\alpha = -\dfrac{1}{\sqrt{10}}$, $\cos\beta = \dfrac{3}{\sqrt{10}}$; $\alpha = 108°$,

$\beta = 18°$ (c) $a = -1$, $b = 3$;

$\cos\alpha = -\dfrac{1}{\sqrt{10}}$, $\cos\beta = \dfrac{3}{\sqrt{10}}$; $\alpha = 108°$,

$\beta = 18°$ (d) $a = -2$, $b = 5$;

$\cos\alpha = -\dfrac{2}{\sqrt{29}}$, $\cos\beta = \dfrac{5}{\sqrt{29}}$; $\alpha = 112°$,

$\beta = 22°$

23. (a) $a = -4$, $b = 3$, $c = 4$; $\cos\alpha = -\dfrac{4}{\sqrt{41}}$,

$\cos\beta = \dfrac{3}{\sqrt{41}}$, $\cos\gamma = \dfrac{4}{\sqrt{41}}$; $\alpha = 129°$,

$\beta = 62°$, $\gamma = 51°$ (b) $a = -1$, $b = 0$,

$c = 5$; $\cos\alpha = -\dfrac{1}{\sqrt{26}}$, $\cos\beta = 0$,

$\cos\gamma = \dfrac{5}{\sqrt{26}}$; $\alpha = 101°$, $\beta = 90°$, $\gamma = 11°$

(c) $a = 3$, $b = 5$, $c = 1$; $\cos\alpha = \dfrac{3}{\sqrt{35}}$,

$\cos\beta = \dfrac{5}{\sqrt{35}}$, $\cos\gamma = \dfrac{1}{\sqrt{35}}$; $\alpha = 60°$,

$\beta = 32°$, $\gamma = 80°$ (d) $a = -2$, $b = 1$,

$c = 1$; $\cos\alpha = -\dfrac{2}{\sqrt{6}}$, $\cos\beta = \dfrac{1}{\sqrt{6}}$,

$\cos\gamma = \dfrac{1}{\sqrt{6}}$; $\alpha = 145°$, $\beta = 66°$, $\gamma = 66°$

24. Vector   Symmetric
$(x-2, y+1) = t(-3, 1)$ $\dfrac{x-2}{-3} = \dfrac{y+1}{1}$

25. Parametric

$x = -1 + 2t$
$y = -1 - t$
$z = 1 + 2t$

Symmetric

$\dfrac{x+1}{2} = \dfrac{y+1}{-1} = \dfrac{z-1}{2}$

26. (a) $\left(\dfrac{2}{\sqrt{13}}, -\dfrac{3}{\sqrt{13}}\right)$ (b) $\left(\dfrac{3}{\sqrt{10}}, -\dfrac{1}{\sqrt{10}}\right)$

27. (a) $7x - 2y + 13 = 0$ (b) $x + 2y + 6 = 0$
(c) $x + 3y - 11 = 0$ (d) $x + y = 0$
(e) $x + y + 1 = 0$ (f) $3x + 2y + 11 = 0$
(g) $x + 3y - 2 = 0$

28. (a) $5x + 2y + 5 = 0$ (b) $x + y - 2 = 0$
(c) $x - 3 = 0$

29. (a) Vector

$(x+1, y-1) = t(4, -3)$

Parametric   Symmetric

$x = -1 + 4t$ $\dfrac{x+1}{4} = \dfrac{y-1}{-3}$
$y = 1 - 3t$

(b) Vector   Parametric

$(x, y-4) = t(2, 1)$ $x = 2t$
                      $y = 4 + t$

Symmetric

$\dfrac{x}{2} = \dfrac{y-4}{1}$

30. $a = -5$, $b = 2$; $\cos \alpha = -\dfrac{5}{\sqrt{29}}$,

$\cos \beta = \dfrac{2}{\sqrt{29}}$; $\alpha = 158°$, $\beta = 68°$

31. (a) parallel (b) not parallel

32. (a) $(17, -22)$ (b) $\left(\dfrac{25}{28}, -\dfrac{13}{14}\right)$

(c) The two equations describe the same line.

33. (a) $\left(\dfrac{3}{2}, -\dfrac{1}{2}, 6\right)$ (b) no intersection

(c) no intersection   **34.** $k \neq -\dfrac{7}{4}$

35. (a) $\dfrac{4}{\sqrt{13}}$ (b) $\dfrac{31}{\sqrt{61}}$ (c) $\dfrac{5\sqrt{10}}{\sqrt{19}}$ (d) $\dfrac{\sqrt{741}}{\sqrt{29}}$

36. (a) $\dfrac{7}{\sqrt{34}}$ (b) $\dfrac{\sqrt{283}}{\sqrt{15}}$ **37.** (a) $\dfrac{61}{\sqrt{86}}$

(b) $\dfrac{10}{\sqrt{86}}$

38. (a) intersecting at $\left(\dfrac{5}{2}, -2, \dfrac{11}{2}\right)$, distance 0

(b) skew; distance $\dfrac{3}{\sqrt{14}}$

38. (c) parallel; distance $\dfrac{\sqrt{4085}}{\sqrt{29}}$

39. (a) $x = 1 + 2s + t$
$y = -1 - 4t$
$z = -1 - 3s - 2t$
(b) $x = 2 + 2s - t$
$y = -3 - 2t$
$z = -3s + 4t$

40. $(x+2, y-1, z-3) = s(5, -2, 4)$
$+ t(-3, -1, 2)$

41. (a) Vector
$(x-1, y+2, z-1) = s(6, -2, 1)$
$+ t(-3, -1, 0)$

Parametric

$x = 1 + 6s - 3t$
$y = -2 - 2s - t$
$z = 1 + s$
(b) Vector
$(x-1, y+2, z-3) = s(1, 0, 0) + t(0, 0, 1)$
Parametric
$x = 1 + s$
$y = -2$
$z = 3 + t$
(c) Vector
$(x-1, y+1, z+6) = s(2, 5, 6) + t(-2, -7, 8)$
Parametric
$x = 1 + 2s - 2t$
$y = -1 + 5s - 7t$
$z = -6 + 6s + 8t$
(d) Vector
$(x, y+4, z+1) = s(-1, 4, 5) + t(2, 3, -1)$
Parametric
$x = -s + 2t$
$y = -4 + 4s + 3t$
$z = -1 + 5s - t$

42. (a) $3x - y + 2z - 5 = 0$
(b) $x - y + 1 = 0$
(c) $2x - y + 3z + 20 = 0$
(d) $4x - y + 11z + 6 = 0$

43. (a) $3x + 3y - z - 9 = 0$
(b) $2x + 11y - 4z - 6 = 0$

44. (a) Vector
$(x-1, y, z) = s(2, -1, 0) + t(3, 0, -1)$
Parametric
$x = 1 + 2s + 3t$
$y = -s$
$z = -t$
(b) Vector
$(x+1, y-2, z) = s(1, 2, 0) + t(3, 0, -1)$

44. (b) cont.

Parametric
$$x = -1 + s + 3t$$
$$y = 2 + 2s$$
$$z = -t$$

45. (a) $(2, 0, -1)$ (b) $\left(-\frac{7}{3}, \frac{14}{15}, \frac{2}{15}\right)$ (c) $\left(\frac{5}{6}, 1, -\frac{1}{3}\right)$

46. (a) $\left(\frac{36}{17}, -\frac{3}{17}, -\frac{13}{17}\right)$ (b) $(-8, 1, -5)$

(c) $\left(2, -\frac{4}{3}, \frac{1}{3}\right)$ (d) The line is parallel to the plane and there is no intersection. (e) The line is parallel to the plane and there is no intersection. (f) The line is parallel to the plane and there is no intersection.

47. (a) $x = 1 - 3t$
$$y = t$$
$$z = 1 + 7t$$

48. (a) $x = 2 + \frac{2}{5}k$ (b) no intersection
$$y = k$$
$$z = 2 + \frac{11}{5}k$$

(c) $x = 2$ (d) $x = -\frac{2}{3} + \frac{4}{3}k$
$\quad y = 1$ $\qquad y = \frac{17}{6} - \frac{19}{6}k$
$\quad z = k$ $\qquad z = k$

49. (a) Type II (b) Type IV (c) Type III
(d) Type I (e) Type III

50. Type III if $k = 2$; Type IV is $k \neq 2$

51. (a) no solution; inconsistent
(b) $(59, -135, -83)$; consistent and independent (c) no solution; inconsistent
(d) no solution; inconsistent (e) no solution; inconsistent

CHAPTER 7 CONICS AND TRANSLATIONS

REVIEW AND PREVIEW TO CHAPTER 7
EXERCISE 1

1. (a) $(x + 5)^2 = 25$ (b) $\left(x - \frac{3}{2}\right)^2 = \frac{9}{4}$

(c) $(2x + 1)^2 = 1$ or $4\left(x + \frac{1}{2}\right)^2 = 1$

(d) $4\left(y - \frac{3}{8}\right)^2 = \frac{9}{16}$

2. (a) The graph is a circle with centre $(-5, -2)$ and radius $\sqrt{29}$. (b) The graph is a circle with centre $\left(\frac{3}{2}, \frac{3}{2}\right)$ and radius $\frac{3}{\sqrt{2}}$. (c) The graph is a parabola with vertex $(-1, 2)$. (d) The graph is a circle with centre $(3, -4)$ and radius 5.

(e) The graph is a circle with centre $\left(-\frac{5}{4}, \frac{11}{4}\right)$ and radius $\frac{\sqrt{146}}{4}$. (b) The graph is a circle with centre $\left(\frac{11}{12}, -\frac{5}{12}\right)$ and radius $\frac{\sqrt{146}}{12}$.

EXERCISE 7.1

3. (a) $4x_P - 2y_P + 5 = 0$ (b) Since $4x_Q - 2y_Q + 5 = 9$, Q is not on l. (c) The coordinates of R are $\left(-\frac{5}{2}, -\frac{5}{2}\right)$.

4. (a) Circle: centre $(0, 0)$ and radius 2 (b) Circle: centre $(-5, -2)$ and radius $\sqrt{29}$ (c) Circle: centre $\left(-\frac{3}{4}, -\frac{3}{4}\right)$ and radius $\frac{3}{2\sqrt{2}}$ (d) circle: centre $(2, -3)$ and radius $\sqrt{21}$

5. (a) $x - y - 2 = 0$ (b) $x + 1 = 0$
(c) $y + 1 = 0$ (d) $y = 0$

6. (a) The set of all points one unit from the y-axis.

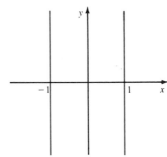

(b) The set of all points such that the sum of their distances from the x-axis and the y-axis is 1. This is a square with vertices $(1, 0)$, $(0, 1)$, and $(-1, 0)$, and $(0, -1)$.

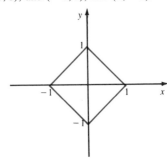

6. (c) The set of all points equidistant from the x-axis and the y-axis.

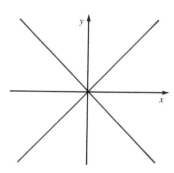

(d) The set of all points such that the square of their distance to the origin is 0. This is the origin.

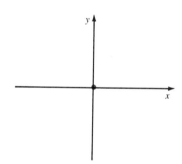

7. (a) $|x_P + 1|$ (b) $PF = \sqrt{(x_P - 1)^2 + y_P^2}$
(c) $y_P^2 = 4x_P$ (d) $y^2 = 4x$: parabola

8. (a) $\dfrac{y_P}{x_P + 1}$ (b) $\dfrac{y_P}{x_P - 1}$
(c) $y_P^2 = (x_P - 1)(x_P + 1)$ (d) $x^2 - y^2 = 1$: hyperbola

9. $\dfrac{x^2}{a^2} + \dfrac{y^2}{b^2} = 1$ where $a = \frac{3}{2}$ and $b = \dfrac{\sqrt{5}}{2}$: ellipse

EXERCISE 7.2

2. (a) $x - y + 2 = 0$ (b) $2x + 3y - 18 = 0$
(c) $x - 3 = 0$ (d) $y - 2 = 0$
(e) $x + y - 4 = 0$ (f) $3x - y - 1 = 0$

3. (a) $x + 3 = 0$ (b) $y - 1 = 0$
(c) $x + y = 0$ (d) $2x + 3y + 9 = 0$
(e) $15x - 43y + 166 = 0$
(f) $197x + 831y - 587 = 0$

4. (a) $r = 2, s = -5$ (b) $r = -1, s = -4$
(c) $r = -3, s = 2$ (d) $r = -4, s = 2$
(e) $r = 18, s = 7$ (f) $r = -194, s = 427$

5. (a) $x^2 + y^2 - 6x + 8 = 0$

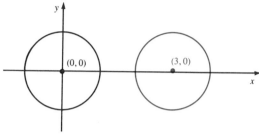

(b) $x^2 + y^2 - 8y + 15 = 0$

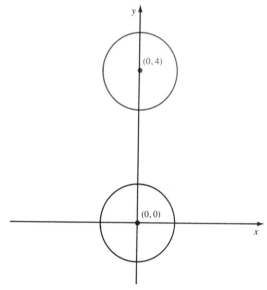

(c) $x^2 + y^2 - 6x - 8y + 24 = 0$

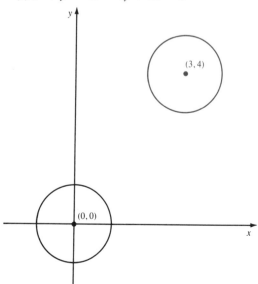

5. (d) $x^2 + y^2 + 2x - 4y + 4 = 0$

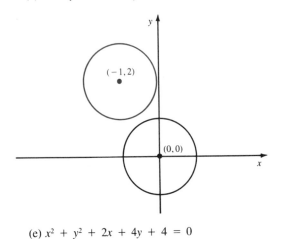

(e) $x^2 + y^2 + 2x + 4y + 4 = 0$

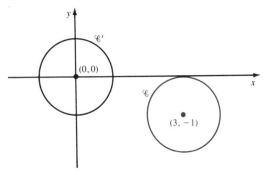

(f) $x^2 + y^2 - 6x + 2y + 9 = 0$

6. $ax + by + c - ar - bs = 0$

7. (a) $(r, s) = t(-b, a)$ The vector (r, s) lies on the line $ax + by = 0$ parallel to l and through the origin. (b) All points on l are moved to the left by same amount, or to the right by the same amount.

EXERCISE 7.3

1. (a) $4x^2 + 9y^2 - 16x - 54y + 61 = 0$

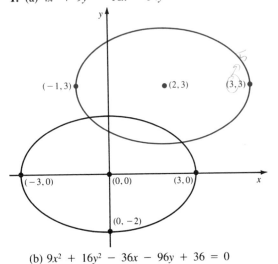

(b) $9x^2 + 16y^2 - 36x - 96y + 36 = 0$

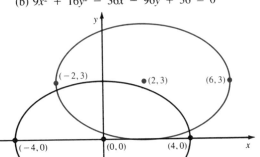

(c) $x^2 + 4y^2 - 4x - 24y + 36 = 0$

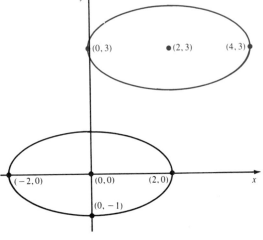
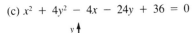

1. (d) $9x^2 + 25y^2 - 36x - 150y + 36 = 0$

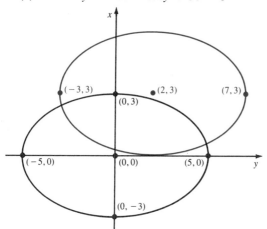

2. (c) $y^2 - 2x + 4y + 6 = 0$

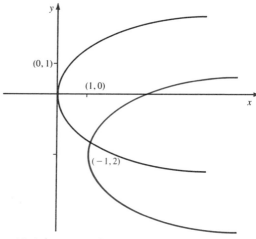

2. (a) $y^2 - 4x + 4y + 8 = 0$

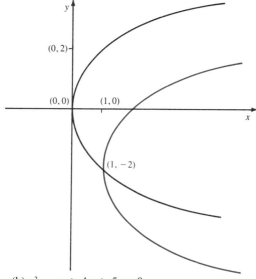

(d) $3y^2 - x + 12y + 13 = 0$

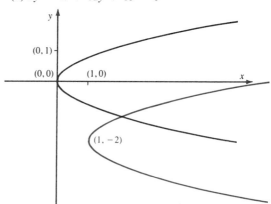

3. (a) $9x^2 - 4y^2 + 36x + 8y - 4 = 0$

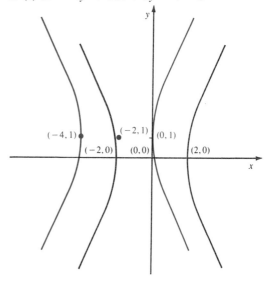

(b) $y^2 - x + 4y + 5 = 0$

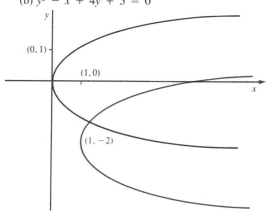

3. (b) $x^2 - y^2 + 4x + 2y - 13 = 0$

3. (d) $25x^2 - y^2 + 100x + 2y + 74 = 0$

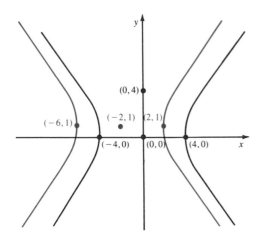

(c) $x^2 - y^2 + 4x + 2y - 1 = 0$

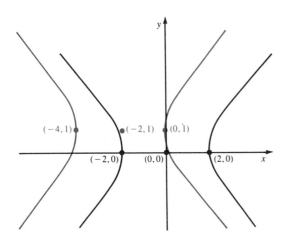

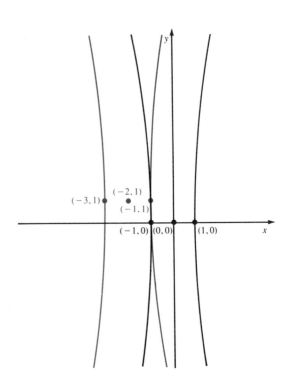

4. $g = -rb^2, f = -sa^2,$ and
$c = r^2b^2 + s^2a^2 - a^2b^2$

5. $g = -2a, f = -s,$ and $c = 4ra + s^2$

6. $g = -rb^2, f = sa^2,$ and
$c = r^2b^2 - s^2a^2 - a^2b^2$

EXERCISE 7.4

1. (a) $\begin{cases} x_{P'} = x_P + 2 \\ y_{P'} = y_P - 3 \end{cases}$ The curve is an ellipse.

(b) $\begin{cases} x_{P'} = x_P - 1 \\ y_{P'} = y_P \end{cases}$ The curve is an ellipse.

(c) $\begin{cases} x_{P'} = x_P - 3 \\ y_{P'} = y_P + 2 \end{cases}$ The curve is a hyperbola.

(d) $\begin{cases} x_{P'} = x_P + 1 \\ y_{P'} = y_P - 1 \end{cases}$ The curve is a hyperbola.

2. (a) $\begin{cases} x_{P'} = x_P + \frac{1}{3} \\ y_{P'} = y_P - \frac{7}{3} \end{cases}$ (b) $\begin{cases} x_{P'} = x_P + 1 \\ y_{P'} = y_P + 1 \end{cases}$

(c) $\begin{cases} x_{P'} = x_P + 2 \\ y_{P'} = y_p + 1 \end{cases}$ (d) $\begin{cases} x_{P'} = x_P \\ y_{P'} = y_P - 1 \end{cases}$

3. (a) $\begin{cases} x_{P'} = x_P - 1 \\ y_{P'} = y_P - 2 \end{cases}$ The vertex is $(1, 2)$.

(b) $\begin{cases} x_{P'} = x_P - 2 \\ y_{P'} = y_P + 1 \end{cases}$ The vertex is $(2, -1)$.

3. (c) $\begin{cases} x_{P'} = x_P + 1 \\ y_{P'} = y_P + 2 \end{cases}$ The vertex is $(-1, -2)$.

(d) $\begin{cases} x_{P'} = x_P + 5 \\ y_{P'} = y_P - 1 \end{cases}$ The vertex is $(-5, 1)$.

4. A suitable translation is $x_{P'} = x_P + \dfrac{p}{2q}$,

$y_{P'} = y_P$

7.5 REVIEW EXERCISE

1. (a) $A'(4, 0)$, $B'(-3, 2)$, $C'(0, -3)$, $D'(2, -4)$

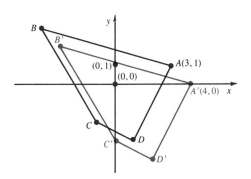

(b) $A'(1, 4)$, $B'(-6, 6)$, $C'(-3, 1)$, $D'(-1, 0)$

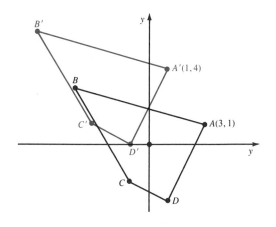

1. (c) $A'(4, 3)$, $B'(-3, 5)$, $C'(0, 0)$, $D'(2, -1)$

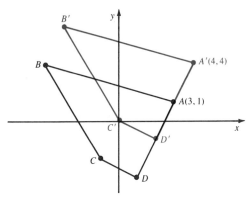

(d) $A'(-1, -2)$, $B'(-8, 0)$, $C'(-5, -5)$, $D'(-3, -6)$

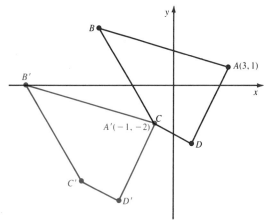

2. $r = 6$

3. (a) $r = 3$ (b) $r = -4$ (c) $r = 2$
(d) $r = 15$

4. The pair (r, s) must satisfy $3r - s = -12$.

5. (a) $x^2 + y^2 - 6x - 8y = 0$

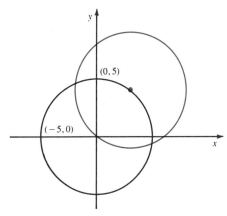

5. (b) $x^2 + y^2 + 8x - 6y = 0$

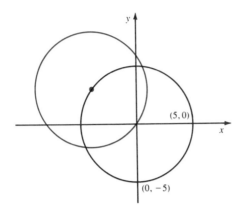

(c) $x^2 + y^2 - 5\sqrt{2}x + 5\sqrt{2}y = 0$

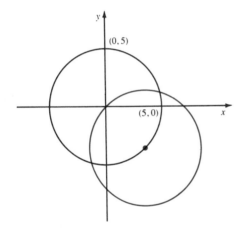

(d) $x^2 + y^2 + 5x + 5\sqrt{3}y = 0$

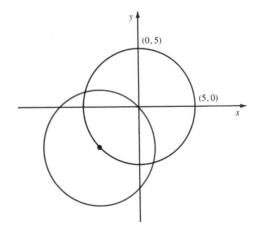

6. (a) $\begin{cases} x_{P'} = x_P - 2 \\ y_{P'} = y_P + 3 \end{cases}$ Image: $x^2 + y^2 = 1$

(b) $\begin{cases} x_{P'} = x_P + 2 \\ y_{P'} = y_P + 3 \end{cases}$ Image: $x^2 + y^2 = 31$

(c) $\begin{cases} x_{P'} = x_P + 12 \\ y_{P'} = y_P + 5 \end{cases}$ Image: $x^2 + y^2 = 169$

(d) $\begin{cases} x_{P'} = x_P - 5 \\ y_{P'} = y_P - 12 \end{cases}$ Image: $x^2 + y^2 = 169$

7. (a) $y^2 - 4x + 2y + 5 = 0$
(b) $2x^2 - y^2 - 2x + 9 = 0$
(c) $4x^2 + 9y^2 + 40x + 54y + 145 = 0$
(d) $2x^2 + 3y^2 - 4x + 18y + 23 = 0$
(e) $3x^2 - y^2 + 6x - 6y - 6 = 0$
(f) $x^2 + 4x + y + 5 = 0$

8. (a) $\begin{cases} x_{P'} = x_P - \frac{3}{2} \\ y_{P'} = y_P - 1 \end{cases}$ The image is a hyperbola.

(b) $\begin{cases} x_{P'} = x_P - 3 \\ y_{P'} = y_P + 2 \end{cases}$ The image is an ellipse.

(c) $\begin{cases} x_{P'} = x_P - 1 \\ y_{P'} = y_P + 2 \end{cases}$ The image is a hyperbola.

(d) $\begin{cases} x_{P'} = x_P + 3 \\ y_{P'} = y_P + 2 \end{cases}$ The image is an ellipse.

9. (a) $\begin{cases} x_{P'} = x_P + 2 \\ y_{P'} = y_P - 3 \end{cases}$ (b) $\begin{cases} x_{P'} = x_P + 3 \\ y_{P'} = y_P - 2 \end{cases}$

(c) $\begin{cases} x_{P'} = x_P - 5 \\ y_{P'} = y_P - 4 \end{cases}$ (d) $\begin{cases} x_{P'} = x_P - 10 \\ y_{P'} = y_P - 9 \end{cases}$

10. (a) $\begin{cases} x_{P'} = x_P + 12 \\ y_{P'} = y_P + 7 \end{cases}$ The vertex is $(-12, -7)$.

(b) $\begin{cases} x_P = x_P + 6 \\ y_P = y_P + 5 \end{cases}$ The vertex is $(-6, -5)$.

(c) $\begin{cases} x_P = x_P + 6 \\ y_P = y_P + 7 \end{cases}$ The vertex is $(-6, -7)$.

(d) $\begin{cases} x_P = x_P + 2 \\ y_P = y_P - 4 \end{cases}$ The vertex is $(-2, 4)$.

7.6 CHAPTER 7 TEST

1. $3x + 5y - 8 = 0$

2. $r = \frac{7}{3}$

3. $(-3, 4)$

4. $(-2, 0)$ and $(2, 0)$

5. $r = 3, s = 2$

6. $c = 7$

7. (r, s) satisfies $r^2 + s^2 = 1$. That is (r, s) lies on the unit circle.

CHAPTER 8 MATRICES AND TRANSFORMATIONS

REVIEW AND PREVIEW TO CHAPTER 8

EXERCISE 1

1. (a) (i)　　　　　(ii)

(b) (i)　　　　　(ii)

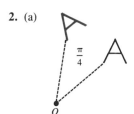
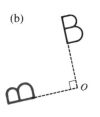

2. (a)　　　　　(b)

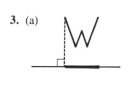
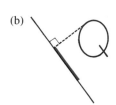

(c)

3. (a)　　　　　(b)

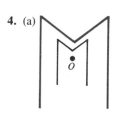

4. (a)　　　　　(b)

EXERCISE 2

1. (a) $\cos\theta$　(b) $-\sin\theta$

2. (a) $\sin\theta_1\cos\theta_2 - \cos\theta_1\sin\theta_2$
(b) $\cos\theta_1\cos\theta_2 + \sin\theta_1\sin\theta_2$

3. (a) $\sin\theta$　(b) $-\cos\theta$

4. (a) $\cos\theta$　(b) $\sin\theta$　(c) $\sin\theta$

5. (a) $\frac{63}{65}$　(b) $\frac{16}{65}$　(c) $-\frac{33}{65}$　(d) $\frac{56}{65}$　(e) $\frac{12}{13}$　(f) $\frac{4}{5}$

EXERCISE 8.1

1. (a) $\begin{bmatrix} 3x - 2y \\ 4x + y \end{bmatrix}$　(b) $\begin{bmatrix} -x + 5y \\ 7x \end{bmatrix}$

2. (a) $\begin{bmatrix} 5 \\ -1 \end{bmatrix}$　(b) $\begin{bmatrix} 15 \\ -10 \end{bmatrix}$　(c) $\begin{bmatrix} 6 \\ 14 \end{bmatrix}$　(d) $\begin{bmatrix} -2 \\ 4 \end{bmatrix}$

(e) $\begin{bmatrix} 1 \\ 8 \end{bmatrix}$　(f) $\begin{bmatrix} 8 \\ 8 \end{bmatrix}$

3. (a) $(-5, 17)$

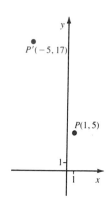

(b) $(4, 2)$

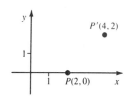

(c) $(0, 0)$

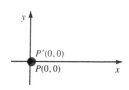

4. (a) $(0, 0)$ (b) (x_P, y_P)

5. (a)

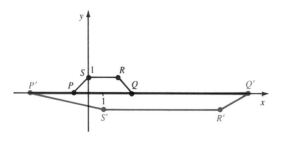

(b)

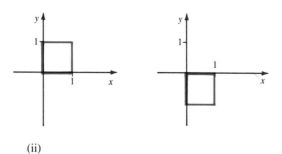

6. (a)   (b) (i)

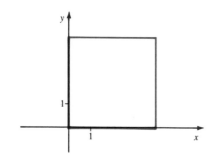

(ii)

5. (b) (iii)

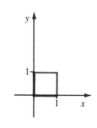

(iv)

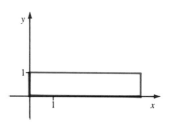

(v)

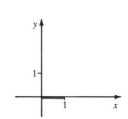

(vi)

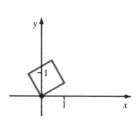

(c) (i) reflection in x-axis   (ii) dilatation by factor of 4 about origin   (iii) reflection in line $y = x$ (iv) horizontal stretch, factor of 5   (v) projection onto x-axis   (vi) rotation of 30° about origin

7. (a) $P'(2, 10)$ (b) $P''(28, 50)$

8. (a) $P'(-x_P + 3y_P, 5y_P)$
   (b) $P''(x_P + 12y_P, 25y_P)$

10. $\begin{bmatrix} 2 & 3 \\ -1 & 5 \end{bmatrix}$ $\begin{bmatrix} 3 & 2 \\ 5 & -1 \end{bmatrix}$

EXERCISE 8.2

1. any point on the line of reflection

2. (a) $P'(-1, -2)$

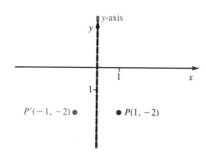

(b) $P'(-2, 1)$

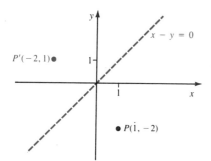

3. (a) $P'(0, -5)$ $Q'(-3, -2)$
(b) $P'(5, 0)$ $Q'(2, -3)$

5. (a) $3\sqrt{2}$ (b) $3\sqrt{2}$ (c) $3\sqrt{2}$ (d) Distance is preserved under reflections.

6. (a), (b)

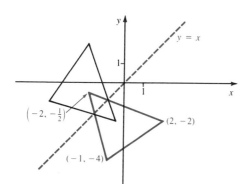

7. (a) $P'(2, -3)$ (b) $P''(-3, 2)$ (c) $P*(3, 2)$
(d) $P**(3, -2)$

8. (a) $P'(-1, -4)$ (b) $P''(4, 1)$ (c) $P*(4, -1)$
(d) $P**(-4, -1)$

10. (a) $x + y = 4$ (b) $5x + 3y - 2 = 0$

11. (a)

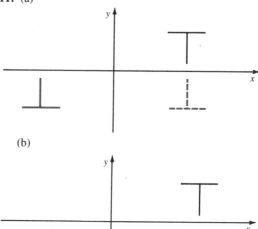

(b)

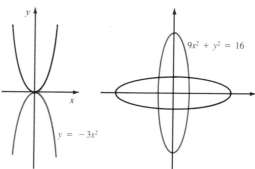

(c) same

12. (a) $y = -3x^2$ (b) $9x^2 + y^2 = 16$

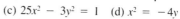
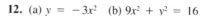

(c) $25x^2 - 3y^2 = 1$ (d) $x^2 = -4y$

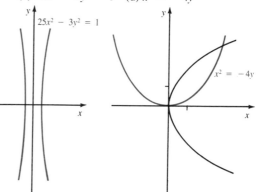

EXERCISE 8.3

1. point O

2. rotation through $\theta_1 + \theta_2$

3. no change because rotation through $0°$

4. (a) $\begin{bmatrix} \dfrac{1}{2} & -\dfrac{\sqrt{3}}{2} \\ \dfrac{\sqrt{3}}{2} & \dfrac{1}{2} \end{bmatrix}$ (b) $\begin{bmatrix} -\dfrac{1}{\sqrt{2}} & -\dfrac{1}{\sqrt{2}} \\ \dfrac{1}{\sqrt{2}} & -\dfrac{1}{\sqrt{2}} \end{bmatrix}$

(c) $\begin{bmatrix} -\dfrac{\sqrt{3}}{2} & -\dfrac{1}{2} \\ \dfrac{1}{2} & -\dfrac{\sqrt{3}}{2} \end{bmatrix}$ (d) $\begin{bmatrix} \dfrac{1}{2} & \dfrac{\sqrt{3}}{2} \\ -\dfrac{\sqrt{3}}{2} & \dfrac{1}{2} \end{bmatrix}$

5. (a) $P'\left(\dfrac{\sqrt{3}-3}{2}, \dfrac{1+3\sqrt{3}}{2}\right)$ (b) $P'(-1, -3)$

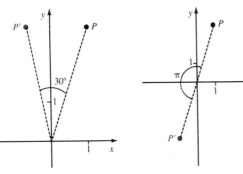

(c) $P'\left(\dfrac{-\sqrt{3}+3}{2}, \dfrac{-1-3\sqrt{3}}{2}\right)$

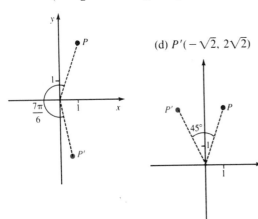

(d) $P'(-\sqrt{2}, 2\sqrt{2})$

6. (a) $P'(-1, \sqrt{3})$

$Q'\left(\dfrac{-\sqrt{3}-5}{2}, \dfrac{-1+5\sqrt{3}}{2}\right)$

$R'\left(\dfrac{\sqrt{3}}{2}, \dfrac{1}{2}\right)$ $S'\left(-\dfrac{1}{2}, \dfrac{\sqrt{3}}{2}\right)$

6. (b) $P'(-\sqrt{2}, -\sqrt{2})$ $Q'(-2\sqrt{2}, -3\sqrt{2})$

$R'\left(-\dfrac{1}{\sqrt{2}}, \dfrac{1}{\sqrt{2}}\right)$ $S'\left(-\dfrac{1}{\sqrt{2}}, -\dfrac{1}{\sqrt{2}}\right)$

8. (a) $\sqrt{10}$ (b) $\sqrt{10}$ (c) $\sqrt{10}$ (d) Distance is preserved under rotation.

9. (a)

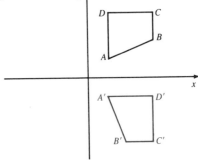

(b) $A'(1, -1)$, $B'(2, -3)$, $C'(3, -3)$, $D'(3, -1)$

10. rotation through π, reflection in y-axis followed by reflection in x-axis

11. (a) $P'(x_P \cos\theta - y_P \sin\theta, x_P \sin\theta + y_P \cos\theta)$

(b) (x_P, y_P)

12. (a) $P'(1, 2)$ (b) $P''\left(-\dfrac{1}{\sqrt{2}}, \dfrac{3}{\sqrt{2}}\right)$

(c) $P*\left(\dfrac{3}{\sqrt{2}}, \dfrac{1}{\sqrt{2}}\right)$ (d) $P**\left(-\dfrac{1}{\sqrt{2}}, \dfrac{3}{\sqrt{2}}\right)$

13. (a) $P'\left(\dfrac{3\sqrt{3}}{-2}, \dfrac{3}{2}\right)$ (b) $P''\left(\dfrac{3\sqrt{3}}{2}, -\dfrac{3}{2}\right)$

(c) $P*(0, -3)$ (d) $P**\left(\dfrac{3\sqrt{3}}{2}, -\dfrac{3}{2}\right)$

14. Order of performing rotations does not appear to matter.

16. (a), (b)

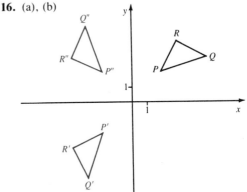

(c) rotation through $90°$

17. (a) $(3\sqrt{3}+1)x + (3-\sqrt{3})y = 0$
(b) $3x - 5y - \sqrt{2} = 0$
(c) $x + 3y + 2 = 0$

18. (a) $\dfrac{3\pi}{2}$ (b) $\dfrac{\pi}{2}$ (c) $53°$ (d) $\dfrac{5\pi}{3}$ (e) $\dfrac{5\pi}{4}$
(f) π

EXERCISE 8.4

1. (a) any point on the line 5 (b) the centre of the dilatation (c) horizontal stretch — any point on y-axis; vertical stretch — any point on x-axis (d) horizontal shear — any point on x-axis; vertical shear — any point on y-axis

2. (a) dilatation (b) none (c) none
(d) horizontal shear (e) vertical shear
(f) none

3. (a) $\begin{bmatrix} 3 & 0 \\ 0 & 3 \end{bmatrix}$ (b) $\begin{bmatrix} 1 & 0 \\ 0 & 2.5 \end{bmatrix}$ (c) $\begin{bmatrix} 1 & 1.4 \\ 0 & 1 \end{bmatrix}$
(d) $\begin{bmatrix} 4 & 0 \\ 0 & 1 \end{bmatrix}$ (e) $\begin{bmatrix} \frac{1}{4} & 0 \\ 0 & \frac{1}{4} \end{bmatrix}$ (f) $\begin{bmatrix} 1 & 0 \\ 1.5 & 1 \end{bmatrix}$

4. $\begin{bmatrix} 0 & 0 \\ 0 & 1 \end{bmatrix}$

5. (a) $P'(-1,0)$ $Q'(0,0)$ $R'(1,0)$ $S'(0,0)$
(b) $P'(0,2)$ $Q'(0,5)$ $R'(0,0)$ $S'(0,1)$

6. (a) $\sqrt{10}$ (b) 1 (c) 3 (d) Projections do not preserve distance.

7. (a), (b)

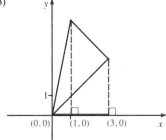

8. (a), (b)

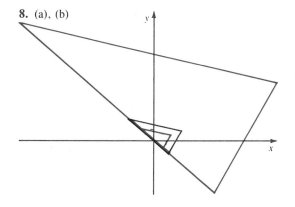

9. (a), (b)

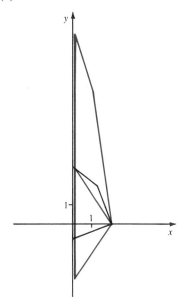

10. (a)

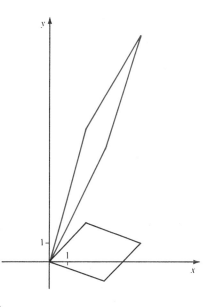

(b)

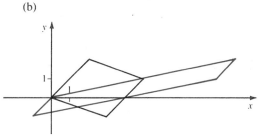

11. (a) $P'(0,6)$ $Q'(2,-4)$ $R'(2,0)$ $S'(0,2)$

(b) $P'(0,2)$ $Q'(\frac{2}{3},-\frac{4}{3})$ $R'(\frac{2}{3},0)$ $S'(0,\frac{2}{3})$

12. (a) $\sqrt{26}$ (b) $2\sqrt{26}$ (c) $\frac{2}{3}\sqrt{26}$ (d) Under a dilatation distance is multiplied by the dilatation factor.

13. (a) $P'(0,3)$ $Q'(0,-2)$ $R'(2,0)$ $S'(0,1)$

(b) $P'(0,2)$ $Q'(0,-\frac{4}{3})$ $R'(1,0)$ $S'(0,\frac{2}{3})$

14. (a) 5 (b) 5 (c) $\frac{10}{3}$ (d) no effect

(e) Vertical distance is multiplied by factor of vertical stretch.

15. (a) $P'(3,9)$ $Q'(-5,-15)$ $R'(1,3)$ $S'(0,1)$

(b) $P'(3,0)$ $Q'(-5,0)$ $R'(1,0)$ $S'(\frac{3}{5},1)$

16. (a) 8 (b) $8\sqrt{10}$ (c) 8 (d) Distance is changed. (e) no effect

EXERCISE 8.5

1. (a) $\begin{bmatrix} 3 & 12 \\ 1 & 4 \end{bmatrix}$ (b) $\begin{bmatrix} 0 & 2 \\ 11 & -3 \end{bmatrix}$ (c) $\begin{bmatrix} 5 & 2 \\ 1 & 3 \end{bmatrix}$

(d) $\begin{bmatrix} -7 & -4 \\ -4 & -3 \end{bmatrix}$

2. (a) $\begin{bmatrix} 12 & 14 \\ 8 & 12 \end{bmatrix}$ (b) $\begin{bmatrix} 4 & 11 \\ -2 & 1 \end{bmatrix}$

3. (a) (i) $\begin{bmatrix} 6 & -3 \\ 20 & 4 \end{bmatrix}$ (ii) $\begin{bmatrix} 6 & -4 \\ 15 & 4 \end{bmatrix}$

(b) (i) $\begin{bmatrix} 18 & -27 \\ 2 & -11 \end{bmatrix}$ (ii) $\begin{bmatrix} 2 & 11 \\ 14 & 5 \end{bmatrix}$

(c) (i) $\begin{bmatrix} 4 & 4 \\ -3 & -7 \end{bmatrix}$ (ii) $\begin{bmatrix} 4 & -4 \\ 3 & -7 \end{bmatrix}$

4. not commutative

7. $\begin{bmatrix} \dfrac{2.5}{\sqrt{2}} & -\dfrac{2.5}{\sqrt{2}} \\ \dfrac{1}{\sqrt{2}} & \dfrac{1}{\sqrt{2}} \end{bmatrix}$ **9.** $\begin{bmatrix} 0 & 0 \\ 0 & 0 \end{bmatrix}$

10. $(-9,12)$ **11.** $\begin{bmatrix} -ab & -b \\ -b & 0 \end{bmatrix}$

12. For $B = \begin{bmatrix} b_{11} & b_{12} \\ b_{21} & b_{22} \end{bmatrix}$ (a) $b_{21} = 0$ and $b_{11} = b_{22}$

(b) $b_{12} = -b_{21}$ and $b_{11} = b_{22}$

14. dilatation by factor $ad-bc$

EXERCISE 8.6

1. (a) yes (b no (c) yes (d) no

2. (a) yes (b) no (c) yes (d) yes

3. (a) $\begin{bmatrix} \frac{3}{5} & -\frac{4}{5} \\ -\frac{4}{5} & -\frac{3}{5} \end{bmatrix}$ (b) $\begin{bmatrix} -\frac{7}{25} & \frac{24}{25} \\ \frac{24}{25} & \frac{7}{25} \end{bmatrix}$

4. (a) $\begin{bmatrix} \frac{1}{2} & \frac{1}{2} \\ \frac{1}{2} & \frac{1}{2} \end{bmatrix}$ (b) $\begin{bmatrix} \frac{1}{5} & -\frac{2}{5} \\ -\frac{2}{5} & \frac{4}{5} \end{bmatrix}$

(c) $\begin{bmatrix} \frac{16}{25} & \frac{12}{25} \\ \frac{12}{25} & \frac{9}{25} \end{bmatrix}$

5. (a) $y = 0$ (b) $\frac{4}{5}x + \frac{3}{5}y = 0$ or $4x + 3y = 0$

6. (a) y-axis (c) $\dfrac{1}{\sqrt{5}}x + \dfrac{2}{\sqrt{5}}y = 0$ or

$x + 2y = 0$ (d) $\dfrac{1}{\sqrt{2}}x + \dfrac{1}{\sqrt{2}}y = 0$ or

$x + y = 0$

7. (a)

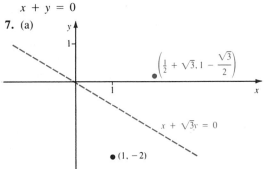

(b)

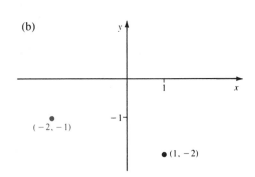

8. (a) $P'(-3,-4)$ $Q'(-\frac{18}{5},\frac{1}{5})$ (b) $P'(-\frac{7}{5},\frac{24}{25})$

$Q'(\frac{58}{25},\frac{69}{25})$

9. (a)

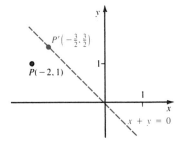

(b)

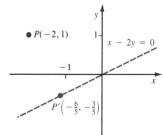

(c)

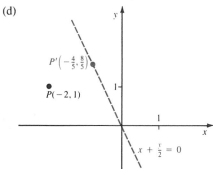

(d)

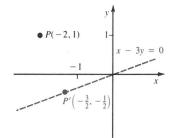

10. (a) $bx - ay - bx_P + ay_P = 0$ (b) $bx_{P'} - ay_{P'} - bx_P + ay_P = 0$ (c) $ax_{P'} + by_{P'} = 0$
(d) $x_{P'} = b^2 x_P - aby_P, \ y_{P'} = -abx_P + a^2 y_P$

12. (a)
$P'((b^2 - a^2)x_P - 2aby_P, \ -2abx_P + (a^2 - b^2)y_P)$
(b) $P''(x_P, y_P)$
(c) same as identity transformation

16. (a) $P'(b^2 - a^2)x_P - 2aby_P + 2ac_1,$
$-2abx_P + (a^2 - b^2)y_P + 2bc_1)$
(b) $P''(x_P - 2a(c_1 - c_2), \ y_P - 2b(c_1 - c_2))$

(c) $X_{P''} = X_P - 2(c_1 - c_2)\begin{bmatrix} a \\ b \end{bmatrix}$

18. (a) projection on l (b) identity transformation
(c) matrix of projection

8.7 REVIEW EXERCISE

1. (a) $\begin{bmatrix} 3 & -2 \\ 1 & 1 \end{bmatrix}$ (b) $\begin{bmatrix} 0 & -1 \\ 2 & 0 \end{bmatrix}$

2. (a) $\begin{bmatrix} 2 \\ 2 \end{bmatrix}$ (b) $\begin{bmatrix} -2 \\ 3 \end{bmatrix}$, (c) $\begin{bmatrix} -6 \\ 3 \end{bmatrix}$ (d) $\begin{bmatrix} -7 \\ -23 \end{bmatrix}$

2. (e) $\begin{bmatrix} 6 & 2 \\ 2 & 2 \end{bmatrix}$ (f) $\begin{bmatrix} -3 & 23 \\ 7 & -7 \end{bmatrix}$ (g) $\begin{bmatrix} 3 & 2 \\ 2 & -1 \end{bmatrix}$
(h) $\begin{bmatrix} 14 & 19 \\ 11 & 1 \end{bmatrix}$

3. (a) $P'(-10, 10)$ (b) $P'(9, 6)$

4. (a) $(3, 0)$ (b) $(9, 15)$ (c) $(3, 5)$ (d) $(3, -5)$
(e) $(-5, 3)$ (f) $(3, 20)$ (g) $(3, 3k + 5)$
(h) $(-5, -3)$

5. (a) projection on x-axis (b) dilatation, factor 3
(c) identity (d) reflection in x-axis (e) rotation

through $\dfrac{\pi}{2}$ (f) vertical stretch, factor 4

(g) vertical shear, factor k (h) reflection in
$x + y = 0$

6. (a) $(0, 0)$ (b) $(0, 4)$ (c) $(12, 0)$ (d) $(0, 4)$
(e) $(4, 0)$ (f) $(4, 0)$ (g) $(-4, 0)$

7. (a) $(0, -1)$ (b) $(1, 4)$
(c) $(12, -3),$ (d) $(-1, 4)$ (e) $(-1, -1)$
(f) $(4, -2)$ (g) $(-4, 1)$

9. (a), (b)

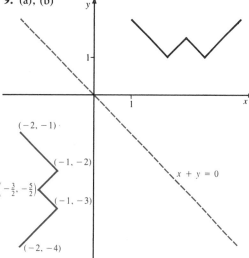

10. (a), (b)

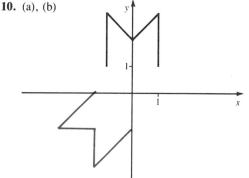

11. (a) $(0, -12)$ (b) $(4, 3)$ (c) $(0, 3)$
(d) $(-5, -10)$

15. (a) $\begin{bmatrix} 1 & 0 \\ 0 & 1 \end{bmatrix}$ (b) $\begin{bmatrix} 0 & 0 \\ 0 & 0 \end{bmatrix}$ (c) $\begin{bmatrix} 5 & 0 \\ 0 & 5 \end{bmatrix}$

16. $53°$

17. (a) projection   (b) rotation   (c) rotation
(d) rotation   (e) projection   (f) reflection

18. (a) 17(f) reflection in $y = 0$ (b) 17(b) rotation
through $63°$ 17(c) rotation through π
17(d) rotation through $135°$ (c) 17(a) projection
on $x + y = 0$ 17(e) projection on
$\sqrt{3} - \sqrt{5}x - \sqrt{3} + \sqrt{5} y = 0$

8.8 CHAPTER 8 TEST

1. (a) $\begin{bmatrix} -11 \\ -19 \end{bmatrix}$ (b) $\begin{bmatrix} 6 & 10 \\ 11 & 17 \end{bmatrix}$

2. (a) $(-10, 12)$ (b) $(2, 2)$

4. $\begin{bmatrix} -26 & -50 \\ 16 & 2 \end{bmatrix}$ **5.** (a) $\begin{bmatrix} 0 & 0 \\ 0 & 0 \end{bmatrix}$ (b) $\begin{bmatrix} 1 & 0 \\ 0 & 1 \end{bmatrix}$

6.

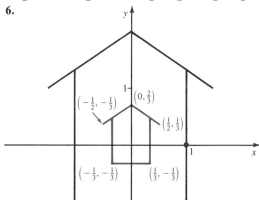

7. π

CHAPTER 9 CONICS AND ROTATIONS

REVIEW AND PREVIEW TO CHAPTER 9
EXERCISE 1

1. (a) $-\frac{7}{25}$ and $\frac{24}{25}$ (b) $-\frac{119}{169}$ and $\frac{120}{169}$ (c) $-\frac{1}{2}$ and
$\frac{\sqrt{3}}{2}$ (d) $\frac{119}{169}$ and $\frac{120}{169}$ (e) 0.28 and 0.96
(f) 0.28 and -0.96 (g) -0.28 and -0.96
(h) $-\frac{7}{9}$ and $\frac{4\sqrt{2}}{9}$

2. (a) $\frac{1}{2}$ and $\frac{\sqrt{3}}{2}$ (b) $-\frac{\sqrt{2}}{\sqrt{3}}$ and $-\frac{1}{\sqrt{3}}$
(c) $-\sqrt{0.8}$ and $\sqrt{0.2}$ (d) 0 and -1
(e) $\frac{\sqrt{2 + \sqrt{2}}}{2}$ and $\frac{\sqrt{2 - \sqrt{2}}}{2}$
(f) $\frac{-\sqrt{2 - \sqrt{3}}}{2}$ and $\frac{\sqrt{2 + \sqrt{3}}}{2}$ (g) $\sqrt{0.95}$
and $-\sqrt{0.05}$ (h) $-\sqrt{0.45}$ and $-\sqrt{0.55}$

EXERCISE 2

1. (a) $\frac{\pi}{4}$ (b) $\frac{3\pi}{4}$ (c) $\frac{\pi}{6}$ (d) $\frac{5\pi}{6}$ (e) $\frac{\pi}{3}$ (f) $\frac{2\pi}{3}$
(g) 0.570 040   (h) 3.041 924

3. (a) $\frac{\sqrt{2 + \sqrt{2}}}{2}$ and $\frac{\sqrt{2 - \sqrt{2}}}{2}$

(b) $\sqrt{\frac{1}{2}\left(1 + \frac{7}{\sqrt{130}}\right)}$ and $\sqrt{\frac{1}{2}\left(1 - \frac{7}{\sqrt{130}}\right)}$

(c) $\sqrt{\frac{\sqrt{10} - 3}{20}}$ and $\sqrt{\frac{\sqrt{10} + 3}{20}}$ (d) $\frac{3}{5}$ and $\frac{4}{5}$

3. (e) $\frac{\sqrt{3}}{2}$ and $\frac{1}{2}$ (f) $\frac{\sqrt{2 - \sqrt{3}}}{2}$ and $\frac{\sqrt{2 + \sqrt{3}}}{2}$

EXERCISE 9.1

1. (a) Symmetric   (b) Symmetric   (c) Not
symmetric unless $c = d$ (d) Symmetric

2. (a) -25 (b) 0   (c) -7 (d) -69

3. (a) $-x^2 + 2y^2$ (b) $2x^2 - 6xy + 7y^2$
(c) $-2xy + 2y^2$ (d) $4x^2 - 4xy + 4y^2$
(e) $3x^2 + 2xy + y^2$ (f) $6x^2 + xy$

4. (a) $\begin{bmatrix} 1 & -3 \\ -3 & 9 \end{bmatrix}$ and 10   (b) $\begin{bmatrix} 16 & -28 \\ -28 & 49 \end{bmatrix}$ and 65

(c) $\begin{bmatrix} 0 & 0 \\ 0 & 36 \end{bmatrix}$ and 36   (d) $\begin{bmatrix} 25 & 0 \\ 0 & 0 \end{bmatrix}$ and 25

(e) 65 and $\begin{bmatrix} 64 & 8 \\ 8 & 1 \end{bmatrix}$ (f) 85 and $\begin{bmatrix} 4 & -18 \\ -18 & 81 \end{bmatrix}$

(g) 65 and $\begin{bmatrix} 16 & -28 \\ -28 & 49 \end{bmatrix}$ (h) 125 and

$\begin{bmatrix} 4 & -22 \\ -22 & 121 \end{bmatrix}$

5. (a) $[1 \ \ 1]$, $\begin{bmatrix} 1 \\ 1 \end{bmatrix}$, and $\begin{bmatrix} 1 \\ 1 \end{bmatrix}$

(b) $\begin{bmatrix} -5 \\ 2 \end{bmatrix}$, $[-5 \ \ 2]$, and $[-5 \ \ 2]$

(c) $\begin{bmatrix} 6 & 8 \\ 0 & -6 \end{bmatrix}$, $\begin{bmatrix} 6 & 0 \\ 8 & -6 \end{bmatrix}$, and $\begin{bmatrix} 6 & 0 \\ 8 & -6 \end{bmatrix}$

6. $\begin{bmatrix} 29 & 53 \\ 53 & 97 \end{bmatrix}$

EXERCISE 9.2

1. (a) $\begin{bmatrix} 1 & 0 \\ 0 & -1 \end{bmatrix}$, $x^2 - y^2$

(b) $\begin{bmatrix} 0 & 1 \\ 1 & 5 \end{bmatrix}$, $2xy + 5y^2$

(c) $\begin{bmatrix} 5 & -3 \\ -3 & -7 \end{bmatrix}$, $5x^2 - 6xy - 7y^2$

(d) $\begin{bmatrix} 3 & -0.5 \\ -0.5 & 5 \end{bmatrix}$, $3x^2 - xy + 5y^2$

(e) $\begin{bmatrix} \frac{1}{a^2} & 0 \\ 0 & \frac{1}{b^2} \end{bmatrix}$, $\dfrac{x^2}{a^2} + \dfrac{y^2}{b^2}$

(f) $\begin{bmatrix} \frac{1}{a^2} & 0 \\ 0 & -\frac{1}{b^2} \end{bmatrix}$, $\dfrac{x^2}{a^2} - \dfrac{y^2}{b^2}$

2. (a) $\begin{bmatrix} 1 & 0.5 \\ 0.5 & 0 \end{bmatrix}$ (b) $\begin{bmatrix} 0 & 2 \\ 2 & 0 \end{bmatrix}$

(c) $\begin{bmatrix} 3 & -1 \\ -1 & 7 \end{bmatrix}$ (d) $\begin{bmatrix} 0 & 5.5 \\ 5.5 & -1 \end{bmatrix}$

(e) $\begin{bmatrix} -1 & 0 \\ 0 & 2 \end{bmatrix}$ (b) $\begin{bmatrix} a & h \\ h & b \end{bmatrix}$

3. (a) $\begin{bmatrix} 0 & 2 \\ 0 & 5 \end{bmatrix}$ (b) No; it is not symmetric.

4. $M = \begin{bmatrix} 0 & c \\ -c & 0 \end{bmatrix}$, $c \in R$

EXERCISE 9.3

1. $\begin{bmatrix} 1 & 0 \\ 0 & 1 \end{bmatrix}$

2. (a) $-x^2 + y^2 = 1$

(b) $-\frac{1}{2}x^2 + \sqrt{3}xy + \frac{1}{2}y^2 = 1$

(c) $\frac{3}{5}x^2 + \frac{8}{5}xy - \frac{3}{5}y^2 = 1$

(d) $-\frac{7}{25}x^2 - \frac{48}{25}xy + \frac{7}{25}y^2 = 1$

3. (a) $\frac{17}{225}x^2 - \frac{16}{225}xy + \frac{17}{225}y^2 = 1$; $ab - h^2 = \frac{1}{225}$

(b) $\frac{7}{75}x^2 + \frac{8\sqrt{3}}{225}xy + \frac{13}{225}y^2 = 1$; $ab - h^2 = \frac{1}{225}$

(c) $\frac{61}{1125}x^2 - \frac{64}{1125}xy + \frac{109}{1125}y^2 = 1$;

$ab - h^2 = \frac{1}{225}$

(d) $\frac{41}{625}x^2 - \frac{128}{1875}xy + \frac{481}{5625}y^2 = 1$;

$ab - h^2 = \frac{1}{225}$

4. (a) $\frac{1}{2}x^2 + \frac{3}{2}y^2 = 1$; ellipse

(b) $-x^2 + 3y^2 = 1$; hyperbola

(c) $\frac{1}{2}x^2 + \frac{7}{2}y^2 = 1$; ellipse

(d) $-\frac{1}{2}x^2 + \frac{9}{2}y^2 = 1$; hyperbola

5. (a) $4x^2 + 8y^2 = 1$; ellipse (b) $4x^2 - 4y^2 = 1$; hyperbola (c) $2x^2 + 6y^2 = 1$; ellipse

(d) $\frac{1}{2}x^2 - \frac{3}{2}y^2 = 1$; hyperbola

9. $X'(MAM)X = k$

EXERCISE 9.4

1. (a)
$$R = \begin{bmatrix} \sqrt{\frac{1}{2}\left(1 + \frac{3}{\sqrt{13}}\right)} & -\sqrt{\frac{1}{2}\left(1 - \frac{3}{\sqrt{13}}\right)} \\ \sqrt{\frac{1}{2}\left(1 - \frac{3}{\sqrt{13}}\right)} & \sqrt{\frac{1}{2}\left(1 + \frac{3}{\sqrt{13}}\right)} \end{bmatrix}$$

(b)
$$R = \begin{bmatrix} \sqrt{\frac{1}{2}\left(1 + \frac{3}{\sqrt{10}}\right)} & -\sqrt{\frac{1}{2}\left(1 - \frac{3}{\sqrt{10}}\right)} \\ \sqrt{\frac{1}{2}\left(1 - \frac{3}{\sqrt{10}}\right)} & \sqrt{\frac{1}{2}\left(1 + \frac{3}{\sqrt{10}}\right)} \end{bmatrix}$$

(c)
$$R = \begin{bmatrix} \sqrt{\frac{1}{2}\left(1 + \frac{1}{\sqrt{17}}\right)} & -\sqrt{\frac{1}{2}\left(1 - \frac{1}{\sqrt{17}}\right)} \\ \sqrt{\frac{1}{2}\left(1 - \frac{1}{\sqrt{17}}\right)} & -\sqrt{\frac{1}{2}\left(1 + \frac{1}{\sqrt{17}}\right)} \end{bmatrix}$$

(d)
$$R = \begin{bmatrix} \sqrt{\frac{1}{2}\left(1 - \frac{1}{\sqrt{10}}\right)} & -\sqrt{\frac{1}{2}\left(1 + \frac{1}{\sqrt{10}}\right)} \\ \sqrt{\frac{1}{2}\left(1 + \frac{1}{\sqrt{10}}\right)} & \sqrt{\left(\frac{1}{2}\left(1 - \frac{1}{\sqrt{10}}\right)\right)} \end{bmatrix}$$

(e)
$$R = \begin{bmatrix} \sqrt{\frac{1}{2}\left(1 - \frac{1}{\sqrt{2}}\right)} & -\sqrt{\frac{1}{2}\left(1 + \frac{1}{\sqrt{2}}\right)} \\ \sqrt{\frac{1}{2}\left(1 + \frac{1}{\sqrt{2}}\right)} & \sqrt{\frac{1}{2}\left(1 - \frac{1}{\sqrt{2}}\right)} \end{bmatrix}$$

(f) $R = \begin{bmatrix} \dfrac{1}{\sqrt{2}} & -\dfrac{1}{\sqrt{2}} \\ \dfrac{1}{\sqrt{2}} & \dfrac{1}{\sqrt{2}} \end{bmatrix}$

2. (a) Using R from Question 1(a) the equation of the image curve is
$$\frac{7 - \sqrt{13}}{2}x^2 + \frac{7 + \sqrt{13}}{2}y^2 = 3$$

(b) Using R from Question 1(b) the equation of the image curve is $\sqrt{10}x^2 - \sqrt{10}y^2 = 4$

(c) Using R from Question 1(c) the equation of the image curve is
$$\frac{-1 - \sqrt{17}}{2}x^2 + \frac{-1 + \sqrt{17}}{2}y^2 = -1$$

2. (d) Using R from Question 1(d) the equation of the image curve is
$(3 - \sqrt{10})x^2 + (3 + \sqrt{10})y^2 = 9$
(e) Using R from Question 1(e) the equation of the image curve is
$(3 - 2\sqrt{2})x^2 + (3 + 2\sqrt{2})y^2 = 5$
(f) Using R from Question 1(f) the equation of the image curve is $3x^2 + 5y^2 = 1$

3. (a) $a' = -2, b' = 2$ (b) $a' = 5, b' = -3$
(c) $a' = 5, b' = 10$ (d) $a' = -5, b' = 15$

4. If $h > 0$, $\cos \theta = \sqrt{\frac{1}{2}\left(1 + \dfrac{b - a}{\Delta}\right)}$ and

$\sin \theta = \sqrt{\frac{1}{2}\left(1 + \dfrac{a - b}{\Delta}\right)}$

If $h < 0$, $\cos \theta = \sqrt{\frac{1}{2}\left(1 + \dfrac{a - b}{\Delta}\right)}$ and

$\sin \theta = \sqrt{\frac{1}{2}\left(1 + \dfrac{b - a}{\Delta}\right)}$

5. $R = \begin{bmatrix} 0 & -1 \\ 1 & 0 \end{bmatrix}$; a rotation through $\dfrac{\pi}{2}$
Circles: those with $a = b$ and $h = 0$.

EXERCISE 9.5

1. (a) $a + b \neq a' + b'$ (c) $a + b \neq a' + b'$
(c) $ab - h^2 \neq a'b' - (h')^2$
(d) $ab - h^2 \neq a'b' - (h')^2$

2. (a) $\dfrac{\sqrt{5}}{2}x^2 - \dfrac{\sqrt{5}}{2}y^2 = 1$ and

$-\dfrac{\sqrt{5}}{2}x^2 + \dfrac{\sqrt{5}}{2}y^2 = 1$

(b) $\dfrac{3 + \sqrt{10}}{2}x^2 + \dfrac{3 - \sqrt{10}}{2}y^2 = 2$ and

$\dfrac{3 - \sqrt{10}}{2}x^2 + \dfrac{3 + \sqrt{10}}{2}y^2 = 2$

(c) $\dfrac{5 + \sqrt{5}}{2}x^2 + \dfrac{5 - \sqrt{5}}{2}y^2 = 3$ and

$\dfrac{5 - \sqrt{5}}{2}x^2 + \dfrac{5 + \sqrt{5}}{2}y^2 = 3$

(d) $\dfrac{13 + \sqrt{61}}{72}x^2 + \dfrac{13 - \sqrt{61}}{72}y^2 = 1$ and

$\dfrac{13 - \sqrt{61}}{72}x^2 + \dfrac{13 + \sqrt{61}}{72}y^2 = 1$

3. (a) Hyperbola (b) Hyperbola (c) Ellipse
(d) Ellipse (e) Circle (f) Hyperbola

4. (a) Hyperbola (b) Pair of lines through the origin (c) Empty (d) Point: the origin

5. (a) Ellipse (b) Hyperbola (c) Empty
(d) Point: the origin

9.6 REVIEW EXERCISE

1. (c) is symmetric; (a), (b), and (d) are not.

2. (a) 4 (b) 7 (c) $\begin{bmatrix} 1 & 0 \\ 0 & 1 \end{bmatrix}$

(d) $\begin{bmatrix} ad - bc & 0 \\ 0 & ad - bc \end{bmatrix}$ (e) $\begin{bmatrix} 1 & a + b \\ 0 & 1 \end{bmatrix}$

(f) $\begin{bmatrix} -2 & 6 \\ -3 & 9 \end{bmatrix}$

3. (a) $\begin{bmatrix} 1 & 3 \\ 2 & 4 \end{bmatrix}$ (b) $\begin{bmatrix} -1 & -2 \\ 1 & 2 \end{bmatrix}$

(c) $\begin{bmatrix} a & c \\ b & d \end{bmatrix}$ (d) $\begin{bmatrix} 3 & 1 \\ 1 & -2 \end{bmatrix}$

4. (a) $\begin{bmatrix} 5 & 11 \\ 11 & 25 \end{bmatrix}$ (b) $\begin{bmatrix} 2 & 4 \\ 4 & 8 \end{bmatrix}$

(c) $\begin{bmatrix} 10 & 1 \\ 1 & 5 \end{bmatrix}$ (d) $\begin{bmatrix} a^2 + b^2 & ac + bd \\ ac + bc & c^2 + d^2 \end{bmatrix}$

5. (a) $\begin{bmatrix} \dfrac{a - 2h + b}{2} & \dfrac{a - b}{2} \\ \dfrac{a - b}{2} & \dfrac{a + 2h + b}{2} \end{bmatrix}$

(b) $\begin{bmatrix} \dfrac{a - 4h + 4b}{5} & \dfrac{2a - 3h - 2b}{5} \\ \dfrac{2a - 3h - 2b}{5} & \dfrac{4a + 4h + b}{5} \end{bmatrix}$

(c) $\begin{bmatrix} \dfrac{3a + 2\sqrt{3}h + b}{4} & \dfrac{-\sqrt{3}a + 2h + \sqrt{3}b}{4} \\ \dfrac{-\sqrt{3}a + 2h + \sqrt{3}b}{25} & \dfrac{a - 2\sqrt{3}h + 3b}{4} \end{bmatrix}$

(d) $\begin{bmatrix} \dfrac{16a - 24h + 9b}{4} & \dfrac{12a + 7h - 12b}{25} \\ \dfrac{12a + 7h - 12b}{25} & \dfrac{9a + 24h + 16b}{25} \end{bmatrix}$

6. (a) 1   (b) 1   (c) 2   (d) 2

7. (a) $\begin{bmatrix} 1 & 0 \\ 0 & 1 \end{bmatrix}$ (b) $\begin{bmatrix} 1 & 0 \\ 0 & -1 \end{bmatrix}$

(c) $\begin{bmatrix} 0 & 0.5 \\ 0.5 & 0 \end{bmatrix}$ (d) $\begin{bmatrix} 0.25 & 0 \\ 0 & 1 \end{bmatrix}$

(e) $\begin{bmatrix} \frac{1}{9} & 0 \\ 0 & -\frac{1}{4} \end{bmatrix}$ (f) $\begin{bmatrix} 1 & 0.5 \\ 0.5 & 2 \end{bmatrix}$

(g) $\begin{bmatrix} 2 & -1.5 \\ -1.5 & 4 \end{bmatrix}$ (h) $\begin{bmatrix} 1 & 1 \\ 1 & -1 \end{bmatrix}$

(i) $\begin{bmatrix} \frac{1}{4} & -\frac{1}{4} \\ -\frac{1}{4} & \frac{1}{9} \end{bmatrix}$ $\begin{bmatrix} 0 & 1 \\ 1 & -3 \end{bmatrix}$

8. (a) $\begin{bmatrix} 1 & 0 \\ 0 & 1 \end{bmatrix}$ (b) $\begin{bmatrix} 0.25 & 0 \\ 0 & 1 \end{bmatrix}$

(c) $\begin{bmatrix} 0 & -1 \\ -1 & -5 \end{bmatrix}$ (d) $\begin{bmatrix} \frac{1}{9} & 0 \\ 0 & \frac{1}{16} \end{bmatrix}$

(e) $\begin{bmatrix} 0 & 0.5 \\ 0.5 & 0 \end{bmatrix}$ (f) $\begin{bmatrix} 1 & 0.5 \\ 0.5 & 1 \end{bmatrix}$

9. Each product is $\begin{bmatrix} 1 & 0 \\ 0 & 1 \end{bmatrix}$

10. (a) $\frac{7}{48}x^2 - \frac{5\sqrt{3}}{72}xy + \frac{31}{144}y^2 = 1$

(b) $\frac{5}{36}x^2 + \frac{1}{9}xy + \frac{2}{9}y^2 = 1$

(c) $\frac{13}{72}x^2 - \frac{5}{36}xy + \frac{13}{72}y^2 = 1$

(d) $\frac{341}{1521}x^2 + \frac{50}{507}xy + \frac{89}{676}y^2 = 1$

11. (a) $x^2 - xy + 2y^2 = 1$

(b) $\frac{5 + \sqrt{3}}{4}x^2 + \frac{1 + \sqrt{3}}{2}xy + \frac{7 - \sqrt{3}}{4}y^2 = 1$

(c) $\frac{7 - \sqrt{3}}{4}x^2 - \frac{1 + \sqrt{3}}{2}xy + \frac{5 + \sqrt{3}}{4}y^2 = 1$

(d) $2x^2 - xy + y^2 = 1$

(e) $\frac{7 - \sqrt{3}}{4}x^2 - \frac{1 + \sqrt{3}}{2}xy + \frac{5 + \sqrt{3}}{4}y^2 = 1$

(f) $\frac{5 - \sqrt{3}}{4}x^2 + \frac{1 - \sqrt{3}}{2}xy + \frac{7 + \sqrt{3}}{4}y^2 = 1$

12. (a) $\frac{7}{4}x^2 - \frac{\sqrt{3}}{2}xy + \frac{1}{4}y^2 = 1$

(b) $-\frac{7}{4}x^2 - \frac{5\sqrt{3}}{2}xy + \frac{3}{4}y^2 = 1$

(c) $\frac{\sqrt{3}}{4}x^2 - \frac{1}{2}xy - \frac{\sqrt{3}}{4}y^2 = 1$

(d) $\frac{15 + 2\sqrt{3}}{4}x^2 + \frac{-2 + 5\sqrt{3}}{2}xy$
$+ \frac{5 - 2\sqrt{3}}{4}y^2 = 1$

13. (a)
$$R = \begin{bmatrix} \sqrt{\frac{1}{2}\left(1 - \frac{7}{\sqrt{53}}\right)} & -\sqrt{\frac{1}{2}\left(1 + \frac{7}{\sqrt{53}}\right)} \\ \sqrt{\frac{1}{2}\left(1 + \frac{7}{\sqrt{53}}\right)} & \sqrt{\left(\frac{1}{2}\left(1 - \frac{7}{\sqrt{53}}\right)\right)} \end{bmatrix}$$

(b)
$$R = \begin{bmatrix} \dfrac{1}{\sqrt{2}} & -\dfrac{1}{\sqrt{2}} \\ \dfrac{1}{\sqrt{2}} & \dfrac{1}{\sqrt{2}} \end{bmatrix}$$

(c)
$$R = \begin{bmatrix} \dfrac{2}{\sqrt{5}} & -\dfrac{1}{\sqrt{5}} \\ \dfrac{1}{\sqrt{5}} & \dfrac{2}{\sqrt{5}} \end{bmatrix}$$

(d)
$$R = \begin{bmatrix} \sqrt{\frac{1}{2}\left(1 - \frac{1}{\sqrt{2}}\right)} & -\sqrt{\frac{1}{2}\left(1 + \frac{1}{\sqrt{2}}\right)} \\ \sqrt{\frac{1}{2}\left(1 + \frac{1}{\sqrt{2}}\right)} & \sqrt{\frac{1}{2}\left(1 - \frac{1}{\sqrt{2}}\right)} \end{bmatrix}$$

(e)
$$R = \begin{bmatrix} \sqrt{\frac{1}{2}\left(1 + \frac{\sqrt{3}}{2}\right)} & -\sqrt{\frac{1}{2}\left(1 - \frac{\sqrt{3}}{2}\right)} \\ \sqrt{\frac{1}{2}\left(1 - \frac{\sqrt{3}}{2}\right)} & \sqrt{\frac{1}{2}\left(1 + \frac{\sqrt{3}}{2}\right)} \end{bmatrix}$$

(f)
$$R = \begin{bmatrix} \sqrt{\frac{1}{2}\left(1 + \frac{2}{\sqrt{5}}\right)} & -\sqrt{\frac{1}{2}\left(1 - \frac{2}{\sqrt{5}}\right)} \\ \sqrt{\frac{1}{2}\left(1 - \frac{2}{\sqrt{5}}\right)} & \sqrt{\frac{1}{2}\left(1 + \frac{2}{\sqrt{5}}\right)} \end{bmatrix}$$

14. (a) $a' = -\frac{1}{2} - \frac{1}{\sqrt{2}},\ b' = -\frac{1}{2} + \frac{1}{\sqrt{2}}$

(b) $a' = 2 - \sqrt{3},\ b' = 6 - \sqrt{3}$

(c) $a' = -3 - 2\sqrt{5},\ b' = -3 + 2\sqrt{5}$

(d) $a' = \frac{7 - \sqrt{13}}{2},\ b' = \frac{7 + \sqrt{13}}{2}$

15. (a) No value of k.   (b) No value of k.   (c) All $k \in R, k \neq 0$.   (d) All $k \in R, k \neq 0$.

16. (a) For all $k > 0$.   (b) No value of k.   (c) For all $k > 0$.   (d) No value of k.

9.7 CHAPTER 9 TEST

1. (a) $\begin{bmatrix} 2 & -1 \\ 3 & -4 \end{bmatrix}$ (b) $\begin{bmatrix} 13 & -14 \\ -14 & 17 \end{bmatrix}$

(c) $\begin{bmatrix} 5 & 10 \\ 10 & 25 \end{bmatrix}$ (d) $\begin{bmatrix} 1 & -6 \\ 2 & 13 \end{bmatrix}$

2. $\begin{bmatrix} 2 & 1 \\ 1 & -4 \end{bmatrix}$

3. $X^t(RAR^t)X = k$

4. $\frac{13}{16}x^2 - \frac{3\sqrt{3}}{8}xy + \frac{7}{16}y^2 = 1$

5.
$$R = \begin{bmatrix} \dfrac{1}{\sqrt{5}} & -\dfrac{2}{\sqrt{5}} \\ \dfrac{2}{\sqrt{5}} & \dfrac{1}{\sqrt{5}} \end{bmatrix}$$

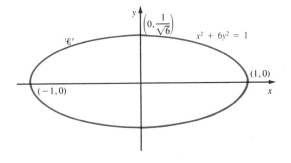

CUMULATIVE REVIEW FOR CHAPTERS 7 TO 9

1. $r = 6$ **2.** $s = 3$ **3.** $2r + 3s = 1$

4. $\begin{cases} x_{P'} = x_P + 2 \\ y_{P'} = y_P - 3 \end{cases}$ Image: $x^2 + y^2 = 1$

5. $3x^3 - y^2 - 6x + 2y + 2 = 0$

6. $r = 3, x = -2$, an ellipse

7. $\begin{cases} x_{P'} = x_P - 2 \\ y_{P'} = y_P + 4 \end{cases}$

8. $\begin{bmatrix} 1 & 1 \\ -3 & 5 \end{bmatrix}$ **9.** $\begin{bmatrix} -2 & 7 \\ 23 & 17 \end{bmatrix}$

10. $P'(-8, 10)$ **11.** A horizontal shear by a factor of 4.

12. $P'(6, -9)$ **13.** $\begin{bmatrix} 0 & -1 \\ 1 & 0 \end{bmatrix}$

14. The angle of rotation has radian measure $\dfrac{5\pi}{6}$.

15. $MM' = \begin{bmatrix} 10 & -11 \\ -11 & 29 \end{bmatrix}$ and
$M'M = \begin{bmatrix} 13 & -13 \\ -13 & 26 \end{bmatrix}$

16. $\begin{bmatrix} 5.48 & 1.36 \\ 1.36 & 0.52 \end{bmatrix}$ **17.** $\begin{bmatrix} 1 & 1 \\ 1 & -3 \end{bmatrix}$

18. $\begin{bmatrix} 0 & -1 \\ -1 & 1 \end{bmatrix}$ **19.** $\begin{bmatrix} 1 & 0 \\ 0 & 1 \end{bmatrix}$

20. $\frac{61}{169}x^2 - \frac{90}{169}xy + \frac{601}{676}y^2 = 1$

21. $\dfrac{1 - 2\sqrt{3}}{4}x^2 + \dfrac{2 + 3\sqrt{3}}{2}xy + \dfrac{2\sqrt{3} - 5}{4}y^2 = 1$

22. $\frac{1}{4}x^2 - \dfrac{\sqrt{3}}{2}xy + \frac{7}{4}y^2 = 1$

23.
$$\begin{bmatrix} \dfrac{2}{\sqrt{5}} & -\dfrac{1}{\sqrt{5}} \\ \dfrac{1}{\sqrt{5}} & \dfrac{2}{\sqrt{5}} \end{bmatrix}$$

24. $a' = -2, b' = 8$, hyperbola

25. $a' = 1, b' = 5$

26. (a) All h with $|h| < 6$.   (b) The parameter h is 6 or -6. In each of these cases $\mathcal{C}$ is a pair of parallel lines.

CHAPTER 10 COMPLEX NUMBERS

REVIEW AND PREVIEW TO CHAPTER 10
EXERCISE 1

1.

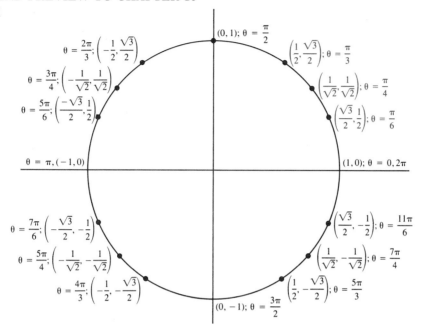

2. (a) $\dfrac{\sqrt{3}}{2}$ (b) $\dfrac{1}{\sqrt{2}}$ (c) 0 (d) $\dfrac{\sqrt{3}}{2}$ (e) $\dfrac{\sqrt{3}}{2}$

(f) $\frac{1}{2}$ (g) $\dfrac{1}{\sqrt{2}}$ (h) $-\dfrac{\sqrt{3}}{2}$ (i) 0

(j) 0 (k) $-\dfrac{\sqrt{3}}{2}$ (l) $-\frac{1}{2}$ (m) $-\dfrac{1}{\sqrt{2}}$

(n) $-\dfrac{\sqrt{3}}{2}$ (o) 0

3. (a) 1 (b) $\dfrac{1}{\sqrt{3}}$ (c) $\sqrt{3}$ (d) undefined (e) 0

(f) $-\sqrt{3}$ (g) $-\dfrac{1}{\sqrt{3}}$ (h) $\sqrt{3}$ (i) -1

(j) undefined (k) $-\dfrac{1}{\sqrt{3}}$ (l) 0

4. (a) $\dfrac{\pi}{4}, \dfrac{3\pi}{4}$ (b) $\dfrac{\pi}{6}, \dfrac{11\pi}{6}$ (c) $\dfrac{7\pi}{6}, \dfrac{11\pi}{6}$

(d) $\dfrac{2\pi}{3}, \dfrac{4\pi}{3}$

(e) $\dfrac{5\pi}{4}, \dfrac{7\pi}{4}$ (f) $\dfrac{3\pi}{4}, \dfrac{5\pi}{4}$ (g) $\dfrac{\pi}{4}, \dfrac{5\pi}{4}$ (h) $\dfrac{2\pi}{3}, \dfrac{5\pi}{3}$

(i) $\dfrac{\pi}{3}, \dfrac{4\pi}{3}$ (j) $\dfrac{\pi}{6}, \dfrac{7\pi}{6}$ (k) $\dfrac{3\pi}{4}, \dfrac{7\pi}{4}$ (l) $\dfrac{5\pi}{6}, \dfrac{11\pi}{6}$

5. (a) $0.983, \pi + 0.983$ (b) $-1.107, \pi - 1.07$
(c) $0.310, \pi + 0.310$ (d) $0.232, \pi + 0.232$
(e) $-0.955, \pi - 0.9555$
(f) $2.419, 2\pi - 2.419$

EXERCISE 2
2. (a) $\cos 3\theta = 4 \cos^3 \theta - 3 \cos \theta$
(b) $\sin 3\theta = 3 \sin \theta - 4 \sin^3 \theta$

EXERCISE 10.1

1.	Real part	Imaginary part
(a)	3	6
(b)	-1	$-\sqrt{2}$
(c)	$2 + \sqrt{2}$	$3 - \sqrt{2}$
(d)	0	2
(e)	π	$-\pi$
(f)	13	0
(g)	$\frac{2}{5}$	$-\frac{3}{5}$
(h)	-7	3
(i)	$\cos 1$	$\sin 1$
(j)	0	0
(k)	1	$\sqrt{2}$
(l)	$-\sqrt{3}$	2

2.

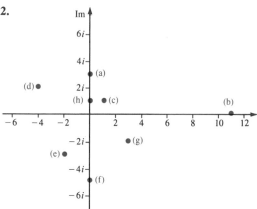

3. (a) $0 + i\sqrt{2}, 0 - i\sqrt{2}$ (b) $-1 + i\sqrt{2}$,
$-1 - i\sqrt{2}$ (c) $1 + i, 1 - i$

(d) $-\frac{1}{2} + \frac{1}{2\sqrt{3}}i, -\frac{1}{2} - \frac{1}{2\sqrt{3}}i$

(e) $-1 + i\sqrt{2}, -1 - i\sqrt{2}$ (f) $1 + \frac{1}{\sqrt{2}}i$,

$1 - \frac{1}{\sqrt{2}}i$ (g) $\frac{3}{2} + \frac{\sqrt{7}}{2}i, \frac{3}{2} - \frac{\sqrt{7}}{2}i$

(h) $5 + \sqrt{3}i, 5 - \sqrt{3}i$

4. (a) $\sqrt{5}$ (b) $\sqrt{2}$ (c) $\sqrt{41}$ (d) $\sqrt{13}$ (e) 2
(f) $\sqrt{34}$ (g) $\sqrt{13}$ (h) $\sqrt{5}$

5. (a)   (b)

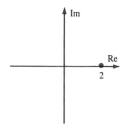

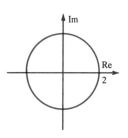

(c)   (d)

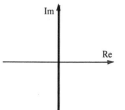

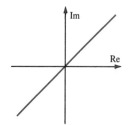

5. (e)   (f)

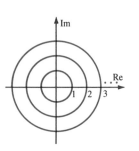

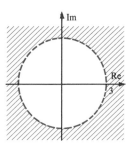

EXERCISE 10.2

1. (a) $10 - i$ (b) $2 + 4i$ (c) $4 + 3i$
(d) $(w + c) + (v + d)i$ (e) 2 (f) 25
(g) -9 (h) 1 (i) 82 (j) $8 - i$ (k) 0
(l) $-4 - 8i$ (m) 149 (n) $a^2 + b^2$ (o) 10
(p) 0 (q) $2a^2$ (r) $-1 - i$

2. (a) $4 + 2i$ (b) $2 - 3i$

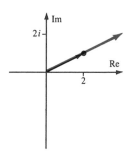

(c) $2 - i$ (d) $3 + 9i$

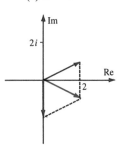

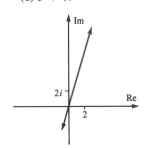

(e) $-6 - 3i$ (f) $3 + 4i$

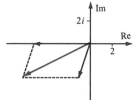

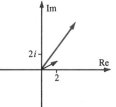

2. (g) $1 + 0.5i$

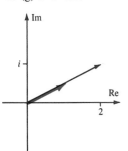

(h) $1 - 2i$

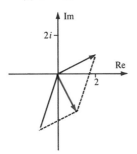

2. (o) $-12 + 4i$

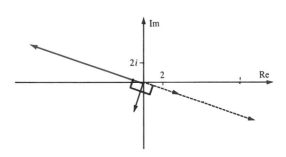

(i) $3 + 4i$

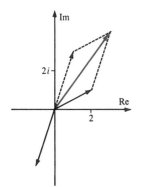

(j) $1 - 7i$

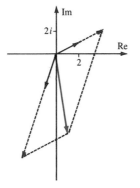

3. (a) $1 - i$ (b) $7 + 3i$ (c) $9 + 2i$
(d) $-3 + 6i$

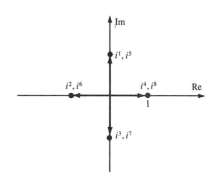

(k) $-1 + 2i$

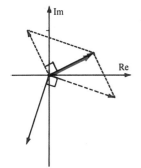

(l) $3 - i$

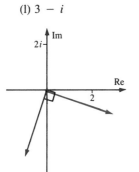

4. (a)

k	1	2	3	4	5	6	7	8
i^k	i	-1	$-i$	1	i	-1	$-i$	1

(b) $i^k = \begin{cases} 1, & k = 4n, n \in W \\ i, & k = 4n + 1, n \in W \\ -1, & k = 4n + 2, n \in W \\ -i, & k = 4n + 3, n \in W \end{cases}$

(c) (i) i (ii) 1   (iii) $-i$ (iv) $-i$ (v) i (vi) i

(m) $2 + i$

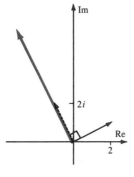

(n) $-3 + 6i$

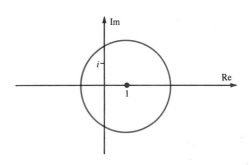

5. (a)

5. (b)

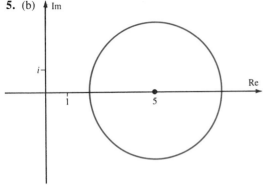

(c)

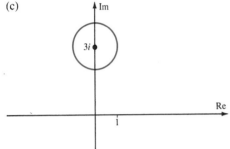

(d)

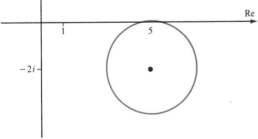

EXERCISE 10.3

1. (a) $3 + 5i$ (b) $9 - 2i$ (c) $-3 + 3i$
(d) $-2i$ (e) $3i$ (f) 22 (g) $17 + 4i$
(h) $3 - 5i$ (i) -1 (j) $-i$ (k) 0 (l) $a - bi$

2. (a) $\frac{1}{2} - \frac{1}{2}i$

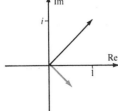

2. (b) $-\frac{3}{25} - \frac{4}{25}i$

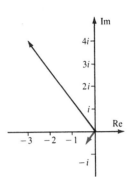

(c) $1 - i$

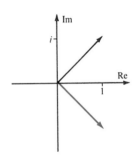

(d) $-3 - 4i$

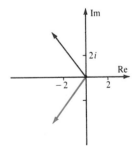

(e) $\frac{1}{2} + \frac{1}{2}i$

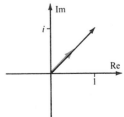

2. (f) $-\frac{3}{25} + \frac{4}{25}i$

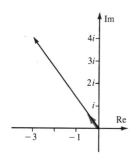

(g) $3 - 3i$

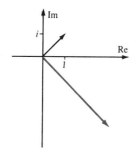

(h) $\frac{1}{2} - \frac{1}{2}i$

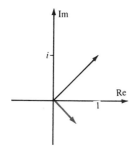

(i) $-\frac{3}{25} - \frac{4}{25}i$

3. (a) $11 - 13i$ (b) $4 - 3i$ (c) $-i$ (d) $8i$
(e) $-2 - 2i$ (f) $\frac{6}{5} + \frac{3}{5}i$ (g) $3i$ (h) $-1 - \frac{2}{3}i$
(i) $-\frac{4}{5} - \frac{2}{5}i$ (j) $-i$ (k) $3 + \frac{13}{5}i$ (l) $\frac{7}{25} + \frac{24}{25}i$
(m) $-\frac{3}{26} + \frac{15}{26}i$ (n) $-\frac{24}{125} - \frac{7}{125}i$ (o) $\frac{5}{2} - 5i$
(p) $1 + i$ (q) $1 - \frac{2}{3}i$ (r) $1 - \frac{15}{8}i$

4. (a) $\frac{1}{5} - \frac{2}{5}i$ (b) $-\frac{7}{2} + \frac{5}{2}i$ (c) $-\frac{1}{13} + \frac{3}{26}i$
(d) $-\frac{2}{5} + \frac{4}{5}i$ (e) $\frac{33}{5} + \frac{4}{5}i$ (f) $-\frac{1}{5} - \frac{3}{5}$

7. (a) $z = i$, $w = 1$ (b) $z = \frac{18}{25} - \frac{24}{25}i$,
$w = -\frac{8}{25} - \frac{31}{25}i$

EXERCISE 10.4

1.

	Modulus	$\tan\theta$	Quadrant/axis
(a)	$\sqrt{2}$	1	1st
(b)	3	undefined	imaginary axis
(c)	$\sqrt{13}$	$\frac{3}{2}$	3rd
(d)	$\sqrt{17}$	$-\frac{1}{4}$	4th
(e)	5	0	real axis
(f)	5	$-\frac{4}{3}$	4th
(g)	$\sqrt{\pi^2 + 4}$	$-\frac{2}{\pi}$	4th
(h)	$\sqrt{2}k$	1	3rd
(i)	$\sqrt{3}$	$-\sqrt{2}$	4th
(j)	$\sqrt{3}$	undefined	imaginary axis
(k)	$\sqrt{5}$	0	real axis
(l)	$2\sqrt{2}$	1	1st

2. (a) $2 \operatorname{cis} 0$ (b) $5 \operatorname{cis} 0$ (c) $2 \operatorname{cis} \pi$
(d) $1 \operatorname{cis} \pi$ (e) $2 \operatorname{cis} \dfrac{\pi}{2}$ (f) $7 \operatorname{cis} \dfrac{\pi}{2}$
(g) $1 \operatorname{cis} \dfrac{3\pi}{2}$ (h) $3 \operatorname{cis} \dfrac{3\pi}{2}$ (i) $0 \operatorname{cis} \theta$, $\theta \in R$
(j) $\pi \operatorname{cis} 0$ (k) $\sqrt{2} \operatorname{cis} \pi$ (l) $\sqrt{3} \operatorname{cis} \dfrac{\pi}{2}$

3. (a) -3 (b) $2i$ (c) $-i$ (d) 2 (e) -5
(f) $1 + i$ (g) $1 - \sqrt{3}i$ (h) $1 - i$ (i) 1
(j) $\dfrac{3}{\sqrt{2}} - \dfrac{3}{\sqrt{2}}i$ (k) $1.081 + 1.683i$
(l) $2.268 + 4.456i$ (m) $-2.970 + 0.423i$
(n) $0.960 - 0.279i$ (o) -2

4. (a) $1 \operatorname{cis} 0$ (b) $1 \operatorname{cis} \dfrac{\pi}{2}$ (c) $\sqrt{2} \operatorname{cis} \dfrac{\pi}{4}$
(d) $\sqrt{2} \operatorname{cis} \dfrac{5\pi}{4}$ (e) $\sqrt{2} \operatorname{cis} \dfrac{7\pi}{4}$
(f) $\sqrt{2} \operatorname{cis} \dfrac{3\pi}{4}$ (g) $\sqrt{34} \operatorname{cis}(-1.030)$
(h) $\sqrt{34} \operatorname{cis}(\pi - 1.030)$ (i) $1 \operatorname{cis} \dfrac{\pi}{3}$

4. (j) $1 \text{ cis } \dfrac{4\pi}{3}$ (k) $3\sqrt{7} \text{ cis}(-0.857)$

(l) $3\sqrt{7} \text{ cis}(\pi - 0.857)$ (m) $\sqrt{3} \text{ cis } \pi$

(n) $\sqrt{3} \text{ cis } 0$ (o) $\sqrt{3} \text{ cis } \dfrac{\pi}{2}$ (p) $\sqrt{3} \text{ cis } \dfrac{3\pi}{2}$

(q) $\sqrt{53} \text{ cis}(-0.278)$ (r) $\sqrt{13} \text{ cis}(\pi - 0.588)$
(s) $\sqrt{265} \text{ cis}(0.829)$ (t) $\sqrt{130} \text{ cis}(\pi + 0.910)$

(u) $\sqrt{0.5} \text{ cis } \dfrac{7\pi}{4}$

EXERCISE 10.5

1. (a) $6 \text{ cis } \dfrac{3\pi}{2}$ (b) $\text{cis } 3$ (c) $2 \text{ cis } \dfrac{\pi}{2}$ (d) $4 \text{ cis } \dfrac{\pi}{2}$

(e) $30 \text{ cis } \pi$ (f) $\text{cis } \dfrac{\pi}{2}$ (g) $8 \text{ cis } \dfrac{\pi}{2}$

(h) $9 \text{ cis } \pi$ (i) $r^2 \text{ cis } 2\theta$ (j) $r^3 \text{ cis } 3\theta$

2. (a) $\frac{2}{3} \text{cis}\left(-\dfrac{\pi}{2}\right)$ (b) $9 \text{ cis } \dfrac{5\pi}{4}$ (c) $3 \text{ cis}\left(-\dfrac{\pi}{2}\right)$

(d) $\frac{4}{3} \text{ cis } 0$

3. (a) $0.183 - 0.683i$ (b) $\dfrac{\sqrt{2}}{4} + \dfrac{\sqrt{6}}{4}i$

(c) $\dfrac{\sqrt{3}}{4} - \frac{1}{4}i$ (d) $-0.555 - 0.674i$

(e) $5.146 + 2.092i$

EXERCISE 10.6

1. (a) $27 \text{ cis } \dfrac{3\pi}{2}$ (b) $16 \text{ cis } 0$ (c) $\text{cis } 0$

(d) $256 \text{ cis } 0$ (e) $\text{cis } 0$ (f) $32 \text{ cis } 0$

(g) $\text{cis } \dfrac{3\pi}{2}$ (h) $81 \text{ cis } 0$ (i) $16 \text{ cis } 0$

(j) $9\sqrt{3} \text{ cis } 5$

2. (a) $648 \text{ cis } 0$ (k) $\frac{1}{8} \text{ cis } \frac{7\pi}{4}$ (c) $0.211 \text{ cis}(0.90)$

(d) $16\sqrt{2} \text{ cis } \dfrac{\pi}{4}$ (e) $\frac{1}{3} \text{ cis } \dfrac{\pi}{2}$

3. (a) $-8 - 8i$ (b) $8 + 8i$ (c) -4096
(d) $4096 - 4096\sqrt{3}i$ (e) $-4096 + 4096\sqrt{3}i$
(f) $564\ 32 + 86\ 193i$
(g) $787\ 717 + 1\ 045\ 282i$ (h) 4
(i) $1.096 + 0.633i$
(j) $-0.008\ 33 + 0.007\ 18i$

4. (b) (i) $-\dfrac{1}{8\sqrt{2}} - \dfrac{1}{8\sqrt{2}}i$ (ii) $-\dfrac{1}{8\sqrt{2}}$ (iii) $\frac{1}{729}$

(c) $2i \sin(n\theta)$

6. (a) $\cos 4\theta = \cos^4 \theta - 6 \cos^2 \theta \sin^3 \theta + \sin^4 \theta$
$\sin 4\theta = 4 \cos \theta \sin \theta(\cos^2 \theta - \sin^2 \theta)$

(b) $\cot 4\,\theta = \dfrac{\cos^4 \theta - 6 \cos^2 \theta \sin^2 \theta + \sin^4 \theta}{4 \cos \theta \sin \theta(\cos^2 \theta - \sin^2 \theta)}$

7. $\tan 5\,\theta = \dfrac{5 \cos^4 \theta \sin \theta - 10 \cos^2 \theta \sin^2 \theta + \sin^5 \theta}{\cos^5 \theta - 10 \cos^3 \theta \sin^2 \theta + 5 \cos \theta \sin^4 \theta}$

EXERCISE 10.7

1. (a) $3i,\ -3i$ (b) $\dfrac{\sqrt{3}}{2} + \frac{1}{2}i,\ -\dfrac{\sqrt{3}}{2} + \frac{1}{2}i,\ -i$

(c) $2i,\ -2i$ (d) $1,\ \text{cis } \dfrac{2\pi}{5},\ \text{cis } \dfrac{4\pi}{5},\ \text{cis } \dfrac{6\pi}{5},$

$\text{cis } \dfrac{8\pi}{5}$ (e) $2 \text{ cis } \dfrac{\pi}{8},\ 2 \text{ cis } \dfrac{5\pi}{8},\ 2 \text{ cis } \dfrac{9\pi}{8},$

$2 \text{ cis } \dfrac{13\pi}{8}$ (f) $\sqrt[4]{2} \text{ cis } \dfrac{7\pi}{8},\ \sqrt[4]{2} \text{ cis } \dfrac{15\pi}{8}$

(g) $\sqrt{2} \text{ cis } \dfrac{\pi}{12},\ \sqrt{2} \text{ cis } \dfrac{13\pi}{12}$ (h) $\text{cis } \dfrac{3\pi}{12},\ \text{cis } \dfrac{7\pi}{12},$

$\text{cis } \dfrac{11\pi}{12},\ \text{cis } \dfrac{15\pi}{12},\ \text{cis } \dfrac{19\pi}{12},\ \text{cis } \dfrac{23\pi}{12}$

2. (a) $2,\ 2 \text{ cis } \dfrac{2\pi}{3},\ 2 \text{ cis } \dfrac{4\pi}{3}$

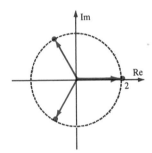

(b) $1,\ \text{cis } \dfrac{\pi}{2},\ \text{cis } \pi,\ \text{cis } \dfrac{2\pi}{3}$

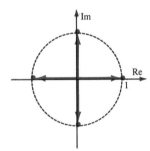

(c) $i,\ \text{cis } \dfrac{3\pi}{2}$

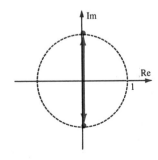

2. (d) 3, $3 \operatorname{cis} \dfrac{2\pi}{5}$, $3 \operatorname{cis} \dfrac{4\pi}{5}$, $3 \operatorname{cis} \dfrac{6\pi}{5}$, $3 \operatorname{cis} \dfrac{8\pi}{5}$

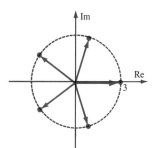

(e) -3, $3 \operatorname{cis} \dfrac{5\pi}{3}$, $3 \operatorname{cis} \dfrac{7\pi}{3}$

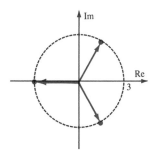

(f) 3, $3 \operatorname{cis} \dfrac{\pi}{3}$, $3 \operatorname{cis} \dfrac{2\pi}{3}$, $3 \operatorname{cis} \pi$, $3 \operatorname{cis} \dfrac{4\pi}{3}$, $3 \operatorname{cis} \dfrac{5\pi}{3}$

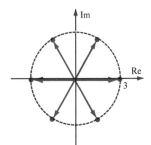

(g) $3i$, $3 \operatorname{cis} \dfrac{3\pi}{2}$

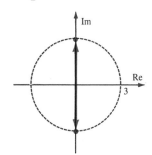

2. (h) $-\dfrac{1}{2}$, $\dfrac{1}{2} \operatorname{cis} \dfrac{7\pi}{5}$, $\dfrac{1}{2} \operatorname{cis} \dfrac{9\pi}{5}$, $\dfrac{1}{2} \operatorname{cis} \dfrac{11\pi}{5}$, $\dfrac{1}{2} \operatorname{cis} \dfrac{13\pi}{5}$

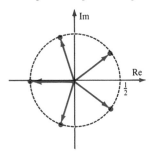

(i) 2, $2 \operatorname{cis} \dfrac{\pi}{5}$, $2 \operatorname{cis} \dfrac{2\pi}{5}$, $2 \operatorname{cis} \dfrac{3\pi}{5}$, $2 \operatorname{cis} \dfrac{4\pi}{5}$,

$2 \operatorname{cis} \pi$, $2 \operatorname{cis} \dfrac{6\pi}{5}$, $2 \operatorname{cis} \dfrac{7\pi}{5}$, $2 \operatorname{cis} \dfrac{8\pi}{5}$, $2 \operatorname{cis} \dfrac{9\pi}{5}$

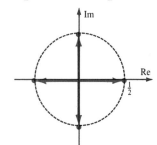

(j) $\dfrac{1}{2}$, $\dfrac{1}{2} \operatorname{cis} \dfrac{\pi}{2}$, $\dfrac{1}{2} \operatorname{cis} \pi$, $\dfrac{1}{2} \operatorname{cis} \dfrac{3\pi}{2}$

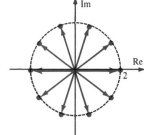

3. (a) 1, $-\dfrac{1}{2} + \dfrac{\sqrt{3}}{2}i$, $-\dfrac{1}{2} - \dfrac{\sqrt{3}}{2}i$ (b) $3i$, $-3i$
(c) $\sqrt{2} + \sqrt{2}i$, $-\sqrt{2} + \sqrt{2}i$, $-\sqrt{2} - \sqrt{2}i$,
$\sqrt{2} - \sqrt{2}i$ (d) 3, $-\dfrac{3}{2} + \dfrac{3\sqrt{3}}{2}i$,

$-\dfrac{3}{2} - \dfrac{-3\sqrt{3}}{2}i$ (e) $-0.366 + 1.366i$,

$0.366 - 1.366i$ (f) 2, $0.618 + 1.902i$,
$-0.618 + 1.176i$, $-1.618 - 1.176i$,

$0.618 - 1.902i$ (g) 1, $-\dfrac{1}{2} + \dfrac{\sqrt{3}}{2}i$,

$-\dfrac{1}{2} - \dfrac{\sqrt{3}}{2}i$ (h) $1.217 + 0.326i$,

$-0.891 + 0.891i$, $-0.326 - 1.217i$

3. (i) $0.758 + 0.758i$, $-0.487 + 0.955i$,
$-1.059 - 0.168i$, $-0.168 - 1.059i$,
$0.955 - 0.487i$
(j) $0.964 - 0.311i$, $0.311 + 0.964i$,
$-0.964 + 0.311i$, $-0.311 - 0.964i$
(k) $0.790 + 0.119i$, $-0.498 + 0.625i$,
$-0.292 - 0.744i$ (l) 1.122,
$-0.561 + 0.972i$, $-0.561 - 0.972i$

4. (a) $0.099 - 0.455i$, $-2.099 + 0.455i$
(b) $0.130 + 0.408i$, $-1.284 - 0.408i$
(c) $-1.039 + 2.443i$, $1.039 - 0.443i$
(d) $-0.193 - 0.850i$, $0.793 + 0.650i$

EXERCISE 10.8

1. (a) $e^{\frac{i\pi}{4}}$ (b) e^{3i} (c) $2e^{\frac{i\pi}{2}}$ (d) $3e^{i\pi}$ (e) $e^{i\pi}$
(f) $4e^{\frac{i\pi}{4}}$ (g) $2e^{\frac{i\pi}{6}}$ (h) $5e^{\frac{i3\pi}{3}}$ (i) $2e^{\frac{i3\pi}{4}}$ (j) e^i
(k) $e^{2.35i}$ (l) $3e^{1.1i}$ (m) $4e^{\frac{i\pi}{3}}$ (n) $\sqrt{2}e^{-\frac{i\pi}{6}}$

2. (a) cis 2π (b) cis $\dfrac{\pi}{3}$ (c) 3 cis π (d) 2 cis 2
(e) cis $\dfrac{\pi}{4}$ (f) cis 3 (g) 5 cis 1 (h) cis $\dfrac{3\pi}{4}$
(i) 2 cis 2π (j) cis 3π

4. (a) $\dfrac{1}{\sqrt{2}} + \dfrac{1}{\sqrt{2}}i$ (b) -2 (c) $-\dfrac{1}{\sqrt{2}} + \dfrac{1}{\sqrt{2}}i$
(d) $\dfrac{3}{2} - \dfrac{3\sqrt{3}}{2}i$ (e) $0.454 + 0.891i$
(f) $-1.399 + 1.566i$

5. (a) $\sqrt{2}e^{\frac{5i\pi}{4}}$ (b) $\sqrt{2}e^{\frac{i\pi}{4}}$ (c) $2e^{\frac{7i\pi}{4}}$ (d) $2e^{\frac{i\pi}{6}}$
(e) $2e^{\frac{5i\pi}{3}}$ (f) $6e^{\frac{i\pi}{6}}$ (g) $\sqrt{5}e^{5.820i}$ (h) $\sqrt{74}e^{0.951i}$

7. (b) $\cos\theta = \frac{1}{2}(e^{-i\theta} + e^{i\theta})$,
$\sin\theta = \frac{1}{2}(ie^{-i\theta} - ie^{i\theta})$

EXERCISE 10.9

1. (a) 12 cis $\dfrac{3\pi}{2}$ (b) $2 + i$ (c) $\frac{1}{5} + \frac{2}{5}i$
(d) 8 cis π (e) $3\sqrt{2}$ (f) 2 cis $\dfrac{\pi}{9}$, 2 cis $\dfrac{7\pi}{9}$,
2 cis $\dfrac{13\pi}{9}$ (g) $10 - 5i$ (h) $\frac{1}{2} + \dfrac{\sqrt{3}}{2}i$
(i) 8 cis $\dfrac{\pi}{2}$ (j) 0

2. (a) $1 + i$ (b) $5 - 6i$ (c) 0 (d) $-2 - 14i$
(e) $1 + i$, $1 - i$ (f) $\frac{3}{2} + \dfrac{\sqrt{7}}{2}i$, $\frac{3}{2} - \dfrac{\sqrt{7}}{2}i$
(g) 3, $3 - 2i$ (h) 4, 4 cis $\dfrac{2\pi}{3}$, 4 cis $\dfrac{4\pi}{3}$

2. (i) -1, cis $\dfrac{7\pi}{5}$, cis $\dfrac{9\pi}{5}$, cis $\dfrac{11\pi}{5}$, cis $\dfrac{13\pi}{5}$
(j) cis $\dfrac{3\pi}{8}$, cis $\dfrac{7\pi}{8}$, cis $\dfrac{11\pi}{8}$, cis $\dfrac{15\pi}{8}$
(k) $0.098 - 0.455i$, $-2.098 + 0.455i$
(l) $4.121 - 0.707i$, $-0.121 + 0.707i$

3. (a) $-\frac{2}{3}$, $\frac{2}{3}$ cis $\dfrac{5\pi}{3}$, $\frac{2}{3}$ cis $\dfrac{\pi}{3}$ (b) $0.171 - 0.046i$

5. (a) $\sin 3\theta = 3\sin\theta - 4\sin^3\theta$,
$\csc 3\theta = \dfrac{\csc^3\theta}{3\csc^2\theta - 4}$
(b) $\sec 3\theta = \dfrac{\sec^3\theta}{4 - 3\sec^2\theta}$

6. (a) $5e^{i\pi}$ (b) $2e^{\frac{i\pi}{2}}$ (c) $\sqrt{2}e^{\frac{7i\pi}{4}}$ (d) $2e^{\frac{11i\pi}{6}}$
(e) $\sqrt{13}e^{5.695i}$ (f) $e^{2i\pi}$

7. $0.290 + 1.084i$, $-1.084 - 0.290i$,
$0.793 - 0.793i$; moduli $= 1.122$

10.10 CHAPTER 10 TEST

1. (a)

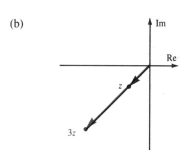

(b)

(c)

1. (d)

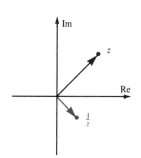

(e)

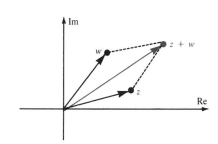

1. (f)

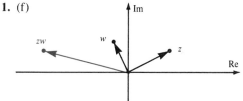

2. (a) $11 - 13i$ (b) $-\frac{1}{3} - \frac{2}{3}i$ (c) $50 \text{ cis } \frac{5\pi}{3}$

(d) $3 + \frac{13}{5}i$

3. (a) $\frac{3}{5} - \frac{11}{5}i$ (b) $-3 + 2i, -3 - 2i$

4. (a) $32 - 32i$

(b) $\cos 4\theta = 8\cos^4 \theta - 8\cos^2 \theta + 1$

5. (a) rotating $q - 1$ times by $\dfrac{2\pi}{q}$

(b) $1, i, -1, -i$

(c) $3 \text{ cis } \pi, 3 \text{ cis } \dfrac{7\pi}{5}, 3 \text{ cis } \dfrac{9\pi}{5}, 3 \text{ cis } \dfrac{11\pi}{5},$

$3 \text{ cis } \dfrac{13\pi}{5}$

6. $\dfrac{\sqrt{3}}{4} - \frac{1}{4}i$

7. $\dfrac{-2 + \sqrt{6}}{2} + \dfrac{\sqrt{2}}{2}i, \dfrac{-2 - \sqrt{6}}{2} - \dfrac{\sqrt{2}}{2}i$

CHAPTER 11 MATHEMATICAL INDUCTION

REVIEW AND PREVIEW TO CHAPTER 11
EXERCISE 1
1. (a) $-1 + 1 + 3 + 5$

(b) $\frac{1}{6} + \frac{1}{7} + \frac{1}{8} + \frac{1}{9} + \frac{1}{10}$

(c) $0 + 2 + 6 + 12 + 20 + 30$

(d) $\frac{1}{2} + 1 + 2 + 4 + 8 + 16 + 32$

(e) $\binom{4}{0} + \binom{4}{1} + \binom{4}{2} + \binom{4}{3} + \binom{4}{4}$

(f) $\binom{7}{0}^2 - \binom{7}{1}^2 + \binom{7}{2}^2 + \binom{7}{3}^2 - \binom{7}{5}^2$

$+ \binom{7}{6}^2 - \binom{7}{7}^2$

2. (a) $\displaystyle\sum_{j=0}^{7} 2^j$ (b) $\displaystyle\sum_{k=3}^{7} kx$

(c) $\displaystyle\sum_{j=1}^{7} a^j$ (d) $\displaystyle\sum_{k=1}^{6} (-1)^{k-1} x^k$

(e) $\displaystyle\sum_{r=0}^{7} \binom{7}{r}$ (f) $\displaystyle\sum_{r=0}^{10} \binom{10}{r}^2$

2. (g) $\displaystyle\sum_{k=0}^{9} (-1)^k \binom{9}{k}$ (h) $\displaystyle\sum_{r=0}^{n} \binom{n}{r}$

(i) $\displaystyle\sum_{j=0}^{n} (-1)^j \binom{n}{j}^2$

EXERCISE 2
1. (a) $5, 8, 11, 14, 17; a = 5, d = 3$ (b) $5, 3,$
$1, -1, -3; a = 5, d = -2$ (c) $1, 4, 7, 10,$
$13; a = 1, d = 3$ (d) $3, -1, -5, -9, -13;$
$a = 3, d = -4$

2. (a) $5 + 120(n - 1)$ (b) $1 + \frac{1}{2}(n - 1)$

(c) $-9 + 1(n - 1)$ (d) $3 - 4(n - 1)$

3. $a = 8, d = -4$

EXERCISE 3
1. (a) $1, 2, 4, 8, 16; a = 1, r = 2$ (b) $3, 6, 12,$
$24, 48; a = 3, r = 2$ (c) $6, 18, 54, 162, 486;$
$a = 6, r = 3$ (d) $1, \frac{1}{3}, \frac{1}{9}, \frac{1}{27}, \frac{1}{81}; a = 1, r = \frac{1}{3}$

2. (a) $5(2^{n-1})$ (b) $5(3^{n-1})$ (c) $7^4\left(-\frac{1}{7}\right)^{n-1}$
(d) $3(5^{n-1})$ or $3(-5)^{n-1}$

3. $a = 9$, $r = \frac{1}{3}$ **4.** $t_n = 10$ for all n

EXERCISE 4

1. (a) 28   (b) $\frac{7}{81}$ **2.** -135

EXERCISE 11.3

1. $\dfrac{n}{3n+1}$ **2.** $\dfrac{n(n+1)(n+2)}{3}$

3. $(n-1)3^n + 1$

4. $n^2(2n^2 - 1)$ **5.** The number of guesses is n.

EXERCISE 11.4

2. (a) $1 + 6x^2 + 15x^4 + 20x^6 + 15x^8 + 6x^{10} + x^{12}$
(b) $a^4 - 8a^3b + 24a^2b^2 - 32ab^3 + 16b^4$
(c) $x^5 - 5x^3 + 10x - 10x^{-1} + 5x^{-3} - x^{-5}$
(d) $x^6 + 6x^4 + 15x^2 + 20 + 15x^{-2} + 6x^{-4} + x^{-6}$
(e) $x^8 + 12x^5y + 54x^2y^2 + 108x^{-1}y^3 + 81x^{-4}y^4$
(f) $16x^{12} + 32x^9\sqrt{y} + 24x^6y + 8x^3y\sqrt{y} + y^2$

3. $x = -2$, $n = 9$ **4.** (a) 2^n (b) 0

5. (a) $\left(\frac{3}{2}\right)^n$ (b) $(-1)^n$

EXERCISE 11.5

4. The 1st, 3rd, 7th. . . . , $(2^n - 1)$st rows.

EXERCISE 11.7

2. (a) False: Induction step (2) fails.   (b) False:
Step (1) fails. False for $n = 1$.   (c) False: Step
(1) fails.   (d) False: Step (1) fails.   (e) True
(f) False: Step (2) fails. (True for
$n = 1, \ldots , 79$)

EXERCISE 11.8

6. f_{n+2}

11.9 REVIEW EXERCISE

7. (a) $(n+1)! - 1$ (b) $\dfrac{n}{n+1}$

(c) $3 - (2n+3)2^{-n}$ (d) $1 - \dfrac{1}{(n+1)!}$

8. (a) 13   (b) 11

9. (a) $\displaystyle\sum_{j=0}^{8} \binom{8}{j}x^j$ (b) $\displaystyle\sum_{j=0}^{7} (-1)^j\binom{7}{j}2^{7-j}x^j$

(c) $\displaystyle\sum_{j=0}^{6} (-2)^j\binom{6}{j}3^{6-j}x^j$

(d) $\displaystyle\sum_{j=0}^{6} \binom{6}{j}2^{6-j}(-3)^jx^{6-j}$

10. (a) $\dfrac{a^3}{b^3} + 3\dfrac{a}{b} + 3\dfrac{b}{a} + \dfrac{b^3}{a^3}$

(b) $\displaystyle\sum_{j=0}^{6} (-1)^j\binom{6}{j}x^{3-\frac{1}{2}j}y^{\frac{1}{2}j}$

(c) $16a^4 + 32a^3b + 24a^3b^2 + 8ab^3 + b^4$

(d) $a^5b^5 - 5a^4b^4cd + 10a^3b^3c^3d^2$
  $- 10a^2b^2c^3d^3 + 5abc^4d^4 - c^5d^5$

11. (a) 55   (b) $\frac{55}{128}$ **12.** (a) 36   (b) 16

13. (a) $n = 101$, $r = 50$ (b) $n = m$, $r = j$

15. (a) False for $n = 1$.   (b) False for $n = 2$.
(c) False for $n = 1$.   (d) True for all n.

11.10 CHAPTER 11 TEST

3. (a) $\dbinom{n}{j} = \dfrac{n!}{j(n-j)!}$

4. (a) $(x+y)^n = \displaystyle\sum_{j=0}^{n} \binom{n}{j}x^{n-j}y^j$ (b) 0

INDEX